Colusa County Free Library

3 0738 00045 1228

D0961543

THE
HANDS
OF
ESAU

C.1

COLUSA COUNTY FREE LIBRARY

The Hands of Esau is the first in a group
of novels called THE GENERATIONS OF ADAM

THE GENERATIONS OF ADAM
The Hands of Esau

IN PREPARATION
Jacob at the Well
The Banks of Jabbok

c. 1

HIRAM HAYDN

THE HANDS OF ESAU

HARPER & BROTHERS
PUBLISHERS
NEW YORK

Library of Congress catalog card number: 62-9920

89B9422

THE HANDS OF ESAU

COPYRIGHT © 1962 BY HIRAM HAYDN

PRINTED IN THE UNITED STATES OF AMERICA

ALL RIGHTS RESERVED

No part of this book may be used or reproduced in any manner what-
soever without written permission except in the case of brief quotations
embodied in critical articles and reviews. For information address
Harper & Brothers, 49 East 33rd Street, New York 16, N.Y.

FIRST EDITION

D-M.

TO SIS AND RANDY

who are everything a father could hope for,
and more than he could imagine

The voice is Jacob's voice,
but the hands are the hands of Esau.

GENESIS 27:22

CONTENTS

1953

May 6

WALTON Herrick took the long way home. From the Northport station to Blake's Wood Road there were two routes. The greater part of one ran a rigidly straight mile and a half through the two lines of small stores and restaurants, gas stations and automobile agencies that were mushrooming haphazardly all along this part of Main Street. They formed a second, auxiliary shopping center for a town that had in the last ten years, as a result of the migration from New York, doubled its previously stable population of nine thousand. The other road that led home was a curving two-lane macadam, broken in many spots, blocked twice now by construction that forced cars onto dirt detours for short stretches—and covering in all, from the railroad station to Walton's home, some two and a quarter miles.

Yet Walton took the second, longer way home, partly because the road twisted and curved past white clapboard houses across whose fresh green lawns the wind-tossed feathery branches made swooping, winking patterns of light and shadow. The late spring sun buttered the willows; a small brook sparkled cold beside the road. Poking its nose between the weathered bars of a split rail fence, a Guernsey raised its vacantly contemplative gaze to the passing car.

Here, then, in pristine tranquillity (once the day's bulldozers and dump trucks had departed), stood the antique Connecticut village— elsewhere mostly overrun with the fungoid growths of suburban life. Yet today, for Walton, there was a reason beyond the obvious contrast between the two roads for choosing the longer and slower route.

He found it difficult to define this reason. To be sure, there was the news he brought. But, since it was both good and startling news, why not hasten home the faster with it?

His meditation was brought up as short by this simple and obvious question as though it were one of the gigantic construction hurdles placed

3

across the road. Was it possible, at the age of forty-five, never before to have wondered at so regular and peculiar a contradiction in one's reactions? For it was true, he could see now, that he always preferred to delay fulfillment of whatever sort, to dally on the road to the moment of completion, realization, triumph. Once it was sure. Once he knew that nothing could prevent its final consummation.

It was perverse, he thought, as the car bumped along the second detour—it was downright perverse not to sail with the full force of the winds of joy when it was possible; the opportunity came seldom enough. What sort of prudence or secretiveness was at work to make him cover with both hands, like a love-starved child, what it would seem natural to hold aloft proudly? What was the origin of this emotional miserliness —if that was what it was that made him want to hug to himself, alone, the news of a distinction won, a recognition granted, rather than to share it with someone?

Someone? With Julie. They had had their seemingly interminable ups and downs, ins and outs, he thought as he cleared the last bump on the dirt road and emerged on the final stretch of pavement leading to Blake's Wood Road; they had, in fact, gone through their particular and exquisite hell together—but when he thought of sharing, he thought only of Julie. And he could not remember a time during the worst of their agonies, at the peak of a period of wild recriminations and long sullen silences (even this spring), when she had failed to respond to such news as he was bringing. At first there might be a dry "That's nice" or "Good. Congratulations," but before long he would hear a humming sound from the kitchen. Then, looking in, he would see that she had begun to glow with that inner light concealed at other times just under the creamy pallor of her skin.

It was always then, at this point, that she would turn toward him, smiling, and then that her large black eyes would lose their somberness and shine with pride and love. She would shyly reach up to lock her arms around his neck and raise her mouth. And later, from another room, he would hear her singing gaily in the kitchen.

He pushed down harder on the accelerator. Suddenly he could not wait to tell her about the call from Abe Fortune. ("Mr. Herrick, this is Abe Fortune. You don't know me, but I know a good deal about you, and I'd like to know more . . .") He turned the corner onto their road so fast that the gravel skittered and clanged under the fenders. . . .

There was an unwonted quietness about the place. In his preoccupation, Walton was aware first merely of an emptiness, an *absence* surrounding the large white clapboard house; then he realized that it was the children he was missing. Almost always at least one of them sighted the car down the road and raced to the driveway to meet him. He felt disproportionately disappointed. Tonight it would have added an extra measure to the plenitude he already felt to be greeted by Jennifer's impish flowerface, Timmy's loving, awkward capers and shy grin, or Peter's intent, searching gaze—as though he sought to read in his father's expression some augury of the future, some presentiment of his own destiny.

Disappointment slipped unobtrusively into a feeling of betrayal; tenderness for the children into a concern lest something was wrong— someone ill, injured or lost. Caught in this anxiety, as yet undefined, Walton noted only morosely and passingly that the whole bed of jonquils was in bloom now; he ducked hurriedly under the rose trellis, taking the short cut to the front terrace and the house. Letting the screen door slam behind him, he dropped his brief case in the front hall and called, "Julie!"

There was no answer. The sound rang up the stairs and thinned out into a flat sweet double vowel far above him. He thought of calling the maid's name, then remembered that it was Wednesday and she would not be here. Muttering half in dismay, half in anger, he stamped through the living room, the dining room, and opened the swinging door into the kitchen.

Julie was there. She was standing before the sink, gazing, in deep absorption, out the window. Walton knew instantly that she had not heard him, that she was not even now aware of his presence. The sadness of her expression was strange to him. He had often seen her sad, but now he was immediately aware of a subtle difference. There was in this expression a resolution, a finality of purpose, it seemed to him, that made it more poignant and at the same time alien.

Silent, motionless, watching her, he felt a yearning that he could not identify. It was so inclusive, it seemed to him, that it could not be related to any single object—it was, rather, a vision, vague and majestic, of the monument that might have been his life—but rimmed round, at its base, with the discrepant failures of daily experience, the broken pots and shards of one unfulfilled intent after another.

And yet he was instantly aware that he was wrong, was romantically blurring the truth. His longing was directly related to this slender supple figure before him. Julie . . . Where she leaned against a cabinet, the rounded line of one slim arm was broken at the elbow, and it seemed to him he could even make out the familiar tender creases on the inside curve of the elbow. And that head, poised, still: the shining black hair, cut short, parted to one side; the full mouth, so oddly sensual in a face that was otherwise delicate, sensitive, brooding.

And then he knew that the longing he felt was for all the lost oc-casions, for all the moments in which he might, given the imaginative understanding—or was it simply the capacity to care: stripped of shallow ego, of all pretenses of devotion and conventional sentiments, all hollow, elaborate assertions of intent and determination?—have stepped across the then small break in the ground between them. But instead, time after time, he had stood where he was as though paralyzed, even pressing down with his feet at the edge of the hole, until the ground crumbled beneath him and widened the gap.

And now here, he thought miserably, she was so removed, separate —suddenly, it seemed to him in this moment of insight—across a very chasm, that he felt, sharply and painfully, that he had lost her, and it seemed to him that he could not bear it. Yet he did not dare to break in upon her silence, to announce himself by so much as the shifting of his stance.

And then at last, without turning around, she said, "Hello. Walton, I've been watching the birds at the feeding trough. I've counted six dif-ferent kinds in only a few minutes. But the bluejays get everything."

He felt as though some tremendous load had been lifted from him, leaving him lightheaded, fatuously relieved. He blurted out the first thing that came to mind, the remnant of his earlier fear.

"Julie, the kids? Where are they? Is anything wrong?"

She finally turned then and faced him, and now he saw that he had not been wrong about her sadness—either about its presence or its quality. And again he felt a seizure of fear—or guilt? or shame? He did not know.

"The children are at the beach for a picnic supper with the Leonards," Julie said quietly. "They won't be back for another hour or so."

She crossed the room with the subtly swaying walk that had been the first thing about her to entrance Walton. It was so delicate and so natural a movement of the hips and shoulders that it bore no relation at all to the usual connotation of a swaying gait as exaggerated, affected, or even a sexual invitation. It was so simple and so fluid a motion as to make most other people seem to Walton ever after to be badly jointed.

Including himself, he thought now, while he mechanically (as though she had bidden him) and awkwardly swung onto the bench opposite the one on which she had sat down. The breakfast table was between them; he thought of it as between them, separating them, keeping them apart. He could not rid himself of his malaise, his sense of imminent but indefinable disaster; for a fleeting moment he remembered the drive home, and his anticipation was now stale and sour in his mouth. He could not overcome this rising panic within him, and he kept futilely repeating to himself, "But there's nothing to be afraid of, nothing really wrong."

Yet their silence persisted, and the notion came to him suddenly—almost desperately—that if he could just reach across the table and touch her, everything would change. But even as an erotic image swam feverishly, but without passion, to the surface of his mind, increasing his tension, he knew that he could not do it—could not, here and now, do anything but wait.

"Walton, I'm going to leave you."

This sensation seemed to be relief: *No worse than that, then?* No worse! What could be worse? In the name of God, what had he been fearing? With what fantastic reassurance was he wrapping himself against the cold?

This was overt. That was all: the very worst, openly said and known, could be dealt with, at whatever cost. He looked directly at her, saw in amazement that the resolution in her eyes had already softened. Pride rose stiff within him.

He felt, rejected it, but knew that the rejection was too exclusively cerebral to have decisive force. Something within him—something he didn't like—was calculating: then if she could so swiftly lose her resolution, this was not the one irrevocable time that only now he realized he had always anticipated—that ultimate arctic time when he would be finally alone. And yet to know reprieve (if only a hinting at it) and to take disadvantage of it, almost spitefully (against whom?) to persist toward the dreaded eventuality: this was worse than perversity; this approached madness. And yet he—whoever *he* was—could gain no ascendancy over this Lucifer-like pride; at the most he could hold it in check. So when he spoke in reply, it was evenly and carefully.

"You've said that before, Julie. And I hope it isn't any more true this time."

Julie's expression had changed again. She was regarding him in steady, dispassionate appraisal. She stretched out a hand and said quietly, "Let me have a cigarette, please. No, I'm really going, Walton. I'm not angry; I'm not saying this because I'm hurt over what happened this morning: I'm too tired, too worn out, to be either angry or hurt."

He found a full package in his pocket, ripped it open savagely, and extended it to her. Watching her hand as though it had a discrete life of its own (the slender, tapered fingers, the soft, slightly plump pad in the palm below the thumb, the finely modeled bones—as she turned her hand over—that led to the knuckles), it seemed to him, in a burst of feeling now, that he could make love to it the rest of his life, without satiety.

Watching angrily the trembling of his own hand as he held out to her the lighted match, he thought wildly, If she goes, I'll cut it off and keep it. Oh, Julie. Oh, Julie, Julie, Julie . . .

"This morning?" he heard himself saying almost suavely. "This morning? You mean losing my temper when I burned myself—"

She broke in, and he could not endure the contempt in her voice and her eyes.

"Losing your temper when you burned yourself! No, I do not mean losing your temper when you burned yourself! But I do mean your saying *that* to describe what really happened this morning. I mean all the little superficial explanations of the real things that neither of us can bear; I mean all the pain and hurt we give each other. But when you start questioning me like that—like some shyster lawyer who is going to win his case by sticking to the surface of things and pretending there's nothing more to it—that *is* what I mean. Part of what I mean. I can't get to you, you won't let me, and you pretend, first of all to yourself, that what happens to us is only little exasperations and quarrels—that we have a deeply happy marriage (I'm so sick of that word 'deeply') with just little scratches on it. And we don't have any kind of a happy marriage at all, not even a shallowly happy marriage. And I can't stand your never looking at what's really there, but only at what you would like to have there!"

Her voice was shaky now, and he saw that she was beginning to weep. Yet he could not resist saying, even knowing the consequences, "What in God's name difference does my vocabulary make? So I say 'deeply' a lot. . . . Is that a criminal action?" But this time he could, and did, reverse himself—and urgently. "Oh Julie, I didn't mean that. I'm so stupid. To *hell* with 'deeply' and any other word. Just let me try to understand better. You're right, of course—my damned stupid and puerile pride, picking at things and not coming to grips with what matters. Don't go, Julie; give me another chance."

She raised her now tear-smudged face, and for a moment smiled.

"Just—just so you know what I'm talking about. Just so you really hear and understand what I mean. Walton, I'm not asking for a divorce. I don't even want a legal separation. I haven't forgotten what it would mean to the children, and I've told you before, I'll do anything I can to keep us from just breaking in two. But we can't go on talking about 'another chance': we've both had too many other chances for it to mean anything any more."

Her earnestness now and this half-reassurance restored him. He asked gravely and quietly, "Then what do you mean by saying you're leaving me, Julie?"

She stretched out her hand slowly, almost shyly, and touched his.

"I thought," she said, "that I'd take the children to Father's—at the Vineyard—for the summer. Only leave early, a little over two weeks from now. They'd miss just one real school week; the one after Memorial Day doesn't matter, it's just closing week, and with Jenny's play school and Tim's kindergarten, it doesn't make any difference, anyway. So if you'd speak to Peter's teacher, and she says it would be all right—"

She stopped abruptly and looked at him directly, with an expression of naked honesty and—it seemed to him—affection too.

"You see," she said, smiling wryly, while her voice grew shaky again. "You see, even when I'm talking about leaving you for a while, I'm asking your help in making arrangements to leave you."

He caught her hand in his, held it tightly; some ferment was working in him now: if, during this summer alone (so he'd already accepted it?), he could really come to grips with himself—or his selves? then, then perhaps . . .

"And after the summer?" he asked.

She looked down, then up again, to regard him steadily, but as though it was difficult to do.

"I don't know. That will depend on you—on what you do about, well, everything. And it will—" here the effort was painful and fully apparent—"depend on me too. On what I learn about myself and what I can do, and then on what I make up my mind to do."

She laid a slight stress on the final "I" and "my." It was as though she were speaking in an unfamiliar tongue and being very careful about her pronunciation.

Walton nodded and they were both silent. Then he finally looked away, through the window at the birds on the feeding trough.

"All right," he said. "We'll try it."

Throughout dinner and the early part of the evening, Walton was very quiet. Then, when the two smaller children had gone to bed and he and Julie had finished the dishes, he said, "I think I'll take a walk in the woods."

Peter appeared as though summoned by the words.

"Oh, Pop, let me come with you," he said. "Boy, a walk in the woods in the dark!"

Walton shook his head.

"Not this time, son," he replied. "There'll be another chance."

Julie patted Peter's head.

"You haven't finished your homework anyhow. Maybe you can take one Saturday."

"In the dark?" the boy insisted, and both Julie and Walton nodded. Their eyes met and they smiled.

It was strange, Walton thought as he left the house, how courteous and friendly they had become.

Almost an hour later, Walton returned from his long walk in the woods at the end of the road. The house glimmered palely in the cloudy moonlight; his footsteps echoed sharply on the terrace. Inside the house, all was quiet; a single lamp burned in the front hall.

He walked slowly to the kitchen, poured himself a drink, dropped heavily onto the bench by the breakfast table. With dull, listless eyes he stared at various familiar objects: a half-drunk glass of chocolate milk, a gaping box of crackers, crumbs scattered on the floor. Tokens and reminders, memories in advance . . .

At last he became aware that the house was not totally quiet. There were sounds above—sounds that were unmistakably those of Julie preparing to go to bed. He stayed motionless. It seemed to him that each further single sound was another step toward the finality of his aloneness —and yet he could not break his frozen state. Unless he could . . . unless he could . . . his mind kept repeating—unless he could before she went to bed, it was all over. The state of resolution in which he had returned from his walk was gone, and each time her light step echoed above him, each time an old floor board creaked, he felt that it was a nail being driven into him.

And yet he sat and stared at his knotted hands. He could not even pick up the glass. He could not move. At last he heard the creaking of the bed and listened to the subsequent absoluteness of the silence and knew that it was now too late.

Almost immediately he felt a relaxing of his tension. The iron corset around his chest and ribs relented; the pressure with which his anxiety had squeezed his biceps and calves was gone. *Too late for what?* His head cleared, and it was as it had been in the woods with him: he was free to think. The objects in the room lost their fuzziness of outline;

to complement the cleansing of his mind, they resumed their unmistakable identities. Here was a drink—a mild bourbon and water; there cracker crumbs. There was again an external reality quite separate from his feelings about it; *here* and *there* were re-established.

And so, too, with Julie. What was the dread, shrouded in shadows and only dimly apprehended most of the time, but literally clinging to him, strangling him tonight as he had approached, entered the house, then finally the kitchen? This dread of aloneness, this certainty of eventually being abandoned? And why, even if he must envision a final loneliness, should it seize him with talons of terror? What about being alone was so terrible, so unbearable, as to conjure up a prospect of bleak and glacial steppes, inhabited only by shadows and whispers and himself?

He did not know, and for a few minutes, sitting there in relaxed relief, sipping his drink, he deliberately invited his mind to float, hoping to feel in the waters below it some ripple, some warmer or colder current that would offer him a subtle intimation of what lurked, hidden and silent, there below. But nothing substantial enough to be really informative emerged. He played lazily with the thought that Julie was eleven years younger than he, vaguely remembered one or two times in his childhood when, apprehensive, he had discovered that he had been left alone by his parents, caught fleeting glimpses again of his first two marriages—Joanna's stricken face when he had left her; his own rage and yes, hatred (dull coals now, but not, even now, dead), when Lydia had left him.

And slowly, as the simple physical comfort of relaxation surged through him, withdrew, and like some lesser tide of salt but inland waters rippled forward once more, his mood turned to lassitude, and he found to his surprise that his meditation, without his being really aware of it, had turned to the freedoms of being alone: to the unfamiliar state of choosing hour by hour (when not confined in the office) exactly what he would do next, without regard for the needs of others, and finally (when had it crept in? Here he was already in an exotic—since unfamiliar—bedroom) to indolent erotic fancies. He shook his head, rose, poured himself a second, stronger drink, and, lighting a cigarette, resumed his seat at the kitchen table.

In a few minutes he realized that he had begun holding colloquies with himself. It was a habit, and one that intensely irritated him. This was no simple Jekyll and Hyde debate, no clear-cut argument between Id and Superego. Yet it took the form of an argument, between one persistent, nagging voice and another dragging, reluctant one, the epitome of passive resistance until suddenly, without warning, it would erupt in a snarling, cursing objection. And sometimes there was a whispering chorus of other voices, admonishing, counseling, enjoining—until their hushed sibilance became a din.

And so it went now, as the liquor in his glass dwindled and the relative peace of a few minutes before vanished altogether. The interior voices went on and on, imagining and damning the various ways in which he might, after climbing the stairs, awaken Julie, with his two hands (what did that mean?) pound out a solution that she—and he—would believe. *A month's absence would give them all a fresh start. . . .* No. *Just now, when only this afternoon he had come home to tell her that he was under consideration for the Democratic nomination for governor of the state . . .* No. Goddam pitiable crawling ridiculous no. *Governor.* He was suddenly saturated in a cloud of black self-loathing.

He would stay in town and come out only weekends so that they need not leave at all. And he would devote all his evenings to straightening himself out. . . . No. That these pitiful little squirming things should be all that he could squeeze out from his brain. That was the trouble—brain.

If she would wait just a little—one more time—until the row at the Foundation was worked out. To go now, in the midst of this worst time for him, and also when a separation would mean the end of his chances for the nomination. No. No. No. Woo't beg? Woo't plead? Woo't eat a crocodile?

He rose and poured another drink. There was no alternative then; he was for the dark. Even now allusions—pompous, play-acting bastard? He could not help it; he drank. Just as he had when Lydia . . .

It was some time later that he rose stiffly, and stiffly ascended the stairs. Slowly, on tiptoe, he approached their bedroom, stood in the doorway and listened to the low delicate sound of breathing. He could not tell her breathing from that of the night air, however, and approached the bed. *There* . . . the faintly scooped-out hollows under the cheekbones, the sometimes quivering chin that one could hold, support in rough tenderness with the palm and heel of one's hand, feeling in one's fingers the articulation of that fragile jawbone. The pale eyelids covering now the black reproachful eyes, and the live tendrils of blackest hair, curling, softly loose now, from the back of her neck, so pathetically, childishly slender and exposed in sleep. The wife. Julie. The beloved. Lost . . .

Then, suddenly, with no warning, his head swarmed. He felt an ambiguous unbearable longing to strain her against himself, to grip her shoulders until he left black marks on them, to shake, to beat her into forgiveness, to force absolution from her. He had now a moment's terrible fantasy of her head bobbing back and forth under the fury of his importunate hands, of shouting at her, "Forgive me, goddamn it, forgive me"—and looked away from her serene and tender face to his spread hands and groaned and turned away.

Irresolute, he paused in the hall. Then slowly, still on tiptoe, he entered Peter's room and crossed it to the bed. For some time he stood there, waiting with an unaccustomed patience for his eyes to become sufficiently used to the gray light to be able to see his son's face.

At last he could make out the features: the full lips parted, as though panting slightly, the curve of his nose, the unbelievably delicate sweep of the eyelashes resting on the softly rounded cheek. He looked and looked, feeling some desperate grim satisfaction in the wild pain now finally unleashed in his heart. Shame? grief? despair?

He did not know. This emotion was not listed and defined in the lexicon of pain. He who could not pray could do nothing but feel this, endure it. His prayer was to feel it; for real feeling, he suddenly knew, was anguish to him, all but unbearable. This he gave to his boy—useless, he thought, valueless, meaningless for Peter. But it was as near as he could come to love, and it was all he had to give—here, now.

Then, after he had gone on to Timmy's room, and to Jennifer's, he slowly made his way downstairs and sank into an armchair in the living room, remembering with a pang his other daughter, Maria, Lydia's child, and a similar moment the last night he had spent with them.

The incitement of the whiskey was gone, the emotion drained out of him. He felt tired but resolved. (He grinned sardonically. How many different times now?) Thank God almost all the turmoil, the wildness, the anguish had been his alone. And he had come out the end of this tunnel: he could always tell, for all his gibes at himself for backing and forthing. It was a physical conviction; when he was out in the open again, his body told him.

And so—he could and would face, go through with it. And with hope. Now, at last, he could see again the softening of Julie's expression, the difficulty with which she had said what she had to say—see it with tenderness. For her, and for the courage and love that made it possible for her to act. He realized, with surprise, that he really did not understand at all what had made all the trouble between them. This, then, was the task that he finally fully recognized only now, in the clarity of exhaustion. He did not know that he could do what had to be done, but he could try. And this was new; he knew with an unmistakable certainty that up to now he had only tried to try.

So, at last now, he could hoist his body onto the couch, lift each leg as though it were an inanimate object, dispose it straight before him, slouch back and close his eyes. But just before he fell asleep,

he lurched up into a sitting position, remembering, whence he did not
know, the words, "But the bluejays get everything." He shuddered,
aware of some final vague obscenity that he could not ward off, and fell
back again. Scarecrows, he advised himself sleepily. He must make
scarecrows to protect himself.

DEPOSITION: 1

A letter to Abe Fortune, dated March 13, 1953, from Anna Manges, chairman of the department of sociology, Graham Institute, Cleveland, Ohio . . .

DEAR ABE—

So there you are, still snooping up and down the corridors of your private city hall, scrabbling through ledgers, and turning the pages of vital psychological statistics. You old soul-scavenger! How I've missed you. And Jane, bless her!

And now you want to know about Walton Herrick. Not a word to indicate whether you want to pin a suit on him, nail him for delinquent taxes, run him for mayor of your beloved Stamford, or ask a favor of him. All right. I remember that with you communication is a one-way street, and it doesn't upset me particularly.

But first—he and I began as instructors at Graham together in 1930, when I went there straight from working with you, and we went up the academic ladder more or less together. Then he left for foundation work in 1943. But we served on the same faculty for almost fifteen years, and, although in different departments, saw a lot of each other through committee work, especially during one trying stretch when he led the fight to breathe some life into our moribund curriculum. We saw eye to eye.

Yet, when you ask me, I do hesitate. For *which* Walton Herrick shall I describe? The one I first came to know—bright, tense, eager, desiring affection and approval, and clumsy in his attempts to disguise the desire? Or the later one who was more relaxed, less questioning, and baffled by his success with work and people, who could neither believe nor accept that things were going well with him? Or the one who came after, the recent one whom I've seen only from time to time, but who

15

seems so to have assimilated the knowledge of his strengths and his weaknesses that he is looking for new ones?

Our relationship has been singular in its durability, its solidity and isolation. Rarely has it been allowed to enter the general context of either of our lives, and it was almost always a mistake when this happened. We have shared few of the intimate details of our lives, and it was, I believe, this lack of curiosity about the day-to-day affairs of the other which gave us our freedom. Both of us were constantly struggling, learning how to feel, then how to trust the feelings, and finally trying to convince ourselves that all was well. We entertained the same devils, though under different names, and with what was sometimes an almost foolish faith we searched for the same angels. Theology! From me!

Walton has a great general appeal for both men and women, which has nothing to do with manners and poise. Occasionally I have seen him aware of his own charm, and these were golden moments for all who were with him. But he has always been suspicious of charm, in himself and in other people, and I think it is just as well that he has never learned the full potential of his own. He could be frightening in his great onrushing haste to get on with living and feeling and knowing, sweeping people and things aside in an attempt to make up for lost years, the early ones in which he seems to have numbed himself so that nothing stirred. He has little talent or time for small talk or small action, although he can be unbelievably literal, tedious and difficult on small details. He is bluntly honest. I have seen him slow the tempo of conversation and finally bring it to a halt with his frequent question: "But what do you mean?" At a social gathering he is both fun and confusing to the sheep and the goats.

Walton is the kindest man I have ever known, always a source of warm knowing and caring. But this is true only for those few people who know the man well and are alert to the sometimes small but important differences between his gestures of kindness and kindness itself. For those few he becomes a frame of reference from which it is possible to move forward to what is best for the person. Many times he has allowed a relationship to drain him completely, even for a brief time of kindness. It is then that he resorts to the gestures, hurting the person who has brought this about, and hating himself. Loving him must be difficult, and being loved by him even more so.

Back in the years when I saw him regularly, every day was Armageddon for Walton. This would have been the undoing of many men, and even with him it took its toll. But struggle was the very essence of living for him; it gave him his reason and his passion for being. Problems large and small, those of a lifetime or a day, took on interest and meaning for him as soon as he saw them as new battles or revivals of old ones. This, I think, was probably the most powerful facet of his nature as it was reflected in his own life and in the lives of those around him. There have been times when, watching him pace the floor over a decision, I could swear that I heard trumpets, the stamping of horses, the clank of metal and the confusion of men in the distance— when I fully expected to hear him call for the attack. These were fine times, with the feeling of early morning about them, when I learned, just from watching him, about decisions and courage, the dignity and the excitement of the fighting which, if done with a flair, almost never meant defeat. For Walton, winning was never a completed act; it was a state of mind, exhilarated and holy.

One was never really alone with him, for he was attended by a small company of old puritanical ghosts which never left his side. They were present in battle and in peace, constantly advising him of the next step to take or, more often, the next step not to take. He was not happy with them, but to deny their presence would be to deny the very roots of his being, and if they were ousted, what unfamiliar spirits would replace them? Walton wished and needed the cock to crow at least three times, for it was only through his denying and being denied that he could make his penance and his peace.

He had a strong sense of not just evil, but a personal evil. Perhaps this is why, even in his younger days, he was a great moralizer. And although his dark red preacher's blood seemed to thin as he got older, I think he continues to live under his own cloud of original sin and to suffer that greatest of all guilts—the one which comes from having been born at all. I don't think he was ever heard to say, "I have no right. . . ." Quite the contrary. To those who know him casually he appears to be an egoist. But the phrase has flickered behind his every action, his every success, and behind his every moment of what might have been pleasure for another man. I found this particularly true when some spotlight for which he had been longing would finally swing full upon him. If it were a moment of general praise and applause, a moment of light without faces, he would rise to it eagerly with warmth and eloquence. But if it were that specific second of a specific devotion or gratitude, he would cover his face and turn away. He had no right.

The difficulty, I think, rests deep in the maze of his need for love; then, when love does come, the guilt allows it only to brush his ego and pass. The fact is that he has found admiration, respect, loyalty, and even love in an assortment of places and people. But somewhere far back in the soul he dreamed—and perhaps still dreams—of the perfect whole, the Grail, the final and full cup of love withheld since man came to know that it was an elixir. This derives, I think, from the discipline and the lesson of his years. Believing as he did that he was not deserving of the love which he was offered—the small, the simple, the unadorned—he set for himself the grand goal, the one which would allow him to live with vitality and dignity while never attaining it. If one identifies with the sun, falling stars are of little interest or pain.

When you can, Abe, tell me what this is all about. My love to Jane.

ANNA

Abe Fortune's reply . . .

April 2, 1953

DEAR ANNA,

A poem. I've read it and reread it. Are you in love with him?

Try again. How did he get on with most of the faculty? The administration? The students? In those years he was married twice and—I think—divorced twice. Why? What were his wives like?

What in the name of the great triple-horned Aesophagus does he have that has so bewitched you? There never was a man like that. And my inquiry is serious. What's become of the sociologist? the observer? What good did it do for me to spend three whole years training you to look at events and people with a clear eye?!

Anna. Come clean. Jane sends love.

ABE

May 10

THROUGH the numbness of the weekend that followed, Walton reached
for work. He spent much of Saturday in his study, detailing a plan for
the new language programs through which the Foundation might help
to improve the lamentably weak national ones. Nor, this time, did Julie
complain about his preoccupation. The only serious interruption all
weekend was Peter's.

Late Sunday afternoon Peter opened the door to the study and
stood there in silence until Walton turned around. Some timidity in
the boy's posture, a hesitance and even apprehensiveness in his eyes
touched Walton, and he checked the impatient question that came to
his lips.

"What's up, Pete?" he asked instead.

The dirty hands, the shuffling feet, the one curl of hair hanging
over his forehead. And the boy smell as he stepped nervously closer—a
mixture of sweat and dirt and some vaguer emanation that Walton
thought of as growth.

"Did you—you forgot about the walk last night."

Walton stared at him.

"Walk? Last night?"

"You said you'd take me for a walk in the dark."

Were the large brown eyes really so reproachful, or did they rather
reflect the feeling that guiltily leapt across Walton's mind? He had just
reached the stage in his work where yesterday's confusions were being
clarified, and yet tonight he and Julie were committed to dinner out—
under the circumstances an ordeal, but if Julie hadn't canceled it, his
pride wouldn't allow him to.

"I'm sorry," he said. "I did forget. And tonight Mother and I
have to go out. Let's take it now."

Walton started down the back road behind the house with the

19

familiar feeling of being wrenched by two conflicting pulls. It was only after they had trudged along for a quarter of a mile that he realized that neither of these pulls represented what he really wanted to do: he felt coerced into the walk in order to live up to the image he wanted Peter to have of him; he felt driven to complete the particular piece of work because, as usual, he had set himself a goal of accomplishment for the weekend that it was impossible to reach.

Peter, however, was quite oblivious of any tension in him. Glowing with the prospect before them, he had been marching sturdily along, hands in pockets and whistling thoughtfully in an imitation of his father that Walton suddenly recognized. For once, he thought, it was not too late. And by the time Peter stopped short, beside a break in the bushes that bordered the road, Walton was cheerfully absorbed in the expedition itself.

There was a low stone wall to get over, a small hill to scramble down and some brambles to avoid. Then they were in a flat valley of meadowland. The tall grasses had been beaten down and bleached by winter storms; they formed a silvery sea that crunched softly underfoot.

"See that hill over there?" Peter asked excitedly, pointing. "With the woods? That's where we go."

His eyes were now so lustrous with life that Walton wanted to pick him up, hug him. But instead he merely said, "It looks good," and the boy rushed off, leaping and racing across the silvery field, uttering the high squeal that meant he was too happy to remember the dignity that he usually felt becoming to eight.

He waited for his father at the foot of the wooded incline, and they followed a clear path upward between small pines and firs. They climbed in silence, except once when Peter said softly, as though he were whispering seriously to himself, "We named it the Woodsy Woods."

At the top he took Walton's hand and pulled him eagerly between taller trees and through underbrush so thick that they tripped several times and barely kept their balance. Laughing, out of breath, they reached a clearing and stood looking out at the land below.

The sun behind them saturated the scene with soft colors, powdery purples and blues and reds. The fields were wheat color; the one directly below, which they had crossed, looked as though touched with some immemorial hoar frost. The houses, white or gray or red, shutter-trimmed, were cut out as clearly against the neutral fields and the soft blue sky as though by a celestial knife. It was, Walton thought —all of it, everything they could see—almost unbearably beautiful in its tranquillity, in its intimations of permanence and peace.

At the end of the dirt road on which their house stood, two boys now suddenly leaped on their bicycles and began to pedal furiously down the road. One drew ahead of the other; he turned and waved, and his shout of joy, thin and clear, reached Walton and Peter where they stood.

Peace was made animate now; a warmer life enclosed the whole sun-softened scene, curled from the chimneys, flashed from the glittering spokes of the bicycles, rose in waves of shimmering silence from the quiet meadow below. Walton turned to Peter and studied his flushed face.

"You see," the boy said, and suddenly he was shy, embarrassed, "I never think when I'm down there—when I'm riding my bike and all—I never think about it at all. That it's my home and stuff, that it's where I live, that it could be so beautiful. I love it the most of any place in the whole world."

They were quiet on the way back until they reached the meadow. Then they chased each other for a while and wrestled on the soft hay. Back on the road, they talked about the arrival of spring and the possibility of a new bicycle. But after Walton was back at work at his desk, the door opened and Peter came in and kissed him, then went out quickly again. Walton sat at his desk for another hour, but he did no more work.

LETTERS *and* MANUSCRIPT: *1*

From Dudley Foote, visiting the Herricks in Northport, Connecticut, to his wife, Cynthia, at home in Ithaca, New York . . .

April 10, 1953

DEAR CYN—

It's been a wearying week, and I'm glad there's only one more to go. I don't see how the Herricks can stand the pace, the way they live. Walton goes at a tremendous clip all day in New York, yet four nights since I've been here we've either gone out to dinner or had people in. It takes him more than an hour on the commuting train, and he gets up every morning somewhere between six-thirty and seven, yet he rarely goes to bed earlier than twelve, and usually it's at least one. It would kill me, but he seems to thrive on it.

He's been wonderful to me, Cyn. Everywhere I've gone, I've been treated as though I were a visiting dignitary. It's downright awesome, the deference everyone shows to him and about him. He's not a foundation executive, but a myth. I haven't been one place for an interview that the man I was talking to didn't say something like "He's a remarkable man. There's no one else like him."

And he is remarkable. But I've thought sometimes during this week that it is almost a disadvantage to come to people with his endorsement. I've been tempted several times to say, "Yes, he is extraordinary, but what I'm wondering is: do you have any job for an *ordinary* man?"

I can hear your response to *that*, all the way from home to here, but I'm not listening. We might as well face it, honey: there are two dozen men like me trying for each of the few openings I've uncovered —in the foundations, the colleges and universities, the publishing houses and magazines.

I'm discouraged about it—and yet I can't help being amused too: at the pompousness of the worst of these people, and the uninspired earnestness of most of the rest. I can't talk either academic jabberwocky or the Madison Avenue kind. But these people keep on trying to pull me together to conform to the right patterns for their mysteries. They really want to take me in hand, in a kindly way, and persuade me to take myself and Life more seriously.

I go through all the motions the best I can, and for a little while I thought I was really going to wind up with a job at one foundation. But then this fellow (he's the managing director, or some such thing—it's the Baldwin) says, "The great thing here, Foote—the great thing here is the sense of team play," and I laughed. Right in his face. I apologized and we talked a while longer, but it was all over right there. I really offended him.

When I set out to come East last week, you know how determined I really was to get somewhere this time. But it's just like it's always been, honey, and I'm afraid we're going to have to reconcile ourselves to my staying an associate professor at Cornell, until I'm so doddering that they make me a full professor to fatten me for the feast of retirement.

I puzzle Walton. And what puzzles me is the way he rates me. I've seen some of the letters he's written for me, and, Cyn, they make me out a combination of Socrates, St. Francis and Ring Lardner. I'd like to know what this kink in him is that makes him so exaggerate.

It has something to do with a few people whom he values so excessively because they have something he wants—no, needs, craves. What I *don't* mean is the kind of person, the kind of feeling in him, that causes him to reach and bear-hug (I don't mean literally). Do you know what I mean by that? Do you remember—or, rather, did you ever see this in him? He absorbs people—just reaches out and draws them into him. It sounds awful, and it is. It's as though at times he squeezes them for their essence. Yet it doesn't seem to me that he wants to; I've seen him draw back in bewilderment, even in pain, as though he never meant to do all that damage.

I think this explains a lot of his anger and the moods he gets into when he clams up and seems so *dried out*, confronts you only with his shell, and seems to find it hard to say even a few words. Then I feel that he recognizes that he has set up a game he doesn't want to play out, and yet that he must—since he started it. He will face the obligations he's incurred. But it's pretty dry fare he hands out when he's caught this way.

But what I started to say is that there are some few of us (I'm sure you'd be another if he knew you better) whom he respects from the word go, and on whom he never tries the frontal assault. So when I talk about the feeling of *craving*, I mean that he feels the lack in himself of our qualities and longs for them, but still likes us for having them. What qualities? Well, humor, easygoingness, simplicity (at least relative, in comparison to himself), tolerance, maybe plain comfortableness. Just as what I most admire in him are his drive, his capacity to stand up and be counted, his ability to go out and, more often than not, get what he wants.

I'm so sleepy I can't keep my eyes open. I canceled two appointments this afternoon to come home and get some rest. I'll write you again, tomorrow or Sunday. Come Monday, I'll be back on the firing line—with no time for letters.

Kiss the kids for me, and if Roger objects tell him we'll fight it out when I get back. Also please tell him I couldn't get the guitar pick he wants, but I have the nearest thing to it I could find. Good night, honey.

DUD

Saturday evening

DEAR CYN,

Your letter came this morning. I already have the sweater for Sarah. I lost the piece of paper with her size on it, but I'm sure that the one I picked (green) will fit her. As for the copy of the Arthur Machen book for Lucy Devere, tell her I'll try in the second-hand shops on Fourth Avenue next week, but I may not be able to find it.

Listen, honey, I think I have a job for the summer! Walton again. Feeling as he does about me, he can't understand why I'm having so much trouble landing something. But when he came home yesterday, we had a few minutes together and he said that he'd had a talk with the president of his own outfit about a new project that's just getting underway on a provisional basis (it's complicated, and I'll tell you about it later) and that they agreed to take me on for three months this summer to handle the preliminaries. Then, while I'm teaching next year, they'll be deciding whether or not to go all the way with it, and if they do, I'm in. It sounds good to me—really down my line (a new language program to help us in the Cold War)—and good pay. So— I'll spend the first part of next week getting briefed, and I may even get home by Thursday—Friday at the latest.

I told Walton I'd love to tackle the job, and he looked at me in that abstracted way of his and said, "You know, I think we've gone about this all wrong up to now. I've never in my life sought a job; they've all come to me. I shouldn't have let you go out for all those interviews."

They've all come to him. I don't know why that seems to me some kind of key to him, but it does. What if "they" *hadn't* come to him? Would he be sitting there yet? (There? where? damned if I know. On a throne in the Sahara Desert, or in an igloo.) Would he sit there through the years in some kind of austere and isolated majesty? But of course they had to come: that's another part of him. People get drawn to him. I've seen him come into a crowded room and watched how the expressions of over half the people present change. They look at him speculatively, with a recognition—as though they'd always known there must be somebody like this.

He's impressive. But he's scary, too. Take him at home—with his kids, for instance. Peter's seven or eight, Timmy not quite five, and Jennifer three. Sweet kids, too. They worship him, and when he comes home each night, they raise such a hullabaloo as you've never heard. Yet they're scared of him, too, I think. Well, what the hell—so am I, some ways. He's unpredictable, but whatever he does is somehow outsized, and often overpowering. Take last Sunday. Something was eating at him anyway, and Peter came tearing through the room like an express train. Walton let go with a blast at him, and I don't know which of us (the boy or me) was more scared.

No, that's not so. I do know: *I* was more scared. I cowered in my chair as though he were yelling at me. Peter was scared, but he's a proud, kind of high-strung youngster, and he eyed his father as if he wouldn't give an inch but expected to be pushed (or blown) a mile. And you could see Walton relent, ashamed, sorry and yet awkward too, and not knowing how to back down and still save face. At last he said very stiffly, "I shouldn't have yelled at you, Peter. I'm sorry. But please walk when you're coming through the living room." Then he got up himself and walked out. We didn't see him again for two hours.

Just think. If he often seems larger than life-sized to me, how must he seem to children when he's angry or upset or even simply filled with the kind of gusto that hits him from time to time? It isn't just his height, his physical size, though that's enough, God knows. There's some kind of extra potency in him; it makes him seem possessed when he gets steamed up.

I keep forgetting that you did meet him once, back when he was married to Lydia. There's a real change in him since then, I think, but the basic elements are of course the same—not that I understand them any better. I remember you said, when we got back to the hotel from the apartment that night, "Well, I do like him, but he scares me, he takes everything so for real, the littlest thing, and doesn't discriminate between what's important and what isn't. He has no sense of humor or perspective. It makes him exciting but scary." It must have been twelve or thirteen years ago.

So why do I remember it? Because he's always been a hero to me since we had our first jobs together, and that night you were meeting him, and he you, for the first time. And he'd taken me aside after dinner for a minute and said, "Dud, you sure have done it. She's as fine as she is lovely, and when she looks at you as though you'd invented both her and the world, I'm so envious I could shoot you."

I never told you that till now. That's funny, too, it seems to me, and even now I don't know why. For it surprised me. Walton has always been so private, so tight-lipped about personal matters (he got that way through feeling that he had to keep buttoned up about his own strange, original family, I guess). So I knew he meant just what he said, and this was embarrassingly naked about Lydia and him. And he said it with so much intensity! Suddenly I knew how desperately he wanted to be loved, worshiped, almost. It made me wonder about his own capacity to love.

Well, I can't doubt that capacity any more. I mean he's crazy about Julie. Doesn't just love her the way most men who have happy marriages love their wives after the first seven or eight years (never mind, it's a good way), but with a crazy desperation.

It gets in the way of their happiness, I think. After all, he's forty-five, two years older than me, and I think she's between thirty and thirty-five. They've been married nine years and have three kids. It's not *decent* to want still to play Tristan and Isolde—or to expect her to respond and put this romanticism ahead of being a mother.

So he's very touchy. If she doesn't, as you say, pay him much mind when he wants it, he gets mad, or sulks. I feel like a heel, writing this, even to you, for he's been wonderful to me. You know, there isn't one touch of condescension or (worse) of that kind of self-conscious equality with which some men who have been outstandingly successful treat the rest of us. Most of them. On the contrary, he sometimes looks at me as though he thought that he could learn something from me that would—I don't know what; I started to write *put him at peace.*

Whatever that means. (But he *is* a tormented man—with all his achievements, accomplishments and rewards.)

And think of the odds he's been up against. That really crazy family of his. I guess his father was quite a wonderful man, though badly crippled, but I barely knew him; what I do know is that Walton had all those years of taking care of his mother (a handful) and his invalid sister, and got himself deep in debt, to boot. And then the marriages— a sea of troubles. He got a late start, and a hard one. Yet here he is, at the top (or near it) of the heap in New York, with a lovely wife and good kids and a beautiful home.

All this makes me—and you?—wonder about Julie. But that's got to wait. And I haven't even started on last night's goings-on. I guess I'll save them to tell you: it's a long story.

Miss you. Night, baby.

DUD

NIGHT THOUGHTS
or Meditations on a Misspent Life

My name is Dudley Foote. I'm forty-three years old, five foot nine, weight 154, a sandy-colored man. Born in St. Louis, Missouri, educated at the University of Illinois. Doctorate from Columbia. Associate professor of Romance Languages at Cornell. For six years past working on a new translation of Montaigne. Working, and meaning to work. So far, only eleven chapters of Book I—through "Of Prognostications"—though I've done "Raimond Sebond" and half of Book III. Why? Because that's the part for me. *And* because order and orderliness bore, torment and baffle me. *And*—often—I'd rather be using the power drill and saw.

I'm intelligent and lazy. I'm unambitious and yet often irritable and dissatisfied with myself. For I'm a novelist manqué. Maybe *that's* why I'm starting this venture, which of course I'll never finish. I'm no Boswell. But I'm inquisitive—most of all about my fellow man. And right now, in particular, Walton Herrick—*mon frère,* but not *mon semblable.* My friend of twenty years, whom I have admired, romanticized, even revered—but don't understand at all.

STUDY OF A FRIEND
DUDLEY FOOTE

The Dinner Party
(NOT CHAPTER I)

The Fairfield County cocktail hour is unique and debilitating. After the hour or two dedicated to this ritual, dinner is almost always an anticlimax. Nobody's capable of tasting the food, which as often as not has become cold, anyway.

People settle in to this thing the way, when I was a kid, we used to go early to get seats at a big game or a Fourth of July fireworks. There's the same kind of maneuvering for place, all the anticipation, hilarity and arguing. Only at the end there isn't any big event to which all this points; you just eat that dinner and either get sleepy or go back to drinking.

But the stances, the styles! There's the specimen, male or female, who begins by saying, "Now make mine very light, a tall weak drink"; in ten minutes forces the glass back on the host, saying, "Remember: weak for me"; but by the fifth, or even fourth glass, is saying nothing— just holding his glass up for attention. I could go on and on about the changes in individual pace, the expressions, the styles of instruction to the host. But enough for now. And much as I enjoy drinking, it's too much for me. Last night I got Walton to give me beef bouillon on ice; it looks like a good dark bourbon, and with most of these people, if you don't want to get into an endless argument, you have to hold something in your hand. Anyway, I had very little to drink last night, and that may be why it all hit me so hard.

Things went along the way I've described until dinnertime. Then everybody got up and went over to the long buffet table to serve himself. Everybody, that is, except one dark little fellow with wavy black hair, who instead refilled his glass so that it was almost black with whiskey, and settled down in his armchair, glowering at each one who came back from the table with his plate piled with food.

I had noticed him throughout the Long Drink, though I hadn't had a chance (or any particular desire) to talk to him. I'd settled down early in a corner with the beef bouillon and a cute little redhead with a sassy tongue and an uptilted nose, name of Abigail Arbuthnot. She's divorced (there are a lot of those around here), about thirty-five and so apparently uninhibited and full of *joie de vivre* that you figure she must have a deep unclosed wound somewhere. She found out early that

I teach at Cornell and that seemed to her the funniest, quaintest and most charming thing she'd come upon in years. I accepted all this adulation with my customary *sang-froid,* once I'd cautiously assured myself that she wasn't really making *mean* fun of me. Then I learned that she had three kids (and it was clear that she was very keen on them) and made her living (presumably with the help of alimony too) by running a hat shop. In Manhattan. Had been in college with Julie.

I soon realized, too, that she had a special eye for Walton. We'd be deep in a discussion of some subject I know a lot about—like women's hats or raising kids—and then her voice would get absent-minded, and when I looked up I'd see her watching Walton move around the room getting fresh drinks, stopping for a moment to talk with somebody, then moving on. Only once did he catch her eye and then he gave her a big smile.

You know, it's a funny thing about him and women. Most of them like him. No—let's see—most of them who are unhappy like him. The way they look at him, they seem to feel he's dependable and understanding and protective. Anyway, something like that. Several of them at these parties, learning he is an old friend of mine, have said this is true. They feel that he has the qualities they miss in their own husbands and ex-husbands. Or he makes them think of the fathers they didn't have or lost or didn't get along with but wanted to. The quality he has that makes them feel this way, I think, is a kind of homespun one with an extra dash of something its opposite—as though he were Will Rogers at home in dinner clothes.

But to get back to Gail Arbuthnot. After one of these times I caught her watching Walton, she smiled, and said, "What was he like in his twenties?"

It caught me off balance, and I was chewing on it when I was saved by a big commotion: loud voices, real anger, the works. A tall blond man with a hooked nose, whom I'd met at one of the other parties (name of David Davis) and learned was a lawyer who wished he was a scientist, was up on his feet, glaring down at this little fellow with whom I started the story—the one who, later on, didn't get up to get any dinner.

I can't quote what Davis was saying, but it was to the effect that anybody who was so callous, cynical and irresponsible as to say that we ought to go ahead right now and drop our whole stockpile of bombs on Russia deserves to be strung up on a public gallows without benefit of trial. The other man didn't say a word, didn't move, just sat there, swishing his glass of whiskey and smiling up at Davis. But that smile, and the downright murderous expression in his eyes! Davis, twice his size, looked like a skinny, gangling, loose-jointed sacrificial calf. And who held the knife? The little dark man, of course.

I turned to Gail and said, "Who in the hell is that?"

She didn't answer me at once, for both of us were watching Julie go over to them (she has the most wonderful walk—no slinking, no gliding, no hip swishing, and yet it's like she invented motion) and save the situation. We couldn't hear what she was saying, but we saw Davis relax, and the man in the chair stop smiling and take a swallow from his drink. After a moment, Davis patted her on the shoulder and moved away to another group; she took his seat and went on talking to the small dark man.

Then Gail sighed and said, "He's Louis Jacoby. He's a genius who's lost his way. I don't understand what he invented, but it was something valuable to do with cameras, and it was a long time ago. Something went wrong about the patent, and he never made a penny from it. It's almost his one topic of conversation. He lives in New York in an attic somewhere, a cold-water flat, and supposedly is working on other inventions, but really is drinking himself to death. Julie and Walton didn't invite him; he's spending the weekend with the Varneys [she pointed out to me a thin, long-necked woman with red jewelry, and a sad-looking, heavy-faced man who carries himself as though he's afraid a building is going to fall on him] and they asked to bring him along."

She stopped talking for a minute, and her eyes followed Walton, pouring a drink. Then she turned back to me and saw I was watching and laughed.

"I can't seem to help it. Don't worry. There's nothing to it. Well, we're all scared of Louis, and especially since his wife finally left him, about two months ago. She's a darling; I'm very fond of her. Most of us who have known them have always put up with him for her sake, and he knows it. But Julie and Walton have never even met him before, and I think it's a shame that the Varneys have to push their missionary work onto innocent bystanders."

That was all there was to it then, though I thought: the Varneys, my eye. It was, it had to be, all the doing of that woman with the red jewelry. Poor Varney, sitting there mournfully, lapping up his liquor, almost pouring it through those jowls of his, would never dream of any kind of missionary work, had even given up trying to salvage himself.

But to go back—or ahead—to Louis Jacoby, sitting there throughout dinner with that black whiskey in one hand and stroking the Herricks' cat with the other. Right after the row with Davis, she'd come up to Jacoby, just walked sedately all the way across the room, past everybody else, making a beeline for him. It was spooky. For a moment she stood there staring at him and he stared down at her. Then she made a purring sound and jumped right into his lap. We held our breaths, expecting him to—I don't know what, maybe twist her neck. But he just smiled and began stroking her, and they stayed together while all the rest of us got our dinner. When he got up to refill his glass, and again when he came back to the chair, he handled her as carefully as though she were made of china.

It was after people had even had second helpings and were starting on dessert and coffee that it all happened. I'd lost my seat by Gail, getting her more salad and coming back to find Walton there. He'd looked up at me with a kind of gleam that in this one week I've discovered means that he's pretty well along with his drinking (he packs away quite a lot, but seldom shows it in obvious ways) and said, "You've had your turn, kid; this is mine." So I was over across the room, between a couple of people whose names I never did get when all of a sudden the room grew awesomely still. It was the kind of quiet that makes you know that somebody has said something so raw, so naked, that no polite social converse can cover it.

I can still see clearly a few faces as they looked during that moment. Walton, really black with anger, his hand gripping in mid-air the bottle from which he was pouring a drink, but the act arrested now, with the neck of the bottle tilted back up. Julie, with so stricken an expression—I don't know how to describe it, but it wasn't in anticipation of trouble, rather as though whatever it was had already happened. Then Gail and Louis Jacoby: that was when I got my bearings and realized that this was between them.

She wasn't the sassy, bright-looking little girl I'd been so taken with. Not any more. Her face was dead white and those big green eyes of hers just blazed. Green eyes, and her red hair. And across the room, still stroking the cat, but with his head kind of sunk into his shoulders, this Jacoby, so that all you could see of him was the hatred in his eyes, that were dilated like he'd been taking dope.

I didn't learn till later what had already been said, but it had gone like this:

JACOBY (out of the blue): How's that floozy friend of yours?

GAIL: I don't know what you're talking about.

JACOBY: My wife, I'm ashamed to say. I know she's living with you.

(And it seems she is, though Gail had not mentioned it to me when she'd spoken of her.)

GAIL: I don't want to talk about it.

JACOBY: I shouldn't think you would, sleeping with her right under the noses of your children.

This was the point at which the great silence came, and the tableau I've just been describing. And then Gail said, in a strained voice, "You're so contemptible, Louis Jacoby, that I almost wish I were— just to see how you'd look then, when you heard it was true. And anyway, I suppose living with you *ought* to make a normal woman into a Lesbian."

There was a moment more as silent as though a huge bell had rung, and when the echo died everybody was waiting for it to ring again. And then Jacoby stood up, with the cat sprawled out in the grip of one hand, clawing at the air and spitting furiously, and let go, hurling that poor dumb screeching animal as hard as he could straight at Gail.

He missed, thank God. But I'll never forget that howling comet of a cat streaking through the air, its claws missing Gail's head by inches, and then the thud when it hit the wall behind her.

That was only one of its nine lives, for it righted itself on the floor and raced away through the dining room, letting out the damnedest falsetto squeaks. And they hadn't even died away before we had the next tableau.

This was Walton. Standing over Jacoby, he looked nine feet tall. From where I was sitting, I couldn't see his face, only the back of his head, but I know how he looked, how those eyes of his can suddenly become hooded, like some predatory bird's. And the steel in his look must have been like the steel of his voice, which all of us could hear, though he spoke very low.

"You get out of my house, and don't come back. Now."

It was like the crack of doom. Nothing of all Jacoby's malevolence, even the act of throwing the cat, held a candle to it. It was daemonic, yet under complete control. Yet! What do I mean, *yet*? That was what gave it its quality. It was the genie bottled.

And Jacoby wilted. He swaggered a little, but pitifully, muttering something about nothing could please him more, he didn't want to be there anyway, and walked for the door.

I guess the reason I got a look at Julie just then was that the Varney woman stood up, spat out something about the provocation being more than a person could bear, and stalked out with Jacoby. As she passed Julie, I suddenly caught Julie's expression. She was staring at Walton with a look that was pure awe, made of equal parts of reverence and pride. I remember thinking right then that if she ever gave him that look when he was able to let it sink in it would probably settle his black moods and the times he feels rejected by her, once and for all. And that means, of course, that I've never seen her look at him that way before or since.

But it was right at this point that I got into the act. I'd risen automatically when all this went on. By the time Jacoby started out and Mrs. Varney followed, I was standing right by the door leading into the front hall. I'm not sure even now why I moved over there, but I did, and Mrs. V. swished by me, all her red jewelry blinking like the eyes of hell. The next thing I knew, my arm was being gripped by something that felt like a manacle, and I was staring into Jacoby's eyes —and *they* looked maniacal.

I've called him a little man, but he was right even with me. Maybe he has one of those swami acts whereby he can make himself taller at will, or maybe—but you figure out the alternative.

Anyway, he said to me (and now I could tell just how drunk he was), "I think it was you put her up to that."

And then I felt Walton there beside me—and I didn't mind it, either. I could feel his arm brushing mine, but even before that I could feel him simply by looking into Jacoby's eyes.

This time he wasn't wilting, and they blazed back at Walton while his grip on my arm tightened till I thought I'd screech like that poor cat. But I didn't. I just said, "You'd better let go of my arm." I wasn't really frightened. I'm no hero—but I'd been so intent on all the melodrama that I didn't feel this part could be real: I was a spectator, not an actor in the play.

Anyway, that murderous hold slackened, and I could feel my arm coming to life again, the way it does when the doctor stops pumping that infernal machine with which he takes your blood pressure. Jacoby didn't say a word, but closed his eyes and stood there, swaying, for a moment, then followed Mrs. Varney out the door.

I looked up at Walton and he smiled. Although he was looking right at me, I don't think he even saw me. And that smile—if there was something like triumph in it, then it was reminiscent triumph, for it was a remote sort of smile, as though what he was occupied with had happened long ago, and had nothing to do with Jacoby or Gail—or me. And he put his hand on my shoulder and said, "Dud, you're not going to think very well of us around here."

What he said clearly had nothing to do with what he was thinking about, so I didn't answer, and we went back into the living room, where everybody was buzzing and bustling, the way people and flies do after a disturbance, and Julie was comforting Gail, who was crying.

The guests began to crowd around Walton, telling him how wonderful he'd been, and spouting their various indignations about the whole business. I got trampled on in the rush, so I started across the room toward Gail and Julie. But before I'd taken more than a few steps Gail jumped up from her chair. I saw her face: it had that kind of blind intensity that means an overpowering need or hunger that drives a person straight from the base of his spine to his objective, like some human missile. Through fire, through ice, through steel or fog— that's what the expression says. Or lack of expression, for it's always a kind of hypnotic mask of desperation that drives him like a loosed arrow. There are no obstructions in his path. There can't be.

And so now Gail just ripped right through that throng around Walton and flung herself against him, crying so hard that although she was talking all the time you couldn't understand a word she said. It all came out muffled and shaky.

Walton looked more uncomfortable than anything else. He put his arm around her shoulders in a gingerly sort of way. (Somehow it gave me the creeps to see his hand there, watch his fingers touch her shoulder and lift away as though they'd been burned, and then settle down again lower, where her dress covered her. I don't know how my eyes happened to light there, but it looked, for just this moment, as though his hand had a separate animate life of its own, replete with a sense of original sin!) And he let her keep her face there against his shirt front (she must have drenched it) but his heart certainly wasn't in it. I could see his face above the heads of the other people, and he kept looking at Julie with a curious expression. It was a pleading look— as though he was begging her to understand that *this* wasn't any of his doing. And he kept patting Gail's back with an automatic, wooden motion; she might have been a bale of hay.

Everybody had hushed all over again, and I guess they all did what I did. Seeing the way Walton was looking at Julie, I turned to look at her too. But Julie seemed perfectly composed and sympathetic, with just a kind of sad smile over Gail's being so upset. And then she walked over and the other people moved aside for her and she joined Walton and Gail and he put his free hand on *her* shoulder and she smiled up at him.

Then she said something in a low voice to Gail and Gail let go of Walton and went off to the back of the house with Julie, their arms around each other.

And the group broke up and returned to normal and made drinks and settled down again. All but Varney. He stood there beside Walton (it was the first I'd realized that he hadn't gone home with his wife and Jacoby), teetering back and forth on his heels, that endless drink in one hand, and gazing up at Walton like a cocker spaniel—no, he looked more like a bloodhound, with his mournful dewlaps and his blood-shot eyes and the whole melancholy careful way he carries himself.

Walton glanced at him once or twice. But the look said that Varney was both inanimate and uninteresting.

I found myself studying Walton's face as though it were new to me. It's awkward and big-boned, and more oval than square, perhaps because his chin isn't up to the rest of it. Once, last week, he joked about his weak chin, as he does, more often, about his big ears. Not good-looking in any conventional sense, he seems so when animated; he has extraordinarily expressive features. And perhaps that, in turn, is related to his wrinkles. They fan out from his eyes to cover all of his cheekbones; there are two or three deep horizontal lines in his forehead and two even deeper vertical ones running from either nostril down past his mouth.

I make him sound like a relief map. At any rate, all these lines and wrinkles, together with his rather thin mouth, which, when set, makes him look pretty forbidding (and yet looks large and generous when he's laughing), give him an appearance of unhappiness in repose— and when, under strain or in anger, his eyes get hooded over, he looks downright scary, as sullen and violent as this fellow Jacoby.

And that's the way he began to look now. He was moving from the embarrassment or distress of the scene with Gail into anger over having been embarrassed, or perhaps in angry resolution of whatever had been troubling him. And with poor Varney hovering around him like a broken-winged pigeon, I decided to go over to see if I could relieve the situation. I reached them just as Varney finally managed to get something out.

"It was great," he said, all flushed and earnest, and took a quick lap at his drink as though overcome by his own audacity.

Walton looked directly at him, a little contemptuously, and then away again. It was as though he were brushing away a persistent insect without raising his hand.

But this seemed only to make Varney more determined. He seemed to have a desperate need to say whatever was on his mind, and Walton's indifference increased this need.

Gazing up at Walton in mournful excitement, he repeated, "It was simply great. Great, that's all." He teetered slightly as he raised his glass again, and I realized that he was even drunker than I had thought.

This time Walton gave him the flattest kind of look—one of subcontempt. "What?"

Varney fairly capered around him now.

"What you did to Louis. The way you dismissed him. The power of it. The strength. Nobody's like that any more. Nobody but you. It's tremendous. It's just great."

At first Walton looked dumbfounded, incredulous, then a little suspicious. He opened his mouth, but closed it without speaking, and his bleak black look returned.

Varney was oblivious of this. He seemed enchanted by his own articulateness, and after guzzling the rest of his drink in two or three gulps that jiggled his jowls, he went on: "Tremendous. I admire you. Reshpect you. You're a man. None of the rest of us are. Any more. I revere you."

His eyes nearly rolled out of sight right then, for Walton reached out and grabbed him by both lapels, almost pulling him off his feet. And now Walton's voice was loud and choked, the very opposite of that fine-tempered steel when he had spoken to Jacoby. "Shut up," he said fiercely, swinging Varney first back, then forward, then back. "Shut up, you—clown!"

And again there was a silence, with everybody just staring in awe, and poor Varney rolling back and forth like a puppet. Then Walton released him, to fall back onto the couch, and without a word or even a glance at the rest of us, he strode across the room fast, right past Julie, who was returning, went up the stairs and disappeared. Over our heads a door slammed.

He didn't come down again.

Julie was magnificent. She remained the graceful hostess she had been all evening, but she took over for him, too. I helped her a little with the drinks, but she didn't need me; she merely indulged me. And all the guests responded and stayed on a while instead of departing two by two, in a state of shell shock. All, that is, except for poor Varney. Another fellow who really did have to leave took him along in a few minutes.

I have seldom known anyone so short a time, been less interested in him as a person and still been so overwhelmed by a sense of the dreadfulness of his fate. To go from that experience with Walton home (home!) to his wife and Jacoby!

When the last guests left, Julie and I cleaned up the glasses and ashtrays. Then we made coffee and sat at the kitchen table.

To go from Walton to Julie is like going from the first to the second movement of one of the Beethoven symphonies—from an allegro vivace e con brio, maybe, to one of those andantes of his—or perhaps the third movement adagio of the Ninth. (Reread this; looks a little pretentious.)

And so it is, I guess—pretentious. Yet my feeling about Julie is genuine. And I've paused here, because I'm sure I'm going to want Cyn to read this, and I'm thinking about her relation to Lydia, and how, consequently, she's felt hostile to Julie without ever meeting her. Yes, you have, Cyn.

Anyway, it's funny about Cyn and Lydia. That one meeting, when Cyn had her doubts about Walton, but none at all about Lydia. And, over all these years, the way the two women have continued to exchange Christmas letters, neither of them ever missing a year! Women!

But not all women. Even after so short an acquaintance with Julie I can't imagine her doing that—with any woman. She's too private.

The poetry enters with Julie. I've already written about the way she walks, the way she moves. Then there's her voice: it's subtle—soft and husky, but naturally so. Not guttural and throaty, but husky in the sense of a natural whispering quality in it, even when she's speaking in an ordinary tone. She's short and slender, with small bones and a very supple, rounded figure.

Her eyes are black, opaque when she's sad or meditative, but tremendously, dancingly alive when she's happy. And her hair is jet black; it shines.

She has a mobile face, with a wide range of moods and expressions —yet through almost all of them I get an impression of two dominant and alternative emotions: joy and sadness. Simple words, but I mean the real things—and they're rare. Not vivacity; joy. Not depression or bitterness; sadness.

Gail Arbuthnot, I said, is so exuberant that she gives a para-doxical sense of some hurt just below the surface that makes her vulner-able. When I speak of Julie's sadness, I mean something quite different, almost the opposite. It's as though her hurt were sealed off long ago; she's not going to let anybody even get close to it, but each new thing that makes her feel bad brings out a reflection of the old hurt.

Am I in love with her, that I write like this? No, but if somebody pushed me a little, I could be. If Cyn weren't there, or Walton. To me, Julie is a rarely beautiful woman—and I mean *that* word, too. Her personality has pure lines. If something prevents her from saying what she really believes, then she won't say anything. She writes poetry— has had some published. But I've never read any, and when I asked her if she'd let me, she said, "No, I haven't written anything in a long time and I don't like the old things any more."

We didn't talk much while we were cleaning up, or even at first when we sat down to coffee. But finally she pushed her cup away and looked up and said, "I don't believe Walton's asleep. I'll go see if he'll come down now."

It was as though she were asking a question. But I didn't have an answer, and after a minute she left the kitchen. I could hear her climbing the steps.

I could hear more—the humming of their voices—and suddenly I thought of the children and wondered how they could have slept through all the things going on downstairs, and how they could be (or seem to be, anyway) such good, normal kids, with all this swirling around them.

Then I heard Walton, his voice raised in irritation, "All right. All right. You go ahead and I'll be down in a minute."

When she came back, her face was composed, but her eyes were sad again. We didn't say much, just sat there sipping coffee and listening to Walton pacing back and forth overhead.

Then there was a long silence, and Julie sat with her head bowed. When she finally raised it again and looked right at me, her eyes were filled with tears. She kept shaking her head, and her mouth trembled as though she wanted to say something but couldn't.

And then he started down the stairs, his footsteps heavy and slow. The picture in my mind had him dragging his feet, a big middle-aged child, pouting, one hand on the railing, stopping on each step and staring petulantly at the wallpaper.

Julie brushed away at her eyes, went over to the sink and poured another cup of coffee for herself and one for Walton. Then she scurried back to the table and sat down, just before he reached the kitchen.

He stood there in the doorway, as irresolute as I have ever seen him. A moment before, hearing him on the stairs and seeing Julie in tears, I'd felt as though I'd like to punch him, but now my heart went out to him. The child image pertained, all right, but the mixture of shame and awkwardness and defiance that I saw on his face now upset me. And then Julie reached out her hand and took his and drew him down beside her and he relaxed and slumped there as though he'd come home.

It was then at last that I came out of my paralysis and asked all sorts of questions about the people who had been at the party. Walton answered most of them, at first almost grudgingly, as though he had to pull the answers out of himself. But he grew easier as we went on, until it became a normal conversation. Now and then Julie would temper some judgment of his with a kinder interpretation or a word about this or that person's good qualities, to balance some sharp thing he had said. But each time she'd squeeze his arm or stroke his hand, as though to be sure that she didn't lose contact with him.

And finally, when we'd got really chatty and comfortable, and Walton was laughing and wholly relaxed, she said, "Walton, whatever did happen with Otis Varney, poor soul? I know he's what drove you upstairs, but that's all I do know. And I feel so sorry for him."

Walton stiffened and his eyes narrowed. He looked at her closely before he spoke, and when he finally did reply he cut his words off as though he were biting them: "He slobbered all over me."

She looked at him gravely. It was as though the question she was going to ask was so important to her that she was afraid it would break.

"What kind of slobbering? You mean he praised you for standing up to Jacoby?"

The look he gave her then was poisonous. His eyes were shining with a concentrate of malice.

"Yes," he said bitterly. "He praised me. Six-foot me, for standing up to five-foot Jacoby. The slob, the clown. He said I was great, that I was the only *man* he knew. All the rest are boys."

And now that look was gone, and in its stead was torment—as though he were at bay. I had the illusion that he was looking first one way, then another, swinging around to face somebody who'd stolen behind him to get at him from the rear, then back again to face the others. What others? For Walton didn't move a muscle.

Julie said softly, "Oh, Walton. That poor man."

He jumped up and slammed his fist down on the table, slopping coffee over the rims of all our cups. His face was contorted and he stood there, looming over the table.

"That poor man!" he shouted. "That poor man! Jesus Christ, what poor man? You don't ever understand." And he reached down, picked up his cup and hurled it, coffee and all, against the stove.

For a moment more he stayed there, staring at the rivulets of coffee running down the white porcelain and at the shattered remnants of the cup, some of them still spinning crazily on the floor; then he swung around, gave Julie one last wild look, and left. For the second time in one evening, I heard him climbing the stairs alone.

It was awfully silent after the door slammed upstairs. I fiddled with lighting a cigarette. And then I heard her voice, so quiet it scared me.

"Dudley, I don't know what I'm going to do."

I had to look up. Her face was set and white. I couldn't think of anything sensible to say, so I mumbled idiotically, "You mean Walton?"

She didn't answer me. But after a moment she said, "It gets worse. I used to think that I understood, at least partly, and could help him. But the longer we live together, the less I think I do. And what's much worse—it's gotten so that I get almost numb about something like this. I expect it to happen, and when it does, while I'm unhappy about it, my feeling's sort of blurred. And I hate that; whatever else happens, I want to feel fully everything that happens to me. Or I'm dead."

I thought of the three tableaux of the evening again, and said, "He was magnificent with that Jacoby."

She looked at me in a tired way and nodded. "Yes, and every so often he's that way again. At first, that's the way I always thought of him, strong and tall and self-controlled, speaking up against anyone and anything he believed wrong, but under control. But how do you put that together with just now—and with Otis Varney? He's at least two totally different men."

I thought again many of the things I had earlier, especially about Gail and the two of them, but all I blurted out was, "But you love him, Julie?"

She shook her head so hard that her hair swirled across her face. I could see that her eyes were wet.

"I don't know," she said, and her voice sounded inconsolable. "I don't know any more. If I am as loving as I used to feel all the time toward him, when I'd blame myself and search for whatever it was in me that caused us to quarrel and become strangers, then it seems to me that he either just takes me for granted or even taunts me. And I can't stand living with him separate and withdrawn from each other: it's so cold and lonely." She wiped her eyes.

"I can't imagine his taking you for granted," I told her. "I never saw a man so much in love with his wife—and after all these years."

She shook her head again.

"That's not loving *me*. I don't know what it is, but it's some secret idea or vision or symbol of what he wants from life that he makes of me. He's a very secretive man, Dudley. When he seems to be most in love with me, there's a whole part of him that isn't even with me, that's holding a dialogue with whatever he's hunting or possessed by, so that sometimes—it's hard to say, but it seems to me that *they're* talking about me quite objectively, even while he's making love to me."

I knew what she meant. And I reached over and took her hand, but she pushed me away and said, "Don't don't don't. Don't be kind to me," and got up and went up to their bedroom. And I sat there a long time but didn't get any very useful thinking done.

March, April

ALL that spring it had seemed to Walton that Julie was pecking at his tired nerves like some exquisite but relentless woodpecker. Rat-a-tat-tat! Rat-a-tat! Rat-a-tat-tat! How, he sometimes asked himself, could the lovely, quiet girl-woman he had married become, in nine short years, a shrew?

And then, in the silence of his mind hearing this unspoken question, an uneasy shame would fill him, and doubts of the validity of his complaint. Doubts—because it seemed to him at such times that there were at least two levels of reality, and he didn't know which to trust. Had she really pressed him so hard last night, been as suspicious and sarcastic as it seemed to him in retrospect, about his account of the struggle at the Foundation over Kiefer's appointment? Standing on the rain- and wind-swept platform at the Northport station, awaiting the morning train to New York, he would search, drain his mind for the exact words she had spoken, but never find them. Or, drowsing on the late-afternoon train on his way home again, he would start suddenly, as though an invisible hand had tapped him on the shoulder in admonition, and he would have a moment's vision of Julie's pleading face last night when he flung his napkin on the table and stood up, preparatory to abandoning dinner for the—third time that week?

Something in him would loosen then, there on the home-bound train, release him briefly from the strait jacket in which he had not known he was confined. Some half-apprehended tension slipped, lost its grip, and he was no longer disturbed by the presence of the stranger between him and the aisle, sharing his seat. Only then did he realize that he had been feeling so hemmed in that he had unconsciously been scrounging himself up against the window. But after a respite of a few minutes fatigue would again clutch at him, stiffening the muscles of his legs and arms. The intrusion of the invisible finger had deprived him of the full nap he so much needed. This sense of deprivation merged into anger at the source of his awakening, then in turn at Julie, who surely must have really been hammering at him last night—else why would he be so angry? And when he finally descended from the train and set his face toward home, he would also set his jaw.

But not always. Not even almost always. There were times when, on his way to the evening train, late and hurrying, he stopped by a flower stand because of his need to bring home in his hands some visible, tangible expression of his love and gratitude. He, Walton Herrick, had actually slipped the gray shroud of years? had such a wife? such children? such a home?

Then, if he was driving his own car from the station, he would take the short way home. If someone else was driving him, he would ask to be left at the corner, so that he might walk across his acre of grass, under his own trees, to his house.

His? Not theirs? he asked himself more than once, when the pronoun intruded in his thoughts more importantly than usual. Even minimal honesty would not allow him to change it. This did not mean that he was impervious to *theirs* or *ours;* this was a solitary thing, the celebration of triumph over loneliness and hopelessness. Once, walking across the yard with no one in view, he caught himself explaining with ludicrous earnestness, "Ours, Julie, ours, but mine too."

And on all these occasions—buying flowers, driving home, arriving and being greeted by the children, especially at the first glimpse of Julie—his heart would fill so that he could never understand, two days later, a week, a month, what had happened—that this should have ended so abruptly, that a curtain should have been drawn, not upon a play, but on life, his life. But Julie shut him out, he would think, and almost instantly: no, no, it was he who was at fault, who must be, with his literalness, his selfishness, his fear of openness, his touchiness. And the fights. And worse, the silences, the withdrawals.

Sometimes he would groan to himself, I have no memory, I cannot learn, or I would understand how what is so beautiful, so filling, can be shattered without my ever catching the instant of transition, the moment of reversal. And then, days later, the pall would lift—and there he would be, he thought with what little humor he could summon, there he would be again with flowers in his hand or a small box in his pocket or simply with a look in his eyes which he knew must tell her how he treasured her. Sisyphus, he thought once, was a piker. But Sisyphus had no Julie.

Ultimately she always eluded him. The thought was torment, most of all because he knew secretly (sometimes he wondered why he did not want himself to know) that what she wanted most was for him to make it impossible for her to elude him. Now, now, he felt sure sometimes, I have her, she's mine to hold, at some intimate moment late at night, holding her heart's face between his two hands. Or when an unaccustomed zeal had led him to respond to Tim's urgent plea, "Some kids' fathers build them playhouses," not with words but with a trip to the lumber yard. Thereafter he had spent two hours in the yard, placing and replacing two-by-fours on the grass, trying to visualize the framework of the proposed house. Once, sweaty, dirty, perplexed, he wiped his brow with his forearm and looked up, to find Julie gazing at him with a look so tender, so joyful, so altogether rewarding that it sustained him through the six weeks during which he built his monument to trial and error.

Then, then, these times, he knew that he had caught her, that he finally understood what she wanted, what she needed from him. Only to feel chilled with the icy winds of total rejection a day or two later when, so far as he could see, nothing had changed. "Julie," he would cry at last, after hours of hurt silence, "what have I *done?*" to be answered dryly, "Nothing. That's the trouble. You never do anything. You leave it all to me—good, bad and indifferent."

But he didn't. He couldn't be that wrong. He loved her, he loved the children, he earned a good living, he took care of them. . . . And then again, after a while, he would come in one night, on the brink of despair, to find the whole world of home blossoming again.

Or so it seemed to him.

One such time was early in April of this year. On a Thursday night he had been delayed unavoidably at the office, and had called to say he would be late. Only after Julie had answered listlessly that she didn't mind and he had hung up did he realize that his relief was so profound as to suggest that an intolerable burden had been lifted from him. Did he dread her disapproval so much then? he wondered in amazement. When aroused, she had a sharp tongue, but no potential scolding or even tongue-lashing could produce such radical effects. Was he a man or— He would not finish the homily. But, as he approached home, he braced himself with a determination to be firm, quiet and sure. Those were the words in his mind, he thought bitterly. The Lion of the Foundation! The man who had braved the Congressional Committee!

But he was greeted, not as husband, father and householder, but as a returning hero!

"What's the matter?" he kept asking as Julie met him with a radiant face and a deep, sweet kiss, as Peter grasped his hand with a fervent shake, and Tim shouted, "Yay for Daddy," with Jenny sleepily providing an antiphonal "fur Dad-dee."

Bewildered, sheepishly pleased, half scared to accept the welcome —as though, he thought in the midst of the hubbub, it might really be for someone else, a case of mistaken identity right in his own home— he appealed desperately to Julie, "Please, please, what is it? Tell me, Julie."

"Walton," she said, and turned and shook her head the way she did to hide a tear, while Peter watched her, half anxious, half clearly filled with a tremendous elation, "there's nothing special. We're just glad we have you."

"Mummy's crying," yelled Tim. "Yay for Dad!" He stopped abruptly in mid-kitchen, and asked Peter in sudden consternation, "Why is that good?"

"Don't keep asking why," Julie said softly as she and Walton were preparing for bed that night. "Just because, that's all. Sometimes I see— But let's not talk about it. We talk too much."

And later, drowsy, knowing so pervasive a contentment that he felt it could never end, Walton whispered shyly against Julie's cheek, "I've had a wonderful time."

But the next morning, after a week's absence, the Spoiler showed up while Walton was shaving, rode silently with him to the station, and climbed aboard the train with nonchalance, airily swinging his attaché case, which was, of course, filled with sheets of complaints. In idle moments, Walton thought of him as wearing a pork-pie hat and a bow tie.

What did all this nonsense mean? Walton asked himself that very Friday morning as the train grumbled along the last mile of tunnel entering Grand Central. For he had been pursuing this fantasy for a half hour, having abandoned the morning newspaper since he found it impossible to read for the hot resentments that kept importuning him: "After last night, Julie might have got up to make your breakfast" . . . "All those sweet things she said last night! She barely said good-bye this morning!" . . . "Making love solves a lot of things—until the next day" . . . "What *was* it all about, anyway?" It was part of the horror of these whisperings that they were so petty, so fatuous, so infantile that one had to whip oneself up into anger to give them sufficient dignity to ward off self-loathing.

But the fantasy? He honestly struggled with his touchiness, his being spoiled and selfish (this was the way he tried to think of the origin of his bill of complaints, whenever he wasn't too angry even to attempt to examine himself), and since he couldn't overcome them by will and clarity, he found that the simplest way to combat them was to personify them in this fashion. The Spoiler lost his grimness and stature if he were made into a commuter (no Lucifer, but a shabby bourgeois devil). Who could be terror-stricken by a man in a bow tie?

To be sure, there had been many times when the Spoiler had represented, rather, that intrusion from outer reality that seemed sure to appear whenever there was the likelihood of a protracted period of happiness. The road ahead was clear; then a shadow fell across it. Whence it came originally he knew well enough: his mother's voice, her quick step. But as time went on, it seemed increasingly true that events proved the actuality of a nemesis that haunted him. At a crucial moment in work, in love, in a decisive conversation—a fist pounded on a door, a hammer shattered the quiet, there came a police whistle or a siren. And he faltered, his heart grew leaden.

Or so it seemed. But now, in these recent middle years, there was a change of costume, of scene. The knocking, the intrusion came to be inner, and he could not bear it. He had to find a new way to meet this threat—of what?

He did not know, but exorcise this Spoiler he must and could. Yet all the time he knew, of course, that the forces so symbolized were part of his own nature, and these no conjuring stunt could dismiss or transform. The fantasy was at best a staying action that enabled him to enter the office with a fair degree of equanimity, until the diversion of work could fill his day and soften the issues of dissension between Julie and himself.

But that very Friday night, at the home of some friends, Walton furiously observed what seemed to him Julie's wanton flirting with a scientist who had newly moved to Northport, endured it in a black silence for an hour, and then, when the man's hand rested for a moment on Julie's bare shoulder, rose and without a word stalked from the house, not to return. The harmonious interlude was over.

It had ended, moreover, in a familiar fashion. He had not, in word or gesture or expression of any sort beyond his bleak and sullen silence, indicated to Julie his jealousy or anger. He had confronted neither her nor the man. He had packed all this feeling deeper and deeper in himself, and finally, when filled with it, fled the scene. Trudging the several miles home—for he had left the car for Julie—he reflected bitterly that it was always he who made the public scene, through commission or omission. For he knew from the past that when his defection was discerned the bewilderment of the other guests would center on the strange behavior of a man with so distinguished a record that they could not believe him capable of a puerile act of this sort. But he was, he was.

Public versus private shame was an empty question to worry, but he persisted—to numb or wholly evade the deeper hurt? This much at least was fact: he had not made up the equally bitter complaints that Julie uttered at home, to him alone. His absorption in work, his perfunctory and inadequate attention to his share of the maintenance of their home, the depletion of his store of imagination and understanding from their full employment during the work day—and his resultant passive indulgence of the children, and apathy over their needs and problems—these were the airs she played, over and over again, with ingenious and unpredictable variations.

Yes, this was fact—but surely fact with some justification. What he couldn't feel, couldn't know with consistent certainty, was whether she really played as loudly and insistently as it seemed to him—or whether, only too deeply aware of these inadequacies in himself, he was so raw to any mention of them that he grossly exaggerated the force and extent of what she actually said.

Whichever (home at last, he directed his tired steps down the driveway to their house), the interaction was fraying and irritating to such a point by now that he did not see how they could hold together much longer. He felt sore and disconsolate and hopeless.

When he had paid and dismissed the high school girl who had been taking care of the children, he slumped in an armchair in the living room. Almost at once his mind was crowded with doubts and fears and guilt.

He saw again the scientist's hand resting lightly on Julie's shoulder: it was the very lightness of the touch, as palpable to him in retrospect as though it had been his own skin that those fingers had brushed, its very uninsistence that haunted him now. This was the mark of sureness, of a confidence that came from steady inner weather. He remembered now noting the man's face and manner when they had been introduced —the humor and liveness of the eyes, the unaffected firmness of the handshake, the comfortable way in which he carried his solid, compact body—all signs of somebody *there,* a man.

And was he not a man himself? Yes, he thought, with anger spurting up in him, he was and had proved it in action. But not this kind of man, not a man of quiet strength, of constancy and balance. Not the kind of man both Julie and he himself wished he were.

He stood up and began pacing the room. The headlights of a car dipped and rose, turning the corner, and he rushed to a window to peer out. But the car gathered speed and passed the driveway. Pressing his forehead against the cold pane, Walton stared out into the black, frosty night, more like November than April.

Car after car, even at this late hour, swung along the main road at the end of their lot, but none turned into Blake's Wood Road, and finally he dropped back into a chair and sat, staring dully before him. Upstairs, one of the children moaned and turned in bed and was silent again. A neighbor's dog let out a long howl. The horn on a distant car blared.

He could see Julie in her gold dress (he had not wanted her to wear the dress, had said it was too formal) entering a strange house with the man—

He did not even know his name. Thanks to his—what? egotism?— he never listened during introductions. He did not know who this man was, where he lived. And Julie—

He saw her now, drunk. Unlike himself, she was a very moderate drinker, but under rare provocation would drink a great deal. It did not make her sodden or quarrelsome or foolish-tongued: she fitted none of the clichés. Julie drunk was a flashing if feverish spirit—sprite? no, spirit. All of the quiet, the sadness burned out of her, she was on fire, too bright and hot for most people. They would admire, they would even look on enraptured, but not draw too close. At such times, it was as though they were afraid even her wit could scorch them. But this man—

Walton looked at his watch. Past two o'clock . . . He must act. But even as he rose from the chair he heard the garage doors being closed and in comic haste snapped on a lamp, picked up a magazine and resumed his seat.

She stood in the doorway. She was not obviously drunk; yet there was, in fact, something more deliberate about her than usual. He watched her remove her coat, light a cigarette, cross the room toward him and then stand a few feet away, motionless, regarding him, slender and intense in the glistening gold dress.

"Well?" he said at last, and cleared his throat.

Her black eyes were mocking, dancing with mockery. She dropped him a demure curtsey.

"Very well, sir," she replied, "and thank you for asking." Blowing out an exaggerated funnel of smoke, she tapped an imaginary ash from the cigarette and, raising a shoulder, moved a few mincing steps in caricature of a fashion mannequin.

This was not Julie. Perhaps she *was* drunk.

She looked at him thoughtfully. Then, in deliberate provocation, she shrugged one thin golden shoulder strap down onto her arm and with her hand combed her hair over one eye. "I feel sooo lan-ger-us"—she drawled the words huskily. "Perhaps you will serve us a leetle dreenk and ve vill tawlk."

Swaying there in her ridiculous parody, she was improbably lovely. So beautiful, so aglow, so—so goddamn full of some new palpitant life that Walton ached, ached with a fury that he did not understand.

"You're drunk," he blurted out, and heard the words fall with a heavy leaden thud.

"Oh!" She placed her fingertips over her mouth and widened her eyes in mock consternation. "Nawt dronk. Just a leetle teedly and so very lan-ger-us."

She regarded him with her head cocked to one side. Then she shook her head so emphatically that her sleek black hair swirled across her face.

"Nooo," she said. "Nooo dreenk. Ees very naughty. Julie naughty, weecked girl. Walton very good, reespectable man. So Julie weell get her own dreenk."

She strutted across the room and made an elaborate rite of removing a bottle of Scotch from the liquor cabinet. There followed an extended pantomime of measuring a drink. But as she started for the kitchen after finding the ice bucket empty, Walton was on her. He seized her so roughly by the arm that half of the whiskey spilled from the glass.

"Will you cut out this damn foolishness?" he demanded. "Did you come home alone?"

Her eyes hardened, and she looked at him with so level a gaze that he released her.

"I came home," she said coldly, with a dignity bordering on contempt, and resumed her way to the refrigerator, "and I came alone. The more fool I."

For a moment he stood there, glaring at her.

"I left," he said, with a kind of rough awkwardness, "because I couldn't stand seeing that man paw you."

She loosened the ice cubes with a savage wrench, dropped two in the glass and walked directly past him, as though he were not there. Raising the bottle again, she poured more Scotch in the glass. Then she faced him.

"No man pawed me," she said, enunciating the words with a chilly precision, "and no man will paw me."

She crossed the living room to the couch, and the very grace of her movement infuriated him. But he could only glower at her; he felt impotent and sheepish. When he spoke, his voice sounded weak and unconvincing to himself.

"I saw him. I saw him with his hand on your shoulder."

She sipped her drink, shuddered delicately over its strength and leaned back. She crossed one knee over the other and swung the toe of her slipper, up and down, up and down.

"He is a very charming man," she said.

Walton clenched his fists. He strode across the room and stood threateningly over her.

She looked up at him blandly.

"Not as tall as you. No, not as big as you," she said slowly, "but a very charming man. We talked most of the evening about his wife, whom he adores, and about their five children. His family arrives to-morrow."

Walton felt the tension in his arms and legs relax. But before he could say anything, she went on.

"When I left, he said he'd be glad to take me home, but since I had our car (he'd looked), he thought I'd probably prefer to drive it. So he followed me in his to the end of our road, and went on to his own home." She underlined the last four words scornfully.

Walton stared at her in silent misery.

She looked him full in the eyes.

"You're a fool," she said slowly and distinctly. "A fool and a spoiled child. And I'm not going to put up with it any more. I'm sick and tired of having *not* to explain to people about your antics, lest they think I'm ashamed of you. Which I am. Tonight I am. How a man can stand up before a Congressional Committee and say things that sound like Thomas Jefferson and Abraham Lincoln, things that no one else in the country has the courage to say, and yet, just because another man finds his wife attractive, run from the house, run away, and leave her there to face all the embarrassment—how one man can do and be both things I'll never understand."

She took another swallow from her drink, set it down hard, and looked up at him again. Her expression softened.

"What will I ever do with you?"

He dropped to his knees beside her, and with a groan buried his head in her lap. As though in pain, he burrowed against the rustling gold dress, against the soft flesh under it, rolling his head from side to side and thrusting it against her. And she began, with her small competent hand, to stroke it.

"I don't know, I don't know," she repeated softly. "I don't ever know what I'm going to do with you."

And his arms reached out and his hands dug deep into her shoulders as he pulled her to him, crushing her and the gold dress against him as though he would destroy them both.

And yet by the following Sunday she was gone, withdrawn again deep into some recess in her life where he could not find her. That familiar and yet to him indefinable constraint was upon her; she was cool and aloof, twisting away from him when he sought to hold her— just sufficiently to avoid his reaching hands, but not so much as to enable him to know with certainty that the movement had been intentional.

His reaching hands—and the reaching hands of his mind. He was not, he felt, permitted contact of any sort. He felt guilty, without any clear sense of a just cause for guilt. Was it because he had spent all of Saturday afternoon in his study, wrestling with his memorandum on the Asiatic Studies program? Or because he lavished such exclusive attention on Gail Arbuthnot Saturday evening? Or his being too tired to get up Sunday morning to drive the children to Sunday school?

Finally, late Sunday, he burst out, "Julie, what have I done? Why are you treating me like a leper? Just because I had that memo to do yesterday—"

She faced him coldly, with what he thought of as her astral face and body.

"Memo, memo, memo," she repeated wearily. "Why do you always think the cause is something that just happened? Or that whenever I'm depressed it has to do with you? Or even that I *am* depressed, simply because I'm quiet?"

He spread out his hands in defeat and left the room. But she was depressed and withdrawn; the ultimate proof lay in the children, in Peter's anxious looks, in Tim's rare floor-kicking sulkiness, in Jennifer's unexplained tantrum. And on Monday morning Walton was too dispirited even to summon up his fellow traveler.

The following week brought Dudley Foote to town, and in that cheerful man's visit and the problem of finding him a job Walton found distraction. Until another Friday night and the explosion over Jacoby and Varney.

Thereafter April ran a somber course. Just as the true spring was delayed by gray skies, raw winds and a steady drizzle, so Walton and Julie lived in a consistently gray weather. For two or three days at a time they spoke only of the daily necessities of schedule or of casual events in the affairs of friends. The children, in keeping with their several temperaments, were moody or almost hysterically loud.

The whole family underwent a bout of some sort of virus flu. As was his wont, Walton was genuinely solicitous, thoughtful and patient with Julie and the children, bringing them soup in bed, and remembering little gifts when he returned from New York. Julie, pale, almost sallow, sat up in bed to open one such package, uncovered a beautiful slender deep blue vase, and said, "I should be sick all the time," so mournfully that Walton roared with laughter. After a moment she joined in, but her laughter turned to tears, and suddenly they were in each other's arms, clinging as though some *force majeure* were attempting to pry them apart.

Then Walton himself succumbed, stayed in bed for two nights and a day, groaning and cursing and barking at the children, before getting up the second day, half-cured, and despite Julie's objections heaving himself off to work, a very articulate martyr—to return in the evening exhausted and with the disposition of a snapping turtle.

And so April waned into May, the air softened, and a pale sun thrust itself through the gray skies. Julie worked in the garden; the children cast off their sweaters and their shrill cries echoed in the early evening as, newly liberated, they rode their bicycles and skated; and Walton, arriving home at the end of the day, took his old-fashioned out to the rustic bench under the big maples and, surveying his greening acre and listening to the tree toads, thought again that they would surely persevere through their vicissitudes and come finally out into some sunlit meadow, level and serene.

DEPOSITION: 2

PARKER, GOODMAN and SYKES
507 Fifth Ave.
New York City

May 11, 1953

DEAR ABE—

Your letter threw me. It's taken me a week to get together with
it. Not because your idea is so far-fetched, but because it's so obviously
right that I keep wondering why I never thought of it myself. Not just
this idea—the governorship—but the whole idea of Walton Herrick as
a political figure.

I think "figure" is just right. That's what he could and would be,
from the start: a *figure*. Not a figurehead. Not a stuffed shirt with a
massive kind of good looks in the Harding sense. But a real figure of
some stature and real individuality.

But it's the assignment that stopped me. I think you must have
picked on me to start with because you knew I wouldn't give you one
of those gilt-edged references, of value only to an advertising agency—
or maybe to the City Council when they're trying to decide whose statue
to put in the park beside a fountain.

Anyway, my trouble's been that I *like* the guy. And liking him—
and being surer that he's right for your purposes than that your idea is
for him—the responsibility of the description has been too heavy to be
comfortable. I don't know the details of his life, but I'd gamble it's
been a tough one, and I'd like to see him take it easier from here on
in. For one thing, his present work suits him fine, and he's financially
secure for the first time. For another, he's in his *third* marriage. I'm
sure this one's for keeps, though. Julie is an exceptional woman: calm
and sweet and sure. (Incidentally, there's no scandal attached to the

53

divorces. But it's not, on the face of it, a good record for your purpose.) Yet perhaps it's the same as it was with the Congressional investigation: he kept his nose clean when it was mighty difficult to, and yet never said an evasive word.

I repeat: I'm sure he's perfect for your purposes, but I'm not sure your purposes are good for him. So I'm just going to set down my thoughts—never mind whether they suit you or not. Then you decide from them—or ask me more.

Thinking of Walton, I always go back to the first time I met him. I'd heard a lot about him from friends before we got invited to the same dinner party (it was two more years before I became his lawyer)— and he was exactly what I expected from descriptions. At least physically and, on the surface, conversationally. He had a kind of gaunt quality both in his body and his speech which encouraged people to use the adjective "Lincolnesque" too loosely.

He'd been a teacher. Everything about him said that he still was. Don't misunderstand. There was nothing pedantic about him. He simply seemed to carry around a kind of U.S.-Mr. Chips air. He was nice and shabby, too—his obvious tweed jacket, his shoes, his hair. (He wears good conservative suits more now.) And then the habit he still uses— the one I'll never get used to: he disposes of his cigarette ashes by flicking them into the cuff of his trousers. I remember wondering that first night what he did when he wore cuffless evening trousers. But then it also occurred to me that he probably never wore evening clothes. (But, of course, he did. That misconception is typical of the many that surround Herrick. The worst of the many is that he is just a simple, warm soul. Warm, yes. But probably the most complicated friend I've ever had.)

We found it easy to talk. His interests and knowledge ranged wide. He lost me when he began his expert rhapsodizing on baseball. But I liked what he said about peace, women and writing—he was for all of them, brightly and intelligently, and, frequently, with depth.

That first evening I was impressed, too, with what emerged as a very important element of his character. His modesty. I noticed it right away—and found it attractive. As I got to know him better, I became even more aware of the quality, however, and began to think it was phony.

Then came the next stage of knowledge of him—wherein I accepted his warmth and his complexities—and liked him very much. Then I decided, and I was right, that his modesty was not phony at all because it really wasn't the cliché thing we call modesty. He was just very straight about himself—he had a sound appreciation of his capabilities, and they were many, and an equal knowledge of his lacks. This let him be quick to admire, respect, praise anybody else. It also allowed him to utter the fast judgment or the quick retort which often sounded cruel and sometimes was.

Are you getting any notion at all of what I mean by his complexities? Sample: he gave the impression of being such a reservoir of self-peace, and yet he would plague himself with neurotic ideas. Another: a very creative man, busy writing, busy teaching (a night class somewhere in the city), busy leading promising young ones by the hand, and yet he insisted on conducting his professional life as if he were an efficiency expert, scheduling appointments, scheduling work as if an unaccounted-for minute would be charged up as a demerit. Or I'd try to make a dinner date and he'd say, so efficiently: "My wife makes all our social engagements."

There was a period, before he learned better (one of his wonderful qualities is his learning ability), when he was just as efficient about his social life. He would drink—too much—efficiently. If there was dancing, he'd dance more than anybody. He'd want you to stay late at his house and then, if he suddenly realized how tired he was, he'd want you to leave—immediately. Sometimes, he just fell asleep or stopped talking.

He never was a small-talk man. I've heard him tell good anecdotes but I can't remember his ever telling a joke. (How much does that matter to politicians nowadays?) He likes jokes—his laugh is speedy and good—he just isn't a joke teller.

Now I make what is my most important statement about Herrick. He is a man of great dignity. You might miss it, looking at him, unless you paid a great deal of attention to his face. The eyes show it, and so does the mouth. That word "dignity" sometimes carries the "starch" connotation with it. But, obviously, not with Herrick. The dignity begins where it should, deep inside, and works out. It includes, first, himself, then his wife and children, then his friends and associates, and then the whole human race. A lot of territory? Well, his whole being is founded on his belief in the priceless worth of every individual. Nothing has ever shaken that. Nothing ever will. The result in him is what they call integrity—a dignified integrity. He doesn't allow himself to be chipped away. Hemingway has written with brilliance and acumen very often about this quality of dignity. But I find that his variety is based a great deal on the male genitalia. I could never visualize Herrick in the bull ring or on one of the green hills of Africa, but I could see him strengthening Tom Paine or staying alive in a concentration camp.

I guess that's it, Abe—for now, anyway. There's a lot more I could guess at, and it's not all good (all good! In whom is it?), but I don't think it's my business to guess here. These are the impressions I'm sure of, and as I reread what I've written my conclusion is that he has real political assets.

Ask me any more questions you want to. And escape from your country estate sometime and come in and lunch with me. Or take dinner with us. Marny would be inviting you if she knew I was writing. But, as you asked, only you and I and my secretary will know. Seriously, tell Jane we want you to come to dinner. We're—especially Marny— kind of lonely without the kids (Jack's doing fine at Iowa—I'm glad he went west).

Best,

(LEON)

LEON S. GOODMAN

P.S. The enclosures pertain to his appearance before the Congressional Committee to Investigate Tax-Exempt Foundations; please return. Exhibits A and B are interesting parts I've copied from the stenographic record of the hearings. I did not, of course, attend the hearings with him, or represent him in any way related to them; his counsel was the foundation's corporation counsel.

Abe, you'll catch his real tone, I know. To me—as I think it will be to you—the really significant achievement here is the way in which Walton stood up to *all* his responsibilities. I mean as a man, as an American, as a liberal, as the representative of his foundation. Study it, Abe, and I think you'll agree with me that the combination of statesmanship, courage and honesty is rare. Not spectacular, but solid.

A last word. I'm asking my secretary to identify the various people designated in the record only by Mr. —— even though you'll probably recognize all of the congressmen.

Mr. Twilley: Leonard A. Twilley, General Counsel to the Committee.
Mr. Graves: Representative Arthur P. Graves of Oklahoma.
Mr. Mackey: Representative Harold Mackey of Ohio.
Mr. Johnson: Representative Clem Johnson of Georgia.
Mr. Callahan: Representative Richard Callahan of Massachusetts.

Exhibit A

Wednesday, Dec. 10, 1952

The committee met, pursuant to recess, at 2 P.M. in Room 1305, New House Office Building, the Honorable Harold Mackey presiding.

Present: Representatives Mackey (presiding), Graves, Johnson and Callahan.

Also present: Leonard A. Twilley, counsel to the committee.

MR. TWILLEY. To resume, Mr. Herrick. Would it be fair to say that the activities of the Schuyler Foundation have been directed along the lines of endorsement of international cooperation?

MR. HERRICK. Certainly.

MR. TWILLEY. And it has done this in pursuance of its belief that that will be a contributing factor to international peace; is that correct?

MR. HERRICK. Yes.

MR. TWILLEY. Now, then, let's move on from that point to this. In your opinion, has any of the Foundation's work tended to weaken the capitalistic system or the Government of America as it is traditionally conceived?

MR. HERRICK. My answer is no, on both counts.

MR. TWILLEY. With regard to attitudes to international cooperation, is there not at one end of the range of possible positions a body of people indulging in a body of thought of internationalism and one world, and at the other end a group of staunch isolationists who disapprove of international cooperation?

MR. HERRICK. Yes.

MR. TWILLEY. They are opposite poles of thought. Now we hear a good deal—and have from you—about foundations and endowments that foster projects for international cooperation. Is there, to your knowledge, any foundation that sponsors projects from the other pole of thought, projects, let us say, favoring the isolationist point of view?

MR. HERRICK. I can't think of any. But let me say a word about those poles you refer to. I don't think of our Foundation as sponsoring the other extreme from isolationism, which would be, presumably, the literal one world idea, as advocated by the various organizations propounding immediate world federation in one form or another. Our attempts in the direction of international cooperation have been more modestly and—I think—more realistically tuned to the idea of promoting better understanding between Americans and the other peoples of the world. But, having made that clear, I must say that neither ours, nor any other foundation I know of, has based any program on the conviction that the best way to promote peace and security and understanding and freedom is to follow the isolationist position.

MR. TWILLEY. Yes, but aren't the views of those who hold this other position entitled to consideration?

MR. HERRICK. Yes and no. Ideally and democratically, yes. Any view. But in simple realism, how can anyone hold such a view validly today, unless he believes either that there is a world-wide conspiracy against us, or that we should become, in effect, a continental fortress against the rest of the world? Or—I add a third—unless he is so ignorant that he believes that merely by playing the ostrich, he will escape notice and be left alone?

MR. TWILLEY. I want to say that my questions are not intended to convey criticism. That is not my function as I construe it. But I should like to know why, in our investigations, we find no foundation that is devoted even to the expression of these ideas at the other end of the—spectrum.

MR. HERRICK. I think I've just answered that, sir, to the best of my ability.

MR. JOHNSON. Mr. Twilley, may I interrupt at this point? Mr.—Herrick may feel that he's answered the question to the best of his ability, but his answer doesn't satisfy me. What's this distinction between "ideally and democratically"—if I quote right—and "simple realism"? Not so simple, I'd say. Why does he thrust "ideal" and "democratic" to one side? What does he replace democracy with—realism?

MR. HERRICK. No, sir, I don't. I don't want to replace democracy at all. What I meant to say was that in a democracy we respect the right of everyone to hold his own opinion, to dissent from whatever majority view, although, once it is voted into legislation, he obeys it as a law. Yet I do not think that faith in democracy, or the practice of democracy, invokes the abdication of our intelligence. And in today's world to support isolation is to my mind either such an abdication or the avowal of a belligerent intent, which is more inimical to the democratic ideal than any sort of internationalism.

MR. JOHNSON. A democrat can't be belligerent? Even in defense of democracy? You want us to be walked over? We're familiar with this kind of talk here.

MR. HERRICK. I do not want us "to be walked over," as you say, nor am I confusing democracy with Christianity. I am saying that aggressive imperialism is not congenial to democracy.

MR. JOHNSON. Why is isolationism aggressive imperialism?

MR. HERRICK. It is not, of course. What I held, sir, was that isolationism in today's world is either a suicidal relinquishing of intelligence or the acceptance of an armed and arming opposition to the rest of the world.

MR. JOHNSON. Why suicidal? Do you mean that we cannot hold our own?

MR. HERRICK. I mean that any nation that attempts to dissociate itself from a world like ours, in view of the shrinking of distances, the ease of all kinds of communication, friendly and unfriendly, and especially the needs of vast overpopulated and underdeveloped areas, is attempting not only an almost impossible thing, but inevitably arousing the resentment and animosity of the rest of the world.

MR. JOHNSON. You seem more concerned about the rest of the world than about your own country. Go on, Mr. Twilley.

MR. TWILLEY. I was trying to get at something quite different, Mr. Herrick. I was wondering—and this has come up in the course of other testimony—whether a good deal of the criticism being leveled at the foundations is not in terms of the foundations exclusively favoring international cooperation and indulging in international operations.

It occurs to me that there might be some justice in the objections of those holding the opposite point of view that there is no support of this sort for the propagation of their view. I was just trying to explore that with you.

MR. HERRICK. Yes. My answer to that would be that I don't think the isolationist point of view is tenable today. I have gone into my reasons. For that matter, I don't think the other extreme, of immediate world federation, is feasible either. Therefore in the light of these findings, we must support studies and activities which seem viable—to the end that our promotion of peace and understanding may be effective.

MR. TWILLEY. But doesn't your reply indicate that foundations do, whether consciously or not, tend to mold thinking, or at least give their support to only one kind of thinking?

MR. HERRICK. I don't agree to that. If we have found that the really large area between the two extremes is the real area of possibility, then it stands to reason that we should work within that area. There are many variations and degrees and attitudes within it— and certainly no detailed unity among the various foundations. The findings that have led to these conclusions, I would stress, have been scholarly studies and attempts to understand the problems, not doctrinaire prejudgments.

MR. TWILLEY. I can understand, Mr. Herrick, why any foundation would today lend itself to further investigations of the physical universe that extend farther the notions of time and space developed from Newton to Einstein, and refuse to make grants to people who still believe in the physical universe of—was it Ptolemy? But when it comes to the question of ideology, where physical and mathematical proof are not available, I am a little disturbed to find among the foundations no support for the people opposed to sponsoring international cooperation. I am not attempting by this statement to indicate my own views at all.

MR. HERRICK. I understand, Mr. Twilley. You are exploring these questions only as counsel. But I can think of nothing to add to what I have already said on this point, except that I cannot understand why, within foundations, every point of view *must* be represented. It is as though, in dealing with the question of marriage and divorce, you feel that one foundation, at least, should support the practice of universal divorce, simply so that every point of view is covered. [Laughter in the audience, quickly suppressed.]

MR. TWILLEY. That's far-fetched, Mr. Herrick, and irrelevant.

MR. JOHNSON. Mr. Twilley, I want to go back to earlier testimony for a minute. Mr.—Herrick, when you explained a while back that you didn't confuse democracy with Christianity, were you suggesting that you find them hostile or contradictory to each other? And were you implying, from what had been said just before, that to be a Christian means letting yourself be walked over?

MR. HERRICK. No to both questions. As for the first, I merely meant that the doctrine of passivity, of turning the other cheek, is traditionally associated with Christianity rather than democracy. Or more exactly, after saying that I did not want us "to be walked over," I added, as I remember it, "nor am I confusing democracy with Christianity." This was a reference to the widely-known Christian approval of forbearance, to an extent well beyond the attachment of any such concept to the idea of democracy.

Further, that democracy refers to a form of government, and, in

extension, of society. The international position of that government and society is not necessarily firmly fixed because it is a
democracy, yet it has traditionally been assumed to be a more
enlightened one, a less *exclusively* nationalistic one, and seldom
(ideally, never), an imperialistic one. In reverse, an autocratic
regime is apt to be state-centered to the point of fanaticism, and
hence inflexibly nationalistic.

MR. JOHNSON. So a democracy can't be pro-isolationism?

MR. HERRICK. That is not what I said. However, in my opinion, no
sound society today, no sane government, can be isolationist. Fifty
to one hundred years ago, probably.

MR. JOHNSON. And your definition of Christianity?

MR. HERRICK. I offered no definition of Christianity. I said that I was
not confusing it with democracy, and I have just elaborated that
point further. The democratic concept I was thinking of was one
of equal opportunity to all and the freedom to dissent, etc. But the
idea of turning the other cheek, giving both cloak and coat, walking two miles with the man who asks you to accompany him one,
paying as much to the workers who began only in the afternoon
as to those who worked all day—these, and other such paradoxes,
are from the New Testament. However, I'm grateful to you for
bringing me back to this point, for I think I made the allusion
too easily. These parables (however dubious as a base for foreign
policy) are not the equivalent of letting oneself be walked over,
and I should not like to leave that impression.
Now, when I advocate international cooperation, I am proposing
give-and-take, an open and inquiring mind and an honest attempt
to understand each other, not a unilateral giving on our part, a
lonely attempt, on our side only, to understand, or a mind that
accepts everything it finds elsewhere. I'm talking about the flexibility, the openness to possibilities, that can help nations to come
together in peace.

MR. MACKEY. If you're through with this line, Mr. Johnson, what Mr.
Herrick has just said makes me want to ask a question. The
Schuyler Foundation has a good many projects involving international matters, and sponsors many individuals who travel to
other countries in the effecting of these programs. When you screen
and select these individuals, to what extent do you consider the
citations by the Un-American Activities Committee, the Attorney
General's office, and so on, as a conclusive factor in your selections?

MR. HERRICK. As far as the Attorney General's list goes, we would not consider giving funds to any organization on the list. Individuals mentioned in the reports of the Un-American Activities Committee are another matter. Certainly such mention would be a significant factor in our decision, but it would not necessarily be—nor do I think it should be—the conclusive factor.

MR. MACKEY. I see. And I assume, Mr. Herrick, that your distinction here is the same as that made by officers of other foundations in their testimony: that Congress itself has not intended such citations (in the index to its hearings, for instance) to be construed as final statements concerning the loyalty of individuals named.

MR. HERRICK. That is correct, sir.

MR. JOHNSON. Nevertheless, and I had not thought it was our function to put words in the mouths—

MR. MACKEY. Excuse me, Mr. Johnson, but with your permission, I should like to follow my train of thought here before we go on to the discussion of the loyalty of individuals associated in one way or another with the Schuyler Foundation. That was the direction in which you were moving, am I right?

MR. JOHNSON. Yes. I only wanted Mr. Herrick to state his own position. But go ahead.

MR. MACKEY. I "put the words in his mouth," as you started to say, only to expedite matters. I do not think anything valuable was lost. Now, Mr. Herrick, I referred a minute ago to *officers* of other foundations. Strictly speaking, you are not an officer, though you are an executive of the Schuyler Foundation. We have on record the reason for the rather novel substitution of yourself for the president of your Foundation, but perhaps you will give us a rundown of that.

MR. HERRICK. Yes. Philip Henderson Gates, the president of the Foundation, will appear and testify, as requested—

MR. JOHNSON. It is not a request, but a subpoena.

MR. HERRICK. Excuse me. Mr. Gates will appear, as required, and I believe, directly after my testimony, to answer questions about the general structure of the corporation. And I think that one of our trustees, Mr. Huntingdon Haldane, is also to testify. But at any rate, when your questionnaires were submitted, President Gates wrote to your committee, explaining the unusually heavy burden he was carrying, partly because of a special commission by the Government that he was undertaking, and his then ill health, and requesting that I be permitted to act for him in assuming the major responsibility for completing the questionnaires and answering detailed questions at this hearing. You generously granted this permission, and this is why I am here.

MR. MACKEY. Yes. Well, we will ask Mr. Gates most of our questions about the structure of the Foundation. But before we go on now to questions about individual grants, there is one general question I want to pursue with you, and that concerns the foundation viewed as a public trust. What do you think about the desirability of foundations making a public accounting or a public reporting of their activities?

MR. HERRICK. I believe that a foundation should make its work fully public. Although our funds are private funds, they are committed to a public purpose, and we enjoy a favored legislative status. We feel, as a foundation, and I feel, as an individual, that it would be contrary to our obligations and to good public policy not to make our work fully public. There is considerable cost involved and considerable work, but we feel them necessary.

MR. MACKEY. Thank you. We may have occasion, I think, to refer back to this statement, as we proceed with more detailed matters. But unless there is some objection, this seems to me a good point at which to break, earlier than usual, as several of the committee members have other obligations.

MR. TWILLEY. Just one point, Mr. Chairman. I think this would be a good place at which to read the following extract from the answer of the Schuyler Foundation, page 41, to certain questions:

> Recently, the Foundation has felt that it must explicitly and openly concern itself, in terms of individuals and organizations seeking grants, with their attitudes toward Communism. In addition to, and apart from, the related questions of national security, the Foundation will not recommend assistance for any scholar or scientist unless convinced that this man is capable of, and practices, sound scholarly and scientific procedures in his work, is convincingly objective in his findings, and open about them (save those involving classified material)—in short, acknowledges no other authority or pursuit than that of the truth. It is very dubious, we feel, that scholars and scientists of Communist persuasion are capable of fulfilling these requirements.

I assume that you would subscribe to this statement, Mr. Herrick, since you have taken responsibility for answering the questionnaire?

MR. HERRICK. I do.

MR. TWILLEY. Then I suggest, Mr. Chairman, that we adjourn until ten o'clock tomorrow morning.

MR. MACKEY. The committee will resume at ten o'clock tomorrow morning.

Exhibit B

Thursday, Dec. 11, 1952

The committee met, pursuant to recess, at 10 a.m. in Room 1305, New House Office Building, the Honorable Harold Mackey presiding.

Present: Representatives Mackey (presiding), Callahan, Graves and Johnson.

Also present: Leonard A. Twilley, counsel to the committee.

MR. MACKEY. The committee will come to order, please. Mr. Twilley, will you begin the questioning.

MR. TWILLEY. We closed yesterday's session, Mr. Herrick, with a reading from the Schuyler Foundation's answer to certain of the questions submitted to it by the committee. Specifically, to the Foundation's answer to be found on page 41, which concludes with the following words (I abridge the first part of the statement in the interests of brevity): "The Foundation will not recommend assistance for any scholar or scientist unless convinced that this man . . . acknowledges no other authority or pursuit than that of the truth. It is very dubious, we feel, that scholars and scientists of Communist persuasion are capable of fulfilling these requirements."

Now, Mr. Herrick, what interests me particularly in this wording is the phrase "We are very dubious" etc. Dubious, mind you. If you compare this statement with those of other foundations on the same subject, you will find that all of them say, rather: "It is impossible" for a Communist to acknowledge no other authority or pursuit than that of the truth. How do you explain this difference in the wording of the statement from your foundation?

MR. HERRICK. I was not aware of the wording of the other statements. I do not find this to be a significant difference; it seems to me simply that we have perhaps been a little more careful and precise.

MR. TWILLEY. Will you elaborate that statement, please?

MR. HERRICK. Yes. We are living in a time when allegations of being

Communist or pro-Communist are being hurled broadside and
without discrimination. Sometimes they hit their mark; sometimes
the innocent are wounded. It is very difficult at times to be sure
of the degree or even the fact of guilt or innocence. Accompanying this tendency is that of saying that since Communism is a
world-wide conspiracy and since all Communists are, in effect, in
absolute servitude to Moscow and its directives, regardless of how
these may vary from the ascertainable truth, then all Communists
and Communist sympathizers are incapable of pursuing or teaching
the truth. They are in bondage to their doctrine—no matter how
often a new directive, as initiated at Moscow, may contradict a
former one and hence radically alter that doctrine.

MR. GRAVES. Well. You've put it very clearly. Don't you believe that?

MR. HERRICK. In so far as I know, I believe that it is probably true for
members of the Communist Party.

MR. GRAVES. Why do you say "in so far as I know" and "probably"? It
seems to me that this is common knowledge, and certain.

MR. HERRICK. I'm not sure that what is called "common knowledge" is
always knowledge. And I say "in so far as I know" because I don't
feel I know much. I have had no experience with the Communist
Party at first hand. I don't understand how other people who
haven't either can feel so sure of their knowledge.

MR. GRAVES. You don't feel sure of the conspiratorial character and
absolute discipline of the Party from recent trials, from testimony
before this and other investigatory committees, and from the wealth
of printed material on the subject?

MR. HERRICK. Yes, I do feel sure of that—as sure as I can be of anything I haven't experienced at first hand. But when I said that I
thought members of the Communist Party were *probably* incapable
of pursuing and teaching the truth, wherever it leads them, I meant
that it is conceivable to me that a few such members might be
"bad Communists"—attracted to the Party through their conviction that only a radical social, political and economic upheaval
could amend the inequalities of our society—and yet, in the teaching, say, of physics or music, be as earnest a pursuer of the truth
as a non-Communist. And I think this much more likely for
someone who is not a member of the Party, but a sympathizer.

MR. GRAVES. The tone you are adopting is almost that of a sympathizer,
Mr. Herrick. At least it is a soft position you hold.

MR. HERRICK. I don't agree with you, sir. All I am saying is that we are
tending in this country to make too many absolute statements, not

documented or backed up with proof. From Senator McCarthy down—or up—we make pronouncements which we cannot support with proof. But I want to get back on the main track. In our statement we used the words "*very dubious.*" Surely this is sufficient to indicate the gravity of our doubt about someone either Communist or pro-Communist and yet to leave the margin out of respect for the truth and for precision and moderation of language —to leave the margin of possibility for an exceptional case. I do not say, you understand, that even with such an exceptional case we would make a grant. I am saying only that I am not eager to add absolutes of ours to all the rest.

MR. CALLAHAN. Why did you say "from Senator McCarthy down—or up"?

MR. HERRICK. Because of my expressed aversion to making categorical statements the validity of which I cannot fully examine.

MR. CALLAHAN. Do you disapprove of the work Senator McCarthy has been leading in the uncovering of Communists?

MR. HERRICK. Some of Senator McCarthy's actions and words certainly seem to me irresponsible and reckless, in the absence of corroborative evidence. I deplore his influence.

MR. MACKEY. I do not believe this side path a fruitful journey. Mr. Herrick, if I understand you, you are saying that the Foundation has phrased its statement in terms of grave doubt about Communists and Communist sympathizers (rather than absolute certainty that no such person could pursue or teach the truth), on philosophical democratic grounds and on grounds of justice to all individuals until proved guilty. Am I correct in this interpretation?

MR. HERRICK. You are, Mr. Chairman.

MR. MACKEY. After the Supreme Court ruling in *United States* against *Dennis*—you are familiar with this ruling?

MR. HERRICK. Yes.

MR. MACKEY. After this ruling, how can you feel justified in your position?

MR. HERRICK. The ruling that the eleven Communist leaders were engaged in a conspiracy to overthrow the Government by force and violence is the final word on that subject. And we at the Foundation are not going to give money and employment knowingly to anyone participating in that conspiracy. Nor, to the best of my knowledge—and I have studied the record carefully—have we done so. Even in those cases where someone is simply suspected, on whatever grounds, of having Communist sympathies, our investigation of him will be painstakingly thorough. The Foundation is deeply loyal to the nation and the Government. Yet we are also loyal to standards of scholarship and to the ideals of truth and of justice. Therefore the words "very dubious" seemed to us the perfect and just words for the context. They are not intended to imply—and in my opinion do not imply—the slightest taint of Communist sympathy or the slightest tolerance for the fellows of those found guilty of conspiratorial aims by the Supreme Court.

MR. MACKEY. I think that statement should suffice for the generality. Mr. Twilley, will you take up the questioning again?

MR. TWILLEY. Yes, Mr. Chairman. Mr. Herrick, there has been considerable criticism leveled at the Foundation's support of the civil liberties study at Maynard University. Will you comment on this?

MR. HERRICK. Yes. Back in 1947 or '48 (I think the preliminary talks occurred in 1947, and the program got under way in 1948) I suggested this study myself. It seemed to me, and it still seems to me, that the greatest single contribution the American tradition has to make to the world in crisis is its concept of liberty—an interpretation of freedom, as I understand it, that means individual freedom under law, within order, and thoroughly consonant with cooperative living. The freedom to explore and fulfill one's talents, to speak one's mind, to dissent, to pursue one's own course—all to the extent that in so doing one does not damage others or impair their freedom, break laws or follow a destructive course. The balance between liberty and license is often a delicate one, that between liberty and security equally so. And so it seemed to me that a study of the relation of the security program of the Government to our basic civil liberties would be particularly useful.

After some discussion, we selected Professor Grainger at Maynard to head the program and, as various documents from his office indicate, in selecting him we chose a man who insisted that the program must squarely face the needs of security as well as those of freedom, must recognize fully that there *is* a security problem as well as problems of freedom.

One important result of the study has been a series of books, which we are well aware have been considered controversial, and which we expected to be, since they deal with controversial subjects in a time of controversy. Yet the first of these, by Nathaniel Heathcote, has been widely hailed as making a useful and illuminating con-

tribution to one of the thorniest areas—the field of the physical
sciences and the application of concepts of security and freedom
to this field.

MR. TWILLEY. Heathcote has been identified with a number of organizations cited as subversive by the House Un-American Activities Committee, has he not?

MR. HERRICK. We listed his name in that connection in our answer
to D-15.

MR. TWILLEY. Yet if he is a Communist sympathizer, you must have
been, in your own words, *very dubious* of his capacity for objectivity?

MR. HERRICK. If we had any slightest reason to believe him a Communist sympathizer, we would never have made a grant to him
to work in this field of all fields.

MR. TWILLEY. You say if you had the *slightest reason* you would not
have made the grant. Yet he belonged to a number of cited organizations. This would seem to me to give you a slight reason, to say
the least. What did you have to balance this knowledge? Mr. Heathcote belonged to, or at least was identified with these organizations,
wasn't he?

MR. HERRICK. It has been so charged.

MR. TWILLEY. Mr. Herrick, you have made a good deal in your testimony of first-hand experience. But we don't really have a chance
for personal knowledge of many things in life, do we? How do you
deal with the questions raised by these citations?

MR. HERRICK. First of all, Mr. Heathcote is a distinguished professor
in one of our leading law schools, with a fine reputation with his
colleagues, students and peers. He has had a strong lifetime interest
in civil liberties, and necessarily from time to time would get involved in one or another protest organization—some of which have
been cited—and necessarily would become interested from time
to time in other organizations and individuals who have become
controversial, because these are the organizations and individuals
who often are the storm centers of civil liberties questions. Yet he
has had and has other connections, groups in which he has played
an important role, and groups not only clearly non-Communist, but
also downright anti-Communist. He has also served with the Department of Justice off and on.

However, not only are these facts true, and not only did his
colleagues and associates give him unanimous support, but he
himself satisfied us with his candor and objectivity in the long and

searching talk we had with him. From that talk I can say with confidence that Mr. Heathcote would flatly deny some of the allegations as to organizations to which he is alleged to have belonged, but with others would put the association back in time to a context in which membership in this or that group would have meant something quite different from what it does today. We are all aware, I think, that a good many liberals worked in causes and organizations at the time when not only our government, but the whole national sentiment was friendly to Russia—worked with causes and organizations they would not consider associating with now. And this was what I meant earlier when I said that we're going through a period of charges of disloyalty often taken out of their proper context.

MR. TWILLEY. If you had the problem of whether or not to select Heathcote on your hands today, would you make the same decision?

MR. HERRICK. We would conduct the same careful exploration, and if nothing new pertinent turned up, then I think we would make the same decision.

MR. JOHNSON. What about Mr. Austin? He wrote a book in this series.

MR. HERRICK. Felix Austin is an educator of impeccable standing— a man I know well, and of whom I know nothing that is a cause for reproach, whether in terms of personal character or national loyalty.

MR. JOHNSON. He preaches—or teaches—the overthrow or the abolishment of the United States.

MR. HERRICK. You mean that he favors world government, of which he thinks—

MR. JOHNSON. He wants to abolish our government, what we have.

MR. HERRICK. In a similar sense to that in which the framers of our Constitution sought to establish what they called "a larger and more perfect union."

[Dear Abe: At this point it gets repetitious. Twilley takes up persons involved in this program, and grants in the area of Russian studies. While Walton does fine, there's nothing distinctively different from what precedes. But finally Johnson picks Walton up again on his own book. Leon]

MR. JOHNSON. Mr. Herrick, you wrote a book yourself in that Maynard University civil liberties series. It was called *The Free Man and Peace* and published in 1949. I've looked through the book and found a number of curious things, but I'm mostly concerned now with your statement in it that you did not favor the enactment of legislation to make the Communist Party illegal. Why?

MR. HERRICK. I also *answered* that question in the book. I said that I
believed the effect of such legislation would be to drive the Party
underground and that this would make them more dangerous, more
difficult to cope with.

MR. JOHNSON. There was something about your phrasing. I copied it.
It reads, "Driven underground, the Communist Party might well
develop into a powerful threat to the health of our body public.
In matters political, as well as medical and psychiatric, it is the
hidden tumor, physical or emotional, that is able to run wild, unobserved." You want everything out in the open, is that right?

MR. HERRICK. That slightly oversimplifies my position, Mr. Johnson. I
think there are some areas in life proper to privacy. But, having
made that reservation, I would answer "yes."

MR. JOHNSON. Then why do you object to investigating committees?

MR. HERRICK. I do not object to investigating committees. Whatever
I have said that has led you to think so has been along the line
of objection to certain methods practiced by some few particular
investigators—and also some witnesses. That is quite a different
matter.

MR. JOHNSON. But to go back to your book. That's a strange way to
put things—that talk about a tumor. Agreed that Communism is a
sore in our society—but that isn't what you meant.

MR. HERRICK. No, not exactly. I meant, and I believe, that everything
most destructive in human nature, whether in individuals or in
groups, is fomented, finally to burst out in some violent form, when
segregation, secrecy and deception are practiced or, in one way or
another, enforced.

MR. JOHNSON. Well. At any rate, I want to go back to your friend
Felix Austin. In your testimony yesterday, you said that your
Foundation did not sponsor projects or individuals favoring world
government. Yet you supported this Maynard University series,
including a book by Austin.

MR. HERRICK. But the book is not about world federation in any way.
It is about security and academic freedom. I do not think of Mr.
Austin as either criminal or disloyal because of his views on
world government. Therefore, when he writes a book on an
entirely different subject, and one on which he is eminently well-
qualified, I don't see that we are either supporting world federation
or supporting anyone in the least subversive.

MR. JOHNSON. You seem to have very little Americanism, Mr. Herrick.

However well you've dodged in and out between our questions, one thing's been pretty clear: you're a stronger supporter of internationalism, of truth and freedom, as you describe them, and even of world federation, than you are of America.

MR. HERRICK. I deny that flatly. There is no conflict between America on the one hand and internationalism, truth and freedom on the other. Or if there is, then something's wrong with the United States. My loyalty to America is not simply a loyalty to the the status quo. Wherever I look and see human beings, I expect to find some faults, nor do I find this a reason for despair. I look at us, these United States, and I see many discrepancies between our ideals and our practices. When I say that my Americanism is concerned with the best that I believe we can become, I do not find this—nor do I see how any sensible person can find it—disloyal. A concept of Americanism that is limited to no dissent from just the way everything is at present seems to me not Americanism at all, but standpatism. It further seems to me in total disagreement with the principles on which this nation was founded and has flourished.

MR. JOHNSON. The Founding Fathers would turn in their graves if they knew how they are used today.

MR. HERRICK. Perhaps. But not because they were afraid of committing themselves to what they believed, of disagreeing among themselves, or of change. All *lived* life—as against mere existence—is commitment, is risk. In our work in the Foundation, simply because we are determined to tackle the real problems, these are ridden with dangers and the possibilities of serious mistakes. There are very few areas of work open to foundations of our sort and at the same time directly valuable to the human cause that are not laced with booby traps. If we refused to run any risks, our work would be of a piddling and fruitless sort. So, knowing to our own satisfaction our basic devotion to the cause of our country and of humanity, which causes we do not believe to be at odds, we know that if we make a mistake in an organization or a person, it will be an honest mistake, made only after all the exploration and soul-searching possible. And if we stay always on the safe side, simply to avoid mistakes and to wear always the air of perfect sanctity, we shall end by being respectable do-nothings.

There is much talk of survival these days—and with good reason. But nobody seems to be asking "Survival—for what?" and I propose to you, gentlemen, that if we so ring ourselves round with cautions, fears, suspicions and safeguards and policings that we begin to resemble the state of affairs in the Soviet Union, we shall have capitulated to the enemy without knowing it and without a blow having been struck. Let us rather, using all the resources of sober and rational men, select those ventures and people we will sponsor with care and thoughtfulness, but without fear, and let us commit ourselves to projects that may really lead to the betterment of the human situation, without being intimidated from this action by the fear that we will be misunderstood or criticized or slandered. To act so, in my opinion, is to act like men, in accordance with the deepest and truest of the American traditions.

Gentlemen, search out treason and disloyalty. But do not invest security with so absolute an authority that we close our windows and lock our doors from fear of the honest air of individual opinion and dissent, or association with people who have minds of their own. For then the locks and bolts will rust and we will neither dare nor be able to go forth even when the enemy's alarm sounds.

If we believe in our way of life, and not simply in talking about it, then we must have the freedom to commit ourselves to it—to act, not simply to react.

[Abe, it was at this point that all the papers reported an unprecedented burst of applause, which the Chairman allowed to continue more than a minute before he called the room to order and asked the Committee if there were any other questions. There were none, and he declared the session adjourned until the afternoon. This was Walton's last testimony.]

May 11–23

In the last two weeks before Julie and the children left, Walton rediscovered the climate of fear and loneliness. Now and then he would catch himself in a phrase or a gesture, familiar but unidentifiable, as though not his own, but that of some old friend. Friend? Acquaintance perhaps.

Memories of early terrors flitted through the landscape of desolation, an empty waste between lonely monuments of loss and solitude. Images of desert and—strangely—water. Sometimes it seemed that he stood motionless for five minutes, on a street corner, in his yard, in the office, while pools of guilt swirled about his feet, withdrew, and returned in swishing eddies, sucking and gurgling where he stood, tugging remorselessly at him.

Guilt? The very diffuseness of his thoughts about the nature of his offense (for although he would not admit it in argument, he never doubted that it was *his*) that had led Julie to take this drastic step— his very uncertainty about the cause of so wide a rift between them— made his pervasive feeling of guilt the more poignant. Faithlessness after deception, lie upon lie, betrayal and defection—big words for the army of his little sins that passed in dress parade before him, a reluctant and impotent general.

Little? Mean, it seemed to him now, often mean, cowering, secretive. At such moments he raged inwardly at himself for these weaknesses, until his guilt over whatever specific harm he had brought to someone else in whatever incident was dissipated in scalding self-contempt. And all this while he was vaguely, uneasily aware that during these days he was so patient, so meek even, with Julie, that both of them were embarrassed. It was, Walton thought, not unlike a small boy hopelessly endeavoring to win back favor, but succeeding only in further alienating the adult by his whining, placating attitude.

73

Hopelessly—for hopelessness was the intimate of the fear and loneliness that haunted him. The fear of loneliness, the hopelessness of this fear, the loneliness of the hopeless.

And then, suddenly, late in the first week, the weather broke. He awoke one morning to find that he was deadened and dulled no longer, that, even while he slept, he had found in himself new resources and regained his manhood. He could face what had to be, if not with serenity, at least with stoicism. More, that he was ready to begin the fight to keep what he was losing—no, to regain it. With cheerful sureness that Saturday morning, he resumed his place at the helm of the family, dispersed the boys to morning chores, proposed they spend the rainy afternoon together at the bowling alley, mended Jennifer's doll in the basement workshop, and joined Julie over a second cup of coffee for a discussion of the logistics of next week's expedition.

The children, as always, responded quickly, brightened and went their ways. Julie eyed him speculatively. During his period of depression, she had remained firmly cheerful, determinedly even-tempered, friendly but a little impersonal. Now, as he insisted that he wanted to drive them up, get them across on the ferry and see them safely stowed away in her father's house on the Vineyard, she looked at him warily.

"I don't think that's a very good idea," she said softly. "It will just make it harder. What I most need help on is the packing and loading. And all the storing away in the attic. And cleaning the house. I've hardly started, and when I think of what there is to do, it paralyzes me."

Walton felt a sort of paralysis, too, as he remembered the long, dreary hours of lugging and loading, tugging and hauling. At such times Julie seemed constitutionally incapable of beginning the necessary work until the last moment. Then, once started, she would work steadily and well, and with a fair degree of calm, while Walton, tensely conscious of the limited time left and of her failure to start the job during his absence all week at the office, would drive away at it as though possessed, bark his shin or smash his thumb, lose his temper and finally blow up in a fury.

Yet now, remembering all this and feeling an almost sick inertia within him at the prospect of so overwhelming a task, the more formidable for the many previous ordeals—Walton, even considering that this time he would in effect be laboring to expedite losing Julie and the children, summoned all his strength and spoke quietly.

"We'll manage, baby," he said. "I'll take Friday off and what you haven't done already we'll start Thursday night and spread it out, so that there won't be so much pressure at the end this time. And as for the trip, I'll do whatever you prefer."

Julie smiled. And it was clear throughout the day that she did believe him and take heart. It was the pleasantest weekend they had all had in months. Only each night, after the children were asleep, did a constraint fall over Walton and Julie. They went to bed silently, self-consciously, at the same moment after the extinction of the light turning on their sides away from each other and saying a subdued "good night."

But by the following Thursday evening this aspect of the final week changed too. Julie had had a good day—with the help of the maid had completed stowing away in the attic the family's winter clothes and blankets (it was a little, Walton thought, like finishing the mowing of two or three acres of hay on a hundred-acre farm, yet he too was cheered). For the first time in months, she dressed for a routine family evening at home as though they were entertaining guests, and her eyes were once more clear and vital. She met Walton at the door and kissed him in a more than perfunctory way.

He sipped his drink before dinner with a heady hope permeating him. At the table, after seating Julie, he held Jennifer's chair for her and she turned surprisingly, with her grave three-year-old fervor, to bestow a sticky kiss on him.

"You are a good daddy," she announced. "I will give you my soup."

Tim let out a braying laugh.

"That's because she doesn't like soup."

"It is *not*," said Jennifer. "And anyway, I do too like soup."

Peter, who had been brooding over these proceedings, broke in authoritatively.

"It all depends," he said. "She likes some soup. If she doesn't know what soup we're having today, then it's really because she wants to give something to Daddy. If she does know and doesn't like the kind we're having, then she's doing it because she doesn't want to eat it. But if she does know *and* doesn't like it—"

Tim, who had been listening with wrinkled brow, concentrating on the logic of his brother's argument, broke in now excitedly.

"You said that before," he shouted. "You said before if she does know and doesn't like it. This time—"

"I did not." Peter glowered at him. "I said—I mean this last time—that if she does know and does like it, then it's a good deed and she's a hero. No, a heroine."

"Hold on a minute," said Walton. "That's a very good analysis, Peter, and shows you really think things through. But Timmy was right, too, though he didn't need to interrupt and to yell. Simply by a mistake, you had started to repeat, for the third choice, what you'd already said for the second."

Peter shook his head.

"Nope, I didn't."

Walton grinned at him.

"It's better to be wrong and right about being wrong when you're corrected than to be right, and wrong in your feeling about being right."

"What's right about being wrong?" Tim asked with rapt interest. The soup had been served and he now ducked his head and rapidly spooned some up, two or three times, before again fixing his intent gaze on his father.

"What I mean," said Walton, "is that if you're wrong and then admit you're wrong when it's pointed out to you, you've then done a right—thing," he ended lamely.

"I know," said Tim, his face glowing and eager. "Like when you get in an argument with Mommy, and you say that someone has taken your brief case and there are valu—valuable papers in it and you get mad and stamp your feet and say that it's too bad if a man can't have some respeck in his own house and then Mommy says it's right where you put it and you say it isn't and shout and then she goes and shows you that it is, only there's some newspapers on top of it so you couldn't see it and then if you—if you—"

Walton nodded.

"I know why you're stopping, Timmy. You were going to say, and then if I admitted I was wrong and said I was sorry, then I would be right about my wrong. But you know that the time I did this I didn't admit it and was still cross. And I'm sorry now about that and about many other things I've done because I lose my temper and don't want to admit I'm wrong. That was the trouble, Timmy, wasn't it?"

Suddenly overcome, Tim nodded shyly and retreated to his soup. In the ensuing silence, Peter laid his hand with an awkward tenderness on his father's sleeve.

"That's all right, Dad," he said earnestly. "We all make mistakes."

Walton squeezed his hand.

"There's one more thing," he said, "about your thoughts about Jenny and her soup. If she didn't know what the soup was and yet gave it to me, then of course she is running a risk of missing a kind she likes and so is generous, as you said. Yet there's also a chance that she isn't really hungry, or that she so much dislikes tomato soup that even though she likes pea soup—and it might be pea—she'd rather take the chance of missing it than have to eat tomato. And all I mean about this is that being generous is fine, and I hope you all will be, but the real test of it is when you *know* what you're giving up and still give it up because you know it's best for someone you love."

Jennifer pounded her spoon on the table.

"But I do like tomato soup. And it *is* tomato. And I've eaten it all up," she declared smugly, with an arch look of self-satisfaction addressed to them all.

During the loud laughter that followed her announcement and increased her pleasure in herself, Walton looked anxiously at Julie, who had remained quiet throughout. Her eyes were soft and shining. . . .

That night he kissed the children good night for the first time in several weeks without a wrenching feeling of deprivation. And when he proposed to Julie that they begin the packing, she took his hands and looked deeply at him.

"Let's not," she said. "Let's go to bed and get up early to start."

He found her sweet and responsive and as yieldingly loving as in the first days of their marriage. And before she went to sleep with her head in the circle of his arm, she whispered, "Dear darling, you've given me such hope."

Throughout Friday morning, with the children spending their last day at school, Walton worked with inspired cheerfulness, whistling, running up and down stairs, racing downtown in the car for rope and cartons.

This was paid labor, he thought with surprise as they sat down at noon for sandwiches and iced tea—hot, dirty and tired, but jubilant over being more than halfway through the task. Paid? Overpaid, by a half-dozen radiant smiles from Julie; by a fiercely passionate kiss she gave him after he cut his thumb, then swiftly bound it and went back to work with only a moment's interruption; by the tenderness with which she stroked his head when after the kiss she moved out of his arms, saying, "We mustn't. I want to too, but we must finish."

After lunch, he urged a nap on her and himself went on working vigorously. She made him promise to wake her in an hour, but he doubled the time and only went into the bedroom a half hour before the children were due back from school. He had made great progress during the two hours; the rest of the job could be completed in easy stages; and he was content as he tiptoed into the room.

Her face was flushed and sweet. Something about her closed eyelids and the way her lashes rested on her cheeks reminded him of the innocence of Jennifer asleep. He remembered with a sharp stab of pain that night two weeks before when he had stood beside her as she slept and watched her in longing and anger. The memory was an uneasy cloud between him and the warmth of his elation. He felt around his chest that familiar painful constriction that meant conflict to him, and realized, but only dimly, that he was angry again in retrospect. Not simply for the pain she had caused him, the vital suffering of these past weeks over her determination to go—that too, but especially, it seemed to him now, because they had both accepted without question his responsibility for their troubles.

A beacon flared in his mind, a warning signal, a directive for a safe landing on the runway of sanity and fairness. *Had* she so accepted his exclusive fault? His chest ached. Yes, surely she had, that first afternoon in the kitchen, when she'd said that there was no sense in talking about another chance, that there had been too many "other chances" already. And there was a kind of condescension, an assumption of superiority in the way she told him that she was tired of his using the word "deeply." In the way she told him *that?* In the way she had looked at dinner last night, just because he'd admitted that he was often wrong, losing his temper and not owning up to his fault. Just because he had talked things through with the children (and not very well, at that; it was a double match laid to the conflagration waiting within him that he had talked to them, it seemed to him now, rather lamely and pedantically)—as though he hadn't ever before. Decorated with the order of the Good Father! Wet eyes! In the name of God, what did she think he had been like all this time? It was insulting.

It was insulting, and so was the disproportionate reward for not getting angry this morning after cutting his finger. What did he usually do when he cut his finger—scream and wail? She treated him as though she were his mother.

He realized suddenly that he was shaking with this accumulation of hidden resentment. To quiet himself, he walked over to the window and stared out at the afternoon sunlight, his eyes burning. At that moment the barking of the town's fire siren rang out. It rattled in Walton's head with each blast, and its insistence set off in him strange quivers of sadness, then fear. Continuing to gaze out the window, he felt a stirring of hatred at the light, the fresh greenness, the soft fragrance of the air stirring the white curtains. All false promise, all deception.

But it was almost time for the children; he must wake her. With an effort, he brought himself back to the bedside, all carefully controlled motion, and touched her head lightly.

"It's time to wake up, Julie," he said in a voice that he could himself hear as neutral. "You've had a good nap and the kids will be home soon."

He watched the slow waking: determined not to be moved, he saw the uncertainty of coming from sleep change into an eager hopefulness, then, finally, fade and dull as she looked at him. Her hand, which had reached for his, drew back. She asked quietly, "What time is it?" The reconciliation was over.

When he replied, she sprang up, an almost wild look of anxiety in her eyes.

"It's all right," Walton said in a voice that sounded smug to himself—or rather, perhaps, simply self-conscious over the attempt not to be smug. "I've done a lot; except for packing the car, there isn't more than a couple of hours' work left to do."

She sank back against the pillow.

"Thank you," she said quietly, and lay there for a moment, looking searchingly at him. Then, softly, "Walton. What's the matter? What's happened?"

He moved swiftly toward the door, and spoke over his shoulder, not looking at her directly.

"Nothing. I'm just tired."

Halfway down the stairs, desolation smote him. An impulse to turn back, to reach out and say, "Darling, Julie, I just went off my trolley again," and hug her, hold her tightly to him, raced through his mind, but deliberately he rammed it down, packed it tightly within him, and pressed the lid back on. On his way to the station wagon, he thought with a strange grim satisfaction, There. There. That does it—and shook his head savagely to rid himself of the pain that suddenly assailed him.

And so he moved through the last night, automaton-like, stiff with fatigue and hurt and self-pity. It could all, he thought to himself, be accounted for by fatigue, and he was not sure himself whether he was really exhausted or willing an increased weariness to cover this unhappiness. The children's happy chatter about the trip, about swimming and boats and Grandpa and renting bicycles, swarmed in his head as jeers and hoots. They were too excited to notice his depression, but it angered him still more deeply that Julie, who could and did notice, could answer the children in as gay a voice as theirs. By the time Peter, the last to ascend to bed, had said good night, Walton found, as he lugged two heavy suitcases to the car, that he was repeating to himself, "She doesn't give a damn about me. She doesn't give a damn."

At ten o'clock the last package, except for two Julie insisted she needed for the morning, had been stowed away, and Walton tightened the heavy ropes around the load with a perverse satisfaction. Here was something to tug at, to heave and haul with all his strength, and feel something give under his furious assault. When he finished, he was half sorry.

Inside the dimly-lit house, Julie was already in her nightgown. She had cold cream on her face and her hair in curlers—both attentions she seldom gave herself.

A new wave of fury throbbed through Walton's head.

"Well," he said heavily in what was almost a sneer. "It's going to be quite a summer."

She gave him one quick cold look, then continued packing things into her cosmetic case.

"It's delightful," Walton went on, "to be the husband who, when he finishes packing the car, finds that his wife will give him the special intimate attention of hair curlers and cold cream. Think of the poor outsiders, who never have the privilege of seeing more than the results."

His heart leaden, he turned and strode into the kitchen to make himself a strong drink. When he returned, Julie was already in bed, curled up on her side and turned away. He sat down heavily, took a swallow from his drink.

"Well, here's to Martha's Vineyard," he said, gesturing with the glass. "Here's to curlier hair and creamier skin."

If possible, it seemed to him that her position became even more rigid, but she did not reply.

For a little while, Walton drank and smoked in silence. Then he stood up, contemplating a second drink.

"It's never occurred to you, apparently," he said a little thickly—and remembered that he had had only a sandwich for dinner—"it's apparently never occurred to you that you haven't exactly been an ideal wife yourself."

Julie sprang into a sitting position. Once again, he saw with surprise, there were tears in her eyes.

"Don't. Don't. Don't," she said. "Don't say anything more. You've said it all. You can never stand happiness. Whenever we're happy for a little while, you always trample on it, stamp on it. Just don't say any more."

The dismay Walton felt was surprise, disbelief and an unbearable regret.

"But you—" he said almost falteringly. "But Julie— You never—" and stopped, shaken and bewildered.

For a moment they stared at each other, searching, probing—for some sign, it seemed to Walton, but he couldn't have said of what. Another of those moments, he thought later, when something almost happened, but during which he could never act. So he dropped his eyes and slowly made his way back to the kitchen. When he returned, half an hour later, Julie was asleep. . . .

And in the morning, under a dark, cloudy sky, he went through the necessary actions in a finally hopeless misery—plodding, it seemed to him, his dark and solitary way to hell.

After the good-byes to the children and the kisses, the final loading, there was a moment beside the car when he and Julie stopped, a foot apart, and looked at each other. He did not understand her strangely disturbing look, but it rendered him speechless.

"Good-bye," she said and climbed into the car.

He said nothing. He stood there and stared after the departing car. When it reached the corner, he lifted his arm in farewell as though it were crippled. Then the car was gone, and as he turned toward the house, the nature of Julie's expression came to him, hit him with the impact of a sledge hammer. It was, he thought, a look of hate.

JOURNAL: 1

from the journal of Walton Herrick . . .

May 26, 1953

Sometimes, as I write my name, it seems alien, unfamiliar to me. At such moments I am aware of the name's having been there all the time, as one may be aware, in a huge multi-celled New York apartment house, of one's neighbor being there—in his own bedroom or kitchen, perhaps—just beyond the wall of one's living room, for months and even years, without knowing what he looks like or how his voice sounds. Then one day, standing in the hall, awaiting the delinquent elevator, one sees him leave his apartment, appraises him, speaks to him and discovers him for who he is—realizing then that one has not only seen him before, many times, but sensed that he was the one—the mysterious next-door tenant behind the impenetrable wall.

So with one's own name:

Walton Herrick
~~Cornelius~~ Walton Herrick
Walton Herrick
~~Cornelius~~ Walton Herrick
Walton Herrick

But do I mean: so with one's own name? Or so with one's own identity, one's own self? Is it not rather myself who seems like the neighbor?

I do not know exactly what I mean by that. Yet I do not really know who I am, either. Asking the question, I am confronted with a convocation of pseudo-selves—types, it seems to me: Herrick the professional man, Herrick the husband, Herrick the father; on another dialectical level, Herrick the dispenser of deliberated wisdom, Herrick the restless loner,

82

Herrick the naïve idealist, Herrick the expedient cynic. I could go on and on in what I suspect are more subtle categories—to no point: these type men do not make a man. Confronted with them, I begin to have a better understanding of those canvases by Picasso and other moderns; those cubistic crazy quilts that violate anatomy may render with some accuracy the soul of twentieth-century fragmented man.

Pause. Stop. My official mission: to find a missing man, to apprehend him, to invest myself with him, and to climb back into my life with him. And already I am turning phrases, pursuing abstractions and generalizations. This is no literary errand.

Yet perhaps this is the only way I can move now. It comes to me suddenly that I have always had to cling to order, surround myself with ceremony, proceed with decorum—even in the smallest matters— lest all chaos yawn under and around me, there where it is, behind my elbow, before my very feet. It seems to me now, tonight, as I begin writing in this notebook that little Timmy gave me on my birthday last fall, that I have always known that I was going to lose Julie and the children—and that, when I did lose them, then I would finally be naked to my enemies.

Pretentious? No. For my enemies, I suddenly believe, are all within me, lurking there so long, packed in like sufferers in some pest house or prisoners in a concentration camp barrack, and now the door will be opened and they will swarm out to confront me, snarling and gibbering.

Perhaps, in any historical review of what has happened, the fault lies with Julie as well as with me. But this is irrelevant; I can do little or nothing now about her share in it. What does come home, like an arrow in the groin, is my own failure as a husband and father, as a human being. My faults . . .

Faults? More nearly in the geological than the moral sense. *We are such faults as our ancient contractions and expansions have made us.* Our mothers' and fathers'. Into what genealogical ice age for information about one's very present self? What petroglyphic rubbings will reveal, after excavation, that such a one was impelled at such a time to turn right and contract, rather than left and expand?

It seems quite hopeless—and yet, if there is any truth in all this, back there someone was tough. Tough, resilient, unyielding. For I will not give up. And since in these matters I cannot yet run, or even walk quickly with confidence, I will plod. And if I fall, I'll pick myself up. I've learned to do that, long since. And though I'm afraid of the dark I'll go into it.

Brave words . . .

Yet true, too, I think. I believe I can—and what I feel sure is
that that is the verb to learn to live with. Not *must*, not *should*, but *can*.
I . . . I . . . I. The page is squirming with them, like so many
earthworms after a spring rain. And yet they are almost meaningless;
they have no solid consistency, no firm identity, no autonomy for me.
The subject pronoun has no sure point of reference in empirical reality,
but the object pronoun does—as the recipient of actions, perhaps as a
sounding board. Lacking the feel, the sense of identity, *I* cannot act, do
not separately and discretely exist. But others can act upon *me,* who
therefore experiences (and exists as an entity), if only passively.

· · Who is *I?* Who *am* I?

Take down from the shelf *Who's Who in America:*

> HERRICK, Walton, found. exec., author; b. Cleveland,
> O., Nov. 3, 1907; s. William and Marcia (Nicholson) H;
> A.B., Amherst Coll., 1928; M.A., Western Reserve U.,
> 1930; Ph.D., Columbia, 1935; m. Joanna Wood Gaylord,
> June 12, 1928; m. 2d, Lydia Brandeis, June 18, 1937;
> 1 dau., Maria; m. 3d, Julie Norton, Apr. 26, 1944; chil-
> dren—Peter, Timothy, Jennifer. Instr. Graham Inst. 1930-
> 35, asst. prof. 1935-41, asso. prof. 1941-43; visiting prof.,
> Aycock College, 1941-42; associated Schuyler Found. since
> 1943, Chmn. Humanities Div. since 1948. Member Phi Beta
> Kappa, Alpha Delta Phi, Century Club. Author: The Free
> Man and Peace, 1949; Essays in Acceptance, 1952. Home:
> Blake's Wood Rd., Northport, Conn. Office: Schuyler Founda-
> tion, 523 Fifth Ave., N.Y.C.

Writing this down is a copy exercise. Halfway through, I realized
that there was nothing pertinent here. I recognize the names of people
and places, posts won and held, but they have no more immediacy
than the anonymous neighbor in the hypothetical apartment building:
parents, wives, children, jobs, books written, achievements (even the
not listed appearance before the Congressional Committee to Investigate
Tax-Exempt Foundations): all.

And with this realization, I feel an irritability almost unbearable—
like a rash on my raw nerves—so that I finished the copying in a stiff,
cramped hand, with a sense of being obligated, *driven* to set it down,
with a compulsiveness that gained power in direct ratio to the emptiness
of the whole act.

But, however remote the names of others—people, places, things—

seem to me, what most haunts me is the strange, removed, almost spectator sense I have now of Walton Herrick: what he has done, recorded there in black type on white paper, what he has been to all these other names, in black on white.

To say this is to say nothing. I know, if I were to read over what I have been writing, my face and my ganglia would pucker with distaste; I loathe exhibitionism (at least in others); and confessional literature, maundering introspection—whether Rousseau, Amiel or the twentieth-century boy-men—bores me and fills me with contempt. The writing I have more often thought of than accomplished was always to be filled with observations, judgments, interpretations and opinions about the world *outside* me.

My two published books bear me out, although there is necessarily some of the subjective and personal in *Essays in Acceptance*. But, to the really discerning, it must be obvious that this is an impersonal personalism—a book in which I play, not the confessor, but the sage.

What kind of sage? How revealing of the ambiguities of personality! A man who writes wise reflections but in his intimate life is irritable, childish, sullen, and given to tantrums! A man who is successful in public life, but thrice a failure in marriage and—is it fair to say?—four times as a father. A man being considered for the governorship of his state and unable to govern himself!

I feel dully that this is self-abuse, partially unjust—but also insincere. It seems formalized, unreal, to me, as though hidden away under it were some kind of cryptic self-aggrandizement. And yet there's the hard, hollow factual truth of it: my family's gone. Julie has left me. And I keep remembering, I'm obsessed with, my birthday last November. My forty-fifth birthday: at breakfast, a lighted candle set in each piece of toast, illuminating, above, the face of each of my children—Maria (how I sometimes long to have her with me all the time!), Peter, Timmy, Jennifer—watching, whether fourteen or two-and-a-half—with eyes magnified and shining with the portentous excitement of a great day. It seems to me that I can feel now the emotion, even the tears that I did not then need to suppress. In retrospect, it was as though I then felt an obligation to be touched, to be grateful, and this very sense of coercion made it impossible for me to feel *anything,* even a conflict about it. So, I now know, I simulated the emotions that it seemed to me I should feel, and the weight of this obligation flattened the whole experience, made me irritable that so much was expected of me—and before breakfast was over, led to my barking at Tim over his sticky hands and at Peter for his grumbling over oatmeal. My thanks for my birthday gifts must have sounded as false to the rest of them as to me. And then a squabble between Peter and Tim over—God knows what: a ball or bow-and-arrow, and I broke out in a rage that was the whole massed-up accumulation of self-reproach and strain over the breakfast party. And tears and outraged child faces and Julie, stricken and hopeless. And I—miserable and divided and hopeless. Then the agony of remorse that I can never express . . .

For ten minutes, I have stood before the mirror, staring at my own face, as though this act could bring back Julie and the children. But it is not even my own face. I am familiar with it, and I can describe it; but it is somebody else's. I repudiate it; that is the thing that strikes me most strongly: I refuse to accept it as my face. I blame it for what has happened, as though I had no responsibility for it.

And I find most distasteful of all the wistfulness I see in this face. Why should it be wistful? How does wistfulness accord with the man whose record is set down above—or, for that matter, with the man setting all this down, with a bitter taste in his mouth? How does wistfulness become six foot two, one hundred ninety pounds of forty-five-year-old man?

But those pounds . . . For a moment, looking into the mirror, I thought of stripping off my clothes and examining all of me, naked as I was on the day I was born—

Needless to say, I didn't. And I think I understand both the impulse and its rejection. I think that for a flash I believed that I could catch myself unaware, surprise all of myself in an unguarded moment—and, almost as quickly, realized that I was afraid to. Or was it, rather than fear, something related to the wistfulness: a certainty that I would look at that big frame with the powerful chest, and wonder, as I sometimes have, why I couldn't *feel* of a size commensurate with my visible proportions?

I am now aware of a curious sense of weightlessness, and it reminds me of what a friend told me the other day: that he could not bear to see something blown down a street by the wind. He may be feeling contented, even gay: let a torn scrap of paper or dried leaves sweep helplessly past him, propelled by a gust, and he is instantly depressed—drained, it seems to him, of his own reality.

So, too, with me. Even when I first sat down here, I was depressed. I have become more so, and the empty feeling has followed. And now, suddenly I realize that I could be a little relieved of it if I were capable of tears.

Tears? My eyes, I find now, *are* wet; I did not know it. I feel no inclination to repress them, to curse myself as maudlin, to remind myself that these are tears of self-pity. Whatever their nature, they are a blessed relief.

The first tears in ten years? fifteen? I don't know—or perhaps I don't dare know. For the identification of the last time would open the door, if only a crack. I wrote the word "door" then as though someone were holding my hand, forcing it to set down those letters— and then suddenly there flashed into my mind a picture of myself throwing my whole weight against this anonymous door, desperately, with horror, pushing against whatever force was irresistibly driving it open. And I had an agonizing sense that in a moment this room of the present would be full, overwhelmed with the tide of the past.

I did not know that I was so ashamed and afraid of the past. Of the past? Of my life. No, not of *my* life. I haven't lived it. How I suddenly long to. That last birthday, the whole year, all the years, my life. Not relive, but *live* my life. How did I get from the frail, pampered little boy I was at, say, eight, to this slightly grizzled, solid, thickened middle-aged man with the tired skin under his eyes concealed by the thick rims of his glasses?

These are perhaps strange questions, yet what seems most strange to me now that I feel a little quieter is that I have not really asked them of myself before. I have thought about time—and change— philosophically (if as an amateur), but I have not felt it. I remember reading some passages a month or so ago in Bergson's *The Creative Mind,* and marking lines with great excitement—then, curiously, never returning to them. The book has lain here unopened ever since.

Here is one long passage I underlined:

> But nowhere is the *substantiality* of change so visible, so palpable as in the domain of the inner life. Difficulties and contradictions of every kind to which the theories of person- ality have led come from our having imagined, on the one hand, a series of distinct psychological states, each one in- variable, which would produce the variations of the ego by their very succession, and on the other hand an ego, no less invariable, which would serve as support for them. How could this unity and this multiplicity meet? How, without

either of them having duration—the first because change is
something superadded, the second because it is made up of
elements which do not change— how could they constitute an
ego which endures? But the truth is that there is neither a
rigid, immovable substratum nor distinct states passing over
it like actors on a stage. There is simply the continuous
melody of our inner life—a melody which is going on and
will go on, indivisible, from the beginning to the end of our
conscious existence. Our personality is precisely that.

This indivisible continuity of change is precisely what
constitutes true duration. . . . *Real duration* is what we have
always called *time,* but time perceived as indivisible. That time
implies succession I do not deny. But that succession is first
presented to our consciousness, like the distinction of a
"before" and "after" set side by side, is what I cannot admit.
. . . In space, and only in space, is there a clear-cut distinction
of parts external to one another. I recognize moreover that
it is in spatialized time that we ordinarily place ourselves.
We have no interest in listening to the uninterrupted humming
of life's depths. And yet, that is where real duration is. Thanks
to it, the more or less lengthy changes we witness within us
and in the eternal world take place in a single identical
time.

Thus, whether it is a question of the internal or the
external, of ourselves or of things, reality is mobility itself.
That is what I was expressing when I said that there is
change, but that there are not things which change.

This is it, and though I cannot really digest it yet, it fills me
with excitement. Time past in time present—time indivisible . . .
*We have no interest in listening to the uninterrupted humming
of life's depths.*

That is true. I have no interest in listening. I cannot hear it. I
have never heard that continuous melody of my inner life to which
he refers. And it seems to me somehow worse that I feel nothing
now when I write this.

But is that true? If true, why do I feel so sure that the vibrations
of which he speaks are *there,* to be heard? Why am I so unshakably
sure that there *is* this melody, if I have never been aware of it?

"Never" is the word to question here. For there have been
moments, hours even, when I have listened and have heard. The

terms in which I have thought of these times have been different,
the experience the same, it seems to me now. On each such occasion I
have felt a true I in me, engaged with a true separate and discrete
other, whether in the most casual or intimate encounter, with children,
nature, music, beloved or idea—an immediacy, a directness of experience that set my whole body to singing. There is then a fullness, a
unity of participation that makes all other living a travesty of the
word.

I have known false ecstasy, too, a delusion of the senses or
the intellect, product of drink or vanity. And the sure and simple
distinction, as sharp and clean as the line of the horizon on a clear
day, is that the true experience remains constant, as full-bodied and
fixed in the following day, week, year as in the moment of delivery—
while the other, when the vapors of justification, rationalization, compulsion have rolled away, lies open to the full daylight of the mind: a
glittering skeleton, old bones encrusted with dime-store rhinestones.
And although these judgments may often coincide with conventional
morality as we know it, they do not necessarily.

But I remember now that Bergson had a final passage to the
chapter I marked that says all this better than I can:

> Thanks to philosophy, all things acquire depth—more
> than depth, something like a fourth dimension which permits
> anterior perceptions to remain bound up with present
> perceptions, and the immediate future itself to become partly
> outlined in the present. Reality no longer appears then in the
> static state, in its manner of being; it affirms itself dynamically,
> in the continuity and variability of its tendency. What was
> immobile and frozen in our perception is warmed and set in
> motion. Everything comes to life around us, everything is
> revivified in us. A great impulse carries beings and things
> along. We feel ourselves uplifted, carried away, borne along
> by it. We are more fully alive and this increase of life brings
> with it the conviction that grave philosophical enigmas can be
> resolved or even perhaps that they need not be raised, since
> they arise from a frozen vision of the real and are only the
> translation, in terms of thought, of a certain artificial weakening
> of our vitality. In fact, the more we accustom ourselves to think
> and perceive all things *sub specie durationis,* the more we
> plunge into real duration. And the more we immerse ourselves
> in it, the more we set ourselves back in the direction of the

principle, though it be transcendent, in which we participate and whose eternity is not to be an eternity of immutability, but an eternity of life: how, otherwise, could we live and move in it? *In ea vivimus et movemur et sumus.*

This is to me a great passage, as majestic in tone and meaning as the most inspired scriptures, or the best of Lucretius, Dante, Shakespeare. It gives me the sense of a great split in the life of the twentieth century, of two worlds coexisting almost without knowledge of each other. Though their margins, their circumferences, touch and even interpenetrate at times and in individuals, this seldom comes to full conscious realization, since the one, having more dimensions than the other, knows the superficially identical experience in quite another way.

The one world is the "static state" of life to which Bergson refers—that "frozen vision of the real" which is "only the translation . . . of a certain artificial weakening of our vitality"—the semblance of life to which I have given most of my conscious rendering of experience. This is his stage, on which I and others move like puppets, impelled to speak the lines that, only half aware, we feel have been given us to speak. It is this denial of true life that drove Julie away, that leaves me wistful, haunted, empty. The communication lines to my genuine self down, I am isolated, deserted, alone and without identity, though moving with the appearance of freedom (indeed, the author of *The Free Man and Peace*) amongst the masses of my fellow puppets.

And all the time, deep within, around, about, the unheard melody, the uninterrupted humming of life's depths. Oh, Julie. "Everything comes to life around us, everything is revivified in us": I cannot express the hope that stirs within me at these words.

How did I begin all this? I cannot remember what I wrote, but I do know that the whole sequence began truly in that sense of wistfulness I wondered at. Wistfulness! My God, the dullness of my feelings. What I called wistfulness is despair, an unbearable desperation. And the tears of my heart reach my eyes without my knowing they are there.

I think of my forty-five years, of all my failures and evasions and betrayals, and I think of the shadows on the wall of Plato's cave. And all the time—yes, *all the time*—there flowed, there flows, this great stream of life, past me, around me, through me. I want my share; I want my immersion; and I am suddenly sure that I can find myself only by finding myself in it—and it only by finding myself.

There is new meaning and hope for me in keeping this journal.

For, as Bergson wrote, such a sense of life teaches us that the "philosophical enigmas" need not be raised at all, arising as they do from the "frozen vision of the real." I must not analyze, describe, record, as I thought when I began writing tonight, but invoke—somehow learn to reach down into the unknown darknesses of my soul with my own dowsing rod, tap resources of which I have not even been aware. Patience and honesty, patience and honesty. And I may, in my measure, succeed, I realize now, if I have the humility to remember all the while that the larger context is all there, in time; if, even as I write my little i's, I do not forget that larger shadowy writing over the earth, on trees and stones and on the walls of buildings men have raised, in the great rolling ocean and on the streets of man and the sky-hooded hills alike, on the very golden fiery air itself—God's signature in time. In it we live and move and have our being.

Part One

THE HERRICK FAMILY PEW

[*Part One*] **1**

AT either end of the hall of childhood stood a magisterial figure. Or so it seemed to Walton Herrick, long years later, when he at last felt able to come in the front door, pay for his ticket, push through the turnstile and saunter about the gallery of the Herricks and the Nicholsons like any other museum-goer. Only then did he realize the extent to which these two figures had dominated the others.

Scattered about in ones and twos were the rest of them, caught and immobilized in some attitude so characteristic, so finally definitive of each impressed life, that they seemed, in the manner of the Homeric gods, more the embodiment of single qualities than complex individuals. Mother, head disdainfully erect, chin lifted in that hauteur with which she denied her fear and defied the demon-peopled world of her imagination—the world that, for her, eventually came to replace all but completely the one of external reality. Father, seated, his short crippled legs not quite touching the floor, seeming almost to be balanced on his enthusiasm alone as he leaned forward to stress some point he was making—his hands extended, palms together and fingers pointed upwards as though intent on prayer. Uncle Lloyd Herrick with his bald head thrown back in ribald commentary; in contrast, Uncle Herbert Nicholson, chin on palm, brooding somberly upon some obscure obscenity implicit in the floor before him. And all the rest of them: grandmothers, aunts, cousins, frozen thus for perpetuity in Walton's memory, so that—no matter how many conflicting or contrasting moods or traits any of them might have possessed; no matter how boldly or subtly they might have altered in the ensuing years; no matter how heroically they might have applied themselves to that most drastic of human disciplines, conscious change—he could never think of them as other than they were, in the hall of his memory, transfixed, trapped as though in stone.

On the whole, they formed a striking group. At first they seemed to capture to an extraordinary degree the diversity and range of life itself—all the way from the hand-locked resoluteness of Grandmother Herrick to the undone laxness of Walton's sister Elinor, reclining on the bed of her disintegration and surveying with lackluster resignation the emptiness of her life. But, the longer Walton looked, the less sure he became of the range and diversity. In all the figures there was an evidence of constraint. The more vigorous ones showed it in the very strenuousness of their rebellion; those who had endured passively, in the rigidity of their compliance. The fragile ones had been broken altogether—into madness or degeneracy or some wasting and protracted illness of, say, the mind or the colon.

And so, in his middle years, looking at the exhibition of Herricks and Nicholsons, Walton Herrick became fully aware at last of the shadows cast by the two great figures facing each other across the hall, his two grandfathers. He found it fruitless to remind himself that they were not *only* prototypes, originators, the great primordial fathers of their groups—indeed, were not *this* at all, but single individuals connecting, as all individuals (even the childless ones) do, the heritage and the bequest, the past and the indecipherable future; that they, in a similar hall in the imagination of someone of another generation, were the slight minor figures of an alcove, a recess in one of the side walls, themselves shaped and conditioned by other, earlier, dominating prophets: patriarchs and matriarchs. The admonition was futile—or, at least, meaningless— for it was only his own gallery that he was necessarily concerned with; in *that*, these two commanded every perspective.

Cornelius Butler Herrick, D.D., LL.D., Walton's paternal grandfather, was the more gracious, the less forbidding figure of the two. Of middle height and comfortable but not excessive flesh, he was impressive for the massiveness of his head and for a certain majesty of bearing. People, Walton remembered, had often spoken of his resemblance to Robert E. Lee—and the shape of the head and the trimmed, barely pointed white beard did contribute to a quick, easy likeness. But Cornelius Herrick's face was broader, the eyes (though sensitive) less wise, less gentle, less candid. They were, in fact (at least, so it seemed in retrospect) troubled and opaque. Yet most people, when they spoke of him, used the word *benevolent*.

He wore his benevolence with an air of urbanity, as he had tempered the putative austerity of a life-long Presbyterian ministry with two "worldly" intervals—one as secretary to the national board of missions of his denomination in New York City, the other as acting president of the university which he had otherwise served for twenty years as a trustee. He achieved an aura of moderation, a blending of Christian dedication and tolerant gentility so irreproachable to people of so many different temperamental colorations that to the young and the acid this in itself constituted a reproach. But these two groups are seldom influential elements of a community. And if those who were bound to him only as sheep of his pastoral flock or as fellow citizens were awed by this commingling of the rounded, complete gentleman and the Christian servant, what should be the effect on his four children?

Devastation, probably, Walton thought—at first, in their trying somehow, not to emulate him (the very thought was sacrilege), but in some small fashion to keep from being wholly unworthy of him; later, when the awful secret of his senility obsessed and scandalized them, to recover some semblance of equilibrium, to find some explanation, some extenuating circumstance, to mitigate the ugly, shameful discovery of his relation to the nurse who attended him when he was past eighty.

"A scheming, common adventuress," Walton's mother, Marcia, had proclaimed, setting her lips. "Taking advantage of a helpless, childish old man!"

Uncle Edgar Briffault, the husband of Cornelius Herrick's younger daughter Rosalind, being a physician and a Frenchman, phrased it more succinctly—to be sure, not in the presence of the assembled family.

"She is a bitch," he said, hissing aspirately, his smart 1910 black goatee dipping briskly. "But she can be bought off."

Not that there was much money—except in Aunt Emily's bank account and investments. But more than blackmail, it was scandal that the family feared—the whispering and pointing, the suddenly averted glances, the abrupt hush in a crowded room as one of them entered it, the bright impudent stares when heads were raised again.

One had an anticipatory knowledge of how it would be if anyone outside the family were to catch even the faintest whiff of the smoke rising from this startling, impossible fire that had caught in some inexplicable way on the hoary plains of late winter. What Cornelius Herrick did was of interest to the whole city of Cleveland. Prominent in its religious, educational and civic life, it was he who joined in marriage its elite of blood and fat securities, baptized its future senators and steel barons, exorcised the devils of infidelity and illness and death that plagued the wives of its bank presidents and corporation lawyers.

So the family had met, in agitation and foreboding: the four children, and those of their husbands or wives who had not died or been divorced. It was extraordinary, in itself indicative of something

febrile and unwholesome in his surroundings, Walton eventually came
to think, that even then (he could not have been more than four) he
learned that such a meeting was taking place at Aunt Emily's house.
He had, of course, heard only a stray reference or two from his parents'
conversation—and understood little of what he had heard—yet that
any of it at all should have been discussed before him suggested both
the magnitude of the crisis to the middle generation of Herricks, and
their inadequacy in the face of not unusual adult problems and responsibilities.

With his new museum-gazer's insight, he had no difficulty in piecing together—or, rather, re-creating—the gathering. His mother had
told him some of it later—in his adolescence, during the period when all
her accumulated resentment of the Herricks, all the real and imagined
slights, all the honest indignation and dishonest self-pity, poured from
her in a prolonged hideous spasm of protest. But his version of the meeting owed only one or two facts to this hysterical, certainly distorted
account. The rest was his own, culled in slow, meditative ruminations.

Aunt Emily would have called the meeting to order, as befitted
her double responsibility of seniority and hospitality. She was the only
child of Cornelius Herrick's first wife, who had died so long before that
she was only a wraith in the tradition of the Herricks, a marginal notation
on the great record. Cornelius' unpublished autobiography (which Walton inherited from his father) allotted her a paragraph from his early
days in Connecticut:

> I now began to make weekly visits to Meriden which
> issued in my engagement at some time to marry Emily Curtis.
> I had held the pastorate at Norwich for a year and a half when
> my eyes troubled me again. Mr. Curtis, who was well-to-do
> and friendly, suggested a sea voyage, a trip in Europe and a
> consultation with a distinguished oculist in Lausanne, and
> put $500.00 at my disposal. My intended was suffering from
> the effects of a burn and a persistent religious depression of
> mind; and it was at Dr. Bushnell's suggestion that our marriage
> was determined upon, and she was to share my trip. We were
> married the first day of May, 1861, soon after the Civil War
> broke out, and sailed in the ship Victoria for London, the 5th.
> [A melancholy prospect! But Cornelius went on to state defini-
> tively:] This was all and altogether a happy marriage so far as
> we were concerned. [Who else, Walton wondered, was "con-
> cerned"? At any rate, it was not a marriage of great duration,
> for Cornelius concluded the same long paragraph:] On June

8th, 1862, my Emily was called home to God, leaving me alone
with a baby five days old. Of this desolate experience, I cannot
write.

This was (except for her own daughter, of course) the family's
whole knowledge of Emily Curtis Herrick. She was a little suspect, a
little alien, invoked most often in poorly-concealed envy, since she had
left her considerable fortune to Walton's Aunt Emily, and thus set her off
materially above the other three children. Yet, as Rosalind Herrick
dryly remarked, the first Emily could hardly have "remembered" the
rest of them in her will, since they were conceived and borne in the
womb of her successor.

Aunt Emily, in her comfortable stucco home, recessed and dark
behind magnificent box hedges and yew trees, with her strangely poignant wish to be thought jolly despite her intense need for privacy,
her nagging and inescapable fastidiousness, her utter inability to elude the
private tyranny within her that drove her to the verge of vertigo when
things were not *comme il faut* . . . Aunt Emily, who was temporarily so
sparkling and so successfully jolly, as she drove from house to house in
her "electric," picking up all the cousins of Walton's generation, her
various step-nieces and nephews, to take them to lunch at DeKlyn's,
where there was a special children's menu on Saturdays—yet who had
never married, and was given to formidable temper tantrums and
migraine headaches that sometimes lasted for ten days . . .

Who knew Aunt Emily? Little Emily, who was but five days old
when her mother died, who spent summers with her grandparents in
Connecticut and never spoke of them, who grew up somehow always
alone in the midst of a large family, set apart by her inheritance and
her inwardness? Big Emily, stout, smiling. with an incongruous tendency
to chatter at social gatherings; yet, caught and rendered off guard, mournful, bitter, grieving—for the life she had never had but only viewed far-
off, as a perennial passenger on a lifetime train catches a fleeting, wistful
glimpse of some scene impregnated with cheerful, bustling life?

At any rate, Aunt Emily, who had introduced into her slightly
baroque but meticulously proper household, some seven or eight years
earlier, a companion known to the Herrick family only as "Miss Sanford" and the subject of much speculation but not discussed openly—
Aunt Emily must have begun the meeting (once the maid had dispensed
orange pekoe tea, in the second-best Worcester china, and little cakes
with pink icing) by saying firmly, "We must take measures."

And then they must have turned to Uncle Lloyd, not because there
was anything in his bearing or in his record that would suggest turning

to him in a time of grave crisis, but because he was the oldest—no, older
—son. And just as the oldest child should have the meeting at her house
and open the meeting, so the older son must be accorded the opportunity
to initiate the action. So they would all (except, Walton, thought, his
mother, who secretly envied Lloyd his casual, irresponsible charm, and
openly denounced him as a coarse wastrel)—they would all have turned
to Lloyd, without expectation, without hope, in empty formality. And he
would not have disappointed them.

"Nonsense," he undoubtedly had said. "Folderol." (A favorite expression of his when the presence of family—rather than the traditional
one of women, with whom he enjoyed a regular success—inhibited his
habitual use of more pungent expressions.) "Folderol. Let the old boy
have some fun. He's had little enough."

The nature of the storm that broke after this was not blurred in
Walton's mind, but it was too familiar to be very interesting. Suffice it to
say that, for various reasons, something had to be done. For obvious
reasons, a man must do it. Lloyd flatly refused, and Walton's father,
William, was ruled out (with affection, with approval, with little, unconsciously condescending shudders over the hurt he might otherwise
suffer at the hands of that vulgar woman) on the score of his unworldli-
ness as well as that of his being crippled. There was, therefore, no choice
but to commission an in-law, Uncle Edgar Briffault, who accepted the
appointment with reluctant relish. Walton had no proof that Dr. Briffault
had thereafter enjoyed an entertaining parry-at-arms with the slightly
faded but pretty nurse who had precipitated the whole matter (to be
sure, with Cornelius Herrick's enthusiastic cooperation), but he had
suspected something of the sort. And for a long time—until the Puritanism he had imbibed with the milk of his infancy (he was bottle-fed) had
subsided to sediment at the bottom of his nature, stirred only rarely—
he had both envied and despised his uncle for his seeming capacity to sin
lightly, urbanely, and without remorse.

At any rate, Dr. Briffault did effect the appointed task; Aunt Emily
footed the bill; a harelipped woman who spoke little English replaced
the offending nurse; and the Herricks breathed more easily. But the secret
flaw at the heart of things had been exposed; with God dead, it was not
easy to rally immediately, or to see a continuing purpose in God's world.
Walton's father, in simplicity and honest faith, prayed for guidance.
Emily confided to Miss Sanford, not without sobs, that this was the final
confirmation of all her darkest convictions about men. Rosalind, the
youngest of the four, in bitter loyalty to her father, fought with her husband Edgar, attempting without success to refute his satirical comments

about the nature of man and—incidentally—fathers. Lloyd, finding in
the incident an easy justification for the course of his own life, rejected
it and suffered for several days from a melancholy malaise. What he had
said to the family had been for the family. As for the several in-laws, they
tried vainly not to express the satisfaction they experienced at this testimony to Herrick frailty, a reassurance that the Family had to face concrete evidence that Cornelius Herrick shared something of the common
human condition.

But they all should have known *this*—or at least suspected it—about
their father, it seemed to Walton, reviewing the matter decades later.
What was the meaning of the flurried, almost adolescent terror the episode evoked in all the children except Lloyd—and even in him, an
uneasiness? Walton could find only two explanations that satisfied him
at all, and they were, perhaps, complementary. One was, of course, the
semi-deification of Cornelius Herrick, to which they had all acceded—
even Lloyd again, in the very violence of his rebellion. The other was
that they had been allowed to encounter very few of the rudimentary
facts of life, except as veiled by some hastily snatched-up covering of
cheery evasion, some improvised scarf of "decency."

Of course the result was patent in their lives; the incident of the
nurse was not really needed to expose it. Three of their own five marriages (three for Lloyd) eventually ended in divorce—and that of Walton's father and mother was a prolonged, though involuntary, war of
attrition. In its own small local way, Walton thought, the record was as
unedifying as that of the Roosevelt family on the grand stage—and as
puzzling to the admirers of the father, the great man.

But there had been various evidences that behind the dark opaqueness of Cornelius Herrick's eyes lay a stormy and troubled nature, a
volcanic sea of emotion with bubbling spouts of hot passion and arbitrary
wrath. To be sure, to the best of the family's knowledge, no alien eye had
ever viewed its eruptions. But it had been part of the ritual of their
childhood to pass on tiptoe the closed study door whenever Catherine
Herrick said, "Your father's not feeling well. He's very tired today." It
was further evident, even to a grandchild, that since Catherine Herrick
regularly sat in a rocking chair with her hands tightly clasped in her lap,
and seldom said anything beyond the amenities required of the wife of a
great man (often, indeed, even omitting these), there was some constraint upon her, an imposed or self-imposed discipline of iron rigidity.

Moreover, on those rare occasions when she did wag her tongue
to any extent, there were a dryness and a wryness to her references to her
husband that confused and upset the children. On such days as these, it

was her turn to retire to her room, inviolate, with a steaming pot of tea and—it was hinted—a novel of no great seriousness.

There were, too, the still rarer times when "Father got mad." Walton never heard the particulars of any of these explosions, but one of the most familiar sayings of the family body of dogma, spoken in wholly unambiguous pride, was "Oh, no! Father seldom got ruffled, but once in a while—say, every two or three years, he'd get in a towering rage. Really frightening." Pride and wonder, as at one of the great natural curiosities or scenic grotesqueries of the globe—eyes glowing as the speaker reached for another Nabisco or a Social Tea wafer.

And then, of course, there was the other Great Scare, preceding the libidinous passage with the nurse by eight or nine years. At seventy-five, Cornelius Herrick, as pastor emeritus and "grand old man" of the Cleveland Presbytery, was invited back to his beloved First Church to preach on the occasion of its seventy-fifth anniversary. (People made much, in easy mysticism, of the fact that he and the church had been born in the same year.)

The children had had their doubts of the advisability of his performing. But all their uncertainties were in terms of his having the physical strength to prepare and deliver a sermon, one that would not overtax him, yet do him moderate justice. Assured by their mother, who was much the frailer of the two and had at that time less than two years to live, that Father felt fine and had written a worthy address (actually she had not read a line of it, but reassurance was her role), they all settled down in the family pew, tightly crowded in, to enjoy to the full the valedictory of Cornelius Herrick. Lloyd, of course, they expected to be bored; yet he, too, arrived on time—indeed, early—in order to be sure of having the aisle seat, with its arm rest.

Hence, they were all unprepared and thunderstruck by what took place. They were horrified, shaken to their foundations—except William, who told Walton, years later, that this sermon was one of the greatest events, the turning points, of his whole life. Yet, he admitted, at the time he had been torn between his sense of exaltation and a very realistic concern over the mundane consequences.

Cornelius Herrick's successor in the pastorate was the Rev. Douglas Barclay, a hearty, stout, vigorous preacher of the faith and a Scot with the integrity of sterling silver and the resilience of tempered steel. Despite many dreary long Sunday mornings spent twitching and shifting and dreaming in the family pew, Walton never felt a grudge against Dr. Barclay. He knew, with the instinctive judgment of a child (which, he remarked to himself, remembering, is too often invoked, yet retains a good deal of the validity it shares with other platitudes), that this was a good man, by which he later realized that he had meant a kind and honest man. Once, when an elder of the church, paying a Sunday-afternoon call on Walton's father, had spoken a slighting word about the minister, Walton had leapt hotly to his defense, summoning all the resources of his precocious nine-year-old vocabulary.

The criticisms of Dr. Barclay were mostly expressions of disapproval over the well-known "facts" that now and then he "took a glass" and that he had "an eye for pretty women"—notably the contralto in the church quartet. At that time Walton (not yet fully infected with the virus of the Calvinist tradition) was not quite sure why these tendencies were evil, but there seemed to be complete unanimity about them—and this increased his rebelliousness and stiffened his loyalty to the Scot (to a point, in fact, during the years of secondary school reading, where he was inclined to identify Dr. Barclay with Roderick Dhu, and, later, Ivanhoe). This was one of the first of a lifetime series of wholly emotional loyalties, matched in ferocity only by his equally irrational antagonisms. In this case, it had something to do (he came eventually to know) with his stubborn refusal to accept the almost universal worship of his grandfather. For the comparison between the two ministers was often made, to the depreciation of Dr. Barclay.

"You see," Walton was to say darkly to his father during a spring vacation in his college years, "Grandfather lies over that church like a blanket, just as he does over the family. And the only difference between him and Dr. Barclay is that Dr. Barclay isn't a hypocrite; he does everything out in the open." His father threw up his hands in his characteristic gesture of hopelessness, of the ultimate defeat he suffered when confronted by the forces of barbarous irrationality—the gesture he usually reserved for one of his wife's more fantastic pronouncements. He threw up his hands and groaned in despair, making no attempt to answer.

But if Walton had been present at the seventy-fifth anniversary service, he would have realized that between old Dr. Herrick and Dr. Barclay there was a communal feeling, a warm, unassailable sympathy that would have withstood, on both sides, all the comparisons and dissension-sowing. When Cornelius Herrick had finished his final, storm-provoking sermon, Dr. Barclay pronounced the benediction with a vigor and yet a serenity that seemed almost threatening in the way it conveyed a sense of his disapproval of those who would take exception to what had been said. And two nights later, at the extraordinary session of Cleveland Presbytery called to consider the case of Dr. Herrick's radical and heretical deliverances, it was Dr. Barclay who turned the tide, with a thunderous citing of whited sepulchres that Walton's father memorized, even to the slightly florid style:

"Would you indict this most devoted and dedicated servant of the Lord Jesus Christ because, in his venerable old age, he has spoken the truth that was in his heart? Or because that truth of a troubled heart is the unspotted, unexplained, unelaborated, shocking truth of the Lord Jesus' unvarnished message? Woe unto us if we adulterate the word of the living God to bring salve and balm to the uneasy consciences of our well-fed parishioners. We have forgotten that Jesus drove the money changers from the temple; we rather sit and hold pleasant discourse with them. We are seduced by the worldly within ourselves and we twist the word of God to our pleasure and convenience. We render unto Caesar those things that are God's. A prophet has been among us. Let us weigh his words, search our hearts, and keep silence."

What had the old man said? Simply this, as Walton had been able to piece it together: Love is the gospel. Love alone means the gift of the self to God. Love accounts for all the parables that seem to exceed or even to deny justice (going the second mile, giving both the coat and the cloak, paying the laborers who came only in the afternoon as much as those who had worked all day long)—for love knows not the laws of justice as they are commonly understood, but dictates the laws of a new and superficially inequitable justice. Love demands giving, giving, giving; it is at once the severest and most gracious of qualities—indeed, it is not a quality, but a life, not a life but life itself. Only if one gives oneself and one's life does one live.

Finally, then, be it understood that one cannot give this ultimate gift, this self, through will and self-discipline. One can give oneself, the gift of love, only if love is there, pure, unforced within one. And while this is a mysterious inner condition—the gift of God in His love, mysteriously bestowed (studying Calvin and Luther, long years later, Walton willfully played with the concept that his grandfather had intentionally so rendered Calvin's theory of the Elect)—yet there are external conditions in which it may not burgeon and flourish: notably, those of riches and comfort and luxury and pride (how different a conclusion from that of Calvin!). Charity, as commonly understood (philanthropy), was not enough—was, indeed, a wholly different thing and quite irrelevant. He invoked the camel and the needle's eye; one saw the camel halt, try again, give up in grotesque despair.

Here the point of friction, here the abrasion that must become an open sore, that prevented a reception otherwise replete with happy sighs of "so spiritual . . . inspiring . . . a benediction . . ." For the old man went on in a sonorous peroration, his eyes glittering, his face flushed, the veins standing out and throbbing in his forehead, to pronounce a jeremiad against the rich and the proud and the powerful of the city and the nation—those very ones with whom he had consorted throughout his life, those very ones who had bestowed upon him, a poor farmer's son, though of antique Anglo-Saxon stock, a liberal supply of those goods, that bounty (as much in terms of a gracious way of life as the money itself) which he was denouncing as irrelevant and even inimical to the Christian life and to individual Christian salvation: "They open their purses but not their hearts. They give with a measured hand, which is not giving. For six days they seek for themselves, averting their eyes when their seeking crushes others, but never turning aside, never halting, bending over, and extending a hand. And on the seventh day they sit, somberly resplendent, in the house of the Lord—yea, like graven images do they sit in the full panoply of their false righteousness—and seek again for themselves, since though they give to the Lord, they count the interest thereof: 'Do you, in recognition of this gift, accord me full forgiveness, O Lord, for those sins that I may have.' Thus do they pray, asking forgiveness when, in the dark uneasiness of personal communion, they cannot sufficiently forgive themselves to look even a little way into themselves and acknowledge in what they have sinned."

And he concluded with the words, "I say unto you, renounce all these resources of pride and seek love. Seek only love. Seek it in yourself. Find it. Give your goods, give yourself. Love is not merely the greatest of these; it is these and beyond these—it is life. Death is the condition of not loving. Pray for life and find it. Find life and love. For love is life, and he that has it not is dead, past recall at the trump of the Last Day—past redemption, beyond the forgiving grasp of God. Repent and seek love. Love and live. Find ye life therefore, in the name of God the Father and God the Son and God the Holy Ghost. Listen to the voice of the Living God—listen and love and live."

He was an anarchist—a radical—a socialist—one with scoundrels like Debs and Altgeld. Worse—when one considered the advantages he had enjoyed. He was an addled old man—senile, childish, pitiably broken, gone mad. . . . But the ringing anvil of Douglas Barclay's voice prevailed—or perhaps it was only the law of inertia, the great back-tugging inclination to ignore, to pretend, to forget, to "forgive," to overlook. At any rate, Presbytery (which officially ignored the "socialistic attack" on the burghers of the city and concentrated upon the interpretation of dogma, especially one sentence which declared that it was "of little importance, indeed a frivolous and trivial point, whether or not Jesus was the actual and literal Son of God, immaculately conceived")—Presbytery, in special session, resolved to take no action and voted to adjourn.

Within the Herrick family, it might be said that the same results obtained—but with a difference. The scar tissue remained. This time it was William whose interpretation differed from that of the rest; Lloyd, grave, even sulky, refused any comment. But William was forgiven by the others for his excess of spirituality; hampered by his lameness, he was an unworldly man, and the wild advice of Cornelius' sermon actually applied to him, as it did to no one else in their acquaintance: such a doctrine of exclusive love sustained him, no doubt, in his adversity, strengthened him against his affliction.

Lloyd, as usual, did not escape so easily. It was remembered that during the past winter their old father, formerly cold to Lloyd, even embittered against him for his profligacy, had seemed to turn to him for the first time, had almost daily gone riding with him in his cutter. The two of them became one of the city's familiar sights, Lloyd in his bowler, skillfully flicking the whip over the flanks of his dapper bay, the old man, wearing a stocking cap and so bundled up that his face was hardly visible, snuggled close against his son under the plaid lap robe—the bells jingling and the smooth runners of the sleigh scraping lightly the hard-packed snow.

It was Aunt Emily who conceived the idea that Lloyd, who was known to have consorted with esoteric sects, an interest (she felt) only superficially incongruous with his general dissoluteness, must have been seducing their father, taking advantage of his gullible old mind. Emily's idea was entertained by the rest of the family, but discarded. It was rejected by William as a misunderstanding of the whole matter, and by Rosalind because she loved Lloyd, and because she knew that he preferred conservative conduct in everyone except himself: the one marginal comment he had scribbled most often on the pages of his life (though in a language that required translation) was that he wanted the rest of his family to behave with their traditional propriety.

But the days passed; more ordinary matters resumed their dominance in the interests and lives of the Herricks; eventually even Emily resumed her customary coldly cordial attitude toward Lloyd. Perhaps the last reference to the whole affair was made by William, when he finally had his emotion sufficiently disciplined to feel sure that he could, without breaking down, tell the old man how deeply moved he had been by the sermon.

Cornelius' clouded eyes cleared for a moment.

"You," he said softly, "were the inspiration of that sermon."

That one sentence carried William through much of his life. When his cane was insufficient to support him, he would lean upon these words of his father's.

THE uneasy sufferance between Emily and Lloyd was not new. Period-
ically, their distrust of each other would flare up overtly, like some recurring boil or sore. The subsequent suppuration would ooze for days,
thick with pent-up secretions, oily with the angry mixture of blood and
pus. At such times, the other members of the Herrick family would, in
accordance with the varying idioms of their personalities, obliquely work
away at conciliatory measures or express—but never in the presence of
either principal—outright disgust at this perpetuation of a childhood feud.

For Lloyd and Emily had been suspicious of each other from the
outset. Walton could not, of course, discover the specific origins of their
hostility; it had been so long established that it seemed to have been born
with them. He could only surmise that the differences and conflicts between his aunt and uncle were embedded in basic questions of status and
personality.

Emily had become a resident member of the Herrick family in 1869,
when she was seven and Lloyd four; thereafter, she spent only the summers with her maternal grandparents. The advent of a new and *older*
sister must in itself have been shattering to a little boy who for four years
had been the only child in the household. That she should be as strong-
willed as Lloyd himself, and undoubtedly edgy over her transplantation,
must have intensified the conflict between them, and also their parents'
dilemma. Nor was it difficult to believe that when William was born prematurely three years later—weak and crippled (from the delivery?)—
Emily must have felt that *this* was her *real* brother, since she was not
just presented with him, but on the scene to welcome him. If she had felt
alien, a stranger in a strange land, when she had first come into this
household, in which the mother was not *her* mother, now it must have
been Lloyd's turn to feel superfluous, displaced by a rival brother upon
whom all of his parents' solicitude was immediately centered.

At any rate, Lloyd and Emily, as they grew up, were not only bitter opponents; they came to seem almost perfectly opposed archetypes—in outlook, conduct and disposition. Emily, secure in her private means and free to indulge her tastes, increasingly exemplified the correct, conservative and effete in public, while invoking the exclusive prerogative of the well-to-do to enjoy in private one's eccentricities. Lloyd, having only the family's common fortune to sustain him, was defiantly extravagant, whether in terms of money or behavior. She was managerial by temperament, he impatient of instruction, discipline, and even order.

Both had well-developed tempers: Emily's bitter, smoky, low-lying —at its rare worst shrill and hysterical; Lloyd's easily aroused, flamboyant, almost florid. Emily was finicky, fastidious; Lloyd affected a sort of debonair slovenliness. She was precise in manner and diction, although a certain natural robustness occasionally betrayed the artificiality of this precision, and the combination produced an effect of false heartiness. Lloyd was coarse and careless in speech, often deliberately vulgar. Emily, though moderately attractive as a young woman, seemed to shrink from even the most marginal sexual expression, and discouraged any male attention with frozen dignity. Lloyd's affairs, from the age of eighteen on, were a scandal to the family and the community.

There was in Emily, finally, a sense of dark repression, of crusted resentment, and a determination to get even—with what: Life itself? In Lloyd there was a contrary sense of looseness, wildness, and—deep within—a final helplessness and hopelessness. Looking back, Walton thought that he could understand how both of them covered an ultimate pessimism with quite different kinds of superficial optimism: Emily's at once domineering and prissy cheerfulness, Lloyd's boisterous determination to have a good time.

So, well into middle life, they endured each other when it was necessary, Lloyd warily circling Emily's every effort in the name of good breeding—eying her cynically like some old dispirited but still tough game-cock who will eventually strike, but at his own good time and not according to the rules of the contest. He knew that he could hurt her most by accepting her offices at a family gathering, say, with the essential minimum of affirmative and negative grunts—and then, only when she felt temporarily reassured that he was not going to do anything outrageous *this time,* break into the established gentility of the occasion with some such comment as "When are you going to do something about your chastity, Emily? You're as fat as a capon."

The most dramatic outcome of their lifelong opposition involved no face-to-face encounter. Hence Lloyd, in old age, could supply Walton only with certain aspects of a rare family crisis centering in an action of

Emily's. The remainder of the story Walton filled in for himself, piecing together remarks of his Aunt Rosalind's and of his mother's with his own increasingly confident intuitive sense of his grandfather.

The event in question took place some seven or eight years before the incident involving the nurse, a few months after the anniversary sermon, and at a time when Cornelius Herrick still retained the better part of his intellectual vigor. Lloyd dropped in one afternoon to pay his weekly visit to his father and mother (it was only a year before her death), and remarked that he had heard that Emily had taken on "a companion."

Cornelius nodded in benign approval.

"It's a very good thing," he said. "She's been lonely in that big house, and I'm glad she's found a friend to share it with her. I mean to go up there and meet Miss Sanford tomorrow."

Lloyd chuckled derisively, but would have allowed this testimonial of innocence to pass unchallenged had it not been that at that moment he caught his mother's eye. He was not sure of all that her expression meant, but he at least partially understood it, and what he did comprehend both startled and angered him, angered him savagely for her sake.

She had always been his refuge, but now he realized suddenly that this very fact had somehow ironically kept him from knowing her: she had been so sufficient for him simply as protection and comfort that he had not looked deeper. But now her expression was so sardonic that he surmised, all at once, almost overwhelmingly, that she knew the nature of the relation between Emily and Miss Sanford; that she had never loved Emily, but rather done what she conceived to be her duty toward her; that she resented the special privileges and special place in her husband's heart that Emily—and not *her* children—had enjoyed. And thinking of those long years of patient forbearance, of the integrity of Catherine Herrick's peculiarly astringent sort of kindness, oriented by justice rather than sentimentality, Lloyd became enraged at Emily, who had always, it seemed to him now, treated her—*his* mother—with complacent condescension. Looking at his mother, seeing with a newly acute vision that she was dying and that (through his own shortcomings, to be sure, but this only doubled his anger) there were depths in her that he had undervalued and now would never really know, he lashed out at his father in a way he had not done for years.

"Found a friend to share it with!" he snarled. "What kind of a friend is that, for *you* to approve of? And why couldn't she share some of her comfort and luxury with the people who have done so much for her? The whole thing's disgusting—and you don't even know what it means!"

In a moment, of course, he realized that he had blurted something out the way he had as a boy—that he had gone too far unless he was ready to go much farther. He saw the familiar warning signals flickering in the old man's eyes, the momentary saturnine amusement in his mother's, and, suddenly reduced again to the frustrated helplessness of his youth, he limped over to kiss his mother almost roughly, said gruffly, "Good-bye, Father," and slouched out, just as the old man began a formal and indignant request for an explanation.

Cornelius Herrick turned almost irritably to his wife.

"I thought Lloyd was now sufficiently a man at last not to give vent to his spite against Emily. What does he mean? I'm sure she's been very generous to all of us—and I can see nothing 'disgusting' about her sharing her comforts with a less fortunate friend."

Catherine Herrick looked directly into his eyes, and for a moment he was uneasily aware of the irony in hers.

"One sees what one wants to," she said dryly, and picking up her tatting also left the room. . . .

As usual, it took Rosalind's efforts to restore the old man to equanimity. She arrived at Turtle Villa (so the family had named the dome-roofed house in which the old couple lived) an hour later, and Cornelius immediately poured out to her his grievances and his bewilderment.

Rosalind smiled wryly. She was the only member of the family who was equally fond of Lloyd and Emily—and William, too, for that matter. Moreover, she understood and loved her father and mother impartially.

"First of all, Father—" she explained, stroking his hand until the fierce tenseness left it—"first of all, Father, it isn't as though Lloyd was complaining for himself. You know he's worried about Mother, and I'm sure it was Mother he was thinking of. You and I know that Emily's done a lot for you and Mother—for all of us. But Lloyd won't admit any good in her. He and she just can't get along; it's like trying to mix—well, vinegar and maple syrup: if you have both you don't have either."

The comfortable slump of Cornelius' shoulders told her eloquently that he was mollified; his softened expression, the restored amiability in his eyes, announced that he loved *her*—ironically, she thought, simply because she was the only one who would give him (as she tended to give everyone) exactly what he wanted. This was her cross, her trophy, at once the meaning of her life and what deprived her of having a meaning of her own.

Relaxed, Cornelius permitted himself a little slyness.

"Which is the vinegar?" he asked.

Rosalind acknowledged his quip and his chuckle with a smile. Why, she wondered again, were the Herricks so perverse about enjoying themselves? Her father had as good a sense of humor as anyone needed, yet he rarely gave it expression. It was as though he willfully kept to his official personality, with its blend of piety and urbanity, actively suppressing a naturally earthy and informal self. And this, she supposed, was what she loved most about Lloyd: that, alone among the Herricks, he had fun. When not pricked by some special irritant (like Emily) he was openly amused by most of life. The rest of them (herself often enough included, despite her awareness and dislike of the trait) pulled a long face as quickly and regularly as most people extended the time of day. (No, not William. And why was it, when she loved him so much, that she often forgot him in her tabulations of the family?) At any rate, it was as though the Herricks, revering the doctrine of Original Sin, feared the wrath of God if they so far forgot themselves as to enjoy thoroughly whatever they were doing.

And now, as if he were able to read her thoughts, Cornelius urged a little petulance into his voice.

"But that doesn't explain what he meant by calling Miss Sanford's coming to live with Emily 'disgusting.' And telling me I don't know what it means. What does he mean: 'What it means'? Why should it mean anything—except that they're friends, and Emily is being kind to her, while doing something that will be good for Emily, too?"

Rosalind sighed, hesitated—and then sighed again.

"Father, I don't know. But you know that Lloyd uses stronger language than the rest of us and that—he's knocked about in some rough places. I suppose that there are circles in which, whenever two women live together, assumptions are made of the sort that—well, would not be so likely to occur to the rest of us."

Cornelius stared at her blankly for a moment. Then comprehension and anger fused.

"You mean—why, the very idea's disgraceful! I'm ashamed of him. I won't let him come— I—"

He choked himself off, and seemed, surprisingly to Rosalind, to fall into a meditation. It was evident that he was experiencing strong and conflicting emotions; it was, therefore, all the more startling to her that within a minute or two he seemed to have made full peace with himself. His voice, when he spoke now, blended sweetness with resolution.

"I do not believe it. It is impossible. I shall put it out of my mind altogether—even the fact that Lloyd said it. I shall not honor so wild and demeaning a conjecture with any credence; I shall not even refer to it when I next see Lloyd. And tomorrow afternoon I shall call on Emily

and welcome Miss Sanford into the family myself."
    Rosalind rose and patted his shoulder briskly.
    "Where's Mother?" she asked.

    As he mounted the front steps of Emily's house the following after-
noon, Cornelius was aware of a vague uneasiness, a constriction located
somewhere in his lower ribcase. I should not have had those sweetbreads
for lunch, he thought; they never agree with me. But there were few
dishes of which he was so fond, and self-indulgence, he knew well, was
responsible for most of the craven rationalizations he had entertained
throughout his life.
    Throughout my long life, he found himself saying as he paused on
the front porch, peering a little cautiously at the living room window.
(What did he expect to see through the heavy lace curtains? he wondered.) Throughout my long life, he repeated to himself, and was suddenly a little horrified at the succession of self-indulgences, little venial
sins of complacency, even fatuousness, in which he had just caught
himself: satisfaction that he was dishonest to himself only over so minor
a peccadillo as the indulgence of material man; satisfaction over his
longevity, his relatively unimpaired vigor of mind, the enduring quality
of his good looks; finally, perhaps, even satisfaction in his satisfactions.
    But I have genuinely worked in the vineyard of the Lord, he thought,
and instantly felt distaste for the unctuousness of the expression. Better
to say plainly and truthfully, I have overcome the black futility, the fear
of death—and of life, too—the deep pervasive sense of sin and guilt that
were the heritage of my childhood.
    But at what cost? He pressed the doorbell. What did he mean? What
price *had* he paid to be rid of those shadows, those black wings, almost,
that had blotted out the sun in his early days?
    He knew the conventional, devotional answers—who better than
the author of *Brightening the World,* a collection of inspirational sermons? No price, of course: the glad giving of one's soul to Jesus Christ,
and the sun was restored. Yet as he heard the quick tap of Emily's heels
approaching the front door (it was Thursday, and the maids would be
out), from somewhere came the words "An infected will."
    And what did that mean? he asked himself indignantly. Here he
had come to pay a welcoming call on the friend of his dear daughter,
come on a pleasant social and Christian errand—and fallen into disturbing imponderables. He adjusted the black ascot tie he had taken to
wearing in the last year or two, and felt a nervous flutter. (His heart?)
One was safe nowhere nowadays. Here on his own daughter's front
porch—

Nonsense! he thought. You old hypocrite! And as the door was flung open, and he was pressed to Emily's plump, starched bosom, he said mildly, "I'm glad to see you, my dear. I've come to meet Miss Sanford."

Everything was perfectly natural, after all. The tea was impeccable, as always, and Emily had a fresh supply of his favorite biscuits—baked, no doubt, before the cook had left for the rest of the day. They talked about the coming flower show, in which Emily's perennials were sure to win the award; the new Parmalee memorial stained-glass window at the old church; William's having attained the rank of associate professor at the University; Catherine's health and the advisability of prevailing on her to spend the summer somewhere on the North Shore, above Boston. His queasiness disappeared; he felt no hesitancy over accepting a fourth biscuit. Perhaps he had maligned the sweetbreads after all.

Miss Sanford was charming, petite and soft-spoken—perhaps shy, certainly pleasantly reticent, a lady. Indeed, to his surprise, it occurred to Cornelius for the first time that, despite Emily's elegance (for she was elegant; sometimes he was even a little awed by her) and the correctness and precision of her speech, she was in manner almost robust—mannish, even. But that was simply a momentary quirk of thought; Miss Sanford's femininity was so pronounced as to render any other woman the less feminine.

And he liked women to be feminine, to look up at him shyly and yet admiringly—in the sort of sidelong glance that made him feel younger and virile, wise and strong and encyclopedic. He gave her his most benign look of approval, the courtliest inclination of his massive white head.

"We are very happy, Mrs. Herrick and I," he said, "to welcome you into the family, so to speak. We have long hoped that Emily might share this big house with a congenial friend. And it is very easy to see that you two enjoy a compatibility of interests. Are you also a Presbyterian, Miss Sanford?"

He immediately sensed a change in the very air of the room. There was a rustling, a stiffening—as of *wings* tentatively lifted in apprehensiveness, then spread taut for flight. What peculiar thoughts he was having today!

But what had he said? Surely, he had asked the most ordinary of questions. And both because Miss Sanford had not raised her head to answer him and because suddenly all sorts of confusing and somehow ugly, disturbing notions (that was what they were: notions) began to swirl, incomplete, in his mind, he turned, in half-humorous, half-desperate appeal, to Emily.

She was smiling her thin compressed smile. He knew this look so

well—from all those times in her childhood when she had stood before
him and he had known that she was about to confess something that
would, in some strange way, be even more embarrassing to him than to
her. For, really, she never confessed—she told. And there was implicit in
this telling, in this very smile, a suggestion of superiority, of a kind of
impregnability that did not, however, give her any satisfaction. It was as
though she had always hoped that he could see how *thin* her strength was
and so *relieve* her of the burden, the distasteful responsibility of being
invulnerable.

   "Theresa is a Roman Catholic, Father," said Emily.

   Cornelius was hard put not to show his consternation. The attack—
yes, it was an attack—was not only so unexpected; it was two-pronged.
There was the fact that she was a Catholic, and then there was the
indisputably more injurious fact that he had never been able to overcome
his prejudice. He deplored, publicly and formally, any hostility to the
Roman faith, as he did to the Jewish. Were not such feelings antipathetic
to what Jesus had taught and lived? Had not St. Paul said, "We are all
brothers, one of another," with an unmistakably wider sympathy of reference than simply to his little band? But the trouble was that the
prejudice was feeling, not intellectual conviction, and feelings simply
would not always obey one. What was that again about an infected will?
And worst of all, Emily knew all this, and was not lifting a finger to
help him.

   But he was not a coward. However confused and upset, he looked
up and squarely at Miss Sanford, preparing as he turned to her a little
speech about the community of Christians.

   He never made it. For she was now looking directly at him, and for
the first time he saw the pale icy blueness of her eyes. It was as though
all the softness, the feminineness had frozen there into a repellent hardness, even cruelty. Exotic though the word was in this situation, it was
applicable: he was sure; he would not pretend otherwise to himself. But
he could not speak; he could not turn his eyes away: it was as though
she, in some way far more malevolent than Emily's smile, was telling him
with this baleful arctic stare that she knew a secret about him, something
hidden and shameful that he had not known about himself.

   Only when this improbable fancy caught at him did he understand
the power her expression held over him. Only then was he able (able?
God knew he didn't want to) to grope back through the thickets of
associative memory to that other long-buried moment at Sinai when he
had faced El Hani across the campfire and seen those frosty blue eyes,
so unlikely in the hawklike Semitic face—seen in their implacable scrutiny

evil, and the mirror of his own evil, the revelation of what monstrous secret sin and guilt in himself he did not know, but with the power to make him timorous, sick and giddy.

Then, he remembered, a host of obscene and murky images had filled and scalded his consciousness: thoughts, gestures, antic acts that he had not even realized he knew of as existing, let alone festering in his own imagination. It had been months thereafter before he had been able to forget them, felt fully free to move about his daily work in simple Christian faith and warmth.

Now there was no such procession of capering grotesque images. Now there was only a terrible premonition which he dared not investigate further. But even in its inchoate form it gave him a sense of the mockery and ultimate futility of all human lives and aspirations, a deadening certainty that the very faith in which he had labored all his life had no basis in truth. He felt this knowledge rise in him, swell in his throat like some gigantic, unbearable heartburn with which he must burst. . . .

Cornelius Herrick did not see Miss Sanford again that day. Even afterward, he was only vaguely aware of what had happened in Emily's living room from the moment of the long silent exchange with her companion. Dimly he remembered Dr. Peck's round, anxious face peering at him as he lay on the sofa; vaguely he was aware of the relief that finally came over the physician's face after his examination, and of the reassuring words he had then spoken to Emily—words that seemed to be punctuated every sentence or two by the repetition of "rest."

Mostly, however, he remembered Emily's face, close to his, and the words of unrestrained love and tenderness that she stammered out. Recalling these, her tears, and the warm, almost clinging way in which she kept stroking and caressing his cheek, he felt at peace. This was her secret then, he thought drowsily, when later he lay tucked into the huge bed in his own room in Turtle Villa—that all the time, stored away as though in the attic of herself, covered with cobwebs and dust, there was a great carton of love. And love for him—particularly, specifically for him. He smiled contentedly. And then tears came to his eyes and flowed serenely, comfortingly, down his cheeks, unchecked. Poor Emily. Poor little Emily.

A hand covered his where it lay on the blanket, and he turned slowly at its rough, kind touch, his tears still unrepressed, to look at his wife. It seemed to him then suddenly that he knew at last what love was, knew further why he had preached love with such unremitting and paradoxical fury in his anniversary sermon. If he could only say it now to this strange, wry, silent woman with whom he had lived most of his life, this stranger with the enigmatic, almost Oriental eyes, with whom he had lived in conjugal intimacy without any corresponding spiritual intimacy. But he could not—he could only feel it—and so he reached out his other hand and patted hers.

She smiled, for once without irony, without the satirical, deprecatory quality her smile always had. And then, suddenly, he knew that it would be useless anyway. For the conviction came to him that she knew, that she had known all along—she alone—what love did mean. Only— perhaps because she saw its application, its reciprocity, as quite hopeless —she had always given this knowledge an ironic accent.

"You are a good woman, Catherine," he said.

And all at once it came to him that this was the nearest he had ever been to humility.

In two days Cornelius felt much stronger, and Dr. Peck, paying an evening call, told him he would be able to get up the following day. He was not sure, he said, exactly what sort of attack Cornelius had suffered, but in old age there were many insolubles that came and passed: "Best to take it slow for a few days; then you'll be as good as new."

"As good as new." That, Cornelius thought, enjoying the quiet twilight alone, was unlikely. But then it was a good thing in a doctor to remain so cheerful—certainly a good thing in anyone. It helped, however temporarily and superficially, to assuage that ultimate loneliness of mortal man which only love could bridge. If one was open to receive it.

He realized now, with surprise, that in these few days he had more and more come to think of human love, less and less of the love of God. He felt strong enough tonight to probe further into this realization. But the words "human love," almost, it seemed, against his will, brought back thoughts of Emily and Miss Sanford—and that had not been at all what he meant. Incongruously (at least he could not see the connection) he remembered now for the first time the ride back home in Emily's electric car, and the clear, sweet quality of the late afternoon sunlight. He had kept muttering to himself, "The blessed sun, the blessed sun," and, when Emily had asked solicitously what he had said, replied with dignity, "I am invoking the source of sanity"—and felt well enough to enjoy her alarmed look that suggested his own sanity was in question.

The whole afternoon had been a shock, but he had endured and survived it, as he had so many others. He was sorry, tiredly sorry, that he had caused Emily and her friend first embarrassment, and finally real concern. He wondered what they had said to each other on Emily's return. They could not possibly know what had caused his attack. (What a comforting, blanketing, soporific effect this word, intended to convey an aggressive meaning, really had!) In one sense he was distressed that they must think it was all caused by his abhorrence of Catholicism; in another, he supposed that it was just as well.

Of course, her Catholicism actually had nothing to do with it. Had it not been for her eyes, his fragmentary uneasiness over having asked if she were a Presbyterian would have disappeared. None of that had distressed him, beyond the realization that he had never actually overcome the reflexive reaction of prejudice. No, no, it was the eyes—and he was going to face the issue.

As surreptitiously as though intent upon a theft, he heaved himself cautiously out of bed and moved slowly to his bureau. Removing a key from the top drawer, he unlocked the second one and drew from it an old faded notebook. He pulled on the light chain over the headboard of the bed and put on his spectacles.

His hand trembled as he turned the pages. Ah, here it was—the trip to the Holy Land: 1870: He followed line after line with a shaking forefinger until he reached the passage he was seeking.

> The outcome of it all was that we bargained with El Hani, a Beirut dragoman, well recommended, providentially in Cairo, having just finished with another party, to conduct eight persons, in first class style, to Sinai, and straightaway North thro' Beersheba and Hebron to Jerusalem, and thro' Palestine at a napoleon a day each person. All this seemed wonderfully providential, as was my going at the first. We were a congenial company. The weather till we got into Palestine, fine, the whole trip full of scriptural suggestions, and unforgettable memories.

That was all. Reaching up with an effort, he pulled the light chain again. Then he placed the book and his spectacles on the table beside him, and lay still. He had forgotten how almost Biblical his prose style had been. "El Hani, a Beirut dragoman, well recommended, providentially in Cairo . . ."

"Providentially . . ." and "full of scriptural suggestions, and unforgettable memories"! No, it was no use. He was too old, and his will *was* infected. *Those words,* he realized, had come back to him again. That was what he had meant by them, then: that some somnolence of the spirit, some lethargy connected with a perverse love of easy, undisturbed self (this part of it he still did not understand), had always kept him from the full Christian adventure, from exploring the ultimate frontiers of good and evil, without, within—and that this failure of nerve, this infection of the will, had impoverished his purpose and his life.

The horror over the moment at the campfire with El Hani he had characteristically refrained from mentioning—perhaps on the principle that was all too familiar to him: if you lay still, perhaps *it* would not notice you and would go away. It had really only been a *moment,* and he would never know what the dragoman's expression (an obscene invitation, perhaps?) had meant to himself. But to him, to Cornelius Herrick, it had meant this disastrous reflection of all the kinds of evil and perversity potential within *him,* and become a symbol of the depths of life he had never found the courage to investigate.

Nor would he ever, now. This new incident had been only a final minor flare-up. The time for grappling, for decisiveness, was long past; he had somehow missed the road at a crossing way back there when he had been young enough to take it. Looking fearfully over his shoulder, he had fled from the way ahead that led down, through the dark woods, into the ultimate cave, not daring to enter it for all his intimations that if he won his way through he would then be on the true road of his journey. He had raced down the side road, fleeing the strait way—fleeing to love. Or so he had thought.

But one could not find love that way; one could only chance upon love, through the grace of God, if one had the humility to forgive oneself for all one's fears and shortcomings and weaknesses—forgive and plod on, a foot soldier of the Lord. He had possessed neither the necessary humility nor the strength. And now he was an old man, too weak and corrupt to begin the journey; he could not bear to look into himself, to explore that dark and shadowy interior land.

"Father, forgive me," he thought, but could not speak the words aloud.

[*Part One*]   *3*

LLOYD Herrick seemed to most people an unusually satisfying embodiment of the platitude about ministers' sons. But those who knew him well were aware that his nature was streaked with sensitiveness, tenderness and generosity—to be sure, exercised in an unpredictable way, so that within the course of a single day he might consummate the wildest and most harebrained of pranks and the gentlest of kindnesses. But only the former were duly recorded, even widely reported.

He attended five colleges, being dropped from one of them because of his poor academic record, three for "conduct unbecoming a gentleman." He remained at, and was graduated from, the fifth, it was generally agreed, only because his father was, during those years, first trustee, and then acting president, of the institution. And even under these circumstances Lloyd required an extra year to complete the course.

Among his more prominent college escapades were the smuggling of a town girl into his dormitory room; the painting of a beard and outsized genitalia on the statue of the founder of another college; the playing of strip poker in a convivial mixed company which included the wife of a young instructor, on still another campus; and the "borrowing" of the president's buggy to call upon his sweetheart of the moment. These escapades, and his others of these years, showed little enough originality. They seemed to emanate from a compound of restlessness, inquisitiveness, a refusal to "take a dare lying down," and an almost dogged determination to shock. (The only misdemeanor with which he was charged but of which he was not convicted was also the only one of a different character. It involved stealing a "stiff" from the medical college of the university he then attended, and hanging it from the branch of a tree fronting the library, providing some twenty or thirty of the student body and faculty with a moment of vivid horror. Lloyd always denied having had anything to do with this gruesome affair, adding, on several occasions, that he didn't consider it funny.)

How great the emptiness of purpose underlying his escapades, how overshrouding the apathy and ennui he felt, became fully apparent only after Lloyd left college. For his father to find him employment was relatively easy; for Lloyd to hold any job longer than a week or two was rare. He wandered casually from a post in a wholesale firm handling "dry goods" to a cashier's cage in a bank, to manual labor in a lumber yard (on the premise that "good, hard work would straighten him out"), to clerking in the city's only fashionable hardware store. Thereafter, it became more difficult to find anyone who would even give him a chance; his father's intercessions began to meet with all sorts of ingenious evasions. Lloyd spent a good part of the time from the age of twenty-four to that of thirty without a job.

It was during these years that he first heard of, and eagerly pursued, various esoteric religious sects. The Rosicrucians, theosophy, spiritualism, the school of Madame Blavatsky—these and other occult movements of the time engaged him, one after another. For the first time he read omnivorously; he attended meetings, alternately gave up alcohol, tobacco and cards, and (as he grew disillusioned with each spiritual adventure in turn) went on prolonged debauches. His father, who had whipped him for his early peccadilloes (though with evident distaste), now tried to reason with him; they were closeted in the study for hours at a time. But Lloyd's ingenuity at pleading for religious tolerance was boundless: his father had, he pointed out again and again, always deprecated his lack of religious interest; his father always preached the direct relation of the individual soul and conscience to his God, and hence the right of the individual to choose his own form of worship; his father, himself, had been converted at a revivalist meeting while attending college, and after a hitherto dissipated youth.

This last was the final point made at most of these sessions. In a careless moment, or perhaps on an occasion when the guard of Catherine Herrick's silence had slipped because she was more than usually outraged at her own frustration, she had told her favorite child the story of his father's conversion. Lloyd's references to it—even though he necessarily softened them—so pained his father, so rankled in him, that they often led to two or three days of hostile silence between Cornelius and Catherine.

At last, when Lloyd was twenty-eight, and convalescing from his second marriage, he made what was to be the last of his feverish occult associations—with the Secret Seven in Denver, Colorado. Punctuating his account with many chuckles and descriptive gestures, he finally, when in his seventies, told Walton, then in his early thirties, the full story of his initiation—a story he had veiled in seductive hints some years before during one of Walton's college vacations. Not that even in his old age Lloyd had entirely lost his credulousness: the difference was that finally he had become disenchanted with all the established and organized forms the Search took; the Search itself he never relinquished.

Lloyd had heard of the Secret Seven several years before, from a shabby hanger-on who peeked over the shoulders of the elect in a circle of theosophists that had intrigued Lloyd for a few months. This man, by name Alfred Fenner, was, despite his unsavory appearance and reputation, an acknowledged veteran of the byways of the occult; the very adepts who would suffer him to come no closer than the suburbs of their particular *civitas dei* granted freely the wide range of his experience and acquaintances. And Lloyd endured the rheumy eyes, the sycophantic hands and the expense of three meals to hear the full story of the Secret Seven.

Nor, although it was two years before he acted upon his impulse, could he thereafter shake from his mind the mystical and erotic images Alfred Fenner invoked. They haunted his daytime fantasies; they rose up in his dreams to beckon beguilingly. At last, the torment (this was the only time, he realized much later, that he embarked on an esoteric voyage for the sake of a particular anticipated experience as the end in itself, rather than in a hope that this would lead to God, to certainty, to the apprehension of cosmic meaning)—the actual torment of these images—became too great to endure further; seeking Fenner out again (to find him given over to heroin), he finally secured for a price the address of the only one of the Secret Seven whom the man had actually known.

Days of waiting . . . Then, at last, a crudely written note informing him that one of the Seven had died in the last few months and that no successor had yet been chosen. Lloyd's hands, holding the sheet, trembled in his excitement, and he immediately set out to find which of his few wealthy friends, sons of his father's associates, would lend him the fifty-dollar "application fee" which was, not requested in the postscript, but demanded, together with the writing of a full spiritual and sexual autobiography. He sat up until three the next morning to complete the account of himself; failing to negotiate the loan, he pawned a watch and three of his four suits to enable him to send a money order.

At last came a reply, brief but at once disheartening and intoxicating:

The Six have found you worthy of an initiation. If you survive it, spiritually and erotically whole, you may be the Seventh. Wait at the Denver railroad station on the afternoon of Wednesday the seventeenth, until someone taps you on the right shoulder. Bring with you five hundred dollars and tell no one.

BROTHER SEXTUS

The date chosen gave Lloyd almost two weeks in which to secure the money and take the trip. When all other expedients failed, he swallowed his pride (presumably) and went to his first wife, from whom he had been divorced three years before, after only six months of marriage. Celia Lowry had been the favorite debutante of her season; her father had made a fortune in steel, and Cornelius and Catherine Herrick had hoped that her family's social position and her own charm and good balance would bring Lloyd to some sense of responsibility.

But it was not to be. No one ever knew the exact details of the estrangement, for neither Lloyd nor Celia would talk of it. But their incompatibility was, to most people, patent from the beginning: "She was infatuated with him, the way a good woman often is with a bad man. Then she came to her senses." Such an explanation, bearing no resemblance to the complexities of human relations, had never satisfied Walton, but he had been able to piece together only a few possibly significant findings, for Lloyd, garrulous enough in later life about most of his misadventures, seldom talked about Celia.

It was, however, notable to Walton that he referred to her, and only to her, as his "Ex." His second wife remained simply "that bitch," his third, "the late frau." Just why the first designation was preferable to the third would not be clear to anyone who was not familiar with Lloyd's peculiar hierarchy of terms; to Walton, it was immediately apparent. As he came to know Lloyd's intonation and vocabulary better and better, he realized that "the late frau" was replete with a not unfriendly casualness that meant Lloyd could take or leave her, feeling toward her much as he felt toward the job he finally fastened onto at thirty-two (in the county surveyor's office) and held, to everyone's astonishment, until he retired with a pension at seventy. Indeed, he referred to "the boys at the office," "the ponies" and "sparklers" in exactly the same tone. This mixture of prevalent and old-fashioned slang was the currency of one of his worlds—the homely, uninspired, but comfortable one of everyday.

But when he spoke of "the Ex," or "the Great Spook" (God), or "Old Integrity" (his brother William—for he did not share with the rest of the family that patronizing pseudo-reverence of the worldly for the unworldly, perhaps because he was so much the most worldly of them), or "the Peg" (his own wooden leg, acquired shortly after the episode of the Secret Seven), there was a special glitter in his husky baritone that intimated the secret esteem in which he held them— intimated, even, that these were the crucial symbols in his mythology.

Walton, then, contrary to general opinion, was always sure that Lloyd revered the Ex in some peculiar way of his own. The fact that he had turned from her fragile brunette beauty to Jessica Hirsch's lush charms and married her only a week after the final decree seemed to Walton to prove little—or perhaps much of a sort not generally understood. It was, he felt, far more significant that during the three-year duration of this second marriage Jessica was "the ball and chain," to be graduated to the relative importance of "that bitch" only after the termination of their stormy attachment.

No, Walton was sure that neither the second nor the third wife had ever penetrated to the inner circle of Lloyd's life. Jessica, with her synthetic red hair, artificial loftiness of manner, and vulgar taste in clothes, had really shocked the family; they had merely patiently looked down on Martha Morrison, who, as a phlegmatic, full-breasted widow of fifty, married Lloyd when he was sixty-five and then, after three apparently tranquil years, died unexpectedly of a stroke—most unexpectedly, since she looked as though she might live to be one hundred and fifty.

At any rate, it was only a week or two after Jessica and he had been divorced that Lloyd wrote his first letter to the Secret Seven. And it was no more than a month after his second divorce that he paid a visit to the Ex, seeking five hundred dollars.

This was the only incident involving Celia that Lloyd ever related to Walton—and this only as an old man, rocking gently on the side porch of his rooming house.

"At first I thought the Ex wasn't going to see me; she kept me waiting fifteen minutes. But she finally came down—this was in her family's house; she never got tied again. . . ." He paused and rocked a moment in contemplative silence. Then he cleared his throat and resumed his story. "I remember that she was wearing a little yellow flower in her hair, a freesia, I think you call it. She was a looker from the word go."

Again the pause and the silence, while Walton listened to the echo of pride, perhaps of sadness, in the last words. Then Lloyd stirred and spoke, and from there on talked straight through to the end in a more genial tone of reminiscence.

"She asked me what I wanted. I told her—just like that, between the eyes—five hundred dollars. She didn't say anything for a moment; then she looked square at me and said, 'Which is it—women, gambling or religion?' I told her it was the Great Spook again—I was still hoping to meet up with Him. After a minute, she said, 'All right' and went up and got it—in cash! Her father was rolling in ducats—I often hoped he'd smother in them, the old bastard—but he was liberal with the Ex. And when she gave them to me, she said, 'I hope you find Him, Lloyd'—she meant the Spook—and kissed me. Gave me a buss right from the heart. It was the only time I ever—well, that's not the story."

The story was that he was in the Denver station at the appointed time, received the tap on the shoulder, and marched into the strangest and most ridiculous three days of his life.

The initiation took place in a large and desolate house in a defeated section of the city. Aside from the rawboned features, the burning icy eyes and the running nose (Lloyd was spasmodically fastidious in unpredictable ways) of the man in the station, Lloyd saw the august Six only in their masks and cloaks. But he saw plenty else.

Not that he told Walton all of it. It was surprising, Walton reflected later, that he had a sense of being told the whole story of the sequence of three days—yet, when he tried to go back over it in an orderly fashion, he realized that Lloyd had really told him of only two episodes, neither of which, as now related, accounted for the mysterious and titillating tone of Lloyd's abbreviated account of ten or more years before. This second time he told only the episode of the Sacred Book and that of the naked female spirit. They had both, of course, turned out to be hoaxes, but the first, providing the key disillusionment which always materialized, sooner or later, in each of Lloyd's spiritual adventures, had disgusted him with its puerility; thereafter, by anticipating charlatanry, he had turned the second to his own advantage and enjoyment.

The incident of the Sacred Book was brief but decisive. Brother Unus was reading from its scriptures, which purported to be hitherto undiscovered pages from the dogma of Hermes Trismegistus, while the initiate knelt before him, with a cloaked guard on either side. For some reason (Lloyd suspected it was alcohol, rather than the weakness of venerable age), Brother Unus' hands shook so badly that he dropped the book, and even the rapidity of one of the guards was not sufficient to prevent Lloyd from seeing that it was a copy of *A Tale of Two Cities,* suitably rejacketed in black with obscure gold symbols, and that the material from which Brother Unus had been reading consisted of hand-written sheets cut to the size of the pages—sheets which now lay scattered about.

Lloyd's disappointment was not too poignant; the scarred veteran of many esoteric campaigns, he felt contempt for such childish hocus-pocus. Remembering that he had entered upon this particular venture solely for what it might hold in itself, and not from any more serious expectation of spiritual nourishment, he resolved to go through with the rest of it—especially since he had as yet seen nothing of the erotic sort over which Alfred Fenner had lingered so lovingly in the telling. Moreover, with the canniness of experience, Lloyd had withheld half of the initiation fee, depositing it on his arrival in a local bank before he went back to the station, and leaving instructions that it was to be paid out only to himself in person. The Secret Seven had indicated some disapproval of this caution, but Brother Quartus, the treasurer, had finally pocketed silently two hundred and fifty dollars in token of accepting the compromise. And with the incident of the Sacred Book Lloyd resolved that he would find a way to avoid making the final payment.

That night, after resting and eating a meager supper in the bare room on the second floor provided him for the few hours of sleep he was allowed from time to time, he was instructed to prepare himself for a meeting with the spirit of Venus Genatrix, mother of fertility and special patroness to the Secret Seven. His own spirits rose again, decidedly, and he waited for a half hour in eager anticipation.

At the end of that time, Brother Quintus (Lloyd had occupied himself during the duller parts of the ritual by trying to distinguish each of the six by his height and contours) came to him, blindfolded him, and led him out. When the scarf was removed from his eyes, Lloyd was at first aware only of a familiar dim bluish light, reminiscent of squalid taverns. Then, gradually, he made out that he was alone (Brother Quintus had disappeared), and that, at the farther end of the room, behind a huge fishing net that served as a curtain, was a small stage, raised some two feet from the floor of the rest of the room. On this stage had been scattered a pitchfork (beginning to understand the sea motif, Lloyd decided that it must be intended to represent a trident), several large shells, and some dried grasses (seaweed?).

He waited for perhaps ten minutes, but nothing happened. At last, irritated more by the tawdry stage trappings than by the delay, he tried the door. It was locked. He had barely sat down on the floor again and resigned himself to a period of contemplation when the blue lights went off. Then, in the total darkness, there was a creaking sound, as of machinery being hoisted or lowered, a splashing noise, some whispers and even a little tittering.

When the loud noises subsided, they were succeeded by furtive whisperings and rustlings. Lloyd felt a tingling within him that increased as the blue lights were again turned on. And when he took a good look at the stage his blood fairly buzzed. That was his expression: "My blood buzzed."

"My blood buzzed. Up there on a pile of cushions and horse blankets and a bearskin or two was a fine-looking filly, pretty much in *her* bare skin. She had little doodads over the usual places and a paper crown on her head (fine red hair, the real thing), but the payoff was her mermaid's tail. You get it, don't you, Walton—the sheer appalling ignorance of those louts? Somewhere, they'd heard or read of Venus Genatrix—but Genatrix or Aphrodite, it was all one to them. Come to think of it—" he was chuckling now—"the only act as crass as this is the one the Duke and his pal put on in *Huck Finn*—you remember? But the girl was a looker, make no mistake about that. In most of these rackets, when they go in for the erotic, they have to take on a two-bit whore, but not this time. She was the niece of one of the Numbers [for so he came to designate the Secret Seven].

"Well, anyway, as soon as she's sure that I've spotted her, she starts in with her lines. Pathetic—like a schoolgirl reciting poetry. All sorts of stuff about the moment when the sensual and the spiritual merge, and how the great adepts of the ages attain unity with the One—all in pretty carnal language. So I sit and wait and restrain myself from ap- plauding or booing, and watch the way she weaves around and waves those luscious arms—you know, the mechanical way the chorines at a burlesque do, only what's depressing in those tired old bags is cute enough in a young one like her.

"Well, finally, after some starting and stopping and fumbling with her lines, she finishes. (You know that glad rush of relief with which somebody says their last lines, knowing they're almost through?) And then she sort of wiggles on her belly from the cushions right up to where the footlights would be if there were any, and plops down into a tank of water set on the floor in front of the stage. I haven't even noticed it, because all the time I'm watching her. Then she rises up again, all dripping and the little doodads wilting now they're wet, and I'm fairly busting loose from my moorings. So she weaves some more and sings in that same schoolgirl voice—" at this point, Lloyd laughed so hard that tears rolled down the grooves in his cheeks—"I think it was from *Das Rheingold*—Wagner anyway, and a little off key. Then the lights go off.

"I feel sure that she was supposed to do a disappearing act. That's the way it usually works on these circuits: they get you all heated with a really choice morsel, if they can find one, and then they whisk her away and you find yourself back in your room with a frustrated old bag, who, being one of the members, has priority on this way of getting hers.

"Only I was wise to this, of course, and waiting for them to douse the glimmers. So the moment they do, I make a dive for the water tank. I don't know yet just what went on. But I reached her, all right; there was no mistaking her for any of the rest of them, and we clinched and wrestled, with her tugging at the mermaid tail one way and me the other. And there were some of the others mixed up with us—probably the ones who were supposed to slide her away in the tank, or cover for her while she made her own getaway—anyway, they were there, for I tangled with two of them and gave them something with interest for a little rough handling I'd had earlier in the day. Then I'd make a grab for her again, and tug, and she'd screech, 'Don't. Don't. You don't understand. Stop it.' Until I was fit to be tied, the whole thing was so crazy. And finally I got to laughing so hard that I let go and just lay there, howling.

"When the lights came on, they'd all gone. There was only me—and the tank, with water splashed all over the floor. And one of the little doodads lying there; it had busted off, and I put it in my pocket for a memento. I think it was the one for her navel."

He sat there in meditative silence for some time, chewing on an unlighted cigar (his physician had forbidden him to smoke) while Walton ruminated a little bitterly on the difference between his uncle's mermaid and the naked nymphs of his own dreams, wet-gleaming too, and disappearing. Bitterly—for the difference, he realized immediately, was not so much in the objects of their longing as in their own contrasting tempers. It was Lloyd's comic spirit, his relaxed enjoyment, that Walton envied, even while, in some perverse way, it offended him.

"What happened after that?" he asked abruptly.

Lloyd shifted his weight in the rocking chair and grinned.

"We had a reckoning. Brother Duos (the one who'd been in the station) came to give me hell, but the cops must already have put the finger on them, for he was scared. He just said they'd decided that I wasn't spiritually fit for membership, and that they'd let me go after I'd paid the rest of the fee. I told him I'd see him in hell before I'd pay the rest of it, and what was more, if they didn't give me back the original two-fifty I'd forked over, I'd have the police on them. I'd given the bank a time limit, after which they were to turn over to the police a letter telling the whole story. He fussed around some, but didn't put up much of a fight, and I figured that out, too. They kept on initiating the Seventh whenever they could find a fall guy, so they could afford to pass up the dough when someone of tougher fiber raised a row. Probably they hadn't ever had an unsolicited victim before, either, and they weren't too sure just who or what I might be. It's like the famous Mexico deal, where the sucker's picked with care from a special list—you know: the letter telling about a man who's in prison because of customs difficulties, and hasn't access to a trunkful of money stashed away secretly. You'd be amazed how many people fall for it."

Walton, deep in his own thoughts, was silent. Lloyd tugged briefly at the fastenings of his artificial leg, grunting in discomfort. When he was settled again, he gave Walton a shrewd, specious look.

"But I didn't lose out on the girl," he said. "I tracked her down before I left Denver. She was a mighty nice number, too—a good kid."

The glib plausibility of his voice was so obviously false that Walton looked at him in open astonishment. It was, of course, by then a familiar experience: the discrepancy between your reason for liking someone and the peculiar individual vanity and self-deceit that made that person assume that you would admire him only for something totally different— something even alien and opposite to the real basis of your feeling. But this time, Lloyd's assertion struck so discordant a note against the tonal background of the rest of the story that Walton could not dissimulate. Hurriedly he reached for the first distraction that came to his mind.

"What did Celia say when you gave her back the money?" he asked, and then stopped abruptly, realizing the question might embarrass them both. But the response on Lloyd's face reassured him instantly.

"She had a sharp tongue," Lloyd replied. "She said, 'I didn't think He was in Denver.'"

They both laughed—more, perhaps, than the occasion merited. But the old man stopped short and looked at Walton almost accusingly.

"These stories don't mean a thing," he asserted, "except that I was a fool. I'm still looking, but I'm through with the shenanigans. I'm still expecting to find Him when I kick off—only not walking along any diamond-studded streets, draped in purple and gold. And no wings— it's good enough for me without wings and all that singing. People are egotistical bastards." He sighed, and there was a fierce, hunted look in his old blue eyes, under the craggy white eyebrows. . . .

But Lloyd had given up the search for a while after the trip to Denver; for at least two years, he acted as though he were finally convinced that the Great Spook was a phantom induced by desire and fear. It was only a slight exaggeration to say that he returned from his aborted initiation into the Secret Seven to go on a two-year binge.

It was during this period that he became wholly alienated from the family, no longer living in the house on lower Euclid Avenue, but in a disreputable hotel. Cornelius Herrick discontinued his allowance, but he was more than ordinarily successful at poker during the first months of this stretch, and for a while he lived high. By the time his luck changed, he had re-established his credit, and could begin piling up debts again.

During all this period, which was finally terminated by the episode in the railroad yards, he saw but two members of the family—William and Rosalind—and each of them only once. William sought him out when his resources were still ample, and they talked for a painful hour. Lloyd brought the meeting to a close by standing up, handing William the cane without which he could not walk more than a few steps, and saying, with his hand on William's shoulder, "It's no good. You like me—God knows why—and I like you. But we're from different hemispheres; we've lived in different climates; we've spoken different tongues and worshiped different gods. We can't bridge it. The only things we have in common are the old man and poor Mother."

William would have taken up the theme of their mother as a possible last inducement, but Lloyd firmly ushered him out. Rosalind had a happier session, but that was because her realistic devotion to Lloyd was mingled with a certain awe for this older brother who flouted the traditions she did not dare to challenge openly. They met by accident on the street, and stayed together while she had an ice and he a black coffee. Aside from a veiled reference or two, they did not discuss his expulsion from the family.

Other than these two meetings, the only word the family had of Lloyd came in the unwelcome form of stray gossip. Someone had seen him strolling along Euclid Avenue or Prospect Street with a disreputable woman (so they put it, although they knew nothing of her reputation); someone else had spotted him emerging, drunk, from an infamous saloon (anyone who came out of a saloon was drunk); a third person saw him regularly at the races, red-faced and betting heavily. (The poverty of imagination!)

That was all—until the evening on which, really drunk, he decided to take the short cut home, through the railroad yards. He was halfway across the maze of tracks (so he told it later, in his hospital bed, to a forgiving family, clustered around) when he first heard the bell, first saw the light close upon him—enormous, like the eye of the Great Spook Himself. He couldn't remember later whether, in his befuddlement, he had simply thrown himself down between the rails of a track with a drunken sense of its affording protection, or whether he had known that he was lying between the very rails on which the train was coming and, in equal confusion, had felt this was the only way to save himself—that there was no time in which to move off the track altogether.

Whatever the motivation of the impulse, he did throw himself down, and the train, built high off the rails in the fashion of those days, did pass over him. He lay there for the eternity of its passing, unharmed except for his right leg, which he had neglected to pull within the rail. It was cut off neatly, just above the knee.

He would probably have bled to death had it not been for the fortuitous almost immediate appearance of a night watchman. He was found unconscious and taken to the nearest hospital, where the threat of infection was checked. And the family forgave him and took him back without question. It was William who remarked, with as much bitterness as he ever showed, remembering his futile pleas on Lloyd's behalf to his father, that the ways of men were passing strange: they always ministered with tenderness to the victims of physical hurts, but seldom to those of psychic or spiritual ones.

Lloyd took to his artificial limb with only a few complaints. His inexhaustible resilience was never more apparent. (The last time Walton ever saw him, when he was eighty-three or four, and had lived in Florida for ten years, he was still playing a daily nine-hole round of golf. A letter written a few months later explained that he had given it up, because there were so many gopher holes [*sic*] in the rough of the course that he was afraid of catching the Peg in one, and breaking it!)

But something about the experience with the train had sobered him; he was much quieter, and, when finally he was able to navigate freely, began looking for a job with a seriousness of purpose that was wholly new to him. To be sure, he still frequented the races from time to time; he still drank; he was not celibate—but he indulged in all these activities with a relative moderation of which he had before been incapable.

He did not refer to the accident, except in the most superficial way, yet to Walton, listening to the family's version with greedy interest (it was somehow an heroic tale), and impatient with their shudders over the *wrong* details, it was clear that the Great Eye of the locomotive must have become one of those central mythical symbols of Lloyd's life. . . .

This was the man, then (acquaintance with whom, except under the strictest supervision, was forbidden Walton in his boyhood)—this was the man and this the life that Walton felt could best illuminate the hidden aspects of the life and nature of Cornelius Herrick. Not directly, of course. He did not mean anything so crude or oversimplified as a conviction that Lloyd's escapades literally reflected with any precision the wild, buried strains he hypothecated within his grandfather.

No, he meant rather that his own father and his two aunts were, in their various ways, so weighed down by the greatness and authority of the father that, far from rebelling, they sought to be other than their own inclinations might have made them—all, somehow, in an attempt to be worthy of Cornelius Herrick. It was not quite true, of course, to say that they were never rebellious; each eventually was, in his own way. Yet even Rosalind, perhaps less affected than the other two, staged her revolt so late in life that it lost for others any sense of being directed against the supreme deity of her childhood; it was inevitably adulterated with an admixture of all the other shaping forces of her later years and sur-roundings.

To be sure, rebellion, as well as obedience, might immediately derive from the impact of a dominant personality. Lloyd's true nature, Walton realized, might have been as thwarted in rebellion as those of his brother and sisters were in emulation or submissiveness. More, the irony of Lloyd's unceasing search for the Great Spook must have been evident, even in those pre-Freudian days, to everyone in the family except his father.

But whatever the truth behind these subtleties and ambiguities, Lloyd did—in sharp contrast to the other children—cut up directly in defiance of his father's image. (It had to be so stated, Walton reasoned, for he knew that the actual practical authority in the family had been Catherine Herrick; it was Cornelius' *presence* that was dominant, rather than his voice issuing decrees.) Lloyd boldly rebelled, was expelled, and then reinstated, with peculiar affection, in his father's old age—indeed, *promoted* to a place at his right hand (a source, Walton suspected, of secret bewilderment and perhaps pain to William, who must have pondered the parable of the prodigal son with new interest). And some-how, Walton was sure, when the reins that Cornelius Herrick had held so tightly on himself finally slackened in the enfeebled hands of his will, and (a strange paradox!) the eyes of the old man, childish or not, became clearer than they had ever been in the days of his power and authority, with their opaqueness finally dissolved—somehow, it seemed mystically clear that Lloyd's revolt had brought a catharsis to his father, had enabled him thus to lead vicariously the life he had beaten down dis-approvingly in himself.

JOURNAL: 2

from the journal of Walton Herrick . . .

May 29, 1953

Size . . . I am obsessed with size. I tend to inflate and invest with false grandeur—whether quantitative or qualitative—what is primarily a local and domestic matter. I reach unconsciously for a larger stage to lend dignity or excitement to some particularity of my life or observation. An argument with someone in the office is worth the telling only if it can be dressed up dramatically to be a part of a crucial issue. A poignant situation in the neighborhood gains tragic stature because I exaggerate the moral courage or the wasted potentialities of the participants. Tragedy is *better* than pathos; a dramatic conflict is *more important* than, say, a lonely individual decision or the resolution of a disagreement in a quiet conversation.

And so it is, then, with the events of my life—the turning points, the climaxes, the terminal situations. When one surveys one's life, I suppose it is always tempting to entertain a traditional vision of births and deaths, loves and hates, meetings and partings—and thus to give oneself a sense of the portentous and the mysterious: profound visions of beauty, compassion, suffering; ordeal and renewal. But I suspect most people don't strain this process as I do.

Size again: human dignity, death and transfiguration, "the tragic sense of life": the phrases of the romantic humanists roll majestically through my mind as though they were quotations from Cicero or Daniel Webster.

This is not written to belittle or deny human aspirations and passions. It is a warning to myself to remember the value of tonal honesty. The telling of a flagrant lie is easy and even tempting only to the pathological (who don't recognize the temptation) and the desperately vindictive—which may come to the same thing. Lying to others is almost always a secondary manifestation of internal lying. And flat, unqualified lying to oneself is difficult to sustain unless one has come close to losing all touch with external reality. But what is easy, for almost everyone, I think, is tonal lying—shaded partial lying: the deception embodied in briefly acknowledging the truth about one's motives or feelings or contradictory desires, but not permitting it to sink in. One bows to it, and hurries off; one blurs the image: it is as though one took off one's glasses and deliberately blew on them; then, replacing them, walked on in false serenity, unseeing and suffering only from a minor queasiness in the stomach or a hardly noticeable tic in one's temple.

So, if I look back on my life, it is easy for me, through the blurring process, to call up, as the occasion or my mood prompts, heroic or brilliant episodes; generosities and sacrifices (modestly understated, of course) that can stir the tender sympathies of an unwary listener; racy and dashing anecdotes of marginal veracity. Grief stoically borne, enchantresses seduced, friends and family supported to the bleak outposts of loyalty, loneliness endured, obstacles heroically overcome . . .

This partial lying, this self-deception, is fatefully easy for me—and my taste pushes it in the direction of the heroic, the many-sided, the richly endowed. There have been times, I am afraid, when I saw nothing essentially incongruous in fancying that I possessed, and at once, the attributes of Caesar, Christ and Casanova. And so, contemplating my life, I could, with incandescent facility, and persuading myself as I went of my integrity, paint it with sweeping strokes and raw, jarring colors.

Having been so obsessed with size, with grandeur, with profundity, with tragic conflict, I could—I know—tell a high and gusty tale of the tragic disintegration of my family, my triumph over fear and loneliness as a boy, my travels and adventures, my years of asceticism, my three marriages and my more than three adulteries, my late coming to a new career in New York after fifteen years of almost willful isolation and obscurity and my impressive success in this career, culminating in this possibility of a governorship. (But there has been no further word from Abe Fortune; we have not set up a meeting—and this upsets me, even when the whole thing is impossible.)

All this I could tell and probably convince many, even half believe it myself, so mystifying is the ambiguity of personality; so easy is tonal lying, since it is usually unconscious.

God knows I could tell it another way, too, concluding with Julie's leaving me. Is that why I need to invest the story of my life with Gothic qualities—because the unadorned story seems to me so pitiful a succession of moral failures, unresolved fears and conflicts?

I mean this to be a journal of the inner weather. It is my nature to be most honest with myself when alone, and my habit, perhaps, to think most clearly then, as well. I know no other way than this to go about facing what I now must face.

Am I castigating myself? I do not think so. What is lacking in the picture I have been drawing of myself? Any trace of humility, plainness, a sense of humor. These now, at last, I would like to cultivate. Probably, as Montaigne puts it in Florio's old translation, "Not my bellyful, but all I dare—and the older I grow, the more I dare."

Plainness . . . I think how often I have scorned the factual, even the scientific account, as prosaic, even prosy and unimaginative. I forget where I read the other day of the way in which astronomers sometimes refer to our great blazing sun: "a main-sequence dwarf of spectral class G2." None of the visible splendor, none even of the mathematical and physical majesty of the sun is to be found in such a classification, yet for an attitude like mine it furnishes a sound corrective.

And how much more I need to employ some of this toning-down process in my attitude toward the common human experience, and especially my share of it. The heroic yardstick is equally fatal to expectation and to self-appraisal. It establishes impossible goals and sets one to screaming like a fishwife at oneself for the failure to meet them. It helps one to revel in fantasy (even, sometimes, to try to live it) and leads one not even to see, let alone value, homely real achievements. It stakes out the province of one's life in a climate half ephemeral, illusory glory, and half black misery.

At the moment, I understand all this with painful clarity. Yet I will betray this horse sense—perhaps before I go to bed tonight. I have always felt (and to what pains I would go to deny this to anyone in the world!) that there was greatness in my destiny. Perhaps—though I have never thought of it before—this explains my always feeling younger than I am: the discrepancy between my aspirations and my record, between the dream and the actuality, is so great that I must unconsciously assume that, with my glory all before me, I am necessarily young. One further thing is certainly plain: when I learned from Leon Goodman what Abe Fortune wants of me, I felt no considerable surprise, although the idea of a political career had seldom crossed my mind.

The earliest image that comes to my mind in the context of my imputed greatness is that of the elders of the church of my childhood, going forward to the altar to dispense the cup of communion and the sacramental bread. This familiar and recurring scene, although I actually observed it only after my grandfather's active pastorate was over, has always been associated, for me, with his presence—perhaps because of the similarity of appearance between him and one of the elders, Ellsworth A. Lyman.

Here I am struck by my use of Mr. Lyman's full name: I would not dream of referring to him in any other way; this is, in some obscure fashion, a part of the myth. At any rate, in a group of really distinguished-looking men Ellsworth A. Lyman stood out as peerless. Like my grandfather, he had snow-white hair and a short beard too rounded to be called a goatee. Like my grandfather, he had a courtly manner. But the quality that remains unique in my experience was his unfaltering kindness. His eyes literally shone with a gentle constancy that I find it impossible to describe, but it does me good forty years later simply to remember it.

Singing "Just as I am, without one plea, Save that Thy blood was shed for me . . . O Lamb of God, I come, I come," the elders would arise, in their black cutaway coats and dark striped trousers, and from their individual pews in all corners of the church advance toward the altar. Each, holding his hymn book, would walk down the aisle with firm and reverent gait. The organ and the voices of the congregation would swell with the apostrophe to the Agnus Dei, only to diminish heart-breakingly on the reiteration of "I come"—and from the pew behind ours, Ellsworth A. Lyman would arise, pass nearly within hand's reach, and proceed to the altar.

To the altar? Advance, it seemed to me, beyond all altars in a quest for some unimaginably ultimate grail; and my heart would threaten to burst from its moorings to set out upon its own imponderable and glorious mission. The elders marched into heaven. . . . As I look back on the scene now, I remember these grave and austere men raising the spotless white cloth from the bread and wine it covered, and I am reminded in some oblique way of the quality of the faces of the men clustered around the coffin in the scene of the funeral of Count Orgaz: it is a vision compact of gravity and elegance and spirituality, a peculiar blending of reverence and courtliness that almost made a tournament of the commemoration of the blood and body of Christ. Yet, at the time, it was for me quite a different experience, informed wholly with its promise of the beauty and adventurousness, the high quest that would be my life. The elders marched into heaven. Of that there could be no doubt: *surgunt docti* . . . And I—I marched into the future.

In such ways was the heroic romantic dream engraved upon the chain mail of the armor I was to wear against reality. In those early days the imprint of the dream and its symbols were fashioned of the dominant visions of my parents—hence largely religious, or at the least idealistic; later, they were almost all invoked in defiance of their values. Then they symbolized outward achievements to come; once I was "hospitalized"—sentenced at seven by my mother and my uncle Edgar to one and a half years in bed, because of alleged "valvular leakage of the heart"—they turned inward and came to fruition exclusively in dreams.

But there was another association—at that time, latent—which these visions were to have, whether in my parents' tradition or the reverse of it, an association which I am sure has been deeply harmful to me. As I grew older, I found far too little, in myself and in the life around me, of the heroic of whatever sort, to match even approximately the glorious destiny I had foreseen. Increasingly, this discrepancy led me to my own version of the conviction that there is nothing in the present to equal the old days; I began to believe that "there were giants in those days."

I honestly don't know whether the conception of the past as heroic or my dissatisfaction with myself in the face of early intents and heroic fantasies, my tendency to self-depreciation, came first; whether my dreams were so majestic (however unrealistic) that life was bound to be disappointing, or my disappointment with myself so acute as to lead me to distort and aggrandize the past, as though the substance of my dreams must once have been realized in actuality. But whichever was cause, whichever effect, whatever the proper chronology, it is true that I think of the heroic as possible only in my imaginative forays or in the past.

And so I have been prone to think, for example, of that forefather of mine whom I call the Great Original. William Herrick (for whom, some three and a half centuries later, my father was named) was the first of my line in America. He arrived on a ship called the *Mary and John*, at Dorchester, Massachusetts, in 1630, and while I have cousins who trace the lineage all the way back to a bondsman named Jehan who won his freedom and surname at the Battle of Hastings, I have been content to stop what little study I have made of my ancestors with the first one to cross the ocean.

Ancestor worship has always seemed to me the stupidest of snobbisms, yet the figure of William Herrick, the Great Original, has inflamed my imagination. To me, with no specific knowledge of a European past, beyond the certainty of an English heritage, it is as though the Herricks sprang full-born from the forehead of the new land, indigenously American. The first William is, to me, Adam in America. And the

generations of Adam, the names in the line of succession down to my
grandfather, father and myself, unanimously evoke New England, seem
to have suckled at the breast of a stony pasture-and-meadow sort of
mother: William's son Daniel, then Ebenezer, Nathaniel, Hiram, Peletiah, Aaron—before descending to Cornelius, William and (Cornelius)
Walton.

Two things I note about these names with particular interest. There
is little repetition: not a single son or grandson is named for father or
grandfather; and only with my father is there the reappearance of any
name in the line. It is as though, grimly continuing to wrest survival from
the rocky soil (for, from the Great Original to my grandfather, all the
men of our line of Herricks were farmers, and several also had their own
stone quarry), each contemplated his life, peered backward and forward,
and then, sardonically contemplating the infant son in the cradle, bestowed upon him the one sure gift in his power—to name him Other.

There they stand:

William (-1669), farming and stone quarry. Windsor, Conn.
Daniel (1640-1712/13), farming and stone quarry. Windsor,
   Conn.
Ebenezer (youngest son), (1681-   ), farming. Herrick, Conn.
Nathaniel (1715/16-1772), farming. Harwinton, Conn.
Hiram (1738-1813), farming. Harwinton, Conn.
Peletiah (1768-1857), farming and drinking.
   Removed to Pompey, N.Y. in 1816.
Aaron (1808-1883), farming. Pompey, N.Y.
Cornelius (1831-1913), minister & educator. Cleveland, Ohio
William (1872-1938), minister & teacher. Cleveland, Ohio
Walton (1907-   ), teacher, author, foundation executive.
   Moved to Northport, Conn., in 1950.

Perhaps I shall sometime find out more about the men behind the
names from William to Peletiah, the outstanding eccentric of the line,
who moved his family to New York State and spelled his name Herri'k,
to cut himself off more decisively from the rest of the Herricks. But at
present I know of Daniel, Ebenezer, Nathaniel and Hiram nothing more
than this chart provides.

The other point of interest for me is how different a note from those
of the rest of the line is struck with the name Cornelius. Surely this
name is Dutch, and I wish that I were able to ask my father how it found
its place among those Biblical–New England ones. No one alive seems to
know.

Not knowing, I can only ruminate. But if my half-playful conjecture about the naming of male children in the line holds any truth, then surely Aaron—of all of them, except possibly his father, Peletiah—would most cherish the exotic, most wish to make the break with his heritage and surroundings a radical one. My grandfather, in his autobiographical journal, has written of Aaron:

> It should be said that my father was an only son: self-willed, strong, of good natural abilities untrained, who had in him the making of a man of mark without the opportunity of proving it, born to a farm but never liking it and never able to leave it, but getting some relief thro' his shop in which he exercised himself in self-taught handi-craft. . . . He was not an easy man to get on with, either for my mother or for us children. His government was capricious and his demands often unreasonable, and enforced with severity. . . . He was easily elated over trifling successes and depressed by little misfortunes.

To this Aaron, perhaps, never able to leave the environment he hated, a repudiation of the traditional New England names and the introduction of a wholly new sort was the expression of a dream projected into the future. It has never before occurred to me that he may simply have had a friend named Cornelius.

At any rate, there is ample testimony in Grandfather's journal that *he* was born to and raised in as bleak a context as anyone else in the line. I have always been haunted by an early sentence in this journal:

> The three things of which I am certain as among my earliest recollections, are the cold face of my aunt, after death, the death of my little brother in the dead of winter and the deep snow; and my grandmother, Hephzibah Herri'k, going out to the currant bushes for a switch to use on me—for what, I have no idea only that it was Sunday and I had been left in her care. This is the only reminiscence I have of her.

What a heritage of memories! And yet, despite this early vision of death and punishment, of Calvinist Sundays and currant switches, Cornelius Herrick seems (except for one of his sons) the blandest of the Herricks of whom I have any knowledge—the one most to value pleasure, the one least obviously haunted by the wingèd stinging messengers of guilt and duty. Yet I know, of course, that there were many shadows below the surface.

At any rate, lacking family portraits, I have within me a dim gallery whose walls are lined with strong, gaunt, dream-ravaged faces: Daniel, Ebenezer, Nathaniel, Hiram, Peletiah, Aaron—the generations of Adam. For me, they are figures of massive taciturnities or (like Aaron) of savagely frustrated volatility. But this is not the way I feel about William, the Great Original.

He had left Massachusetts for Connecticut at least by 1637, and was settled in Windsor by 1640, the year in which Daniel was born. In the summer of 1637 William took a vigorous part in the war with the Pequot Indians, serving with the colony's military force under the command of a certain Captain Mason.

Mason led his little army into Indian territory, and attacked the Pequots' stronghold. The captain has left a record of this encounter, which tells how he was "beset by many Indians waiting all opportunities to lay hands on me" and taken prisoner. Thereupon, "William Herrick espying a breach in the wigwam, entered, and in his entrance fell over a dead Indian; but speedily recovering himself, the Indians some fled, others crept under their beds."

I realize now, as I hunt up this passage to be sure that I quote it accurately, that I have always read it with a sharp and exhilarating feeling of pride. It has meant to me that the first Herrick in America was an intrepid man of action—even that the American line of the family began in heroic fashion with William Herrick's apparently single-handed rescue of Captain Mason.

But this time I read this passage from the Pequot wars from a different angle of incidence. The words that caught and stung, as barbed wire penetrates cloth to tear the flesh, were "and in his entrance fell over a dead Indian. . . ."

The Comic cauterizes the Heroic. This rip in the heroic flesh of the Great Original has humanized him for me. I no longer see a massive avenging figure before whom hapless Indians creep away and hide futilely under beds, but a wholly fallible and human man. A brave man, but not a titan. A strong man, but not a cyclops. A resilient man, but not an unerring deity. Suddenly the achievement is warmer, more meaningful to me. The ironic juxtaposition of epic past and lilliputian present is dislodged: I am free to feel a kinship, a continuity and a consanguinity that would until now have seemed almost sacrilegious to me.

Perhaps—no, surely—there *is* a lower-case heroic in human lives. But just as surely it is conceived in conflict and (frequently reluctant) resolution, and executed with that rare combination of earnestness and unpretentiousness, humor and determination. It has as little to do with Achilles raging among lesser warriors as it does with Zeus sitting enthroned on an artificial satellite that watches the globe it circles, and hurling thunderbolts like some celestial bombardier in an arbitrarily punitive war. What is more nobly human than to know within, to recognize and face a conflict between two incompatible goods, and then to choose effectively, with however great difficulty and reluctance, between them?

The comic spirit does not belittle the truly heroic, but it reduces the Heroic Image to human proportions. We are most truly men when we are neither gods nor dwarfs in our own minds. Let a man blow himself up past those true human proportions, however privately, and it's most salutary if he should sneeze, or forgetfully pick his nose. The man who loses his dignity under such circumstances has no real dignity, because no humility. And that William Herrick should fall over a dead Indian, fall, presumably, flat on his face; and then pick himself up and effect the rescue of Mason—this endears him to me.

Indeed, I realize even as I write that this incident of the sword is bound hereafter to be replaced in my mind as the most memorable one pertaining to William Herrick. In 1645, he built his own homestead in Windsor, hard by the Connecticut River. Between the house of "clove boards" and his stone pit, on the one hand, and the river on the other, lay meadowland, this particular stretch of which was known as Sequester Meadow. In 1885 the whole Herrick clan, or as many of them as could be found and acknowledged the summons, assembled here to dedicate a memorial stone to the Great Original.

Once I visited this spot, and found a huge boulder that must weigh two tons. It is egg-shaped, of flint stone, and some five feet at the line of greatest length, perhaps three and a half feet in breadth. It lies half-buried in the earth and at the highest point extends above ground only a foot and a half. On it is engraved—not in the usual parallel lines, but in accordance with the best surfaces of the stone on which to drive the chisel—the following inscription:

MEMORIAL STONE

WILLIAM HERRICK

BORN IN ENGLAND

DORCHESTER MASS   1630

HARTFORD WITH FIRST SETTLERS

WINDSOR
1640

SETTLED HERE

1645

DIED ON SEPT 27. 1669

HERE HE REMOVED, UNTO SEQUESTER

MEADOW, IN THE PEACE OF EARLY

EVENINGS, WHEN HE WOULD INTERROGATE

HIS SOUL AND HAVING TAKEN

THE SOUNDINGS THEREOF

RETURN

TO HIS FAMILY AND

TO THE HOME HE HAD BUILDED

This final sentence was taken from a letter written by his first son Daniel. In the peace of an early summer evening about twenty years ago, I stood by the stone and watched the night mists slowly rise from the tranquil river and swirl and settle over Sequester Meadow. It required no very vigorous imaginative effort to entertain the scene of some two hundred eighty-five years before—to see William Herrick, gun in hand, walk briskly from the house he had builded to the meadow, and seat himself there, perhaps on another great boulder, to interrogate his soul and take the soundings thereof. Gun in hand—for all about lay forest, tracked only with a few Indian trails. The little house was then an outpost of civilization, claimed from the very wilderness, and when he returned from his meditation he must have barred the door with a sense of shutting out more than the chill night air.

So, too, each morning must have brought more of a sense of deliverance and refreshment than is the common experience of those of us living in Connecticut today. I see him emerge from the house in the early sunlight—envision this perhaps most clearly of all these pictures. For I see him, axe shouldered, standing in the doorway; I see the dew flashing on the grasses, and—frail bridge between a sturdy sapling and a corner of the house—the iridescent strand of a spider's web. The slow aromatic smoke curls upward from the chimney. And all about is a stillness reminiscent of the previous evening's hour in Sequester Meadow—reminiscent but different, as the joyful tranquillity of promise differs from the peace of fulfillment.

Other moments in the daily cycle come to mind as well, many of them loud with the ringing of the axe and the cries and shouts of children's voices, others murmurous with the mid-day's multitudinous sounds of birds and insects. Amidst the hum and bustle of this little community, I see the first mother, William's wife, trudge slowly into the sun-flecked clearing before the house, burdened with the clothing she has washed. I watch her work-marred hands and forearms, bared to the elbow, move nimbly and swiftly, fastening the clothes to her rude structure to dry them in the sun. It even seems to me that I can see her brush a stray lock of hair from her forehead, sigh, lean backward from her perpetual stooping position to ease tired muscles. She smiles at one of the children, and suddenly the plainness of her face is transformed into something akin to radiance.

But of all of these scenes, that moment in the morning, as dew-glittering and still as though it were Creation Day, and the evening sojourn in mist-enfolded Sequester Meadow, are to me the most vivid: the day revisited and the day renewed.

Curiously enough, I *believe in* this first Herrick family tonight in a way I never have before. They have for me now, after my new reading of the Pequot War incident and the inscription on the memorial stone, a palpable humanness, an immediacy that I have never felt in them before. The past is very close; in its unadorned chronicling of the common human lot, however different in detail, it is almost indistinguishable from the present.

Bergson again—let me see if I can find the passage:

> An attention to life, sufficiently powerful and sufficiently separated from all practical interest, would thus include in an undivided present the entire past history of the conscious person—not as instantaneity, not like a cluster of similar parts, but as something continually present which would also be something continually moving . . . a perpetual present . . . a present which endures.

In my first entry, I remember asking, "How did the boy become this slightly grizzled man?"—and for the moment I find an answer in what I have just quoted. I find an answer too to the origins of what I think of as "the ambiguity of personality." In its simplest, most literal sense I mean by this phrase, of course, the extraordinary variance in the versions of a particular individual entertained by one acquaintance, another, a third, and still others—as well as by the individual himself. But more subtly, I am referring to the enigmas presented when what we call the past bursts the moorings of its alleged "pastness" to break incongruously into the present. I am thinking of the way in which one reacts to an immediate situation not in direct reference to its limited immediate aspects, but in terms of some ancient grudge, some "long-forgotten" fear, some hidden associative connection with an event of twenty or thirty years before. And I am thinking of how, waking or in dreams, we sometimes find what we call the past more vivid and urgent than the empirical actuality around us.

All this, but the word I am searching for in Bergson this time would go beyond "the entire past history of the conscious person" to a past that included genetic experience dating back hundreds of years before the birth of this conscious person. I mean nothing facilely mystical, nor even "the collective unconscious" of certain psychological theorists. I mean nothing more than that, if there is a large continuity of what we call the past with what we call the present, if one is interested in all the forces and elements that have shaped one and one's life, then perhaps William Herrick and his family have as direct and meaningful an impingement upon me, on who and what I am, as do the observable events of my childhood and adult life.

I cannot find the passage I sought. Perhaps it is not there. The nearest to it that I can discover is only a philosophical generalization:

> The preservation of the past in the present is nothing else
> than the indivisibility of change. . . . Reality is change . . .
> change is indivisible, and . . . in an indivisible change the past
> is one with the present.

Any really forceful generalization escapes me; what remains is the vivid and urgent sense of the reality of the Great Original and Sequester Meadow—in honest human terms. And a further afterthought—that in tonight's entry, without planning or deliberation, I have actually done what I promised myself in the first entry that I would try to do: not merely "analyze, describe, record," but "invoke." Perhaps in time I shall be better able to understand in some fullness what I am invoking and what it can mean to me.

A last word: in Grandfather Herrick's autobiographical journal, he writes of the house in Pompey in which he was born, and the very room: "The old house still stands, and the room given up to sickness may still be seen, tho' alas, the whole place has fallen into degenerate hands."

At the moment I am not interested in the point of view that makes no distinction between birth and sickness, though this is worth studying further in terms of the Herrick heritage. My point is that, although I have not consciously realized it before, I have accepted this sentence as rendering symbolically the history of the family from the first William Herrick to myself. But now, as I free myself, however temporarily, from my obsession with the Heroic Past, I no longer find it applicable. Today, more of our frontiers are internal than external, but I am not simply the degenerate dregs of a once heroic line. In discovering the first William's humanity, I have discovered a little of my own—and found some comfort and hope, too; so I shall, I know, sleep better than I have in a long time, and survive better a holiday spent alone.

[*Part One*]   *4*

CORNELIUS Herrick's autobiography (if one can so describe the notebook in his bureau drawer) opened with his birth; it ended incomplete, with these words:

> We began our life in Cleveland on Case Ave.; the first residence then south of Prospect St., on the west side of the street. Rents were very scarce, and we had to go out this far. Here William was prematurely born, October 13, 1872, before we were fully settled—his mother having over-exerted herself. That we should raise him seemed doubtful for some time.

A persistent family legend had it that William had been dropped on his spine when only a few weeks old, and that the culprit, the attending nurse, was instantly dismissed. Yet Cornelius Herrick's journal entry is clear and specific. Walton felt sure that the prematureness of his father's birth, with perhaps some further complication in the actual delivery, was responsible for the paralysis of the legs from which William Herrick suffered throughout his life. He could not walk at all until he was twelve years old, and then only after successive operations in Cleveland, Philadelphia and at the hands of the Mayo brothers in Minnesota. Until then, a self-propelled wheel chair; thereafter, first crutches, and finally, and permanently, a shuffling walk with the help of a cane, his knees bent inward grotesquely.

Yet the story of the accident for which the nurse was to blame persisted. It was as though the Herrick family felt that this version removed some vague stigma from the family record. Perhaps they feared that prospective marriages might be canceled through a suspicion that the affliction could be inherited; perhaps it was only the humiliation felt at the suggestion of a taint in the family. Either the medical knowledge of the period was not equal to positive diagnosis of the trouble, or the family's prejudice was too strong to permit access to the precise details: for whatever reason, Walton was never sure of the exact origin or nature of his father's injury.

"That we should raise him seemed doubtful for some time. . . ."

In the most precise sense, they did not raise him; he raised himself. Never given to sustained self-pity, he talked to Walton about his childhood and youth only rarely; however, even these few accounts were sufficient to make it clear that the Herricks, while observing all the forms of tenderness and affection (and doubtless, especially in the case of Catherine Herrick, with genuine feeling), discounted William as a *regular* member of the family. That is, when they spoke of him, it was with a conscious regretful softening of their voices; when they spoke to him, it was with that special deference that masks the unconscious condescension accorded the crippled or maimed in American society.

He raised himself, then, in the sense that he was himself the only person in the family—or, for that matter, in his whole early environment —who did not consign him to that special providence God accorded those unable to take care of themselves. One of the sternest admonitions Cornelius Herrick was wont to impose upon Lloyd was to remind him that he must not only learn to assume responsibility for himself, but also prepare himself for the eventual need to support and care for William. And when Lloyd chafed all the more under this injunction, Emily would step stoutly in, secure and powerful in the knowledge of her special fortune, and assert that, so long as she lived, William should never want.

It was interesting, Walton eventually came to realize, that these were the figures he evoked when he tried to remember all that his father had told him of his childhood. Cornelius and Catherine, William's father and mother; Lloyd and Emily, the older brother and sister assigned to the guardianship never to be required—these, and only these. Interesting, because in the end the member of the family who came to be closest to William, with whom he eventually was on the terms of warmest intimacy, was the youngest of the four children, Rosalind. Since she was some eight years younger than William, she could not, of course, have played a part in his earliest years, yet Walton found it worth his time to ruminate on the fact that she, the only one of the family not pressed officially into service to "see William through," was (perhaps freed for her ultimate role by this very fact) the one who meant the most to him. . . .

Thrown into the water, the theory ran in the early part of the century, the child will swim. Walton, little by little, came to believe that this was generally true. The trouble was that it was a truth that became a pseudo-truth because of what it left out: the effect upon the child in other respects. Applied to William Herrick, it was probably true that being deserted psychologically—that is, given no support in his conviction that he could make his way to independence and the approximation of a normal life—actually helped him directly to the redoubling of his determination to make his own way. Yet, Walton was sure, it also left him with scars that never wholly healed.

William's version of the experience laid quite a different emphasis and, perhaps, Walton came finally to reason, went more directly to the heart of the matter than his own did. Finally—because Walton was well past thirty before he succeeded in distinguishing clearly between simpleness, which he had often reluctantly decided most clearly characterized his father, and simplicity, which did characterize him. Simplicity: the faculty of brushing aside all subtleties, shadings and ambiguities, to come directly to grips with the essentials and to state them without adornment, act upon them without evasion.

At any rate, William put it this way: despite an inclination to kindness and even to love, his busy, active family had little enough time to give him, and little or no faith in the possibility of his making his way to a useful and vigorous maturity. Sorely needing a friend capable of encouragement and solace, he searched for one, and found two. He turned inward and found God. He inquired and hunted in the world without, and found Charles Dickens.

Perhaps it would seem inevitable to a passing observer that the son of Cornelius Herrick would turn, under tribulation, to God. And indeed, from William's earliest period of receptivity, before he was able to walk at all on his crippled legs, his father had earnestly instructed him in the mysteries of God's hidden ways and exhorted him to believe that, concealed behind the pain and helplessness of his affliction, there lay a secret blessing that he could find if he would.

Yet this explanation of William's all but unconquerable faith (the day before he died—and in the face of Walton's well-established agnosticism—he said, simply and directly, "Get yourself a strong faith, son; I don't know any other way to endure all the troubles life brings") was superficial. He never elaborated, at least to Walton, on the bare statement, "I needed a friend and found God." Yet during the last ten years of his life, when his extraordinary qualities at last became fully clear to his son—when Walton was finally able to evaluate them with an eye and mind no longer seasoned with his mother's judgments—Walton had ample occasion to judge the nature of his father's relation to God, if not its origin.

It was evident in William Herrick's large and eloquent eyes when he faced a crisis; they took on a luminousness that seemed to make him almost of a species different from the ordinary human one: it was as though there were a deep well, a reservoir way down within him, to which he had descended, to return—once bathed in those waters—transformed. It was not a difference of degree, but of kind: this rich, unearthly (but not at all ascetic or other-worldly) serenity, this full and really joyous acceptance of life.

"Dr. Herrick is a saint" . . . "Your father was a saintly man"—these and other similar remarks attended Walton all his days. At first they annoyed him, making him feel that his father—and thus himself—was being singled out for some unnatural and not wholly respectable distinction. But as time went on, he became able to distinguish between those who said it perfunctorily, as a way of dismissal ("He is a saint, and therefore we need not worry about having to deal with him in our really important activities"), and those who said it earnestly, grasping as best they could at his peculiar and exciting quality.

The last step in Walton's understanding of the love between his father and God (even when putting it thus through an effort to conceive imaginatively of the relationship as his father did literally, he winced at the phrasing so alien to himself) was to recognize the ordinary human frailties in his father—to see clearly that he was right about the scar tissue on his father's soul—while at the same time recognizing that his father was right about his authentic friendship with God. William Herrick had a seldom-exercised temper of feverish potentialities; he had an undiminished basic conviction of his own inferiority, as a result of his physical deficiencies, and this led sometimes to an irrelevant display of false humility; he was inclined to sentimentality; he was very occasionally prone to short bouts of self-pity and the feeling that his disability warranted more consideration than he received. Yet at war with these tendencies were their assertive and prevailing opposites: an iron will, active most of the time in his determination neither to ask quarter of the brutally curious or indifferent, nor to accept any but essential help from the solicitous; a dislike of pretentiousness that was at direct odds with his own sentimentality; and the freedom to love and to communicate that love. He had looked inward, made his peace with himself as best he could, and turned outward again. When William was able to take hold of God's hand, as he himself once put it, he could confront whatever phantom of fear or pain or hostility.

In a strangely appropriate way, it seemed to Walton, his father's friendship with Charles Dickens complemented and balanced that with God. Despite the simplicity and the lack of mystical hocus-pocus in the latter relationship, the radiance it generated in William Herrick—a radiance that literally seemed sometimes to produce in the complexion of an aging man the freshness one expected to find in that of a boy or a young girl—this radiance was perhaps a little frightening to many people. It at least tended to make them self-conscious, and to cause them to prefer to admire him from a distance. But the Dickens strain in William Herrick gave him the common touch.

He first read Dickens in a hospital in Philadelphia, where, ten years old, he was awaiting an operation, upon the outcome of which hung the possibility of his being able to walk. He was alone, because the preliminary treatment he must undergo had taken longer than the family had expected and the new date for the operation came some ten days after the time established for the beginning of summer residence on Cape Cod. William had assured the family that he was quite content to be alone, except for Dr. Wilkins, the kindly physician who attended him, yet when they left him he found that for some reason he could not this time grope his way to the presence of God.

The physician, arriving several hours later, found him in a state of barely-repressed panic. After a long and reassuring talk, Dr. Wilkins had the happy inspiration of going out and buying a copy of *David Copperfield*. It was scarcely an exaggeration, William once told Walton, to say that his impatience with the operation was as much over the delay in continuing his reading of Dickens as over the necessary ordeal of pain and his concern about the result of the surgery.

David Copperfield was succeeded quickly by *Oliver Twist, Old Curiosity Shop, Nicholas Nickleby* and *Pickwick Papers*—eventually, by all the others. By the time he was sixty, William Herrick had read every novel by Dickens at least six times. The habit of turning to him for relief from stress persisted throughout his life. And when, in his last five years, he made the acquaintance of a woman fifteen years his senior who loved Dickens equally, he experienced a new delight in at last having another person with whom to share the joys of his secret world.

Mrs. Harris was the grandmother of a friend of Walton's. She was a wealthy widow who had somehow never found satisfaction in the traditional interests of her family and economic peers: in their round of clubs and parties, volunteer social service, civic obligations, sports, and the official cultural life of Cleveland. She would contribute money regularly —herself seldom. Her grandson was very fond of her, and on one of the visits he and Walton made with fair regularity her devotion to Dickens came up. A few weeks later, Walton arranged for a meeting with his father; thereafter, Mrs. Harris and William Herrick carried on a love affair.

Needless to say, it was not what the world understands by the term. Nor was it, Walton used to remind his mother (who was jealous, not of William's interest in Mrs. Harris, but of the fact that Mrs. Harris, though courteous to her, Marcia, preferred William), the silly, pretentiously soul-invoking sort of relationship miscalled "Platonic."

It amounted rather to this: on those afternoons on which William Herrick finished his classes at the University fairly early, he would drag his crippled legs the few blocks to Mrs. Harris' residence (on a street tented with magnificent old trees, a street that had defied commercial progress and remained elegantly residential in the heart of a district given over to small shops, the outlying buildings of Western Reserve, and shabby rooming houses). There, in her Victorian living room, they would sit in communion.

But again, in no attenuated, anemic relationship represented so frequently by the euphemism of "spiritual." There were tea and sandwiches and cakes, served by a female Sancho Panza named Katherine, who advised them freely on what and how much to eat; and there were long bouts of laughter, punctuated by periods of silently gazing at each other with eyes still brimming with the overflow of happiness.

"And, oh, Sairy Gamp," Mrs. Harris would say, and shake helplessly in delicious remembrance.

When they recovered, William might manage to get halfway through a sentence without chuckling: "Now, Betsy Trotwood—" only to succumb again.

Walton supposed that they must sometimes hold an uninterrupted conversation replete with rounded sentences. But the one time he accompanied his father, although they began on a more sophisticated level, presumably for his benefit, they soon gave over to these broken, evocative utterances of names—and to laughter.

This one meeting enabled him to understand fully, with mixed feelings (for at this time he still felt a compulsive sullen loyalty to his mother), the meaning of the sly looks exchanged by the two Dickensians on those state occasions on which Mrs. Harris entertained the whole Herrick family. Walton's mother would be pursuing the conventional amenities, making a bid now and then for special attention through what she considered one of her more challenging opinions (for she wanted desperately to impress Mrs. Harris), such as: "I don't think that going to church is the test of true religion" or "A real gentleman or lady may hold any station in life with serenity"—and Walton, looking up, would catch his father and Mrs. Harris exchanging surreptitious twinkles.

Their looks left everyone else out, but held no malice, contained no evident sense of superiority or of offensive exclusiveness. Yet they would anger him, even while he recognized their decent, joyful and even earthy quality—anger him only because of the way they left his mother out.

Possibly the looks did hold an implication that Marcia Herrick's sententiousness was not unlike that of some figures whom Dickens ridiculed; possibly they were secretly fitting Marcia into one of the novels. Yet William Herrick, whether through discretion or blind loyalty to Marcia, seldom made fun of her, tempting though the prospect must often have been. Actually, Walton eventually decided, it was simply that his father valued peace even more than humor. At any rate, what was paramount in his exchanges with Mrs. Harris was happiness in their shared Dickensian world and the impropriety of their secret amusement over what would happen if one of them were suddenly to say, "There, take Mr. Micawber. Or Sam Weller—" and rock with mirth.

Looking back on this relationship, Walton came to realize that while this was a world the two of them shared, its basis was not the basis of his father's own separate relation to Dickens. A chance remark of William's led him finally to see that his father's private friendship with Dickens must actually have begun with a feeling that in these novels he found a society into which he himself fitted.

In the first place, it was a world of grotesques (many of them, to be sure, kindly, likable grotesques): primary, uncomplicated people who were not complex individuals but recognizable, in clear blacks and whites, as the possessors of one or two dominant traits—a simplification of human character that was congenial to his own tastes and convictions, a simplification missing many subtleties but frequently conveying essential truths.

And it was also a world containing many physical grotesques, stunted or maimed bodies as well as minds and personalities suffering from wounds that either never healed or, healing, still left their mark. Resigned in the world of external reality to the position of being singled out from the crowd as an exception, a freak, William finally found companionship on an equal basis. (No other emotion that his father ever displayed so moved Walton as William's incredulous pleasure over his son's statement "You're more of a man than I am.")

Moreover, Dickens' sentimentality over the unfortunates who ranged over, or huddled together on his pages, matched a similar quality in William. And without any pronounced morbidness, he found a release from his long-inhibited suffering through the anguish and grief and mistreatment of the characters in the novels. They helped him to pity others, because he felt less isolated and pitiable himself; unquestionably they contributed deeply to the unselfishness that grew in him.

There were still other elements in Dickens' attitude to which he responded. The anti-aristocratic bias warmed him and balanced his Cleveland associations; it suited his early-established feeling that he didn't belong in the lofty social climate in which the Herricks moved (to be sure, except for Cornelius himself, and to some extent Emily, they moved only on the outskirts to which the families of those who served the rest—whether as preacher, teacher or "companion"—were relegated). It reinforced his democratic viewpoint, which probably had its origin in his own adversities, but which took strong root, to grow in a positive way.

And what was more, Walton noticed, when Dickens' own sympathies narrowed and failed—through lack of the imaginativeness to extend those sympathies to their broadest human application—William's own fine-tempered generosity supplied what was lacking. He felt, and sometimes expressed, a gentle disapproval of, say, the conventional estimate (and even the racial chauvinism) Dickens accepted in his portrayal of Fagin.

All this went into William's friendship with Charles Dickens—surely a friendship more real to him than most of those he formed with people living in Cleveland. And eventually (of this Walton felt sure, although it was never made explicit between him and his father) William came to see Cleveland this way, too. The barbers, streetcar conductors, policemen, even the baseball fans whom he sat next to at League Park—all these he finally came to see through Dickensian lenses. Moving more freely and comfortably through this larger cross-section of the city than through that frequented regularly by the rest of his family, he could and did detect a representative of the genus Squeers or Jarley or Peggotty or whomever—here, there and everywhere.

There was simple comfort for him in discovering in some person who was unable to conceal his revulsion at the sight of William's crippled, twisted legs a likeness to one of Dickens' less savory figures, just as there was solid satisfaction in discerning the soundness of heart and generosity of someone pursuing unheralded one of the humblest tasks in the huge interwoven economic structure of the great sprawling, growing city.

In his turn, he became The Professor to thousands of the inhabitants of that city as he made his way through it with his cane, day after day, year after year. Day after day, falling flat a dozen times in the midst of the rumbling, screeching traffic of Euclid Avenue, picking himself up, grinning painfully at his own discomfiture and the angry squawking of horns and bells, indignant only if some overzealous well-intentioned passerby took hold of his arm and tried to propel him to safety. "I can't give in," he once explained to Walton. "I mustn't give in to these people. They mean well, but if I let them help me, the next step will be not even to go out by myself."

He developed, of course, compensating strengths and agilities of an abnormal sort; the human body, as it will, made extraordinary adjustments. In his twenties and thirties, he could actually run, in a queer, shambling way, waving his arms and his cane for balance. Around the house, using objects of all sorts for crucial balancing support, he even dispensed with the cane. And he acquired a prodigious strength in his arms—his arms and shoulders were proportioned for a man of much greater stature—just as he taught himself to relax and fall with the effortless ease of a baby.

And so he made his way. This, Walton often thought, was the shortest, the clearest and truest manner in which to describe this extraordinary man and his equally extraordinary, if quiet, life: "He made his way."

People knew this. Despite the numbers who were not capable of seeing more than the crippled body or, even while prating of "courage" and "goodness," were congratulating themselves on being hale and whole—despite these many, there were many others who knew this of William and, as a result, found their own capacity to endure increased. There was the Italian barber who had not heard of William's death when Walton met him on the street a few days later: when Walton told him, he wept openly, burying his face in his hands, his big shoulders shaking. Then he grasped Walton urgently by the arm.

"He was a good-a man," he said. "He was good. He love."

And so he did. Dragging that weary, half-broken body on its course day after day, year after year, love still shone from his face. If one loves, one cannot be bored, and a part of his peculiar radiance consisted in the eagerness, the searching curiosity, with which he surveyed the world. The intimations of spring, the final green and gold thrust of Indian summer (as though for a moment all Nature had forgotten its inevitable cycle) the first light fall of snow—these delighted him.

"See that!" he would exclaim, balancing himself and pointing with his cane. "See that. It's beautiful."

The catholicity of his tastes and interests gave endless testimony to his capacity for love. How the locks of a canal operate, the niceties of dentistry, the structure of a fugue, the questionable wisdom of a baseball manager in replacing a given batter with a pinch hitter—all the myriad problems of cause and effect, of interaction and interrelations, could bring this luminous excitement to his eyes, and he would literally give off such an intensification of inner life as to make one believe that it was light he shed from his pores.

As with his tastes and interests, so with his friendships. The Italian barber, it sometimes seemed to Walton, was less an individual than the spokesman for hundreds of obscure citizens of Cleveland who had in common one thing: their respect for and devotion to William Herrick.

There was, for instance, the big Irish cop at the ball park, who stopped Walton one day in the summer after William's death and said, spitting tobacco, "He was a good little guy, the Professor, a game little guy."

Walton thought of the delight William Herrick would have taken in this, how he would have thrown back his head and slapped his leg and roared in wholehearted appreciation of the "good little guy, the Professor." So Walton shocked a pious admirer at the funeral by saying that his father would have been even more amused than pleased at the fulsome tributes paid in editorials in the local newspapers after his death. For William was quite aware that he was neither, very exactly, "a good little guy," nor, as one of the editorials said, "an intellectual saint of the sort one finds once or twice in a century."

His was no storybook serenity, of the sort that often actually means a resignation from life ("I distrust this exaltation of tolerance," he once said to Walton, "because so often it is only a euphemism for the loss of one's capacity for honest moral indignation"). If he was serene, it was only in the sense of his continuing friendship with God, which gave him his magnificent resilience.

Yet in his last years, despite the increasing pain and disability of his failing body, his fair quota of inner conflicts and divisions lessened perceptibly; he became increasingly *one*. From the now thin face flesh had been burned away; the skin was stretched tightly across the bones and the eyes shone incandescent, deep in the sockets. Walton remembered this face best behind the candles on the altar at the last college Christmas carol service over which his father presided. Walton had been detained, then forced to drive slowly through the heavy snowstorm that had attacked the city, and arrived to stand at the back of the chapel just in time to hear William pronounce the benediction.

The light of the candles shadowed the caverns in his face as he raised his hand. Walton knew suddenly that he was going to die, that no one could burn with such an intensity of love and live for long. Standing there in the rear of the chapel, he wept, but not yet with sadness over the imminence of loss—rather over the unendurable beauty of so much life, of life whittled to so sharp a point of purpose and understanding and tenderness. And when William said, with those enormous eyes black and shining in the candlelight, and his gaunt hand spread, "And now may God come and bring His peace to all of you," Walton realized from the great voice of silence that followed that everyone else there in the chapel felt as he did.

There he stood—now as then. Walton came to feel that before he could harden himself, as he was often to do later, to cheat or lie or practice a cynical indifference, he must first turn his back to his father.

1953

1953

June 8

WALTON Herrick leaned back in his swivel chair, stretched one long leg out until the foot made contact with the edge of his desk, and picked up the intercom telephone.

"Hel-lo!" he called and, clamping the phone firmly against mouth and ear by hugging it with his hunched-up shoulder, reached for cigarette package and matches.

"This is Dennis, Mr.—Walton: Dennis Byrnes."

"Yes, Dennis. Wait a minute. Just—" he punctuated the sentence by the act—"lighting a cigarette. Go on."

"I'd like to talk with you a few minutes when you're free. If you have any time this morning at all . . ."

"Sure. You bet. Let's see. Oh, hell, the other phone. Let me call you back."

He cut short Dennis' muffled agreement (sometimes, no matter how much he liked the boy, it irritated him that Dennis found three sentences the minimum in which to say, "All right")—cut it short by hanging up and turning to the other telephone.

The voice of Peggy, the switchboard girl, was shrill with earnest concern.

"Mr. Herrick, it's a Mr. Fortune. I asked him his business and full name, but he won't say anything except 'Just tell him it's Fortune calling.' Will you take it?"

Walton drew deeply on his cigarette, exhaled in a long sigh. It had come. "Yes, put him on."

"Hello," he said. "This is Walton Herrick."

"Mr. Herrick." The voice was as he remembered it from the first call—almost guttural. No, it was hoarse, with that hoarseness peculiar to inveterate cigar smokers. "Fortune speaking. Abe Fortune. I'm in town. If you're free, I'd like to meet you after you leave the office. Or do you hurry right home?"

"No," Walton replied, peering at his desk calendar. "My family's away, and I'm in no hurry. How about five-thirty?"

"Sold," said Abe Fortune, and suddenly the hoarse pseudo-whisper sounded conspiratorial. "Where?"

Walton scratched his head.

"Would you like to meet me at the Century Club?" he asked. "It's quiet."

"No. It may be quiet, but it's too conspicuous. That's out of my class, Mr. Herrick, but a lot of people know what I look like. Do you know the Swazey Bar? Just a couple of blocks from you."

"Fine," said Walton. "I'll be there at five-thirty."

He replaced the receiver and sat perfectly still for a moment of elation. This Abe Fortune had not, in either call, said a word about the governorship, only that he wanted to know "more" about him. Without Leon Goodman's tip, Walton wouldn't know now what it was all about.

But he did know—and that knowledge was sufficient to wash out the dregs of the lonely weekend just over, and to dissipate the customary Monday-morning tension over the huge accumulation of mail and memoranda. It was futile, he found, to remind himself soberly that, after two divorces, his present estrangement from Julie made his candidacy for the governorship impossible; to realize that he should have told Abe Fortune that he was wasting his time; to call to mind the undeniable fact that he, Walton, had very grave doubts about wanting to run, even to enter political life in any fashion. What remained, bobbing up and down in his mind with the stability and resilience of a buoy, was the feeling of being singled out, of being wanted.

"Dennis," he said into the intercom, "come on in now. I'll let the mail wait. And get two cups of coffee from Evelyn."

Walton was exasperated. The familiar and rhythmic demands of the job were pressing at him urgently again. He had shut off the telephone, once he had decided to relax over coffee with Dennis, but each time he glanced at the five-inch pile of unopened mail he could hear in his mind Peggy's angular but efficient voice repeating, "Mr. Herrick is in conference. May I have your number?" "I can't reach Mr. Herrick just now. Will you speak to his secretary?" "I'm afraid I can't interrupt Mr. Herrick just now. Will you leave a message?"

And Dennis went on talking, hesitating, cocking his handsome russet-colored head as he sought for, found, rejected, found again and accepted the word he wanted to convey a precise meaning. Only, Walton reflected irritably, the solution was almost never worth the pains. They had been here a full twenty minutes, the dregs of their coffee cold puddles in their cups—and still Dennis had come to no perceptible point. He was edging toward the Asiatic Studies program; that was clear. But his approach to it was reminiscent of boyhood thefts of apples: for every direct step toward the tree, he would back, slide sideways, apprehensively scan the horizon, drop flat on his belly and slither a short way, before cautiously raising his head again.

"It does seem to me," Dennis was saying deliberately, "that there are two sides to the question. . . ."

In his present mood, Walton regarded him morosely. This was the young man (twenty-eight) whom he had himself selected as his administrative assistant; this was the young man with the candid eyes and the slow but winningly appreciative smile whom he had not only appointed, but incautiously made a friend, almost an intimate—all in four months.

First, Walton thought, one observed his genuine male beauty, his well-proportioned, sailing-and-swimming trained physique, the boyish appeal of the freckles that kept the sweetness of the expression just safely away from the epicene. Then came the sense of the unusual candor and poise, the modesty with which occasionally the eyes were lowered, revealing long, soft, almost feminine lashes. And then, perhaps, one doubted—only to have those eyes open wide in a strange combination of almost virginal innocence and urchin knowingness, to fix upon one so direct and clairvoyant a gaze that one was found out and ashamed of one's own cynicism. Only again, from time to time—it had slowly come to seem to Walton—to catch off guard a look of almost poisonous sweetness that confirmed one's skepticism.

I sold myself a bill of goods when I took this one on, Walton thought, and what a time to discover it! He said abruptly, "Dennis, what's on your mind? Let's really catch hold of it."

Dennis blinked, then recovered himself, and smiled that strange downy smile, secret and self-bemused, like one of Leonardo's portraits. He spread his hands, palms up, in humorous self-deprecation.

"I *have* been rambling, haven't I? You see—Walton—I find it hard to say this."

He paused, hopefully it seemed, but Walton remained silent, staring at him grimly.

The lashes. The sudden direct look, half virgin, half gamin—and then the knotted fist, big-boned, freckled and masculine, pounded into the other palm. Good God, Walton thought, all that stuff I've been thinking about the ambiguity of personality. And yet this is all an act!

"It's the Asiatic Studies program." Dennis began slowly. "I've been thinking about it almost constantly, and it seems to me now that we're making a mistake to insist on Kiefer. Surely there are other men as competent, and, considering what's at stake, we don't want to sacrifice the whole thing for an indiscreet—New York liberal, do we?"

"We," Walton thought in sudden anger. Where do you get this "we" stuff? But an uneasiness that had been creeping through him for several minutes grew more insistent now—and he abruptly realized the irony of a historical parallel. P.H. had brought *him* in; he had supported P.H.'s crucial program to a certain point, only to back down, partially through Ernest Ingersoll's pressure—but partially also from honest conviction. So now . . .

He kept his voice very calm, with only a faint emphasis on the word "we."

"Dennis, I don't believe we're going to lose this fight. And to me it is a fight, and one that I'm not giving up. I went to considerable trouble to learn everything I could about Clarence Kiefer, and I'm satisfied that he's no more a Communist, or a past Communist, or even a crypto-Communist, than you or I. And after all, what was the point of the struggle with the investigating committee, if we win that, only to have become so intimidated that we're afraid to appoint a man who belonged in the forties—apparently only nominally—to several liberal organizations that were later blackballed?"

Dennis stood up, began to pace about. Then he stopped and stood staring down at the magazine- and report-covered table across the office. He pushed at its leg several times with the toe of his shoe before swinging around and facing Walton.

"As I understand it," he said slowly, "P.H. feels that it's all the more incumbent on us to keep absolutely and finally clear and clean because you did do such a great job at the hearings of convincing the public that we are as American and antisubversive as—as the Chase National Bank. It's sort of like—well, the Civil Liberties Union. Our—your very defense of this branch of civil liberties puts us in a special position, like them. We have a new, almost a unique obligation to be one hundred percent careful and vigilant. It's—it's the simplest public relations."

Well, now, is it? Walton thought sardonically. The impertinent young puppy! The "you" and "your" slipped in so ingratiatingly. And "P.H. feels"—so that it seemed painfully clear that Dennis had his instructions—that, after all these years, P.H. had to resort to cajoling him with a coffee-carrying Ganymede.

He grunted, a sound half growl and half curse. This time he'd caught himself before he lost control: P.H. *hadn't* sent Dennis in with coffee, after all. And whose fault was it that Dennis was here in the first place? Who had hired him after two interviews? More, who had foolishly, with an impetuousness more fitting to an adolescent, "taken" Dennis "in," talked with him time after time after hours on the most intimate and equal basis, even—when they relaxed one night with some bourbon after pounding out a report until ten-thirty—pondered together personal aspects of their lives? Walton felt a murderous desire to punch himself for a callow, immature fool. For now, so soon, he thought he saw the configuration plainly. Yet only this past week he had thought of having Dennis spend a weekend with him in Northport, and had wondered whether, in the relaxed mood of the country, he might not even confide in him about Julie, about the governorship. He felt as angry now as though he had actually told him these things.

"Besides," said Dennis, and Walton realized that the boy was regarding him curiously, with a patent tentativeness, "there's—well, P.H. I hate to see you and him at odds, Walton. His devotion to you is absolute—and you really are putting him on an awful spot. All this for a principle that I think you're misapplying. I know you'll understand that I wouldn't dream of saying all this if I didn't think so much of you—"

Walton cut in at last.

"I think, Dennis," he said coldly, "that in view of that feeling you'd be well advised to leave this to P.H. and me. I appreciate your concern, but in the end it rests with us to work it out. And we've known each other a long time. I've kept you here too long, anyway, for you have a lot of work lined up on that Harvard project. And I've got to do something about this pile on my desk."

Dennis shot him that balefully sweet look. Then he nodded and, with a sudden alien dignity that seemed unusually simple and genuine, said, "Sorry. I guess I stepped over," and left the room.

It was then that the sirens for the city-wide atomic raid drill began their chilling warble. For a moment Walton froze, desolate: he was back in the bedroom at home with Julie, that last afternoon. Then he realized that this was the announced eleven o'clock drill and, cursing at the further interruption, followed those in the outer office into the hallway and to the staircase designated as a "shelter."

Here they stood, packed like sheep on the gray steps, for ten minutes. Walton closed his ears as best he could to the gay and excited chatter swirling around him, finally also closed his eyes. How long he stood motionless, shut off, he did not know, but gradually he became aware of a soft fragrance and of the coolness of supple flesh pressing against his hand.

He opened his eyes on a tousled head of wheat-colored hair, a few inches below his chin, and recognized, without seeing more, P.H.'s new secretary, Sonia—he did not know her last name. Someone was climbing the stairs in haste, and the others were pressing back to make a passage. Hence Sonia's arm against his hand, her head almost touching his shoulder, hence the fragrance of her perfume so close to him.

The man climbing the stairs passed them, with an apology to Walton; the crowding ceased. But as Sonia moved away from Walton, she turned her head, and for a long moment they looked at each other— it seemed to Walton more knowingly than questioningly. Then she smiled faintly, and, as the announcement came for the end of the drill, went up the stairs without a backward look.

With their second glasses of iced coffee, P.H. ordered melon and Walton Brie and crackers. Then they fell into a meditative silence.

But this was a good thing, Walton thought, switching his gaze from the perspective of Forty-third Street and the glassed-in bank at the corner of Fifth Avenue to P.H.'s straight, regular features and his neat, close-fitting skull cap of shining white hair, startling above his tanned skin. It was good because for weeks now they had been unable to remain comfortably quiet together.

When Walton did finally break the silence, it was because he had been thinking about friendship, and this led him to Dudley Foote.

"P.H.," he said abruptly, "how is Dud getting along? Both he and I have been so busy I haven't seen anything of him."

P.H. nodded.

"He's only been here a week," he said, "but the first impression's fine. Very likable."

Again they fell silent, and again Walton experienced the old companionable feeling.

At last P.H. looked up from his melon, smiling ruefully.

"You know," he said, just as though they had been talking about the Asiatic Studies program throughout the lunch, "I feel that I simply must have one more try."

Walton nodded and took out his pipe.

"Go ahead," he said, even chuckling a little. The feeling he had sought vainly in these last weeks came finally back to him now: simply how much he liked this man.

P.H. spread his small, brown, well-shaped hands on the table and leaned forward, looking directly into Walton's eyes.

"I shan't say anything further about the man. You think Kiefer's worth the trouble; I don't. You'll remember that when we first talked, and again when you presented the whole thing at the staff budget meeting, I expressed my doubts about him, but yielded because you felt so strongly. And I—personally, that is—would still be willing to go along with him. But you know that, Walt; you know that your word's good enough for me."

Walton broke in: "But not for Huntingdon Haldane and Butterfield and Cutler and young Schuyler and maybe one or two other trustees. Yes, I do know that."

P.H. shook his head, almost in dejection.

"The one thing I wish I could persuade you of is Hunt's solidity. He's the key to the whole thing, Walt. I don't know why you dislike him so; it doesn't make sense. He's cultured, well-informed, moderately liberal, thoughtful, just and marvelously decisive. Without him, I'd simply give up in despair, trying to handle the Board. I wish, when he comes back from Canada, we three could have dinner together."

Walton sucked on his pipe.

"Well, perhaps we can. But it seems to me useless. I'm sure he's not going to change my mind. If anybody could, it would be you. And of course I don't see him the way you do. Perhaps he has all the attributes you've named: I'll grant them, anyway. I still don't like him. He's too neat—*too* balanced, *too* rational, too damned *perfect* to be real. No, I don't mean to be real; I mean that it is a cardinal principle with me that if any man seems so perfectly to be all these things I'm almost forced to believe that he needs air-conditioning inside. I'll take my people with palpable faults, provided they have compensatory qualities I like. And anyway, Chief, for God's sake, why are we in this mess? Because of Haldane. If he weren't chairing the Executive Committee, the whole thing would have gone straight through, the Board meeting would not have been postponed, and there would have been no stink, even if somebody on the Board had taken exception to Kiefer and in the end he didn't get the job. Isn't that so?"

P.H. stirred the ice in his glass with a long spoon.

"Perhaps, perhaps not. It is true, of course, that it was Hunt who raised the question. He was the only one who knew anything about Kiefer—how, I don't know." He again raised his eyes to Walton's, and this time with an unspoken troubled question visible.

Walton vigorously shook his head.

"I've never given that thought one minute's time," he said quietly. "Now I'm really glad we're having this talk. No, let me say it, very explicitly. I know that you didn't tip him off on Kiefer. The fact that you had your doubts but gave in to me is to me utterly irrelevant. I don't know how Haldane got any dope on him, but I do know it wasn't from you. For Christ's sake, P.H., can you really doubt that?"

P.H. smiled warmly.

"Not any more. And thanks. But we're off now on Kiefer, which is just where I didn't want to be. Anyway, the Board would have to know about his membership eventually. Now I'd started to say that I'd just take your word on it, if I were in a position to. What I want to make you see is this: suppose him to be head and shoulders above everybody else we might consider to head this institute, and yet your refusal to allow us to reject him and choose instead, say, Walters or Pendleton, blocked the whole project, and it had to be abandoned—wouldn't your conscience hurt you worse than it would if the program went through, but without Kiefer?"

Walton looked thoughtfully at the familiar posture. How many times in their relationship, he wondered suddenly, had they faced each other this way, with P.H. pleading? The wrinkles in the forehead that seemed so incongruous in the otherwise unlined brown face, the small deft hands outstretched in an attitude of earnest suppliance that was somehow incongruous in a man whose mind and body were so ultimately competent, assured, even—almost—suave. The people who didn't like P.H. always damned him as an "operator"; the words that Walton himself had just spoken about Huntingdon Haldane were not infrequently applied to P.H.—yet to Walton there was no similarity between the two men. Haldane had a high polish; there was shellac over him. P.H. was this earnest, genuine man across from him, this friend.

But possibly this was the point: others knew only Philip Henderson Gates the administrator; he knew P.H. And so, might he not be just as wrong about Haldane? Again, the ambiguity . . . He broke off, realizing that P.H. was still waiting for his answer.

"I don't know," he said. "I honestly don't know. The way you put it seems to me a loaded question. If I answer it, how can I say anything except, 'Yes, the abandonment of the whole project would be worse'? But I can't see these as necessary alternatives. Listen, P.H., let me go back over the ground, though we both have been over it so many times that we're tired of it. The Institute of Asiatic Studies, as proposed, will operate both here and in non-Communist countries in Asia. We haven't chosen the universities here in which we'd plant the first branches.

Right? Nor have we even chosen—though in both cases we intend to make some recommendations—the places, even the specific countries in Asia, for those branches. Point 1."

P.H. broke in.

"But, Walt—"

"No, please hear me out. I'm not just rehashing. Point of Point 1: there can be no informed opinion that we are interested in locating branches of the proposed Institute in sensitive spots already tagged as possibly susceptible to subversion, nor that we are thinking of establishing challengeable individuals in any of them. Right? Point 2: this is to be throughout an institute of humane letters, of literature, languages, fine arts, music and history. Not political science, not economics, not even sociology. All this, having in mind that the best propaganda is a grant that stays completely out of the literal propaganda field. We know that this is practically unfeasible—that of course there is in reality no international border between these academic fields, yet it is pretty tough to teach Marxism or Stalinism to a class in painting or counterpoint without its being evident. History—less difficult, but still not easy. And the various staffs at both the American branches, where they will study Asiatic literature, languages, music, etcetera, and the Asiatic branches, where they will study the American equivalents, will be under our direct surveillance, as well as Kiefer's—if he were appointed director. Right?

"So—" he paused to relight his pipe, but this time P.H., who was now drawing circles and squares on the tablecloth, did not attempt to interrupt, did not even look up— "so Point 2 is that the subject matter is as removed from the controversial as possible. Point 3 is Kiefer's own professional experience—his excellence as administrator and his exclusive scholarly preoccupation with Oriental *literature*. I'm almost through. Point 4 is that he will be in the central New York office, running the whole project from here, hand in hand with us, and may never do any traveling at all. How safe can you get? And bear in mind that all Haldane has raised against him is his name on the membership rolls of three organizations, all in the mid-forties, only one of which was on the Attorney General's list, and that one which, for God's sake, I belonged to myself—though I never did any more than Kiefer did."

He stopped. He had finished, but he would have stopped anyway, because of the expression of concern on P.H.'s face.

"Were you really?" said P.H. "I never knew that."

Walton let out a sound of weary disdain.

"My God," he said. "Now you're worried about that! P.H., what's happened to you? You've always been a fussy old hen, but who's gotten to you to make you so scared of name calling? I was on a committee with Kiefer; that's how I came to be so sure of him."

P.H. resumed the penciling of his hieroglyphics. It was obvious to Walton that only that rich, handsome tan concealed P.H.'s flush.

"Listen," said Walton, and heard with a slight dismay the iron in his own voice. "Did you put Dennis Byrnes up to giving me that line this morning? All about how, like the Civil Liberties Union, we had to be meticulously, one hundred percent cautious, so that we could operate *sans peur et sans reproche?* P.H., I'll go a step further; I'll answer your earlier question. I really believe now that my conscience— whatever, God help me, that is—would hurt more at dropping Kiefer than at abandoning the whole thing. No, don't look shocked; I know all the reasonable answers, and this is no perverse whim. An institution of whatever sort that begins like a bunch of old maids looking under the beds will never become the real thing, will never accomplish the real purpose that we are both after. Admit to one ghost in the closet, and we'll be seeing more. I can see you getting ready to be administrative, to explain the facts of life to me: that negotiation and compromise are the laws of all successful ventures. But just go back a little to the investigation: do you suppose we would have come out the way we did if we had yielded to expediency, to caution, to alleged common sense— if we had snooped around, negotiating and compromising. There's a ring in the nose of everybody who practices expediency in the name of negotiation and compromise, and all you have to do is spot it, catch hold of it and pull it. But we went into that damned thing whole—no rings—and we came out the same way. And I propose, as long as I have anything to do with the Foundation, that we stay that way."

He realized that his hands were trembling a little as he repacked his pipe from his tobacco pouch. Then, when he looked up and saw P.H.'s face, he knew that he had made a bad mistake. Good Lord, Walton thought, he believes I brought up the investigation to remind him that he passed the buck to me—or, anyway was satisfied to let me carry it. I've hurt him—and everything I'm trying to do, too.

P.H. dropped the pencil, studied his hands.

"Walt, you've put a great deal to me to answer, and some of it I'd rather not go into. I don't believe I'll try to answer any of it, except to say that yes, I did suggest to Dennis that he try to persuade you— after he had brought up his own dilemma over the contradiction between his loyalty to you and the conclusions he'd finally reached himself. He's a fine boy, and I must say that much in fairness to him. But that's all I'm going to say in reply. Instead of answering you, I'd like to ask you one question: have you talked all this over with Julie?"

Caught off guard, Walton was sure that he looked self-conscious. He could feel around his mouth that invisible smile of uneasiness that he always felt there when it seemed to him that he was caught in some— misdemeanor was the word that had come to his mind! He tried to find in P.H.'s expression some indication of the knowledge that Julie and he had broken up, but if P.H. knew, there was no evidence of it.

"No," Walton said shortly. "She and the kids are away for the summer, as I told you."

P.H. was looking at him now with what Walton thought of as his "level administrative look."

"Yes, I know that," he said quietly, "but I think it might be worth the effort either to spend a weekend with her and tell her about it, or at least to write her."

It was a little ambiguous, but Walton was inclined to believe that all P.H. meant was that he trusted Julie's dispassionateness, her balance, and her influence on him, Walton, to constitute the most likely means of persuading him to change his mind about Kiefer.

"Well," Walton said stiffly, "not even Julie can change my mind about this. My back's up, Chief, and you know it. But let me ask you a question in turn—and give me the straight answer you always have about anything important. Would the best solution be my resignation?"

P.H. straightened up, dropped his hands in his lap and, for the third time during their talk, looked Walton full in the eyes.

"Never," he said, and his voice trembled a little; Walton had never heard a voice more persuasive of conviction and strength of feeling. "Never. And I don't think you should have felt it necessary to ask that question. I just wish you'd confided more to me earlier."

As though in agreement, they stood up. On their way down the stairs, past the Century Club's art gallery, Walton put his hand on the shorter man's shoulder.

"I hate all this too," he said. "And I think I'd better bend this much. When Haldane comes back, I'll have dinner with you and him."

Despite the many years he had known P.H., he was amazed at the warmth, almost the radiance, of his smile now.

Abe Fortune was a swarthy man. As Walton followed the head-waiter to their table, he was surprised to realize that his first impression was of an Oriental cast to the dark face eying him dispassionately, almost inscrutably.

They shook hands. Fortune did not actually rise, only hunched himself up from his chair an inch or two, in a way that called such open attention to the act that in another man it would have served as insolence. In another man—for his handclasp was warm and strong, and the smile that flickered briefly suggested a sardonic sort of friendliness.

The two studied each other silently across the table for a moment, ignoring the solicitous waiter. What Walton had thought of as Oriental, he decided now, was probably a particular kind of Semitic looks. No, Circassian perhaps—or (suddenly remembering a visit long ago with his mother to a carpet store) an Armenian rug merchant. The slightly beaked nose, the weary droop to the mouth, the large but not massive head held—apparently perpetually—slightly to one side, the dark, almost grayish-brown skin mottled here and there with tannish birthmarks, the whole suggestion of a squat, powerful frame now beginning to loosen and sag—these attributes suggested somehow a tired seaman, a fiftyish Odysseus: but no Greek. A Phoenician, Walton thought, and something about the phrase, Abe the Phoenician, held and pleased him.

But at this moment Fortune's heavy lids lifted a little and Walton saw that everything else about the man was subordinate to his eyes. A rich dark brown, they were opaque, and yet this did not result in the kind of blindness, spiritual deadness, that opacity in eyes so often suggested to Walton. These were, he thought, of a different order from most human eyes; their intelligence, immediately apparent, was irrelevant, it seemed, to what was familiar and recognizable as human intelligence. They were birds' eyes, perhaps—no, he rejected this: the best he could do was that they suggested a highly developed species of an unfamiliar but superior sort.

Fortune chuckled.

"Well, now that we've had a look," he said, "what will you have to drink?"

Walton asked for a bourbon and water, and Fortune turned to the waiter.

"One bourbon and water," he said in that pseudo-whisper that hinted at something illicit, "and one gin and bitters."

The waiter looked perplexed.

"Gin and bitters," Fortune repeated in a patient tone that implied the frequent recurrence of this situation. "Some people call it pink gin. British drink—colonial. Put just one or two drops of Angostura bitters— no more, be sure—in the bottom of an old-fashioned glass, and fill it with gin. Beefeater, please. One ice cube."

The waiter dispatched, he turned back to Walton.

"I'll bet Leon Goodman has told you what I'm thinking of."

Walton nodded.

"Just as well. What do *you* think of the idea?"

Walton began packing his pipe. He always felt at a disadvantage with the direct-question, I'll-put-you-on-the-spot-and-make-you-do-the-revealing sort of man, but he knew there could be only one outcome to this proposition, anyway, and this mitigated his dislike of this approach. And there was a difference in Fortune: unlike vice-presidents and account executives of the Madison Avenue variety, this man's directness accepted you, took you in as a partner in maturity who would no more want to fence with indirections and circumlocutions than he would himself.

"Pleased," said Walton at last. "I don't think it makes sense for either of us, but I like being considered, and I'm curious."

Abe Fortune smiled again. It was as though he used his smile in the interests of economy, with a reluctance to acknowledge with words what he could record with an expression. Hence the smile's brevity and genuineness, Walton thought: it was useful, and this man liked usefulness. Yet he also had a new sense now of Fortune's laconic terseness; it was as if he pushed words from his throat in that husky whisper only with a real effort—as if he were tired of talking.

"Curious?" he asked now. "About our reasons? About me?"

"Both," Walton replied.

"Reasons." Fortune pushed the word out and fell silent. The drinks arrived; he took a thoughtful sip. "Well. Some are obvious. The Schuyler report. Good administrator. Liberal but sound. Gentleman—important for Fairfield County and upstate. Yet liberal—important for Bridgeport, Hartford, Norwalk: workers. And—not so obvious—intellectual. We're playing with the meaning of the Stevenson vogue."

"But the Stevenson vogue seems to have turned out to be mighty limited," Walton remarked.

Fortune shook his head. Only then did he carry it upright. The motion over, he cocked it again; it was like his speech, Walton thought: as though it were too heavy to hold up.

"Never greater than right now," said Fortune. "This trip around the world. Willkie again. We'll watch it; you may turn out right. We've another year, you know—state elections in '54."

Walton pushed the ice in his glass around and around with his finger.

"And you?" he asked.

Fortune lifted his lids and gave him an enigmatic look.

"Really don't know?" he asked.

Walton shook his head. "I'm not very knowledgeable on politics," he said.

"Good for me." Fortune smiled. "Get to thinking I'm as notorious as Frank Costello or Lucky Luciano. Well, it's easy. I'm the poor man's Jim Farley."

When Walton did not comment, only smiled, he continued, a little as though he were chiding himself for his levity. "In Connecticut, all Democrats are poor, even the rich ones. I'm a semi-regular in the organization. Useful because I'm shrewd, able to work full time, and disinterested. Don't think I mean moral. I mean no personal axe to grind, no spoils—money or office. I'm in it because I'm infatuated with politics—that is, with life."

Walton grinned.

"That's quite a little to digest in one lump," he said. "You mean you have the money, don't need a job at all?" He was secretly amused at himself for clipping off part of his sentence in semi-Fortune style.

"That's right. Made it. Retired. Tell you about it someday. Let's talk about you."

"All right," said Walton. "Where do you want to begin?"

Abe Fortune looked at him long and hard again, with that slightly cryptic expression Walton had noted. The Full Treatment, he thought now: that's what that look means.

"Leon says you're much married," said Fortune slowly. After the look, the quality of gentleness in the guttural voice was surprising—and likable.

Walton nodded. "I've thought of that, of course. Leon told me that he told you, including assuring you that there was no public row in either divorce. But that doesn't seem to me to make much difference. Certainly one thing that we learned in the presidential campaign was that—whatever the national divorce statistics are—voters don't like divorced candidates."

Abe Fortune replied in a voice that was for him incongruously amiable, almost gossipy.

"I don't know about that. Let's not oversimplify it. What about your present wife? Leon says she's pretty and bright and sensible. Would she back you up on this—you know, appear enough, not too much; say enough, not too much; let her intelligence be obvious but not forbidding?"

It was almost a speech, coming from this man, Walton thought, and hesitated, wanting at once to be truthful and yet discreet.

"I don't know," he said at last, not satisfied with his reply. "She and the children are away for the summer and I haven't seen any point in writing her when it was still so vague."

He braced himself for a further probing question: "Don't you know your wife well enough to know how she'd respond?" but it didn't come. Instead, with a courtesy (for surely Fortune would have had his version of this thought) the more graceful for its apparent effortlessness, the other man shifted his field of questioning.

"What would the Foundation think of this?"

Walton rubbed the top of his head with the flat of his hand.

"I don't know. Various things from various people. Pleasure and pride mostly, I think. There are some who'd be mighty glad to get rid of me." He chuckled, then went on deliberately. "We're having quite a hassle over a new project of mine. There's some feeling on the Board that the man I want to head it has a bad political reputation."

Abe Fortune gave him the Full Treatment look. But all he said was "Oh?" which, in that hoarse whisper, was almost a croak, yet one that indicated no great concern.

Walton again fell to stirring the ice in his glass with his finger.

"Yes. I'll give you the details eventually if you want to hear them and there seems to be any need to. At present, with decisions pending, it's really still intramural."

Abe nodded, jerking his head up to make the necessary movement. They fell silent again—Walton stirring with his finger, Abe apparently sunk in contemplation.

At last he roused himself, but for once did not look directly at Walton.

"Marriage is hell," he said mournfully. "Monogamy. Congeniality is overrated, gets boring. And lack of it is worse—snarling and screaming and wounded silences. I can stand anything but wounded silences." He paused, then went on in the same lugubrious voice. "My wife's cute. Jane. Forty-seven and still trim and cute. Paints. Great sweeping, swooping things. She's five foot one. Has a tongue like a needle."

Walton surveyed him thoughtfully.

"What did you mean," he asked abruptly, "by saying that being infatuated with politics is the same as being infatuated with life? On the face of it, I don't think that's true. I should have thought that infatuation with politics is infatuation with manipulation, with pulling strings, with what the public relations fellows coat with the noble term 'human engineering.' "

He could not tell from Fortune's expression whether he was considering the question or Walton's abrupt change of topic.

"Well," said Abe Fortune. He always came to a full stop after the word "well." This time it was an even longer pause than usual, and then he repeated the word. "Well. Power politics? Machiavelli? The boys in the smoke-filled room. Some of that, I guess. But more. Much more. All the shadings and variety of human motivation. The spectacle. The deceptiveness of personality. I don't believe in evolution."

It had all been said in his mildest manner. But suddenly, in some inexplicable fashion (for Fortune had not said anything really that remarkable), Walton felt a deep confidence that this was the most interesting man he had met in years, and that he could learn a good deal from him.

As though he, too, had come to a sudden decision, Abe Fortune looked at his watch and signaled to the waiter.

"I'd like to catch the six-forty, you know," he said as though he had told Walton from the beginning that this must be a short meeting. "And I'd like to see you again when we can sit for a whole evening. My home. Near Stamford. Spend a night with us?"

"I certainly would," said Walton with an eagerness he made no attempt to hide.

Fortune acknowledged this with a smile. Then, dumping a five-dollar bill into the waiter's hand, he stood up and took a step away from his chair. Only then did Walton see with surprise that he was lame, that he limped.

"I'll call you." Fortune extended his hand. "Have to be away for couple of weeks. Maybe we could do it early next month—maybe Fourth of July weekend."

He began to limp away, but stopped after a few steps and turned back.

"You have four kids, don't you? Two boys, two girls—one from former marriage. Good stuff. Guess it better be next weekend after Fourth. So. Leave the cigar store Indians alone."

As he walked slowly toward Grand Central (since Fortune had left so abruptly, there had been no opportunity to point out that they both commuted to Connecticut and might well take the same train), Walton found himself pondering Abe's last flippant sentence. Or was it flippant? In tone—whatever it meant—it sounded like the tarnished injunction not to take any wooden nickels. But interpreted this way it was simply flip and cheap, and wholly unlike the man with whom he had just spent three-quarters of an hour. And the reference to the children, while it could easily be accepted for its literal value—still, in juxtaposition to "the cigar store Indians" . . .

What *cigar store Indians?* Walton shrugged. He suddenly realized that he had had a painfully full day, and was tired, hungry and depressed. The excitement of the meeting with Abe Fortune had already dropped away; the prospect of the train, the empty house at home, and then the morning train back tomorrow seemed unbearable.

He stopped short on the pavement, a block from where he usually entered the Hotel Roosevelt to pursue the muggy, steamy tunnel to Grand Central. He would stay in town—anywhere, even a hotel; he could buy a shirt in the morning.

But where to eat—alone? He suddenly knew that what he would like most would be to spend an evening with a beautiful, uncontentious and charming woman. But who? He recognized only too well the slender figure with the short black hair who rose in his mind, and for a moment the bleak desolation with which he had been living chilled him through. Then he shook his head resolutely, and turned to retrace his steps, remembering a French restaurant that was cheerfully lighted. He would buy a paper and read it during dinner.

MANUSCRIPT: 2

STUDY OF A FRIEND (*continued*)
BY DUDLEY FOOTE

notes—June 15

Friday evening, over a lot of bourbon at the kitchen table, with a wild thunderstorm going on outside, Walton told me about Julie—about their temporary (?) separation.

I should have seen it coming, of course, that night in April. Yet somehow it shocked me—not so much that it has happened, as the confessional way he told about it. He embarrassed me, both by this tone and by making me realize that, although he takes all the blame, he doesn't really understand why it happened. That is, he says that he isn't worthy of her, and that it took a foolhardy courage for him to marry at all (especially a woman of Julie's calibre) after having made a failure of two other marriages—and at the same time, when I nervously skirted a question or two about why he wasn't worthy of her, he could only answer vaguely something about not being man enough for her, blaming his early life, the domination of his mother and the fact that his father was crippled and couldn't take a full man's part. He even seemed bewildered at the questions, as though he wasn't used to asking himself why anything he stated about himself was true. (Yet, at the same time, he does demand that his friends understand him and love him—or not—for what he is. And the few times I've ventured even close to doing just that his face has darkened, and once he jumped up as though he'd been stung. So he wants you to know him just as he is, but he feels a powerful hope that *that* will turn out to be the best picture he has of himself. 'Tain't easy.)

And the longer he talked, the more sympathy I felt for Julie and the less for him. After the way Julie affected me this spring, to have

176

Walton expose like this his blindness to his own nature just doubled my partisanship. And I'll be damned if I'm going to be guilty over my feeling for Julie.

Anyway, the evening that began as a bout of camaraderie and bourbon ended as a confessional, with me feeling more and more scrounged up inside, and Walton getting more and more expansive—as though the genuine sadness he felt and showed, telling me, became absorbed in the strange exhilaration (relief?) he found, after a while, in the telling. I went to bed worn out.

But not before some strange moments. *Item:* He had been berating himself, whipping himself almost, for his failure to hold Julie, and citing a number of examples of how neurotic he is—common enough things like fear of airplanes, dislike of being alone, fear of heights. I said that my worst kind of neurosis was inertia, that I found it hard to get started on anything, and even harder to do whatever it might be in an orderly way. As example, I told him that Cyn and the kids would be coming on in two weeks, yet I hadn't even made a move to rent a house or an apartment. He jumped up, all excitement, and said, "Take my house. I'm lonely here, and I hate commuting, anyway. With vacations coming up for the staff, I can easily work out the loan of apartments." Plural, yet.

And still, I half believe he could. But I don't want his house; I even—and it's a mean feeling—resent having it pushed at me. It isn't giving: it's insisting; it's swallowing you up. In the end, of course, we came to a compromise, and on Saturday he helped me with good will, though a little stiffly, to hunt for a house. We found a satisfactory one for July and August at a reasonable price, down near the Sound. But he was hurt, and we both were uncomfortable.

Item: He told me about an experience he'd had with his older boy, Peter, just after Julie had told him of her decision to leave. They'd walked together up a nearby hill and looked down on the neighborhood, and Peter had said how much he loved it. Walton got almost tearful over the boy's having such a sense of home, of roots. The two things that struck me were that he was as excited over the feeling of closeness with the boy as though such experiences weren't the regular diet of parents—and at the same time, when it meant so much to him, that he should tell me (or anybody) about it. Yet I can't doubt that his feeling was genuine.

Item: He asked me a lot of questions about Cyn, and my relations with her and the kids. This is not, to me, something to talk about this way. I don't mean anything stuffy, just that it's something to live, not to talk about—except with Cyn herself, and even then not a lot. Yet I knew that his interest was real, again; he wasn't being polite. So I did my best, but I could tell from his expression that he wanted more, and more intimate things. Several times he'd start to ask a further question, and then stop and just say, "I see" or something like that. Finally, though, he said as though he were puzzled, "But don't you and she ever have periods when you've just rubbed each other so wrong that you go around for days not saying anything more than the few words that—that have to be said?"

I took another pull at the whiskey and said no, that we had our fights, all right, but that usually we yelled so loud that before long we had to laugh, and that almost always broke it up.

He looked downright sad and said, "I can't yell."

For a moment I thought how crazy wrong he was, remembering his thundering at the kids, and confronting, in such different ways, those two men at the April party—Jacoby and Varney. I remembered, too, his throwing the coffee cup. But I thought about it a little and realized that wasn't the same thing—realized that he had a very careful control of a strange sort on a lot of his actions, and when he burst out, it wasn't yelling like Cyn and me, but a dam breaking. Then, too, I remembered his feeling for Julie and saw that he'd find it hard to have just an ordinary husband-wife tug-of-war with her.

And anyway he has a very low tolerance for criticism, disagreement, or proof that he is wrong about something. *Item:* When I got as risky as I dared and said that on my April visit I'd come to feel that he robbed Julie of something every real woman needed, a feeling of plain closeness and give-and-take between her and her husband—that he robbed Julie of this by making such a faraway princess of her, he got angry immediately, for the only time all evening, and, controlling his voice with real difficulty, said, "Oh, you've got it all wrong, Dud. We're very close, just the way you're talking about. No, it's something else."

Something else! And he doesn't know, clearly doesn't have the faintest idea *what*. I kept hearing, under the words he spoke, a question, over and over: "How did we get so far apart?"

Item: Once, when I'd been kidding about sex (nothing to do with Walton at all), he looked at me suspiciously and said, "Now see here, Dud. If you're trying to get at the possibility that the trouble between Julie and me is sexual, you're way off base. We're good together that way." It was hopeless; I didn't try to explain.

Item: Twice I started to get up, saying that I was so pooped I had to go to bed. Both times he almost begged me not to, and I sat back down and poured another drink, goddamned weakling that I am. And then his storytelling and his questions and conjectures got almost feverish; he became an entertainer, trying to keep me absorbed. Even a short silence seemed to worry him, and after a slightly longer one he said, "Dud, I know you're sleepy, but I want to tell you something. I haven't told anyone, and won't again after this once."

He didn't seem aware that these were the exact words he'd used when he first told me about Julie, and I didn't remind him. This time, however, he told me about a man named Abe Fortune, who had approached him to ask him if he were interested in the Democratic nomination for the governorship of Connecticut!

For a few minutes I thought he'd gone clean out of his head, that this was a really screwy fantasy. But as he went on, and was quite realistic about his lack of qualifications, I grew sure that there really was a Fortune and that he really had sounded Walton out. And then I felt very proud of him, and the feelings I'd had about him for years came back: I lost track of all the confusions and illusions I'd been listening to and observing, and I saw again the man I've always admired so much. As he talked, I remembered bits of his testimony at the Congressional hearings (I read every scrap of the record), and began to wonder whether he might not make a good governor, at that.

"But I lack political sophistication," he said suddenly, just as though he hadn't been saying throughout that he wasn't really considering the whole thing at all. "I've always really been apolitical."

And there was on his face an expression that was almost fatuous; it was just as though he were seeing himself in the governor's mansion. And when his face fell suddenly, I wondered if he was remembering how it was with Julie and him. On an impulse, I blurted out, "Does Julie know about this?"

He shook his head. "I didn't think it would be fair to tell her, when it's all so remote anyway. I was afraid she'd think I was trying to use it as a way to get her to stay."

And a few minutes before, he had said, "You've got it all wrong. We're very close, just the way you're talking about"!

Item the last:

Finally, I couldn't keep my eyes propped open any longer. As I started upstairs, he stopped me. He put his hand on my shoulder and said, "You're one of the best friends I have, Dud. You're the best friend I have."

So what could I say, short of dropping to one knee and intoning,

"I don't deserve this honor, your majesty. But I accept: go ahead and knight me."

Mean? But I hate people to put me on the spot like that. I couldn't say anything, just sort of patted his hand and stumbled up to bed.

Then I felt really sorry as I undressed and heard him playing some Beethoven sonata on the record player. It was a quiet one, a sad one, and I kept thinking, as I lay there with sleep just pouring over me: the poor lonely old bastard, the loneliest man I know.

SATURDAY NIGHT

The loneliest man I know had himself a ball on Saturday night. We went to a dinner party at the Leonards', friends of Walton and Julie I'd met in April. They're nice people. Andrew Leonard is a successful novelist, tall, bald, with a beaked nose that lends him an extra air of distinction, somehow. He is something of a bibliophile, a connoisseur of music and wines, food and clothes. Yet, with all this sophistication, he's genuine and solid, stopping short of both the intellectual snob and the dandy.

His wife, Caroline, I like particularly. She's tall, also, and big-boned—has a sort of sportswoman look, and, I believe, rides and plays tennis very well. She's from the Middle West, and as a matter of fact looks as though she belongs on a ranch. Very plain, outspoken and direct—a real person.

When Walton told me they'd asked us to dinner, I was pleased, for I'd thought before that I'd like to know them better. But shortly after we arrived, I realized that I wasn't going to have much chance to, for there must have been between thirty and forty people there. Celebrities—an actress and her husband, a musical comedy librettist, a moving picture director, two or three well-known writers, a leading woman painter, and assorted nabobs and executives. For someone with my background, this is rich fare (and not necessarily digestible); Walton seems to have come to feel very much at home with them.

Japanese lanterns on the lawn; music on what must be a very expensive record player, booming and blaring through tremendous speakers; caterers and bartenders; and colorful summer dresses on the most attractive crowd of women I've seen together in a long time. Dancing, laughter, champagne and excellent liquor: the works.

I ran into the wife half of a pleasant couple I'd met at the Herricks'—a Mrs. Reese, blonde, plump, sensible—and we chatted comfortably on a bench under a big maple, watching the moon come up behind the terrace on which a few couples were already dancing. What with waiters offering trays of drinks every few minutes, I felt as though I were on a Mediterranean cruise.

A man whose name I didn't catch joined us and began to monopolize Mrs. Reese. This gave me just the chance I wanted: to sit and watch. If somebody would subsidize me, I could spend my life watching—and listening: scenes like this, children at play, the whole gamut from committee meetings to a crowd at a beach. I can sit for hours watching other people being active: at a bowling alley, a fairground, a picnic, a political rally.

But before long at the Leonards' that night, I found that I was concentrating on Walton again. He was dancing or drinking with one pretty woman after another, and I had to revise, for this one night anyway, my previous discourse on Walton and Women. I said before that all unhappy women seemed to seek him out. But these weren't unhappy women, by a long shot. Not that night. And I don't think I've ever heard Walton laugh so much. He and all of them were having a good gay time, and I could see why, in this mood, he is so attractive to women. He gives off sparks. And incidentally, he dances well, too. This surprised me, for I have thought of him as heavy on his feet.

Once, he spotted me watching, and grinned and waved. But most of the time he was fully taken up with whichever partner; in fact, dancing, he seemed to draw her into him, surround her, almost absorb her. Sounds absurd, but it's hard to describe. Walton's dancing, at least that night, was not social dancing at all, but had more kinship to ritual and ceremony.

There you are. I don't see how the really good writers are able, as they are, to describe something like this. "Ritual and ceremony!" I don't mean primitive or pagan rites, and I don't mean using dancing for sexual titillation. But this tall cranelike man, both in the motion he created and in the way he held the women, was doing something quite different from the other men who were dancing. A phrase just hit me: he was showing these women the dark side of the moon.

Sense? No, but later, in the unlaced part of the evening, I overheard one woman tell another, "I'd rather dance with Walton Herrick than go to bed with most men." I took a good squint at her and could tell that she was expressing in her way what I've just tried to in mine. (Incidentally, I would have been glad to oblige her either dancing or the other way, but after how she looked while speaking about Walton I knew this was out of my class.)

And then, just before dinner, Gail Arbuthnot arrived, and for the rest of the party Walton never left her. That first time, I had thought her sassy and cute, very attractive; but now she was beautiful—with a heavy tan, those green eyes and red hair, and wearing a chartreuse-colored dress that looked insubstantial enough to be blown away. Every man there—me among them—just held his breath whenever he looked at her, but there was nobody there for her but Walton. After dinner, they danced and danced; she just kind of melted into him, and with her eyes closed and a rapt look on her face she was really gone, over on that other side of the moon for keeps.

She had no time for me this evening, and my nose was really out of joint. Oh, she was sweet and pleasant enough, but I'm sure equally so to everyone else there—neither more nor less. She was alone with Walton on the moon.

And when the party got small (somewhere around one o'clock, there were only a dozen of us left) they did some really fancy stuff, leaving each other, swinging and turning with only their hands touching, returning, tap dancing—I've never been able to distinguish the different kinds of jazz and the different styles of dancing that go with them. But if you've ever seen Ray Bolger, that gives you an idea of Walton at this point. Like some big grasshopper, a sort of daddy-long-legs whose dancing had a dark quality despite the humor in it, and although energetic, somehow gave off more of passion than joy. And he was surprisingly good—loose-jointed, agile, yet in his own peculiar angular way graceful too. But intense, feverish: a dancing dervish. And little Gail was—well, just edible.

About this time, I was getting tired, and I wandered off to a corner of the living room and sat down. Before long Caroline Leonard came in and joined me.

"I've never seen Walton like this," she said without any preamble. "You've known him a long time. Have *you*?"

I shook my head. "I don't think I even knew that he liked dancing. Until I visited him and Julie in April, I hadn't seen him for a number of years."

"Julie is lovely." She gave me a candid look of inquiry.

I mumbled a yes, feeling uncomfortable. Did she expect me to act as Walton's guardian?

"So is Gail," she said, "and she and Julie are close old friends."

I nodded, and punched out my cigarette.

"So are Walton and I," I said irritably and stood up. "I guess I'll see if I can persuade him that it's time to go home."

I said it, it seemed to me then, almost rudely, and my irritation mounted, for I'd liked this woman and hadn't wanted an exchange like this. I found that I was angry now with him, and blaming him.

But I didn't have to hunt him out; he was looking for me.

"Dud, I know you're tired. Take the car and go on home——" he extended the key——"Gail will bring me later."

His face was flushed, his eyes glittering, and he had his arm around Gail, holding her tightly. She was watching him with that openly adoring look that women in love wear—a look that's always embarrassed me, even the few times it's been directed at me. It's both so naked and so frighteningly worshipful: it accepts and yet demands the impossible—everything.

"O.K.," I said shortly. It was beyond me. On my way to find my host and hostess and, if possible, make amends to her, I looked back and there, in the middle of the terrace, in plain view of everyone, were Walton and Gail in a clinch.

"I hope he's really drunk," I muttered to myself.

What did I mean? I suppose only that, if he was, then what he was doing was a little more excusable, and he would be genuinely sorry the next day.

But he wasn't—visibly sorry, I mean. I didn't hear him come in, but it must have been very late: he didn't get up on Sunday till noon, and we didn't have much to say to each other. He was cordial—never more so—and urged me to stay over Sunday night and go in with him Monday morning, but I pleaded work and took the two-thirty train in the afternoon.

This weekend upset me. I had to readjust my sights too rapidly and often, and I find I'm resenting what Walton did and—foolishly, perhaps—even what he is, or seems to be. He never asked me to make a hero of him, and I have no business giving him moral lessons. Nor do I blame him for being bewitched by Gail; probably part of my soreness is that she had no time for me. Still, I couldn't have done what Walton did; I'm no Christer, but I couldn't do that to Cyn. And after Friday night's talk, and considering the fact that Gail is Julie's close friend (is she?), I just don't get him at all.

And it bothers me the more because I owe him the job, and am working at the same place he is. I don't like to feel a constraint of the sort this makes for, and I'll be glad when my family's here, and I'll have a good reason for not stagging around with Walton. Maybe it was a mistake, though, to take a house in Northport. We can't avoid him all the time.

Nor, it comes to me suddenly, do I want to. I'm still fond of him, and I'm still proud to be his friend. But I keep hurting for Julie.

The Unobserved Observer

Eye believe that in all fairness to Walton Eye should set down a few notes. Eye see that as he presents himself he tends so to magnify his faults as to make himself out worse than he is. So, in reverse, a number of others, presenting their depositions to Judgment Court, exaggerate and even distort his good qualities.

Eye am interested in a fair presentation. Indeed, how could it be otherwise? We who have withdrawn from the battle of life have a strong distaste for partisanship. Life is, as much as any other single state, Eye suppose, commitment. And this means taking sides, making decisions, suffering from inner conflicts—all that dreadful churning and heaving! Pain and the fever of lust and competition and, worst of all, grief and hurt: Eye can't stand them.

But now to introduce Eyeself. (Eye am a Private I, but this is a public record.) Eye am that extension of Walton that withdraws and observes his actions, and not to be confused with the writer of this record. Walton functions in his own fashion, driven here and there by the fury of his compulsions and the passivity of his will—while his essential self, as Eye conceive it, sits here, removed, observing, with Eyeself. (You, too, have experienced something of the sort?)

Eye observe, but not altogether without sympathy. Eye observe that Walton is choleric; intolerant and intemperate; ambitious but disinclined to admit it; selfish, and, in many respects, infantile. But Eye have also observed that he is tenacious; on occasion genuinely kind and thoughtful; capable of love, but not of sustaining it with constancy for very long; limitedly honest, more often honorable; and in some ways courageous. Finally, he is wickedly driven by elements he does not understand. Indeed, there are times when Eye even endure a little suffering Eyeself, through the Eyedentification Eye am doomed to have with him, over the frenzy that possesses him at such times, which Eye *know will bring him so much contrition the next day. But Eye must remain objective; such weakness might quite destroy Eyeself.*

In particular, Eye cannot bear the physical pains with which he is racked when enduring conflict. Great constricting bands confine his chest, or a snakelike rope, pulling tighter and tighter, squeezes his waist, or giant coils clamp his biceps and calf muscles like manacles. Laocoön. Eye have felt only the beginnings of these pains; then Eye flee.

And since Eye have learned to avoid the madness of feeling (Eye now speak metaphorically, for Eye am, of course, completely freed of religious superstition), at the first indication of some outburst of passion, Eye make the Sign of the Cross, double, and, averting my little-eyes, absorb myself in the contemplation of any inanimate object. This is the only piety Eye practice: to rejoice rationally in the tranquillity of the inanimate. To be where nothing stirs, breathes, longs, grieves: ah, then, then, Eye am on the heights.

Hence Eye can only surmise those experiences of Walton's involving emotion; Eye have observed only the first flickering flames of those sulphurous crackling fires that from time to time engulf him. Eye say this with confidence; sometimes Eye share these experiences with him in retrospect. Even then, there are times when Eye withdraw from the refracted heat. For example, Eye am not sure whether he and that fiery-headed woman, Abigail, consummated their pain (Eye can call it nothing else) the evening they were together. When he remembers her and that evening, Eye retire. Consummate—consume.

But if Eye find his lusts distasteful, what shall Eye say of his tenderer longings—for Julie and his children? Nothing. Nothing—for here the anguish, if more subtle, is also more piercing.

Eye have observed much more than what Eye have just set down, but space is space and time is time: perhaps you and Eye will meet again. At any rate, Eye wished to convey the speculation that Walton may be far from being all bad, and that Eye hope, to the extent that Eye experience that ambiguous emotion, that things will be better for him. It doesn't seem likely. Indeed, it seems the more unlikely as Eye remember that some years ago there was not this cleavage between Walton and Eyeself. In those days, there was only an occasional little pang of feeling, a bubble that rose to our lips (genuine togetherness), a twinge of pain from gas, alas. There was a we, and as free from the torment of emotion as though anesthetized. (I-less in Gaza, at the mill with slaves.) To be sure, that rude fellow who inhabits the cellarage from time to time railed and pounded on the locked door, but we could pretend we did not hear, invoke some nobler and gentler emotion as a compromise. Those were the antebellum days: the days, as Eye put it—rather neatly, Eye think—before the War Between the States of Being.

To some of you, Eye may seem cold-blooded, even apathetic and cynical. But this is not really true. The only aspiration Eye have is to achieve the tranquillity of the gods whom Lucretius describes in DE RERUM NATURA, *but it is not an easy realization—particularly since Eye am Eyeself an aspect of Walton. A revolting condition, really—like being one of a set of Siamese quintuplets. But enough—Eye deal with it as best Eye can, through Passive Acceptance, a cousin to Passive Resistance. Eye shall train Eyeself in this course as best Eye can, in rational anticipation that, little by little, Eye shall find peace.*

Read on, then. Eye shall be with you, or some of you, or part of some of you. Perhaps you too have an Eye, and Eye shall meet it.

DEPOSITION: 3

A confidential letter, dated June 16, 1953, from Philip Henderson Gates to Huntingdon Haldane, Partner, Curtis Parmalee and Company, New York, New York; trustee of the Schuyler Foundation, and chairman of its Executive Committee—presently vacationing in Canada . . .

DEAR HUNTINGDON,

I've been longer than I expected to be in the preparation of this letter. I think you'll understand why I've put extraordinary care into its drafting, for although you referred to "a simple, informal letter with no copies," the present entanglement and its importance to the rest of Herrick's career makes the task one of major importance. Once in the past the shoe was on the other foot: it was (or seemed to be) my future that was at stake. At that point he finally withdrew his support of my plan, and that hurt. Yet I have always been persuaded that he pursued the whole matter with complete fairness and in accordance with his own deepest convictions. Even if I am wrong about this—and I do not believe I am—you can see why I feel so weighted by a heavy moral obligation as I set down for you my account—the account that you are to study at leisure in hope of helping to bring the rest of our colleagues to a just conclusion.

You're fully acquainted with the present situation and the recent past; so I'll begin with Herrick's arrival at the Foundation and cover the intervening years. I first met him a short time before he came to the Foundation in 1943—in fact, I was instrumental in bringing him here. It is a commonplace, now, for people to remark upon Walton's considerable talents. It has always been a source of pride to me that I recognized the range and quality of his gifts at a time when he was working in a field that gave play to only a part of them.

This is the key to my first strong impression of Walton. He had a direct way of dealing, a vigor of attack, a kind of authority vested in no other power than that of himself—and these, I think, are the characteristics that enable men to utilize the abilities latent in them.

He came for a series of conversations with me, looking toward a grant-in-aid for a new humanities program at Graham Institute in Cleveland, where he was then teaching. I enjoyed these encounters and looked forward to them, and a warm personal response sprang up quickly in each of us. It seemed to me that this man had the kinds of perception that shouldn't bring him before the Foundation as a pleader but should place him there as a creator of policy at a high level—not all to be realized in one jump, naturally.

I introduced him to Ernest Ingersoll, then president of the Foundation, as you know. He liked Herrick and associated him with my own humanities department. It must have been a nervous decision for Herrick to make, but at the same time I think it must also have been like first breathing the air on the uplands where at last you can see the sweep of the land ahead. He had a sure instinct for the clarifying and protection of a position. Mr. Ingersoll told me later that Herrick had stipulated that he wanted to be ultimately answerable to the president directly—not to me—and he must have satisfied Mr. Ingersoll completely, for this was accomplished with the creation of a new post of special adviser, which had Herrick technically attached to my department, technically under me, but in reality holding what amounted to a freelance roaming position (he traveled a great deal) and reporting his findings officially to Mr. Ingersoll.

I think you must realize that in setting up this arrangement Mr. Ingersoll, without, I am confident, intending to do so, made my position very difficult. I am not afraid of being misunderstood in making this criticism, for I know that you are fully aware of my deep loyalty to our president emeritus. And indeed he consulted me before making the final appointment and assured me that if I disapproved it would not be made. But he explained that he wanted me to be unencumbered in my administrative work and to have more time in which to conceive and ponder large self-liquidating projects, while Herrick's concern would be almost exclusively with a study of the new humanities programs springing up all over the country—closely in line with Herrick's already established interests and also a subject of special congeniality to Mr. Ingersoll.

I felt that I must acquiesce—though not without misgivings. Mr. Ingersoll's exposition was so logical, and his nature is so candid, that I felt to refuse would be intolerably mean-spirited. I could see no alternative to trusting these two men not to utilize this unorthodox arrangement to undermine my own position.

To a large extent, the rest is history familiar to you. The simple fact that I hold today the post then occupied by Mr. Ingersoll is evidence enough that I was not mistaken. But under the circumstances, in justice to my friend Walton Herrick, I should state explicitly that his attitude in this situation was exemplary. Whatever his reason for making the original stipulation that he be directly responsible to the president, to the best of my knowledge he never took the slightest unethical advantage of it.

As a colleague he was able and generous in spirit. Officially without commitment to me, he nevertheless kept me fully abreast of his activities and, with what I think could not have been a wholly unpremeditated courtesy, always addressed me, in the many informal and even casual talks we had, as "Chief." This, perhaps, is an excellent way of giving you the flavor of this man, whom, you tell me, you know only very slightly. His physical presence and his manner convey a sense of dignity and of integrity. Hence, superficially, there is something incongruous in his using such an expression as "Chief." It should, I think, seem brassy, off-tone, coming from him. Yet it doesn't, and also doesn't convey any sense of a false heartiness, of the intellectual's inverted snobbishness, sometimes leading him to use slang and even ungrammatical constructions in order to seem a "regular fellow." Does all this mean anything to you?

At any rate, those few years in which we worked closely were among my happiest at the Foundation. And it must be said—although I learned about this only some eighteen months after Herrick joined us—that the larger measure of the credit for this highly amicable condition should be Herrick's. For, as I discovered during his second year at the Foundation, things were very difficult for him in his personal life during this period. In retrospect, I marvel that he was able to carry his heavy burden and at the same time function in work and be the warm and rewarding companion that he was. For he had a bedridden sister and an aged mother (who was possibly as much an emotional burden as anything else), both of whom were dependent upon him. There were seemingly endless crises of moving them here and there and arranging for their care. It was not until after their deaths, ironically, that he approached his greatest earning capacities.

Also, in these early days he had just been involved in divorce and was soon to be remarried. But this was a source of his strength, in part. His new wife, whom I met soon after all these things had become known to me—in 1944, shortly after the wedding—was just right for him. Her deep capacity for relaxation moderated his tensions, prevented his drive from becoming frenzy. In the years since, he has mastered the art of pacing himself splendidly. . . .

I pause here, for I find the next period in our relationship the most difficult to set down. But I have assured you that I would hold back nothing. I am persuaded that to follow this course is in Herrick's best interests as well as my own—and especially, of course, in those of the Foundation. And I am deeply cognizant of the value a full knowledge of the relevant past will have for you, and through you, for the Board as a whole.

At any rate, in the last two years of Mr. Ingersoll's administration, Herrick's and my official relation changed. The department was, in effect, for these two years split in two, Herrick heading the new division solely concerned with academic grants, and I remaining in charge of the nominally and, in some respects (notably financial), larger non-academic division. This reorganization was, frankly, a blow to me—yet in all honesty, as you well know, it led eventually to a shift in emphases and to my succession to the presidency.

At any rate, except for occasional consultations involving programs that in some way overlapped, Herrick's and my working association was limited to staff policy meetings—to shared deliberation, to discussion, to affairs, if you will, of negotiation, in our special sense.

It was at one such meeting that we had our first unhappy encounter —our first real tension and serious misunderstanding. I was launching a project in which I felt deeply involved—you may remember the Clark matter; it was too complicated to describe in detail here. But I'd hung everything I had on it at the time, whatever its merits. In the context of that time, there was some feeling of desperation about it, to be truthful.

Walton had helped me generously in the development of the project. It was our first collaboration in a long time. He believed in it, and he wanted it to go through for me as well. I don't know what went on in his mind—now it doesn't matter. But he sat on the body that decided its fate—and it died there.

Understand me—I know he didn't kill it. But he abstained on the final vote. I thought then that he was involved in a play of forces, pressures and counter-interests in which he found it impossible to act to stop the project from dying. It was a crisis for me. I was hurt. I felt some bitterness, even toward him. At the same time I knew that he had been the only advocate I had. Probably the matter had been painful to him. I haven't the ability or the desire to probe the thing any further.

Both of us did manage to put it all aside without irrevocable recrimination, once the pressure was off.

But, Huntingdon, of course I am at this point giving myself away. I have simply refused, I suppose, to probe in order to cleanse—refused because I was afraid of what I would find. I write this because I have just reread (in first draft from my secretary) the preceding paragraph and I find it lame—so I append this admission.

There followed Mr. Ingersoll's retirement, my ascension to the presidency, and my appointment of Walton to the directorship of the once more unified humanities department. No, I am proud to say that our one rift didn't make me hesitate a moment in that appointment—nor have I ever felt that it was an administrative mistake. One more given to self-probing than I (in the sense of motivation, etc.) might find that I had unconsciously feared that Walton would be promoted over me to the presidency, and in my relief made this gesture. But if it is true, I was not aware of it at the time.

The rest you know well. I have unburdened myself to you fully (how often I've given thanks for your presence on the Board) about my deep pride and admiration for Walton's achievement in the drafting, writing and presenting of our report to the Congressional Committee— and especially for his performance under Committee fire. I have developed fully for you my doubts about the wisdom of my having relinquished this responsibility to him, and my conviction that this has weakened my position with the Board. And so we come to the present dilemma: ironic that this man who sometimes seems to me my best friend and sometimes my nemesis should always be in a focal position at the crises of my life, my career.

That was ungenerous: "sometimes my nemesis." But I shall let it stand in the context of our complete mutual trust.

So much for the main points of our past relationship. You have also pointed out to me that some of our colleagues, in view of the nature of the present impasse, will be interested in Walton's position on matters of religion. Here—in *their* terms—I cannot be very reassuring. In *my* terms, and in yours too, I am sure, his attitude is an honorable one worthy of the respect of any open mind. For I shall call him a naturalistic humanist of the clearest integrity.

As a matter of fact, nothing in our relationship has been more interesting than our relative psycho-religious (if you will excuse the repellent term) graphs. When we first met we were almost indistinguishable in a liberal-humanistic outlook. Yet our patterns had been different. I'd been through an early Village bohemianism and was primed for conservatism. Walton had led a much more subdued earlier life and was just breaking fully free. We used to joke about it.

Then I veered into a new course—a "return to religion" that has carried me into a committed and active Anglicanism of pronounced Catholic coloration. Walton, meanwhile, became deeply interested in psychoanalysis. Frankly, I have no idea whether or not he was actually being psychoanalyzed, but I doubt it. I remember a conversation in which we were skirting around the religious question, and when it came to a matter of affirming a broadly humane ethic, Walton said with an intensity near anger, "I'll have mine without God, thank you." I know that Walton's childhood was dominated by the circumstance of having clergymen as father and grandfather, within (I would guess) a rather narrow theology—though I have no actual knowledge about it. Certainly, though, the family environment must have partly conditioned his religious responses. Freedom of mind and spirit, for him, required freedom from religion as he had experienced it.

Circumstances, in a few years, were to find Walton taking his children to Sunday school, and a member of my family gratefully turning to the resources of psychoanalysis. We hadn't switched—rather, in a sense, we had synthesized. Walton laughed, one day, and said to me, "We started off in different directions, then came around and met in the middle." If that isn't absolutely true, there is still truth in it, and in these processes Walton has both matured and mellowed.

The hardest thing for a man to describe is a relationship. The one I have had with Walton has a special place in my experience. I've had many rich relationships, some particularly related either to certain periods or to aspects of my life. The notable thing about the relationship to Walton is that it has been carried on and enriched through a variety of working relationships, reorientations of thought and spirit, and even strains. Both of us have grown in it. Each of us, I think, has contributed substantially to the other. Ours has not been the bond of two people who are "so alike," but of two people markedly different, with no desire to become alike, but with a capacity for creative interaction upon each other.

I've opened my heart, Hunt—I hope to some good end. You know how much I rely on you toward the just settlement of this vexing problem. Please ask me anything else you wish to.

> Faithfully yours,
> (Phil)
> PHILIP HENDERSON GATES
> President

P.S. [handwritten] I have just realized that I have made no direct references to the history of Herrick's political affiliations and convictions. That I could forget to do so, after your specific request for such information, seems to me persuasive evidence that I am not really worried about this aspect of the problem. Actually, I know very little on the subject, beyond the certainty that his position has consistently been left of center—but I should not say so far left as to be considered dangerous by anyone but an extreme reactionary. I draw this conclusion from our many informal talks; and his handsome performance at the Congressional hearings—fearless but clearly independent-democratic in outlook —seems to me to confirm my conviction. Enough.

P.P.S. [handwritten] I had another talk with Herrick last week. I can't move him, but he's agreed very pleasantly to dine with you and me when you get back. Also had talk with young Dennis Byrnes (you remember him—a real comer) who has also tried and failed.

June 17–21

"IF THE rest of the summer is as hot as this, by Labor Day we'll all be drunkards." Dennis Byrnes, more relaxed than usual, spun his infectious smile around the table.

Like a top, Walton thought sourly. Like a bright, shiny new top.

Dudley Foote grinned comfortably and raised his martini.

"To my escape," he proposed. "In two weeks my family will be here, and I'll be commuting. No drunkenness."

Dennis surveyed him slyly.

"They have bar cars on those trains to Connecticut," he remarked. "And they're air-conditioned too."

Dudley shook his head.

"No temptation," he replied shortly. "Go home to your kids drunk?"

Evelyn Onslow fairly beamed at him.

"Good for you," she said, and then quickly ducked her head, as though overcome by her boldness.

Walton, morosely stirring his highball, broke through his gloom only long enough to smile at her.

For Evelyn, who was his secretary, he would always make the extra effort. There were few other people for whom he would, he thought now, but this shy, quiet, sensitive and well-bred Jewish girl was so utterly undemanding, at once so gentle and so self-respecting, that she soothed him as almost no one else—almost? as no one else could. Yet their acquaintance had been entirely limited to their office relationship, and even there was one of warm respect, of a friendship without intimacy.

"You're very silent, Mr. Herrick." Peggy Thomas, the duchess at the switchboard, as Dud Foote called her, challenged him both with words and eyes.

Walton looked at her speculatively, determined not to show his irritation. On the job she was marvelously efficient, conscientious to the point of shrill insistence. And there was, Walton thought, the same thinness and shrillness to her personality as in her body and her voice. But the eyes, dark, burned with some inner urgency that commanded at once curiosity and caution. And now drinking had intensified their heat, lent them some further dimension—a mocking malice?

"The heat got me down," Walton said at last, rather flatly.

Her eyes continued to challenge him boldly. Was it a female challenge? If so, it was mixed in some curious way with a satisfaction in insisting on pushing into the open the change of status involved in "having cocktails with the boss." Why was he always getting himself into such situations? For it was he who had suggested prolonging the air-conditioned day by leaving the office only to stop off together at the Swazey Bar.

It was as though she were reading his mind. "The heat?" She spoke with a slight suggestion of scorn. "Your office has the best air-conditioning unit in the place."

By now the others were aware that this was more than a desultory conversation about the weather. The other two men looked at her curiously, but it was Evelyn who spoke.

"You're tired," she said softly to Walton. "You never stop working. I wish you'd take at least a couple of weeks off and join your family at the Vineyard."

It seemed to Walton now that Dennis and Peggy exchanged a peculiar look. But it's only because I feel so vulnerable, he told himself.

Dudley cleared his throat.

"I thought somebody else was joining us," he said. "I've finished my second drink, and if I have another I'll start flying."

"Sonia," said Evelyn.

"Who?"

"Sonia Wilenski. You must have met her. She's Mr. Gates' secretary, and she's lovely."

Peggy thumped her glass on the table.

"I'll have another. What did Mr. Gates say when you asked him to come along, Mr. Herrick?"

Walton waved to the waiter and suddenly recognized him as the very man who had, only ten days before, been so confused by Abe Fortune's request for a pink gin. "Another round," he said. "That's a whiskey sour, two martinis, and a sherry. No—" he broke off at Evelyn's vigorous shake of her head. Her second glass of sherry was still full—"no sherry, but another bourbon and water for me." He turned back, with a sudden feeling of briskness, to Peggy. "P.H.? I didn't really think he could come. He's due home for dinner."

She lifted her eyebrows.

"But seriously, he wouldn't have come anyway, would he? Not many big shots are as democratic as Mr. Herrick."

Her tone was ambiguous, but Walton caught the way in which the "Mister" was being emphasized more each time she spoke it. He started to answer, a little hotly, but Dennis had broken in.

"You have him all wrong, Peggy. P.H. is no stuffed shirt. He's dignified, all right, but he's also very warm and friendly and informal."

Walton took a mean passing satisfaction in the withering look Peggy gave Dennis, but he had himself in control now and he spoke directly to her.

"What's eating you, Peggy? Why are you needling me and P.H.?"

He was aware of Dud Foote watching him intently, but he kept his own scrutiny on Peggy.

She flushed and raised her thin eyebrows again.

"I didn't know I was needling anybody," she said, with a shriller nasality than before. "I'm speaking plainly, that's all. Rank doesn't hold outside the office, does it?"

Evelyn spoke up earnestly.

"I'm never uncomfortably conscious of it in the office, even," she said. "I think it's a wonderfully nice group of people."

Dennis nodded. "I do too. Exceptional. Cheer up, Peggy. You'll feel better tomorrow."

Whatever had been smoldering in her flared up now. Walton knew only that its quality conveyed some inflammation that must find relief through opening up and draining.

"Not because of you, Buster. Not because of Mama's little boy scout." And even more pungently, "You make me sick."

The silence was swollen with embarrassment. Then Walton, feeling somehow relieved of his own constraint, broke it briskly.

"Here are the drinks. Let's forget the whole thing and start over again. I guess you were right all the time, Peggy: it wasn't the heat that was my trouble. I was feeling some kind of mid-week depression, but I'm coming out of it—and thanks to you."

Although she did not return his smile, she looked mollified. As she sipped her drink, however, Walton noticed that her hand was trembling slightly. But it was Dennis who looked red and angry now, and it was to Dennis that Dudley Foote addressed his rather drawling remark.

"Byrnes," he said, "today I came across that report you wrote last month on the proposal for language training fellowships. That's a mighty good job—helped me no end."

Dennis's face cleared. He shook his head in his familiar deprecatory way, spread out his big freckled hands.

"There's a lot I didn't get in there. There wasn't time to do the thing properly. But I'm glad you found it useful."

Walton packed his pipe, feeling a sudden warmth for Dudley—for this characteristic gesture from the quiet, plain, sandy-haired man who was his friend.

"Here's Sonia," said Evelyn.

As Sonia Wilenski dropped into the empty chair beside Walton, he finally acknowledged to himself why he had suggested this get-together after hours, counting on Evelyn to bring her friend Sonia into the group. And now, while the others were greeting her, ordering her a drink, finding out what piece of work had kept her so late, he simply smiled at her once, and returned to brooding over his drink.

For she had troubled him since she became P.H.'s secretary three months before, constantly since that moment on the stairway shelter. They had exchanged only a few words in P.H.'s office, yet he never saw her, even at a distance, without a quickening of excitement. He was haunted by that aura about her that drew him as exigently as though it were the fragrance of a blossom to which, poor instinctive bumblebee, he was inexorably impelled.

Never since that brief moment ten days ago could he break through the covey of platitudes that swarmed in his mind when he thought of her: "golden" . . . "tawny" . . . "voluptuous" . . . "catlike." Suggestive, perhaps, of her presence, yet painfully inadequate, these words, use-worn and bruised as they had become. Even the ones denoting color would be misleading, for her soft silky hair, cut short and tousled in the fashion of the popular Italian actresses of the day, was not really golden, but the color of wheat. Yet to Walton, there seemed to be golden and tawny lights playing over her.

He had been resolutely pushing her image out of his mind only last week when he remembered (how he made the association he did not know) Hans Castorp's tremulous excitement over Clavdia Chauchat. Despite his resolution, that night he reread the scene in *The Magic Mountain* in which Hans sees Behrens' portrait of Clavdia, and encourages the only too willing Hofrat to elaborate his macabre discourse on anatomy—especially on woman's anatomy, and most especially on Frau Chauchat's.

That peculiar hypnotic fascination Clavdia Chauchat had for Hans

Castorp, "life's delicate child," Sonia Wilenski had for Walton. He took a forlorn comfort in the identification, as though it gave him some little hold on this lovely creature—with whom, God knows, he did not want to get into his familiar difficulties, the round of susceptibility, infatuation, gratification and disillusionment he had given up (forever, he had sworn to himself) when he married Julie. And yet he couldn't forget Sonia, must have some relation to her, even if one realized only in his fantasies. Half aware that he was stoking the fire he meant to extinguish, he extended his "literary" romance by eventually remembering Anita in D. H. Lawrence's story "Once," as another of these tawny women whose x-ray—a twentieth-century daguerreotype—he would gladly carry in his pocket, as poor Hans had carried Frau Chauchat's.

And now—now, on the tail of that desperately near betrayal with Gail—what was he doing? Why had he suddenly succumbed to what he had held out against for these months, and right after the difficult victory over his temptation with Gail? His blood was heated, he thought almost senselessly, and Julie hadn't written him a line. Savagely he wrenched from his mind that lame, easy excuse and, aware that the others seemed to be waiting for some word from him, looked up—instinctively at Sonia.

"I'm sorry," he said. "This seems to be my day for drifting off."

She smiled and lifted her shoulders in a faint shrug. That gesture: somewhere, sometime, someone . . .

"I said," she repeated, with what seemed to him a lazy assurance, "that I was glad to see you in repose."

Walton grinned.

"I wasn't in repose. I was thinking like fury."

"About what?" Sipping her drink, she looked at him over the rim of the glass.

He hesitated. His face burned.

"Oh, literary abstractions."

Evelyn was interested.

"Oh, tell us. What?"

"*The Magic Mountain.* Something about Sonia's—may I call you Sonia?—arrival reminded me of *The Magic Mountain.*"

She cocked her head back to look up at him.

"I'm not flattered. Isn't it about a tuberculosis sanatorium?"

Dennis broke in, and Walton realized that he had been leaning forward farther and farther over the table during this exchange. "Let's see. Frau Chauchat, Walton?" His eyes were bright.

Walton was pleased at his own composure.

"Yes, as a matter of fact. And Hans Castorp. And the Hofrat. But I'm not the casting director."

Peggy broke her long silence.

"Don't let's get intellectual. I've learned a new game. One person gives another the names of three people. With one of them this person has to go to bed, with another around the world, and with the third, play croquet. I'll give Evelyn the first three."

Dennis broke in. His fair, freckled skin was flushed; it was obvious that he was feeling his drinks.

"It would be embarrassing," he said, "if one of the three was one sex and the other two the other."

Peggy uttered a contemptuous snort.

"It wouldn't have to be," she said, "if only one was your sex; then you could play croquet with him. If you wanted to." Dennis gave her a sharp look, but she ignored him. "Now, Evelyn. President Eisenhower, Adlai Stevenson and Richard Nixon."

Evelyn made a face.

"I don't want to do *anything* with Nixon," she said. "I don't like him. I'd go around the world with Stevenson and play croquet with Eisenhower. In fact, I don't want to go to bed with any of them."

"But you have to," Peggy insisted in a petulant, almost childish tone. "It's the rule of the game."

"All right." Evelyn laughed. "Then I'd go to bed with Nixon. But I'd wear a suit of armor and kick him in the shins."

"Let's play it *right,*" Peggy said loudly. Her eyes had once more taken on that brilliant brightness, and again Walton wondered about the pain, the *sore* in her. "Now, Sonia. Your three are Mr. Gates, Mr. Herrick and Mr. Foote." She leaned forward with no attempt to disguise her elation.

"No," said Dudley. "I protest. All my life I've been put in situations like this and been told somebody wanted to play croquet with me. I'm sick and tired of playing croquet." He made a gesture of mock horror.

When the laughter had dwindled, Sonia looked directly at him, smiling.

"Very well," she said in her lazy voice. "I'll go to bed with Mr. Foote. This is the beginning of a new era. And I'll go around the world with Mr. Gates, since I guess he has the most money. And—" she paused, looked at Walton and added, very deliberately—"I'll play croquet with Mr. Herrick. Are you good at it?"

The fleeting red moment of anger and hurt was gone, for her intonation in the words "Are you good at it?" seemed to Walton unmistakable. Her wit pleased him and the implications of a reversal of meanings excited him.

"I'm very good," he said.

"Hey, wait a minute," Dudley demanded. "I'm not sure that I'm not getting the short end of the stick after all. What sort of croquet do you play?"

She looked him straight in the eye.

"American rules," she said gravely. "Long mallet and two balls."

Dudley persisted.

"Wickets?"

"Narrow wickets."

"Stakes?"

"The biggest stake in the world."

Walton was enchanted. He let out a roar of laughter that caused the people at neighboring tables to stare in surprise. But Dennis, it was evident, was not pleased. Walton had never seen him so suddenly and, above all, so openly angry.

"I've got to go," he announced abruptly. "Here's my share." He handed some bills to Walton. "You going my way, Peggy?"

She looked startled and indecisive. For a moment she eyed him suspiciously. Then she said, "Oh, all right. Nobody's playing it right, anyway."

They left with such ungracious, curt "good nights" that the other four were silent for a moment. Then Dudley grimaced.

"That's a funny pair."

Walton looked thoughtfully after the departing couple.

"I never thought of them as a pair before," he said.

Evelyn was standing.

"It was lovely," she said, "but Mother's expecting me. I'll call you later, Sonia. Good night, Mr. Herrick, Mr. Foote."

She slipped away.

"Boy," said Dudley, "did we kill it fast. And just when I'm getting to feel good. I'm a libertine and a drunkard at heart, Miss Wilenski, but I had so much Methodist upbringing that it takes three martinis for me to get back down to good old stripped heart. And now I'm there, for the first time since I've been in New York. Are you two going to desert me too?"

Walton stood up.

"No, we're not," he said authoritatively. "Change seats, Sonia, so that we can have you between us."

She obeyed. . . .

Dudley Foote was uproariously funny. Through another round of drinks, through dinner in the adjacent dining room, and well on toward midnight, he kept the others laughing constantly. At the climax of one of his stories of academic life, the account of a hoax he had played on one of his stuffier colleagues, by wearing a beard and French clothes, and posing as a distinguished scholar from the University of Grenoble, Walton went into a choking spasm that had Dudley and a waiter pounding his back, and Sonia gazing at him with eyes big with anxiety (or was it curiosity?), her hand pressed to her throat. He was still gasping and sputtering when Dudley finally said, "I'm a joker, all right. Boy, Walton, I'm not going to tell you any more stories—ever."

Sonia, regarding Walton intently, murmured, "You are a very violent man."

Walton was still unable to speak. He could only look at her questioningly, almost beseechingly, over the glass of water he was sipping.

"Yes," said Dudley, suddenly serious. "Yes, he is. Sometimes he scares me."

Walton threw up his hands.

"Can't a man choke—if he has to?" he asked plaintively, and coughed again.

Dudley looked at him quizzically.

"No," he said, after a parody of deliberation. "No, I think not."

"I like it," said Sonia.

As he and Sonia rode away in the taxicab, Walton's last glance showed Dudley standing before his hotel with a hand raised in wistful farewell. There had been no argument over who would take Sonia home; Dudley's hotel was only a few blocks from the Swazey, and Sonia lived on Morningside Heights. Walton explained (rather elaborately, he realized later) that he would cross town from there, and catch the late train home at the 125th Street station.

But when they reached Sonia's apartment building, after a completely silent ride, and stepped out into the still hot night, he paid the cab driver.

"I'm coming in," he said.

She didn't answer, but led the way. Her apartment was a third-floor walkup. She snapped on the light to reveal a large, almost bare room. That was the first, overwhelming impression: no feminine frippery, no soft curtains, no cushions, no nuances or decorative touches.

"The cell," said Sonia, a little defensively, he thought. "And I'm sorry, but no air-conditioning. I'll be right back." She disappeared into the bathroom.

The room was stuffy. Walton raised the Venetian blinds and opened two windows that looked down on the street. The air that entered was hot, steamy and redolent of the great enfolding city. Turning back, he observed details of the room: a neatly made-up but severe daybed, covered by some Indian material; two shabby stuffed chairs with plain summer covers on them; a small nondescript desk flanked by a straight chair; a filled bookcase; on the walls, a Degas print, a small tapestry that suggested Mexico, and a large charcoal sketch of Sonia, thumb-tacked into place.

Remembering Hans Castorp before the portrait of Frau Chauchat, Walton moved closer to the picture. Though not altogether persuasive in detail, it was Sonia—the wide face, the Slavic cheekbones, the soft chin, the slightly slanting eyes. He remembered the Hofrat's clinical explanation of such eyes—the way the oblique effect is caused by a ridge that runs from the bridge of the nose to the eyelid, and down the inside corner of the eye.

She had returned. Without turning, he knew it and spoke.

"I like it. You wore your hair differently then."

"Yes," she said dryly, "I've cut it. Sit down and I'll make you a drink."

He turned then and walked over to her. She was of middle height, but now she seemed to him very short—small. Their eyes met and fastened in a long explorative look. He, a foot from her, was motionless; she was swaying slightly, an almost imperceptible movement. They did not touch each other, except for their eyes.

At last she sighed, lowered her eyelids and moved to the kitchen. He heard her rattling ice cubes, but he made no move to help her. He stood there, lost in the moment that was past and, sequentially, other moments from the still farther past.

When they were seated with drinks, she studied him in silence, and then said, "Tell me about that Chauchat woman."

He did. It was very fresh in his mind and he retold the story in detail, lingering over the chapter called "Walpurgisnacht," and the dia-logue in French between Castorp and Clavdia Chauchat. It was clear to both of them that he was telling an allegory, that this was a récitatif d'amour, elaborated by the hot intensity of his gaze.

"But you are not Hans Castorp," she said at last.

"No," said Walton. "I am not. I am not really at all like him."

"And I am not like her," Sonia went on. "That leaves as the only similarity the infatuation."

"Don't call it that."

"Yes," she said quite decisively. "I like to call things just what they are, when it's necessary to call them anything. But I have no objection to another word you may like better, if it's also accurate."

Walton kept holding her eyes with his own burning scrutiny.

"You've tormented me ever since I first saw you," he said.

"No," she replied softly.

"I mean I've been tormented by the sight of you, by the thought of you, by the memory of you. I've wanted to shut you out of my mind, and I can't."

Again she made that barely perceptible shrug of her shoulders, lifting faintly the cloth of her dress. The earlier memory returned to Walton now—it had been way, way back in his college days, and it had been little Irene Wertz. More than twenty-five years . . .

"Why not?" Sonia asked. "Why have you wanted to shut me out?"

He drained his glass, stood up and began pacing back and forth.

"Your gestures," he said. "Like the way you shrug your shoulders. I was once in love—I think it was being in love—with a girl who did that. Her last name began with W too. Perhaps I was not in love, but I could not leave her alone."

He stopped, close to her, and said suddenly, almost savagely, "It's something to do with the way you move inside your clothes. I was thinking in the bar how in this hot weather the other girls strip down and you're all covered up, yet I can't forget your body. All in green and gold —your dress, your necklace, your bracelet. . . ." His voice had softened, become husky.

Sonia rose and reached for his glass.

"I'm not a girl," she said.

He stopped her with his outstretched hand, but the touch of her arm, even through her sleeve, made him draw back as though stung.

"I don't know if I want another drink," he said lamely. "I've had a lot already."

"All right," she said. "Help yourself if you change your mind."

He watched her make her (sinuous, he thought, and growled at the word) way to the kitchen. As she came back, drink in hand, the telephone rang. He watched the fluidity with which she sank on the couch, glass in one hand, the telephone receiver raised in the other, and with a pang was reminded of Julie's movements.

"Hi. Oh, Evelyn."

"   ."

"No, the three of us ate there. I just got home."

"   .
.   .
.   .
. . . . ?"

"Well, settle down and I'll tell you. He's quite a man, I agree, but not a bit like you described him." She turned a mocking look on Walton. "You didn't prepare me for how violent and—smoky he is."

"   .
. . . . ?"

"Oh, nothing. Don't get so indignant. I just see it in him. But held in rigid control too. Sometimes he holds himself as though he has a brace on. I was so relieved when he let go and roared with laughter over something Mr. Foote said. Suddenly he was—huge, outsized, and—so vital. Even when he choked once, at the end of dinner, it was like a volcanic eruption. It's a good thing I'm not his secretary."

"   .
. . . . ?"

"I don't know, Evelyn." Her voice grew softer, lazy again. "I do know I'd love to have an affair with him—"

Walton jumped up abruptly and made for the kitchen, but her voice, raised, followed him.

"No, of course not, silly. I'm just ruminating. But I'd be afraid of it, too—afraid that he'd be full of guilt and make us both miserable. What?"

"   .
. . . ."

"But *I* don't know his wife, so stop preaching. You know I always talk like this. Just because it's your beloved boss, you suddenly get virtuous."

Walton returned to the center of the room and stood there, staring at her. There was apparent a transition in the conversation now, which led Sonia to describe Dudley Foote as "great fun," Dennis Byrnes as a "mama's boy," and Peggy Thomas as "a psycho." After a few more exchanges, she said good night and hung up.

"Well," she said. "Look at you. Scared? Angry?"

The mood had been broken for Walton. He felt calmer, and in some subtle but decisive way she did not look the same to him as before. The golden shine was off her, the bells were silenced, the fragrance fainter.

"I guess I'm a little dazed by your candor," he said.

She smiled and stretched. The cat, he thought.

"I say what I think. But I guess saying that before you is more than candor. I'm pretty honest, but I'm a bitch, too."

He looked at her levelly.

"Are you?"

"Some ways. I like to surprise people by saying right out what's in my head. You can trust me, if you don't mind all the ventilation."

He sat down beside her.

"Tell me more about you."

Her smile was mocking again.

"End of infatuation. Beginning of practical interest. I'm Polish, but born in Cleveland—"

Walton interrupted her.

"You were! So was I!"

She looked at him quizzically.

"I knew that—but not my Cleveland. Not the steel mills. I know all about you, your father and grandfather. Pillars of the church and the University. It's a wonder you've come through so well—at least I *think* you have."

Walton ignored the challenge.

"And after Cleveland?"

"Two years of college there. Then two at secretarial school. I've been in New York eight years; I'm thirty now. Eight years of working for publishers and theatrical agencies and a magazine; I've had it."

Walton leaned back and took out his pipe.

"Why aren't you married?"

"I was, for two years. He's an artist, and he let me support him. I was quite tied to him sexually; it was a wrench to give him up that way, but that's not enough. I like sex, but I shouldn't have made a foolish marriage because of it. I wouldn't now."

Walton began studying her again, over the lighting of his pipe.

"What do you see through all that smoke?" she asked.

He punctuated his reply with puffs on the pipe.

"I'm not sure," he said. "Something's puzzling me, though."

She laid her cool fingers on his wrist, and a shiver he could not conceal ran through him. She laughed and drew back her hand.

"There. It's still there then. I know what was puzzling you—if it was *puzzling*. I deliberately broke the spell. I wanted you to know something of *me*—not just your romanticized version. I wanted you to know how tough and hardheaded I can be. How cool a customer. Look at my room. I hate romanticism as much as I do sentimentality and sentimentality as much as I do fluffy, frilly feminine things. And what's more—" she leaned closer, so close that her fragrance, though delicate, dizzied him—"and what's more, Walton Herrick, I've been just as aware of you as you of me, ever since we first saw each other. That much is authentic. But if we're going to come any closer I want you to know whom you're dealing with—not find it out and draw back because you expected or needed something else. Or in fear: a lot of men are afraid of me."

Walton's pipe was out, and his hands, clenched, rested on his knee.

"And finally—" her voice was soft again—"I don't want to come any closer if you're thinking only of a casual night or two. There. Have I broken something?"

It was Walton who refilled the glasses this time. From the kitchen, he said, "No, I think you've mended something. It comes hard to me, but I'll try to be as honest as you've been. I haven't been thinking of a casual night or two—or of a real affair. I've been thinking, until today, alternately of how I could pull myself away from you, and how I could have you without losing my self-respect. That's as far as I got."

Something about her position as he handed her the glass told him she'd been hurt, that however tough she thought herself she was vulnerable.

"For God's sake," he said hurriedly, "don't misunderstand that last. I mean that fidelity has always come hard to me, but I have been faithful to my wife this time—you knew that I've been married before? And things are bad between us right now, and I don't want to lose her and I think of this summer as a time when I've got to find myself and make my way back to her. If I'm unfaithful now, of all times—" He broke off, staring at the floor.

Her voice, to his surprise, resumed the slightly insinuating lazy drawl of the early part of the evening. There was in it no element of the sympathy he only now realized he had expected.

"That makes me poison to you—pure poison. It's a good thing I broke the spell. For you do know what would have happened, don't you? I spotted one thing fast: you're a voluptuary, like me. But unlike me, you're riddled with guilt."

He nodded miserably, without looking up. She reached out and stroked his head gently, meditatively, but again, he thought oddly, it was not sympathy.

"I guess I *am* quite a bitch. Now I want you more than before. But I hadn't guessed at this—this boy side of you. As I told Evelyn, I thought of you just as dark and exciting." Abruptly she stood up, and the way her hands came down her sides, smoothing her dress, smote Walton.

"You'd better go," she said, and he saw suddenly, for the first time, the peculiar gray-green of her eyes, widened now, watching him intently. "You'd better go now. I'll be here. We'll see. If you're really wholly committed to your wife, then you won't come back. We'll see. But now— you'd better go."

Startled, he stood up, stared at her for a moment, struggling to resist the contradictory invitation he found there in those widened, tantalizing eyes. Then, without another word, he swung himself around and left, slamming the door behind him.

To walk the corridors of hell the rest of the week. His work suffered; he went to bed late and could not sleep; he woke early, dry-mouthed and dreary.

What was the matter with him? Oh, he knew, he knew, but now, in middle age (when else? a mocking voice sang out), in this dry summer without Julie (when else, indeed?), where he walked, parched and dogged—all for the promise of water and green growth there, there at the end of it.

Promise? Mirage? What had he accomplished of what he sought— of what was needed? What did he understand?

And wasn't he hopelessly naïve? absurdly puritanical? Wouldn't a mature man, wise in the animal limitations of human nature, burn out the fire instead of trying to quench it, burn it to fine white ash and return to the hearth of home, having done no harm?

But this is not true, he answered. Harm is done. Then, then I cannot look at Julie in the same way; I cannot touch her, kiss her, hold her without our knowing—together. This was no original virginal fidelity he invoked; even in that tormented brief first marriage with Joanna, he had finally been faithless, when to wait for its termination would have been a matter of weeks. And how else had he struck back at Lydia when her sharp and incisive tongue, intoning the decalogue of his inconsistencies and insufficiencies, had become unbearable? (Was it striking back, or was it fleeing, in desperate pursuit of comfort? Sometimes he had thought the long line of girls and women he had sought out, the rooms, darkened, where he had lain, the heads beside his head, were number-less—all part of some endless night through which he fled, his coat collar turned up, his hat pulled down, a fugitive of night streets, searching, fleeing, searching—for what? he cried and did not know.)

And between Joanna and Lydia, and after Lydia, still others. And only once or twice a peace, a negotiable peace and a resting place. Was that it, then? Peace? And why did it come so rarely? Why must he be a loner, a fugitive, a dark traveler?

Then Julie. What was it Dud had said he made of her: "a faraway princess." And no wonder: it was coming home; it was finding and having and giving and taking, the dream made real, the promise kept. The third year passed, the fourth, the fifth—and now he was remembering his own voice suddenly, "Seven years, Julie, and I love you as much as when I married you. I want only you." And the slow stirring of her head on the pillow and the widening of her eyes: "Of course. Did you expect it to change?" and an expression he thought then one of contentment and amusement at his (*his*) naïveté. But now, in painful retrospect, it seemed to him it might have been suspicion, and a new pondering on new questions.

This then was what had caught at him on Saturday night, with his hot hands on Gail's hot sunburned shoulders and her mouth sweet on his, drunk, both of them, on each other and their movement in dance all the summer night. She had wrenched her mouth away in a sudden spasm, averted her head, twisted from his grasp, and suddenly cried, "Oh, no, no, no. Julie."

She had thought first, had acted first—she, the friend—he thought miserably; and he, the husband, only thereafter, and even then reluctantly. Passionately, blindly, he had reached after her, savagely brought her back, muttering, "Gail, Gail, I can't help—"

For a moment Gail had clung to him again, but then again pulled away, saying, "Walton, we could never again—" and this time it came home, and suddenly he was cold, shamed, stricken. She had driven him to his house then in silence, and only in his driveway had she spoken again. "Dear Walton, I'll always—"

He had flung himself away, a petulant, middle-aged boy, muttering, "Don't."

That was the way it had really been, heroics, clichés and all, and yet at the Swazey Bar, when Sonia entered, he had thought of this new ordeal (ordeal? and who had arranged it?) as coming right after the difficult *triumph* (*that* had been his thought, his word) over his temptation with Gail. Triumph! Had he really come to lie so to himself? Was it, even, so very new?

As old, perhaps, as the dark pursuit, the dervish dance, the nocturnal flights of his life. He knew that line, from the adolescent dreams behind his closed bedroom door, through the long years, the many nights, to Sonia Wilenski and now—the need, the fierce, obsessive need to meet, to win, to celebrate again the erotic ritual which had shifted slowly over the years from storied encounters in the fabled settings of his early fantasies with enchantresses he had read and dreamed of, to the more mundane rites of Cleveland homes and New York apartment buildings.

But had it ever changed—except for the cyclic waxing and waning of the urge? Was it Jane (or Helen or Katie) with whom he'd sat, matching drinks in the rosy dimness of a room in Shaker Heights, savoring the postponement of that moment when the word became touch, the sight flesh? Or was it rather Leda or Deirdre of the Sorrows with whom he waited in that anticipatory hour? Had he really climbed the stairs (or pushed the button in the self-service elevator) to Celia (or Karen or Rosalind), wet and ruddy from Manhattan's snow? Or instead, had Iseult of the White Hands unlatched the door, Mélisande, well after midnight, slipped out of her gown?

He didn't know how, wondered if he had ever met any of them (until Julie) as she really was, wondered how much he had invested each with her bright aura from his early dreams. But this much was different: here and there, along the winding road, someone emerged, possessed of some further golden sheen, some way of moving, some wantonness of eye that caught and held him irresistibly: this, then, was one of his early princesses truly brought to life—and such a one was Sonia. What had she said? "You're a voluptuary, like me." And though the plainness of much she had had to say had disconcerted him, in retrospect it delighted him feverishly.

In comparison to his encounter with Sonia, the evening with Gail distressed him more and more. It had been real, he knew, real in their feeling, in its lesser measure, as Julie's and his feeling for each other was. It belonged, for all the moonlight and champagne, to the daylight world of reality. Gail was a friend, a part of his and Julie's life, and she had brought him and herself to their senses, to their love for Julie. She was still a friend, to Julie and to him, whatever twinges their next meetings might bring. How could he have come so close to—

It was late on Friday night that he began to understand some of the confused and tortured thoughts and feelings he was having. He *thought* he was thankful to Gail (he *knew* he was thankful they hadn't done it); what he *felt* toward her, though, was resentment. For the incompletion? For having gone so near the line? For putting Julie first? He didn't know, but he didn't like the feeling.

And then, equally suddenly, he felt the emergence in him of a familiar but long-absent elation that was like a dilation of his whole body; all his senses stirred; some long-lost lubrication washed him, and he felt an easing of his tension-stiffened body, a new resilience in his limbs.

He would return to Sonia. She would be there, she'd said, and she belonged to the other order, to that separate life along whose black corridors he had sped so many times, nimble and flexible and fleet of foot, free of that heavy, ponderous body he must carry so solemnly and carefully through the daylight world, lest through a crack there showed a shadow of the dark one.

And now Julie had released him. Released him. Driven him back there, whence he had emerged, painfully, limpingly, so long ago—for her. To live as best he could, the dark and light together, bringing the dark into the day. But Peter had come, in the first year, and then a change. There was no place for the dark, then; he tried to press it down, to carry it hidden, to shake it off. But now, now, she had driven him back.

Yes. How fond-crazy he had been to suppress, to pretend he hadn't seen the look of hate. Not a word, not a letter—he should have known. Only because he had so desperately wanted not to know, he had refused to. But now he could go to Sonia, for Julie did not want him. And somehow his despair over losing Julie became relief, as though a terrible weight had been lifted from him.

He did not consider going back to New York and Sonia that night. No, he would stay here, he thought, and for tonight listen to the sirens' song. Like Odysseus, lashed to the mast.

It came to him that that was what he had often wanted most, even more than the experience of going ashore—or onto the rocks? he wondered suddenly. He wanted the rest of the family safely home, tucked away, while himself listened to the song. But the lashing to the mast had its good side, he thought: it meant an unwillingness to shut oneself off from experience—and exclaimed aloud in impatience at his fatuous earnestness, his false self-righteous reasoning.

Drowsily now, he reinvoked the golden image. Sunk in reverie, he sat at the kitchen table, slowly drinking his beloved bourbon, and dreaming of Sonia. Sonia the Egyptian princess, Sonia the Venetian courtesan, Sonia the hetaera, Sonia le Fay, wiser than Merlin—but always golden, tawny Sonia of the widened gray-green eyes and the catlike movements. . . .

It must have been toward three o'clock in the morning that Walton awoke—cold and terrified. The light still burned, but the kitchen seemed strange; he was in some alien cubicle, and he knew that he was finally bare and alone and bereft. And then he realized, as a door opened in his heart, that he had been awakened by the sound of a voice, Julie's voice— sweet and lifted. And though he knew already that she was not there, that he had dreamed of her and heard her in his dream, warmth returned to him and this kitchen was in his home, Julie's kitchen, where she and Peter and Tim and Jennifer came and went—their voices now a loving, homelike counterpoint—and he could see her cooking, washing dishes, smiling, weeping, and it seemed to him his heart would break, thank God!

And all the other moments of their marriage flooded him at once, so that it was like polyphonic voices, or figures when a film has been doubly exposed, intricate human patterns, blessed human figures, in the dance of life: Julie and he at the altar in the church, her face when he went in after Peter's birth, Julie at night nursing a child or singing a lullaby, her beloved face on the pillow, or bending over him and whispering.

He wept.

And after the healing, he wrote her a letter. On and on, his hand moving in such furious haste that he despaired, when he looked back over it, of her being able to read it.

At five o'clock, with the birds singing in his ears and the early light blessing the trees and grass, he climbed the stairs to bed.

DEPOSITION: 4

A letter from Julie to Walton, written on June 24 . . .

DEAR WALTON,

I've read your letter over four times, and I love it. There's so much I didn't know—that you never let me know.

The last time I read it—just now—I got the funny feeling that maybe you don't even know now what you've written. It's as though you just poured out everything you could find in yourself, and it came so fast you won't be able to remember it afterward.

What I'm trying to say is that, first of all, the first two times I read your letter, it just made me terribly happy. I cried. I left home with no hope at all, and then, not hearing from you, I spent all this past month trying to teach myself how to live without you. I haven't gotten so very far, but I've made a start. And then your letter came and I knew that what I most wanted in the world had happened, that you'd come back and opened up.

And I almost called you—that was Monday night—and said, yes, come, come as quick as you could. But I decided not to, at least till the next day, that I would just go to sleep with your letter.

And now I've read it again twice and I think I see that it's better for you not to come till September. You see, I know one thing now that I didn't know before: you really have those feelings—and you have them for me and the children. That doesn't mean, though, that you can keep on feeling them all the time. Even now (I can't explain; I just feel it) you may be wondering why you don't feel the way you did when you wrote it. *Something has happened* (I know it from your letter), but maybe it's just the beginning. And if after this first month you can feel and say what you did, then I want you to have another couple of months to live with that and get to know it more and more (it's hard to express),

212

not risk coming now before you're really ready to, and both of us getting hurt and disappointed because we pushed it too soon.

Darling, I would love for you to come now. I've missed you so and felt so awful. But you know I've had reason before to hope that everything would be different—the last time just the day before we left—and while your letter *is* different, and *I believe you,* no one could go on feeling the way you did when you wrote it and not burst. And you can change so violently and I can get hurt so quickly and easily. I want us *really* to come together when we do. See—I wrote *when.* But do write me again—only when you really feel like it, and really want to.

The Vineyard is fine for the children. I let Peter ride his bike down to the beach (don't worry; it's a very safe road and everybody here is bicycle-minded) and he's learning to sail. Timmy is just beginning to learn the crawl and is very full of himself. And Jenny loves it here, has a little neighbor girl for a friend. And it's done wonders for Father; I didn't realize how lonely he's been.

I've begun to write a little.

With love,
JULIE

P.S. What did you mean about "governor"? Near the end of your letter you wrote something about "a fine governor," but I can't read the next sentence.

Part Two

THE NICHOLSON DAEMONOLOGY

[*Part Two*]   *1*

THE Hon. James H. Nicholson, Walton's maternal grandfather, stood six feet three. A daguerreotype of him as a young man showed a handsome face—a little like an early picture of Beethoven, but with a more disciplined strength, and less wildness in the eyes. His hair was very black, and once he had grown the beard which he wore most of his life his portraits made Walton think of the Union generals in his picture book of the Civil War. Why Union? He was not sure, for the factual basis of the Nicholsons' Connecticut heritage played no part in this feeling. Moreover, Jeb Stuart and Longstreet looked just as black as Sheridan and McClellan and Grant—at least in these pictures.

No, it had something to do with Walton's early convictions about the tonal qualities of the North and the South in the War Between the States. He did not mean the respective geographical areas—nor, for that matter, the armies representing those areas. It was not the political or moral issues involved that interested him—he was seven or eight years old at the time. It was rather an aesthetic alignment and loyalty that he derived, ironically enough, from his mother.

To her, the South (an essence, a quality, a Platonic idea, a Polar Absolute in her spiritual cosmography) was the Sun, Light, Beauty, Graciousness, Good; the North, conversely and respectively, the Night, Darkness, Duty (which, rather than Ugliness, she opposed to Beauty), Grimness, Commonness (which, in the same manner, rather than Evil, complemented Good). To be sure, she was fiercely proud of, and loyal to, Connecticut and New England. But somehow, in her strange transvaluations of values, geography was swept regally aside: the culture of New England was aristocratic (by which she meant old), and hence a part of the Southern heritage. And within this fantastic genealogy, Robert E. Lee was the grand scion, a truly great gentleman whom she admired beyond all other figures in American history.

Lincoln, she admitted publicly, was a great man, but secretly she found him a little common.

It was ironic that Walton took over from his mother and adapted to his own tastes this body of dogma—ironic for two reasons. The lesser was that Walton's mother had never been south of Sagertown, Pennsylvania. (It was there, indeed, that she had met the Misses Peyton, the only Southern friends of her life, spinsters who, unlike their grim Northern counterparts, still—in their indeterminate forties—rouged and giggled and even were *pretty:* "Those dear little ladies," Mother would say. "*They* are *true* ladies," with a mixture of beatific approval and unwitting condescension that Walton always found a bit confusing.)

But this was the lesser irony—an irony characteristic of situations involving Mother and those attachments of hers which were motivated by so deeply hidden a twist in her nature that it was all but useless to try to trace their origin. This was that lesser irony implicit in all enthusiasms based on a close to total ignorance.

The greater irony was one of an inversion occurring in the pattern of cause and effect, as Walton "inherited" her ideas. Mother frankly (though perhaps not consciously, for once she believed something, it immediately became a *fact,* and anyone who doubted it was hopelessly "prejudiced") indoctrinated Walton with her North-South mythology (she particularly loved the word "Confederate," which she invested with an aura of chivalry that reduced the medieval codes, Castiglione's gentleman-courtier and Sir Philip Sidney to sheer boorishness), and applauded his demanding a picture of Lee on his wall. At the same time, Mother did not, of course, foresee that her devotion to the South and her aversion to the North would somehow become mixed in Walton's own version with his conception of the Herricks and the Nicholsons. (But wasn't there a hint, a presagement of this, however unapparent to her, in the fact that while she invoked the admirable and felicitous qualities—Beauty, Graciousness—in the name of the South, her own life was always shadowed, and even controlled, by their opposites, as she construed them: Duty, Grimness?) At any rate, a vague glimmer of the analogy between the families and the sides in the Civil War must at some moment have crossed her mind, for she not only repeated, with evident pleasure, the common assertion that Cornelius Herrick looked like Robert E. Lee, but developed and elaborated it to such a point that Walton, at the age of four or five, was not quite sure but what his grandfather *was* General Lee.

There was, for that matter, a decided ambivalence in Mother's attitude toward the Herricks—or, at least, toward Cornelius Herrick.

On the same day, she might say, "Of course, if they think Walton is bright, they say, 'How can he help it with the father and grandfather he has?' Oh, I get that all the time"—and, "Your grandfather is a true gentleman. I have never had a harsh or unkind word from him since that day I married your father."

She liked him, that is, almost in spite of herself, for he had, indeed, always treated her with a gentle and deferential courtesy, touched lightly by the flattering implication in his eyes (not uncommon in fathers-in-law) that she was a beautiful woman. She would call attention to this by pretending to dismiss the whole thing on the grounds that he was "quite a ladies' man, in a thoroughly nice way" (which he was). But she was pleased, all the same. Yet she resented him in so far as he represented and headed the Herrick clan and the Herrick tradition— this, because it seemed to her, in some way both insidious and invidious, to depreciate the Nicholsons. And had she not given up the majesty and prestige of her family's name and position in Connecticut to come to this barbarous Ohio, this common Middle West ("Flat," she would say with a fastidious shiver of disgust, "not a hill anywhere. There is a commonness to people here. . . .") only to find that here everyone worshiped the Herricks?

She was wrong on two counts, Walton came to know: everyone did not worship the Herricks, and some time before she had married William Herrick and migrated to Cleveland, the Nicholsons had fallen on evil days that had considerably reduced their prestige in the Connecticut town. But she was adamant about her version; indeed, her ritualistic insistence upon her family's importance was one of the major pretenses of her life.

At any rate, Walton's lexicon of the great polar forces of the North and the South, slightly different from his mother's, went something like this:

The South (and the Herricks) = Daylight, Urbanity, Success, Good—and they wore the gray of the Confederacy.

The North (and the Nicholsons) = Darkness, Passion, Destroyed Success, Evil (which was a paradoxical composite of sin and sternness, suffering and the strict enforcement of duty—"It is my New England conscience," his mother often lamented proudly)— and they wore the black (so it looked in the picture book) of the Union.

He actually compiled such a table when he first, in his late thirties, began taking thoughtful looks back over his shoulder. Of course he had not used these words as a boy, even to himself. Yet they approximated with fair accuracy the feelings he had experienced then. And as he studied the equations, which he had first put down jocularly, although trying to reproduce his actual boyhood feelings as faithfully as he could without analyzing their implications—as he studied them, some insights he had never had before were immediately clear to him.

First of all, he had always dreaded and at the same time been fascinated by the night. Day was sensible and meant work; night was dangerous but exciting. A success which had vanished (the fall of a great house) was tragic and hence had more value and dignity than a continued success, which smacked of commercialism and vulgarity. Here, of course, he had been totally at the mercy of his mother's perverse evaluations; they grew for her out of her need to redress—or at least dignify—the calamities that had befallen the Nicholsons, but they had a wholly gratuitous value for Walton, and became the foundation of his peculiar aesthetic, shoring him up years later at the time of his deepest descent into misery and despair—when he gradually and almost unconsciously gave them a new twist that found nobility and tragic stature in sickness, meanness and prosaicness in health.

One of the most interesting attendant ironies that came to light from the formula he wrote down was the equating of the South with success, the North with vanished success. Here, it was patent, the Herricks and the Nicholsons took over completely, to subvert history. . . . Another feature of the equations that interested him was the way they tipped the scales heavily in favor of the Herricks. But a balance was restored before long, he remembered; by the time he was nine or ten, he had stripped the Herricks, so to speak, of their soft gray uniforms (Confederate gray remained his favorite color for a long time) and given them to the Nicholsons—because by this time he was already well warped by his mother's dominant influence and sufficiently enamored of his tragic vision to feel that gray was a *sad* color and hence appropriate to defeated grandeur and lost greatness. A final irony: the further he moved toward an unhealthy outlook, the closer history was restored to its familiar perspectives.

All this nonsense (the little he was allowed to hear and perceive of it) flabbergasted Walton's father. William Herrick, on the day that the picture of Robert E. Lee was hung on the wall of Walton's room, over his bed, shook his head, though more in sorrow than in anger. "Lee was a fine man and a great general," he said in perplexity, "but Lincoln was a great man. When you say you like the South best, you're

not even thinking of what they fought about. You're forgetting that
the South kept slaves, that they treated human beings like domestic
animals, sonny."

Walton was unimpressed. His mother, standing by his bed, tossed
her head. "That's what all Northerners say," she remarked acidly.
"Actually they treated them better than they've been treated since."
And when William shook his head again, and emitted a sound somewhere between a groan and a chuckle, Elinor, then ten, holding with
one hand to her mother's voluminous skirts, stuck her tongue out at
him and said, "Yes they did. They did too." He gave up then, despite
a twinge of sudden and unaccustomed fury that made him want to
slap his small daughter (it never crossed his mind, apparently, that
it was his wife whom he might better slap), and retreated to his own
room, muttering, "All Northerners! What does she think *she* is—"
which confirmed the three of them, overhearing him, in their long-
standing conviction that Father was literal-minded, made of not quite
fine enough stuff to appreciate this sort of thing. Marcia Nicholson—
for it was by her maiden name that she continued to think of
herself, whenever really challenged: often, in the middle of a harangue
about the departed glories of the Nicholsons, Walton was to see her
cross her bedroom and look at herself sternly in the mirror, compressing
her lips, smoothing out her dress, then turn, with her head newly high,
to say, "Marcia Nicholson has not forgotten"—Marcia Nicholson,
rallying from the almost staggering defeat and dissolution of her family,
had marshaled her new forces with astonishing vigor.

For somehow, Walton thought, looking back on it all with more
surprise than he would have believed possible at this late date—
somehow there was always war imagery about. And despite his later
reversal of the uniforms, the Hon. James H. Nicholson, his maternal
grandfather, who had died fifteen years before his own birth, remained
for him a black Union general. The black, the antagonist of his favorite
gray, applied to the actual color of his grandfather's hair and beard,
to the picture-book uniforms of the Union troops, and to his grandfather's generally forbidding quality. For both the pictures of the
mature man and the word pictures which Walton had from his mother
stressed this quality. To complete the Civil War frame of reference,
and to complement the identification of Cornelius Herrick with Lee,
Walton came finally to envision his maternal grandfather as a sterner
Abraham Lincoln, a more famished-cheeked, stronger-chinned Lincoln,
without the humor, without the sorrow and the kindliness of the eyes,
but always with the tall silk hat that became a most frightening symbol

of his inexorable severity. And thus, put bluntly, for some years Walton
was inclined to confuse Abraham Lincoln with the Bogey Man—and
both of them with this grandfather.

Actually, James H. Nicholson *had* been a severe and overbearing
man. He had also been a man of strong ability who had left his mark
on his city and his state. There had been, oddly enough, at least a
loose general parallel between his career—up to middle age—and
that of the pre-presidency Lincoln. Born in Ridgefield, the ancient
site of his family (Marcia Nicholson never tired of referring to the
Revolutionary memorial there, with three Nicholsons among the
names engraved upon it), James Nicholson had been one of nine
children in a family of moderate means, and he had been required,
to a large extent, to make his own way. He had had almost as difficult a
time managing the study of law as young Lincoln had; when he finally
set himself up in practice in Stamford, he was still a poor man.

But he prospered. An iron will and a reputation for stern integrity
brought him the confidence and respect of the town; his marriage to
Patience Walton, daughter of Colonel Thaddeus Walton, brought him
moderate wealth. He was not, however, the man to rest, leaning
comfortably on his wife's money. Together with another promising
young lawyer, he founded the highly successful firm of Nicholson and
Burgess and in a fairly short time was ready to indulge the political
ambitions he had always quietly nurtured.

At this point in his life, however, the parallel to Lincoln, rough
and easy at best, ended. James Nicholson was not equipped for the
large stage of national events, although he did become a power in the
state. There seemed to have been something cold, glacial almost, about
the core of him, under an impressively stately and courteous exterior,
that repelled those who had occasion to see it exposed, even while
it wrung from them, as often as not, a reluctant admiration that he
was not, as other men were, deterred from his purposes by ordinary
human softness and affection. Apparently he really could not experience
the gentler emotions: Marcia, among the rest of his family, had copious
opportunities to discover the truth of this—that he was actually puzzled
when arraigned in the domestic court for his lack of understanding
and kindness (not that anyone dared to indict him very often).

At any rate, the most conspicuous success of his career was as
State's Attorney. Working often in this capacity with "Pinkerton's
men," he was as active outside the courtroom as he was eloquent within.
There was a famous case about which Walton was to hear again and
again (as told by his mother with ambiguous pride). In this case, the

most unsparing of James Nicholson's cross-examinations, the drilling fire of his questions, the adroitness with which he changed the angle of his attack—all his resources failed to trap, or even to involve more deeply, the defendant charged with grand larceny. Manifestly piqued by his unwonted failure, James Nicholson left the case in the hands of his assistants and, after spending two days in the process of making himself as plausibly unkempt as possible, persuaded the sheriff in charge of the jail to slip him into the defendant's cell as a convict. The third night, he won the prisoner's confidence, and obtained from him as a "friend" the confession he could not wring out of him as the prosecutor.

When the prisoner was sentenced, he stood up and pointed his finger at James Nicholson. "I'll get you," he shouted, "if I have to wait fifty years. You're not a man, but a fiend, a bloodhound—and I'll see to it that you're in Hell ahead of me."

The threat was not fulfilled, although it provided the Nicholson girls with several years of delicious apprehensiveness, and again, some ten years later, when this prisoner was paroled against the protest of their father, a more drastic and less titillating period of fear, as a Pinkerton man stood guard by day and by night on the grounds of the Nicholson estate.

This episode, and other similar though less extreme ones, strengthened an already well-established public opinion. Nicholson was a wonder, an incorruptible, dedicated public servant, and a peerless guardian of the general security. But he went too far; he had none of the milk of human kindness; he was insatiable, cruel and unforgiving: you could admire him, but he made you shudder a little too, as you thought how he would deal with you if—in your quite unexceptional human frailty—you were to be found out, even in one of your least peccadilloes.

For his attitude was not confined to the jurisdiction of the law. It had occasionally been whispered about, for example, that the Rev. Harry Snow, young, popular, generous, was "a little too fond" of Emmy, the beguiling wife of Sam Burgess, junior partner of Nicholson and Burgess. The Honorable James H., now in his early forties, overhearing (for no one would dream of telling him anything of the sort directly) some of this talk, employed a secretary to stalk the pastor of his church for a week, finally learned that he had entered the Burgess home, one afternoon on which Sam Burgess was at the Capitol in Hartford. Hurrying to the scene, James H. peered through the windows to ascertain that there was more to the matter than a thoughtlessly timed pastoral call. He watched for a full ten minutes (he carefully stated in his full account of the incident); then he went off to summon the other elders of the church. The poor minister found them waiting for him on his own front porch when he returned home a few hours later.

The resultant dismissal of Dr. Snow and the dissemination of the juicier particulars brought no thanks to James Nicholson. Emmy Burgess' reputation, it was pointed out, was irreparably ruined (whereas, had the thing been handled quietly, people would have continued to accept her, whatever they thought); her husband, in a fury, dissolved the partnership and took Emmy to Europe for two years, during which time he sold his house in Stamford. On his return, he practiced in New Jersey.

Yet, when Patience Nicholson, an exceedingly gentle but shrewd wife (Walton, remembering her dimly as a very old lady, coined the phrase Patience in a Rocking Chair), quietly pointed out to him just what he had done, James Nicholson protested, with utter astonishment on his face, "But they did it, Patience. It never crossed my mind that Sam would be fool enough, subservient enough, to want to go on living with her." Nor, he thought to himself, that he would be discussing such matters with his wife, a lady.

That word *subservient*. Marcia had listened on the stairs to this conversation; she repeated it to Walton several times, on the occasion of reminiscent interludes, monologues really, devoted to a clearer understanding of her father and of the combination of passionate loyalty and fear he inspired in her. But Walton did not think she fully recognized the importance of the word "subservient" in the pattern of her father's relations with others. . . .

It was to James Nicholson's credit, to be sure, that he replied to his wife with the degree of forbearance that he did. He had just come from a stormy session with Aaron Hayes, one of the elders, who had tartly advised him to confine his prosecuting to his professional duties, and there had been, in the reluctant and disapproving faces of most of the other elders, too clear a censure for him to ignore—unaccustomed though he was to observe the reactions of others when they were not in the witness seat. What had most provoked him was that they all seemed less concerned over the disclosure of the defection of one consecrated to God than that of the frailty of a young and bewitching member of the notoriously susceptible sex—a frailty of the most ancient lineage. This induced in him black thoughts and blacker conclusions about the nature of man. . . .

From then on, it was obvious to everyone except James Nicholson himself that he would never hold any high office of an elective sort. Something about this incident made it the agent of a shift in popular opinion: from a regarding of this austere figure as one for whom you would vote despite his lack of warmth and human appeal, to a fixed decision that you would not vote for him, for all his extraordinary ability. There had been several previous incidents (including the case of the feigned convict) that had met with general disfavor: they were recalled now, tossed onto the conflagration of James Nicholson's dreams. But it seemed probable that there would never have been such a ground swell of disapprobation had it not been for the question of Emmy Burgess. The public humiliation of a beautiful and well-liked woman produced a curious reaction in an essentially conservative, God-fearing community: they could not approve what she had done, nor (except for the boldest, like Aaron Hayes) censure openly what James Nicholson had done; they could and did decide—whether separately or concertedly—that they would quietly abstain from helping him to realize his ambitions.

This did not prevent him from holding appointments of a high order, made by people who were not party to local loyalties and prejudices. As judge of the Probate Court, he made so fine a record that Walton, buying a house in Connecticut nearly eighty years after the "ruin" of Emmy Burgess, was informed by a lawyer present at the closing that his grandfather's decisions "on probate" were frequently still studied and quoted. And James H. went on to the capital, as he had always hoped to, as judge of the appellate court. But it was a fore-gone conclusion when, at the age of sixty-three, he ran in 1892 for United States Senator, that he would be defeated. Those few who remained loyal to him had later a way of saying that the stroke he suffered early in the campaign, forcing his retirement, was "an act of kind providence."

Needless to say, Judge Nicholson would not have agreed with them. The more aware he had become of the general withdrawal from him, the haughtier his manner had become. He was hurt, deeply hurt—or perhaps it would be more exact to say that his pride was deeply hurt. (But, for that matter, Walton sometimes had the feeling that he was not an individual man, but the walking incarnation of pride.) So, in a way that was to become familiar to Walton through his mother's similar dubious strategy, James H. covered the hurt by an even more arrogant front. After the incident of the minister and Emmy Burgess, he made little or no attempt to conceal his scorn for the average muddle-headed, sentimental mollycoddle—and this was his summation of most of the people he knew. Woe to that individual who came under his judicial jurisdiction without a good case, founded on "hardheaded sense and fact"! And yet, despite his refusal to be conciliatory in any way, he felt confident, up to the moment of his stroke, that he could be elected. Something in him that cleaved to the inevitability of the triumph of the righteous persuaded him that people who disliked him would still be unable to reject him on the ballot.

Actually, popular favor waited upon James H. Nicholson only once more: at his funeral. With further embarrassments and hurts at his hands now impossible, with that long, menacing forefinger no longer able to point, with the inflexible severity of that voice forever stilled, his neighbors and associates gathered to pay tribute to his achievements and his harsh integrity. He lay in state—or so Marcia Nicholson was to describe it—for two days; the funeral itself was a solemn and impressive occasion. Marcia dreamed that night that great men lined the shores of the River Jordan, while an unmanned boat crossed the water to receive the body and carry it to the other side. As the boat floated back unerringly with its burden, white-robed throngs on the farther side sang "Washed in the blood of the Lamb." She awoke trembling, exalted but desolate with the knowledge that she was alone in a world of which she was afraid. . . .

Struck down and paralyzed at the age of sixty-three, her father had lingered on, a gaunt ghost confined to a wheel chair, for a little over a year, able to speak only a word or two, unable to move his right side. It was then (at least, so Walton surmised) that he actually came to look most like Lincoln—then that there were deep caves carved in his cheeks, then that his eyes finally showed distress and suffering. Yet not quite like Lincoln—rather like his unredeemed brother. For it was Stoic, rather than Christian suffering: Marcia, who attended him all through that tedious and painful year, saw none of the softening gentleness that often accompanies the crippling of the strong. On the contrary, he almost certainly sat there on the veranda day after day, strong bony hands on the arms of his chair, contemplating the Sound, which his estate bordered, and his own plight, the wreckage of all his secret dreams, his insatiable ambitions, with the same implacable, dry-eyed stare of desolation.

And so, although in the family museum Walton thought of his two grandfathers as standing in impressive dominant postures at opposite ends of the hall—Cornelius Herrick with his hand raised, palm down in benediction, James H. Nicholson with his massive frame bent forward and his long index finger pointed in commanding accusation—he *felt* them most poignantly, perhaps, as they were when old men —or, rather, as they were in their so different brief intervals between full life and actual death.

For, whatever had happened to Cornelius Herrick in the two years between the dismissal of the nurse who had so scandalized the family and his death, Walton—perhaps influenced by Lloyd—saw him waited on, caressed by soft hands, stroked and cherished, pampered and prepared for the visits of his children so that they should see his silken white beard shining, his hair combed, his face washed, and his hands folded in contentment. And Walton always saw him enjoying this late Indian summer indulgence fully, sensuously. But he saw James H. Nicholson (although he knew that he was undoubtedly attended with equal devotion, if without the special zest the first Herrick nurse provided) as terribly alone—flinty-eyed and inconsolable, hating the gestures of affection and pity even more than he hated his affliction.

And somehow this difference, beyond that between the postures he envisioned in his family museum, seemed to Walton representative of the final, basic difference between the two men and the two lives. Whatever dark frustrations and secret suppressed rebellions Cornelius Herrick endured, he actively *loved* the image of himself that he had created. Whatever wild compulsion or fiercely reawakened defiant integrity had caused him to burst out into the jeremiad of his seventy-fifth anniversary sermon, he consistently over the years looked into the mirror as Narcissus gazed into the pool.

On the other hand, Walton was equally sure that, however confident—no, arrogant—a bearing James H. Nicholson presented to his world; however forcefully and unremittingly he applied himself to the pursuit of success and prominence and real achievement—he *hated* himself. Not for those qualities that alienated his neighbors and colleagues: this was a far more fundamental, a more central hatred. Whatever its origin (Walton did not pretend to know much about this grandfather's childhood), a black stony hatred of the essential self lay where his heart should have been. Not a hatred of what he did, not even of what he was—but, somehow, *that* he was. That, Walton thought, was as close as words could come to describing what must have been a lifelong torture, an ultimate heaviness within him that would give, every so often, an unbearable lurch.

JOURNAL: 3

from the journal of Walton Herrick . . .

June 27, 1953

I have been dipping back into my Grandfather Herrick's auto-biography, and have just been struck by a passage about his early childhood in which he says that, to add to his mother's burden of the farm and her growing family, her own father and mother and her husband's father (the cantankerous Peletiah Herri'k) came to live with them. The grandmother was apparently of a gentle and harmonious disposition, a help rather than a burden. "But," Cornelius Herrick adds, "my grandfathers were very unlike, and the bringing of them to live together was not the happiest thing imaginable."

To me it sounds prophetic. For there are times when, half-credulous, I indulge the fancy that *my* two grandfathers have come together to live with me, *in* me—and it is not the happiest thing imaginable.

Fancy, symbolism—and yet, when you come right down to it, from all that I can discover I am much more like my two very dissimilar grandfathers than I am my mother and father. But I am content not to press the point beyond its symbolic value. The two forces that are in me, and war in me, are well enough represented, at any rate, by Cornelius Herrick and James H. Nicholson. I call them Narcissistic Man and Daemonic Man.

The first of these two terms certainly does violence to any fair portrayal of Grandfather Herrick. The more I read back in the auto-biographical essay that he wrote, the more I recover from my early prejudice against him, induced by the all-but-worship of *his* children. Interspersed in the bland, full flow of his prose there are short passages of unusual poetic beauty; expressions of generous feeling that seem unquestionably spontaneous; even rather touching moments of wistfulness that suggest, in a man of real achievements, a humility seldom revealed.

Yet, at the same time, behind (or rather, embedded in) his formal style, there is evidence of a preoccupation with self that extends beyond the requirements of the first-person narrative: not merely a preoccupation—that is not the word—but a lingering, a dwelling on self as of superlative and almost exclusive importance. It is a mood, a tone, soft, reflective, pleased—as though he were peering into the mirror and stroking that silky beard of his. When it is developed explicitly, even though so briefly as to be almost parenthetical, it fringes the fatuous, yet never seems to me to lose balance and fall wholly into it.

Take the one example of his summary of a pastorate at Painesville, Ohio, thirty miles from Cleveland, that began in 1865, a few months after Uncle Lloyd was born. He writes, "This was a beautiful town of five thousand people, a strong church for Ohio, and specially attractive because of the presence in the congregation of about a hundred young ladies of Lake Erie Seminary."

Now it is common knowledge in the family that Grandfather, as Mother always put it, "was sweet on the ladies"—and this sentence in itself is simple and pleasant enough. He goes on to say, a little later, "My relation to the Seminary as Pastor and friend was intimate and fruitful. Many were led to Christ and edified." The first time I read these lines the *doubles entendres* amused and delighted me, but never have I doubted, of course, that Grandfather meant literally and precisely what he wrote. In fact, these two sentences stand, for me, as a superb illustration of the full swing upon the semantic axis that may take place in less than a century. Yet what these words do lead me to is a picture of him, seated, somehow with dignity, under a summer sycamore, gravely instructing, edifying, the Gibson girls (I suppose really pre-Gibson) dispersed around him in the dappled shade, voluminous black skirts spread, yet trimly covering their ankles. I see white shirtwaists and gold lockets, broad-brimmed sailor straws scattered on the grass like huge daisies or black-eyed Susans, and the girls all intent, earnest, even decorously ardent and glowing. But I see too a Mary among the Marthas, a face more delicate, *spirituelle,* a more languid disposition of her limbs under the incongruous primness of the black skirt—and a heat-dampened curl grazing her cheek. Her gaze, dreamy, touched with intimations she would never own to, meets his and troubles it, though no flush appears on his face to match and confirm the subtle heightening of color on hers. For, whatever more lively stirring takes place within him, this is first of all confirmation of the loved image that blooms, like Yeats' rose, in his heart.

I know that my picture is historically as inaccurate, anachronistic and absurd as my mother's forays into history. At its best, I am invoking in it the Pre-Raphaelites, and 1865 is a little late for their flowering. At its worst, this is a Howard Chandler Christy, and the discrepancy in time is even greater the other way. But here is where my imagination fails; I always think of Grandfather as fixed either in vigorous middle age or in old age, and almost always surrounded by women, usually young, wearing the garb of the first decade of the twentieth century.

But that loved image: he sums up the stay in Painesville (at last the *explicit* statement): "This was a precious pastorate. I was fully appreciated."

I am trying, however circuitously and at however leisurely a pace, to get at something like this: I find in myself—totally irrelevant to the self than I can soberly conjure up by thinking about and really looking at myself literally and with the interior eye—I find in myself a soft, passive, *loved* image of this same sort. Is this part of what Julie has felt?

"Loved" is the crucial word, I think, as it was in Grandfather. He loved it, I have loved it and often still do, but for this dark rose to bloom it must be nurtured and cherished by others. This is not the simple and healthy self-liking that completes a cycle in the very recognition of being comfortable with oneself and therefore free to turn outward and *to love;* this is a sickly obsession and a morbid though lordly dependency upon the assurances of others. Grandfather (if I am right about him) and I both might well twist the familiar quotation to "I could not love thee, dear, so much, wert thou not loved yet more by others"—addressing ourselves!

And this hesitant infatuation with a fictitious self has a further characteristic—again, in both of us—of claiming, for this cherished being, special privileges that it is (unfortunately, for them) in the disordered constitution of certain other kinds of people to feel that they must grant when asked. In this context, I think of Grandfather as an old king who suffered no real winter of discontent, of myself as a boy king under a misguidedly benevolent regency. Let the regent abandon his benevolence—I am disconsolate, inconsolable: worse, desperate and terrified.

Of course, again, I do not literally blame Cornelius Herrick for this condition in me. It may well have developed in me during that year and a half of childhood when Mother and Uncle Edgar Briffault kept me in bed with "valvular leakage of the heart," not allowed to lift a hand—only my voice, which became more and more petulant, alternately arrogant and wheedling. May have? Must have.

Yet it is not far-fetched to see this same tendency in Grandfather. I do not have to induce or force the analogy. Time and again he left Catherine Herrick to take care of the children (eventually four, after Rosalind was born) while, all perfectly in the line of duty, he set forth on some extended and delightful voyage. The autobiography contains several passages of the following sort:

> Mr. Chas. A. Maynard was the progressive man in town (Painesville) and in the Church, taking the initiative in new measures, full of Eastern ideas of progress and not quite popular for this reason. It was through him first of all that the way was open for me to accompany my friend Winston, who had entered upon his Chicago pastorate, and was out of health, in a trip to Egypt, Sinai and Palestine in the Winter of 1870. Mr. Maynard caught at the idea, talked it and carried it with the good will of all the people. The Oberlin Professors, Thornton and Fuller mainly, were my supply, paid out of my salary, but the rest was mine to go on and keep the family. Emily was now living with us, and my wife bravely carried through the family side. This was for me a great opportunity. I sailed January 1st, 1870.

This was no isolated instance. Indeed, the pattern had been set with Mr. Curtis, in Meriden, nine years before. His wife "bravely carried through the family side" time after time. Two years later:

> At 1 P.M. my wife took train to Painesville, and I to St. Louis, en route to San Francisco. By some means [!] I was to supply the Second Congregational Church for a month, and this gave me a coveted opportunity to make the trip across the continent, to see the Yosemite, the big trees, San Jose, and the quicksilver mine on the coast, the geysers at the north of San F.—all of which I was eager to do. It was a fine trip—the big trees and the Yosemite in the last of May, the falls and the rivers at flood—one of the events of my life. Incidentally, and as falling in with my life work without much planning of mine, I had become quite a traveler. I have never ceased to be grateful to God and the congregations that have made such experiences possible, and I owe much to my wife

Catherine as well, who on this occasion cheerfully returned
home to set up housekeeping alone, since Emily was in
Meriden with her maternal grandparents for a few months,
and Lloyd visiting cousins near Pompey for most of the time.

The point I am making is that the two of us have also been alike
in the sense of somehow being what I call Blue Ribbon Boys; we have
never lacked for long some admiring and, to use Grandfather's word,
providentially rich or influential patron to provide us with pleasures or
material opportunities on which it would seem we had turned our
backs when we chose professions that are better known for their
spiritual or intellectual satisfactions than for any financial reward. We
have, each in his own way, kept our cake and eaten it too, while
bearing witness before God to our regret that the Catherine Herricks
must not only eat bread, but bake it as well.

And all this is a part of the record of Narcissistic Man. People
refer easily and superficially to "charm" and "magnetism." Perhaps I
dig no deeper when I think of "Narcissus gazing in a pool," but I
see the process as that of the loved image blooming so lushly within,
when and if fertilized fully by others, that it illuminates the outward
self and the unwary "buy" it as the genuine, wild, free-growing thing—
perhaps through a desperate need of their own to bring *this* into their
lives—instead of the carefully nurtured, artificial hothouse plant that
it is. And, of course, there must have been in Grandfather, as there
has been and is in me, a host of half-conscious stratagems, the devices
and pretenses that enhance and maintain the illusion. Without (I think
I say in fairness) being consciously hypocritical, we have ourselves
worked furiously at the weeding. *But who can destroy the canker at
the heart of the rose?*

And for all the special privileges, the admiration and even adoration, the blue ribbons and the cakes and honey, there is a heaviness
to this task—I say task—of carrying around this image; at times,
and increasingly, there is an unbearable heaviness to it. It is secretly a
Midas treasure, an iron rose, the heaviness of which one would relinquish
joyfully, were it possible. But it is not possible without humility, and
humility grows wild among the acknowledged weeds, blistered by
a burning sun, rocked and drenched by fierce storms.

Grandfather found a release at last, I think. I have often speculated about his (at least locally) famous jeremiad at the age of
seventy-five, his fierce exhortation to love. I know that he told my
father that *he* had inspired it, but I am inclined to think now that

Grandfather was also both castigating and purifying himself, rather than aiming his words at his congregation. Whenever I reread those words and the reiteration of "love . . . love . . . love," I feel the anguish and joy that he felt over at last coming upon and making his own the wild and tough weed of humility. And this my father, alone among his children, understood; I think he also understood that, if he was the inspiration for the sermon, its tone was as remote as possible from his own.

But then, released, did Grandfather sink peacefully into the relaxed *appearance* of senility, embrace a second childhood, freed from the iron rose, content in genuine humility to have others confuse simplicity with feeble-mindedness? Clearly, I want to believe so, yet I know that, to the contrary, the last stage of Narcissistic Man may simply be a reversion to the first, most primitive aspect of demanding to be, and being, loved. And this would consist simply of snuggling up to whatever human warmth one might find, insisting only upon cherishing arms around one. Is this what "the return to the womb" means?

If so, then Grandfather only snuggled, whether with his Abishag, the delinquent nurse, or under the blankets, close to Lloyd in the cutter. Lloyd—because he alone had never worshiped at the feet of the idol; there was no lingering compulsion to maintain any pretense with Lloyd.

Whichever explanation the true one—or a mixture, a blend that stubbornly resists analysis—somewhere hereabout lies the explanation (as nearly as I can find one) for the comfort (peace? animal equilibrium?) of Cornelius Herrick's last days, so precisely opposite to the stony end of my other grandfather.

A long pause. After the subtemperate climate of Narcissistic Man, one cannot leap directly into the chill in which James H. Nicholson lived. "The stony end of my other grandfather," I just wrote—and for some reason checked myself from writing, "of my black grandfather." Pity? If so, for him, the prototype of Daemonic Man, or for myself, the possessed?

I feel as though I must approach him, and that part of myself that he symbolizes to me, circuitously, warily. The thought occurs to me that I am less willing to be open about this aspect of myself. Or is it that I know less about it, am able to learn less?

I'm not sure, but as I wrote "the prototype of Daemonic Man," I suddenly thought of an incident of some five years ago, when I was traveling in the South. Waiting for my train to pull into Richmond,

I stood in the corridor of my car, directly behind a man I had noticed earlier with interest. For the next five minutes, I was absorbed in my examination of this man. He haunted me, and when I crossed town in a taxi to get my train back to New York, I determined to try to set down my thoughts about him while they were still fresh.

I did this. Sitting in my roomette on the New York train, I wrote some six or seven pages at a furious pace, savagely, illegibly, as though I were possessed.

I saved them, and I'm now going to copy them here, persuaded that they have some connection with my concept of Daemonic Man, even though the Southerner about whom I wrote and Grandfather Nicholson could not be more dissimilar in most respects. Perhaps, too, I can in this fashion better ease into what I have to say about my black grandfather in me.

Herewith the passage written in Richmond:

Who is this man? For years I've been trying to describe him, to define him, to single out that particular discriminating trait, to draw that single final line that would distinguish him from his brother in New England, in the Middle West— and never have I been able to. Yet he is not really like his brethren; there is no one like him—gentle, amiable, ready with a smile and a summoned greeting. Summoned—this is the trouble; it is summoned from a place no deeper than the larynx. Observe him in what passes for repose; come close and watch him when he is alone, unengaged, relaxed, simply waiting. What has become of the gentleness? Where has the amiability fled?

Coming up in the Chesapeake & Ohio from Hampton to Richmond, leaving the strangely poignant flatness of that flatly brooding land, half marsh, half fir, leaving the warm house three parts surrounded by water, where the wind mutters in the pine trees like the ocean, and pulling into the Main Street Station, I stood behind one of these men for five minutes, close behind him in the corridor of our car—so close that I could see the pores black on the back of his roughened, maplike neck as though I were studying them through a magnifying glass.

I gazed at them in fascinated absorption, as though hoping to read in their leathery topography some sign, some mystical adumbration of this recurring question—who is this

man? this middle man of the South? This man neither aristocrat nor poor white trash—weatherbeaten, weather-roughened,
silent, bleached and lonely.

In repose—or that lack of animation that passes for
repose—he is forbidding. The thin sharp nose, the thinner
lips, the shadowy hollows of the cheekbones, the grooved lines
so deep in the forehead that dust could lie in them, un-
deterred, the mouse-gray hat with the thin band, creased to
make it as anonymous as possible, the string tie, the dun-
colored clothes: he purses his lips briefly, shrugs or twitches a
shoulder, turns and turns back.

This is granite, and one watches the work-hardened
hand, the veins prominent, the square blunt fingernails corrugated but clean, as it clutches the window rod for support.
Strong honest hands—this is granite and one is moved to
hyperboles about the strength of a democratic nation. Until
one sees the eyes.

Hard too—agate hard, blue of a blueness close to absolute, but expressionless, as though from squinting defensively
against the sun. Only there is no sun, it is night, and still
they keep this steely, meaningless glint. There is no depth to
them, or at least the depths are wholly, finally hidden by the
film of blue—obdurate, constructed to endure, cold, frightening. Whatever tenderness, whatever general concession to
human frailty lurks behind, would be denied. There is a set
to the blueness that is final. The lines around the eyes may
crumple in friendliness, the lines around the mouth crack
into a smile of welcome, the thin, tinny voice say flatly,
nasally, "Hey, h'y yuh?" as he spies someone he knows. The
hands might twist in spasmodic tenderness—touching a grandchild. But the glacial austerity of these eyes is locked there,
permanent. Gestures may be made to cover their intransigence;
the finality is in them: they hate.

I felt all this, wondering about him, wondering why, staring at the thick, round, implacable toughness of his neck—
seeing the skin as elephant hide, in its way as tough and impenetrable as the eyes. Why? Why did he hate so? And how,
when his name is multiple and legion, could we ever placate,
satisfy, win him? How could we melt the ice age that dwells in
his eyes, hope to prevail against the glacial hate—bring green
birth, green peace into the gentle land that he inhabits?

The anonymous Southerner and Jas. H. Nicholson are doubtless worlds apart in origin, education and interests, yet I am sure they have in common this central unrelenting hatred. And although I desperately want (never more so than in the last few weeks) the insights that an understanding of the source and motivation of this hatred would bring, I find it just as hard to understand in my grandfather as in the man on the Chesapeake & Ohio train. There is so little of Jas. H. on record except as a public figure.

He himself has contributed one piece of evidence, however, that is both about him as a public figure and smokily revelatory of his nature. This is in an old scrapbook of his which I found after Mother died. In his large and regular but rather spidery hand, he wrote in the front "Jas. H. Nicholson," and the contents thereafter consist entirely of rusty newspaper clippings, pasted neatly on page after page.

They tell of the trial of one Jim Lucas, farmer, held in 1875. Lucas had been accused of impregnating (*sic*) and murdering a girl named Ella Henderson, who had been found face down at the shallow edge of a pond near her home—a girl to whom Lucas had been paying court. There was, of course, no witness, but a great deal of damaging circumstantial evidence.

The clippings provide a day-by-day account of witnesses' testimony, of counsel's questioning and cross-examinations—finally the summarizing arguments of the lawyers for either side. James H. spoke alone for the prosecution, two apparently prominent Connecticut lawyers for the defense. To my intense irritation—and perhaps the further illumination of Grandfather's nature—the clippings end before the verdict. But his whole summarizing speech is there. It begins as follows:

THE LUCAS TRIAL

THURSDAY AFTERNOON

Mr. Nicholson's Argument

At the opening of the court in the afternoon, State Attorney Nicholson began his argument substantially as follows, there being a large attendance especially of ladies:—

and concludes:

> Mr. Nicholson's argu-
> ment occupied nearly three
> hours and was heard amid
> the most profound silence
> in the court room. It was a
> masterly grouping and pres-
> entation of all the salient
> points in the overwhelming
> array of damaging details
> against the prisoner, and
> was delivered eloquently
> and effectively, and with
> nothing strained or labored
> in the manner. If the pris-
> oner is acquitted it will cer-
> tainly not be because the
> prosecution has not been
> ably conducted and the case
> most thoroughly worked up.

But from all the columns of Grandfather's argument, mostly paraphrased, but with some direct quotations, a short paragraph near the
end interests me by far the most. I have read all the clippings carefully
and find the newspaper's summary of the way he presented his case fully
warranted, insofar as one can judge from reading alone. Jim Lucas must
have wished Jas. H. in hell more than once during those three hours;
reading this, I thought of that other defendant who had articulated just
that wish. Grandfather's mind, as illustrated by this argument, was as
relentless and implacable as a steel trap, with a really extraordinary talent for both logical and persuasive structure. There is little suggestion of
any imaginative or literary gift: his imagery and quotations tend to the
florid and lack originality. The over-all effect leads one to think of him
as the Majestic Avenger, as frightening to an offender because of his
stateliness, dignity, calmness, as because of his ability to marshal the
evidence.

But back to the particular paragraph—two from the conclusion of
his argument, and a direct quotation:

"Your Honor, if in conducting this case I have seemed overzealous
to secure a conviction, I beg of the court not to attribute it to any unjust

intent against the prisoner. May the court construe it rather, as I firmly believe it to be, the result of the natural character of my mind."

The natural character of his mind . . . What was it in him that made him so resolutely turn his back always on life—on all the warmth and tenderness; on the giving, supple, rewarding interplay of human beings; on laughter and comradeship with men, the love of women and children. *This is what Julie has meant.*

I do not really know, of course, yet whenever I speculate upon it, I remember a haunting dream—a dream of two or three years ago. Seated with a group of friends upon summer sunlit grass, I felt that I must leave them, must turn my back upon so much laughter and gaiety and love. So I rose and started slowly away, looking back once or twice as though, if one of them were to see me and call me back with a specially affectionate protest—for me alone—then, on those terms only, I might return. But no one did, and as soon as I passed through a grove of trees and lost sight of them, I pulled out a pair of dark glasses and a tin cup, and, sitting by a sidewalk, sought alms, all the time feeling a black hatred for that happy, sunburnt group upon the grass.

If the condition on which I would have returned to that group is reminiscent of the side of me that resembles Grandfather Herrick, the turning away from joy, the pretending to be blind, the torturing of myself with hatred and rejection make me think of my other grandfather.

He called it the natural character of his mind—and he was referring to more than the turning of his back on life; he meant, clearly, the compulsive need, the devil within him, that wanted to go farther and punish others (himself, first of all, then?)—kill, wherever he could, the laughter and the sunlight, the play of life. It was as though, himself ordained never to find joy, he would not permit it to others. There is a terrible, vindictive false righteousness in such natures—and, if one knows about it from the outside, or in theory, one must suppose that if they are so cruel to others they must first be equally cruel to themselves. In experience I have found this to be true. Somewhere, near the source of life, a wound was inflicted, so deep and damaging that the wounded finds it almost impossible to admit its existence. Yet it still stings and burns; outraged, its victim lashes out about him, seeks to cancel the original unidentified grievance by the infliction of more pain, upon himself or others.

There is much, as I have said before, that I do not know about James H. Yet surely, even with this fact, it is significant that I have never heard a tender story about him. (The single exception, the lone intimation of such a possibility in him, I found myself in a fragment of a letter he wrote to his daughter Cora.) I am sure of this much: driven, he drove; wounded, he wounded; haunted, he haunted others. Hurt, he turned his back, to be vulnerable no more; still hurting, he turned around again and, in a cold fury of pain-induced righteousness, attacked.

What then of me? An almost endless conflict. Let someone praise me warmly, lavishly. The Cornelius in me basks in it like a lazy cat. But the James H. part of me scorns it—and the giver. "Consider the source," it points out. "You know it isn't true; this person is a fool." So I distinguish between the two, and how easy and clarifying it is to make the distinction. Yet I realize almost immediately that in the set of Emerson that belonged to Cornelius Herrick, and which my Aunt Rosalind recently gave to me, *he* marked the following sentence in the essay "Circles": "The love of me accuses the other party." In all the four volumes of the set, he marked only some seven or eight places, yet this was one of those!

Sometimes—and this is still worse than their opposition—the two grandfathers become tentative, suspicious allies. Let Julie really open her deeper feelings to me in a moment of mutuality: Cornelius responds, but always with an accent on self—or if on her, on her as *his* wife; James H. is openly determined to hold such love, such life, such mutuality, at arm's length, and finds a way to reject the gift, through coldness or sarcasm or blunt irrelevance. The one deadens through his drowsy, narcotic and indolent response, as though nodding to his wife while looking away into a hand mirror; the other kills outright, whether violently or through slow suffocation.

The one is life, but weak, fed as it were intravenously. The other is death, but filled with a dark daemonic energy. Both are afraid of life, but one cajoles and wheedles it, the other turns savagely away from it or attacks it.

Somehow the energy must be purified. I believe that it can be. These last two weeks have been bad ones for me, filled with uncertainty and conflicts. I have had little heart even to attempt to write in this book. P.H. has seemed cold to me; I haven't heard again from Abe Fortune. Dud Foote is busy with his family, and Dennis and I have become nodding acquaintances—ever since that night at the Swazey. He always looks reproachful, though I didn't do or say anything to cause this reaction. That night—it seems so remote now. The experience I had when I wrote to Julie deadened the other thing, made it meaningless. There's been no recurrence of *that* feeling.

Why am I listing all these people and relationships? To keep from writing about Julie and *her* letter, her reaction. To blur and soften my disappointment, my hurt. Though God knows much of what she said is true, and often I believe just what she said, literally—and do respond to it. But I can't help feeling shut out, especially whenever I run across something in the house reminiscent of her or the children: a scarf, a doll's shoe, a comb, sometimes simply the echo of last month's running feet.

Yet a few times during this period I have felt my own particularity, in a soberer, steadier way than I have known before, almost as though it were a premonition of a time when I may have a full sense of self, know daily in my bones that I am one, though not without inner conflicts and divisions to be resolved—a particular, fallible, faulty *one,* given to passions and needs that drive me fearfully at times, but withal myself, and mostly content to be myself.

But until then—if there is a then—I am a battleground. I am inhabited by strangers, who war within me. And chief among these are the two I think of as my grandfathers. Sometimes. For there was also the dream of the ballet of the two clowns.

In this dream I was a spectator. The white clown danced coquettishly, played the soft buffoon, made of every step a matter of self-ridicule, self-humiliation. With exaggerated gestures, he implored everyone to help him, to love him, to cherish him, then would manage to trip himself or tear his costume in some embarrassing spot. His painted smile was a Chaplinesque mixture of ruefulness and self-contempt.

The black clown was savage. All the time the white one went through his antics in the center of the stage, the black clown was dashing, with great leaps and threatening gestures, in a large circle around him. His movements were replete with viciousness, wildness, sadism. And gradually he closed the circle.

I remember the chilly anticipation with which I observed the black clown close in on the foolish white one. I wanted to call out a warning, but I could not.

Then they began to dance together, pantomiming a sort of ritualistic prize fight. The black clown would lunge, the white clown drop, felled. But little by little it became clear that this was not simply pantomime; the black clown was really striking him, brutally, viciously. And always the white clown would stagger to his feet, with a silly, fatuous smile, and offer himself for more punishment. Silly and fatuous—but there was something more in the smile now: a terrible frenetic meekness, a hectic determination to be beaten, humiliated, destroyed. His head bobbed in a sort of idiot dance; his hands opened and shut convulsively.

I pleaded with him to stop, to stay down, to flee this black killer. But he would not, and since it had come to the point where I could stand it no longer I woke up.

[*Part Two*] **2**

WHAT, then, of Patience Walton? How did this woman—always described as small, delicate, gentle—endure all the years of her marriage with so inscrutable and unrelenting a man as James H.?

Walton found it baffling, when he tried to remember everything that his mother had said about *her* mother, to realize that he could recall only two comments, although she had spoken of her many times. When her mother was mentioned, Marcia Herrick was apt to say, "She was a true gentlewoman." And when Walton showed Marcia some of his precocious literary efforts, she remarked, "You must have inherited your talent from your grandmother." Not much to go on.

Yet he had a chance to judge the second remark quite early. One day when his mother was on her knees in the attic, sorting out from a trunk souvenirs to keep, alternately exclaiming in happy reminiscence and in sadness—now saying, "Oh, I simply must tell you about this," now shaking her head meaningfully, thoughtfully, making a sound of commiseration with her tongue against her teeth: "When I think of all I've been through"—Walton inquired whether she had saved any sample of Grandmother's writing. She had, and presented him with five or six stories, written in a clear, serene hand, perhaps a little immature, and rolled and tied with pink and blue ribbons.

He read the first avidly, the others with waning interest. He would not have read the last two or three at all, had his mother not been observing him. She watched him intently, and at last, unable to wait longer for his comment, said in a tense voice, "Well? What do you think of them?"

It shocked him, he remembered, filled him with a sense of impropriety, that (though he could not then so have articulated what he meant) she, a mature woman and his mother, should be waiting anxiously for his verdict—not because she wanted to find out something about him, but because she was secretly so unsure of her own judgment that she would accept an eleven-year-old boy as arbiter. And again, not as a literary arbiter (in *that*, for all her pretenses, for all the pressed flowers and the underlined passages in her copies of the books of James M. Barrie and Henry Van Dyke and David Grayson, she had little real interest; she mooned over poetry and prose filled with noble and beautiful sentiments in a concern to bolster her conviction of the validity of the ideals she professed)—but as the judge who should hand down a sentence, favorable or unfavorable, even life-giving or destroying, upon the merits of the Nicholsons.

Facing this anxiety, and sensing dimly that he was being presented again—there had already been other such occasions—with a responsibility for which a boy was unfit and unprepared, he mustered the best reassurance he could and declared them fine. She gave him a long, searching look, and then seemed satisfied. She was already tending toward a device that was to become crystallized and fixed in her later years, when it sometimes seemed that she possessed a hidden mechanism (an automatic switch like that which turns on an oil burner whenever the temperature of the house drops below the level set by the thermostat) which would not warn her, but actually shut off her inner ear from hearing an unpalatable truth, an unbearable reminder that she had not been right about something to do with the Nicholsons.

In simple fact, Walton found his grandmother's stories trivial. They were pleasant, innocuous romances, old-fashioned stories of virtue sustained, chastity rewarded, evil thwarted: written, however, in a sufficiently decent and viable style, and with some slight saving evidence of humor. She had apparently given little enough of herself to them.

Or was that true? Slowly, without any very active thinking on the matter, Walton came to believe—fully aware that he might be fabricating the whole business—that he had gained a few insights into the character of Patience Nicholson from these fragile stories. He felt confident, for one thing, that her writing had not been merely an "escape" in the easy generalized sense, but a positive way in which to reaffirm to herself the continued existence and meaning of the simple values and principles in which she believed, and wanted to keep on believing. And he felt sure, too, remembering "Patience in a rocking chair," with her lace cap, her tatting, and her really serene expression (the only certain serenity, he realized, startled, in either line of his heritage, except that of his father in the last years before his death)—he felt sure, remembering this quality of hers, that she had possessed a flexibility, a resilience, beyond the power of Catherine Herrick, for example.

True, his mother told him often enough that Grandmother Nicholson never openly opposed the will of her husband, did not interfere with his stern control of the children, did not challenge the punishments (usually corporal) that he bestowed upon them with an impersonal equity —as *he* saw it. But she did comfort them afterward, and in a way that never made them question her loyalty to their father. Moreover, even the one exchange between Patience and James H. that Marcia had overheard and related to Walton—the one about his interference in the affair of Emmy Burgess—was substantial evidence that she was not afraid of him.

Yet Walton did not know, could hardly surmise, much more than these generalizations about the relation between his grandparents. Occasionally he would summon up the image of these two as, for instance, they might have been when preparing to retire for the night. He could see the tall dignified figure of James H. pacing the floor beside a big, canopied four-poster—and always, to Walton's surprise, not even the incongruity of that full black beard over the long nightshirt that clipped his grandfather's shanks was able to destroy the sense of dignity.

And since, Walton sometimes thought in amusement, this largely unconscious attempt of his to despoil Jas. H. of his majesty of bearing failed, he felt obligated thereafter each time to clothe his grandfather in a resplendent black-and-gold dressing gown.

In this imaginative scene, Patience Nicholson was always seated before her dressing-table mirror, brushing her hair in long, even strokes, sometimes pausing, hand and brush uplifted, the wide sleeve of her silk kimono slipping back to expose the delicately rounded lines of her arm above the elbow—held there, in arrested fluid motion, to await the climax of the torrent of anguished words from her agitated husband.

For in this game of ancestral paper dolls, as Walton called it to himself, in this setting of a boudoir that probably never existed, James H. finally lost his otherwise unshatterable calm ("with nothing strained or labored in the manner") and became overtly the tormented man that one could otherwise only guess at. And in Walton's perhaps febrile imagination, as the gobbets of self-reproach and self-hatred gushed from the lips of his grandfather, Patience Nicholson would slowly put down her hairbrush and deliberately stare for a long moment at her image in the mirror, until a smile that Walton could hardly define appeared almost imperceptibly at the corners of her mouth and her eyes suddenly became languid, softly enfevered. Then she would rise and slowly, almost as though she were sleepwalking, glide to him and place her slender white hands upon his arms. Standing there in flat bedroom slippers, the top of her head reaching only to his chest, she would lift her face and offer her lips. . . .

On the marital bed thereafter, the scene lost for Walton the sharp, clear outlines it possessed until this point. He knew only that his grandfather raged like Zeus or Vulcan, or perhaps Samson in torment, driving, as it were, all his accumulated agony into the tender flesh of Patience, burying his self-hatred in her receptive body.

One visual image only of this fierce mating emerged. This was the transformed, luminous face of his grandmother. At the moment of realization, her face grew smaller, its bone structure still more fragile behind the now radiant, almost transparent texture of her skin. A fire burned there—and a black tenderness deep in her suddenly enormous eyes.

Musing now in middle age, on the nature of this transformation, in particular his emphasis upon how the face of the woman became smaller, Walton's interpretation was different from what it had been in the past. For he had himself actually observed this diminution of the beloved face a number of times with a number of women, always assuring himself that this was a subtle symptom, a sure symbol, of the presence of *love.* When this tender shrinkage, with the corresponding dilation and deepening of the eyes occurred, the woman loved him. When it did not, it was merely a question of a sexual encounter.

But now, in this imaginary mating of his grandparents, and seeing his grandmother's face, as it were, through the eyes of James H., he was freed of a preoccupation with self, and the unconscious bias of an interpretation favorable to self. It finally occurred to him that it was very strange indeed that love should be registered by any diminution of the beloved object—with a complementary implication about the lover!

Uneasily, he ducked around the corner of his mind, to get out of sight of this proposition before a direct confrontation of it became unavoidable—muttering as he went that it was at least possible, since he envisioned his beloved's eyes larger and more tender, that it was a question of the spirit waxing greater and the corrupt flesh waning. With this genuflection to his Calvinistic heritage, he returned skillfully to his initial premise about the *presence of love.*

What remained, in terms solely of Patience and James H., was his grandfather's need of his wife as a vessel for his violence, his raging and passionate hatred of himself and his need to project this otherwise insupportable burden away from himself, to divest his loins of their accumulated anguish. And Patience? With this fantasy, Walton's formalistic sentimental portrait of a meek but strong little woman, shored up by a

profound religious conviction, was wholly dissipated. Patience in a
Rocking Chair was exorcised, transformed into a wraith; the conventional
virtues of her pastel-ribbon-tied stories took on an entirely new significance: the semblance of a blind, behind which to hide an uneasy sense
of a reality too violent to accept or endure consciously. The need of
James H. became crude and obvious beside that of his wife; Walton had
a completely new and inclusive understanding of how the "true gentlewoman" could have borne a life with her black, forbidding husband—
and an uneasy intimation that, if shrinkage of the face meant love, he
had better extend his definition of love.

But, of course, he reminded himself, this *was* fantasy. He *knew*
nothing of this sort about his grandparents; the conclusions he should
draw from these feverish reveries were conclusions about himself. Yet
no documented history of the life together of James H. and Patience
would ever be available, and eventually the power of the recurring image
became sufficiently strong to assert itself as a different but even more
urgent reality than that empirically demonstrable.

And, granted this hypnotic suspension of disbelief, one could make
a sufficiently plausible case for the validity of something approaching
Walton's general hypothesis. What, for example, could one expect of the
offspring of such a union?

Exactly, Walton thought, what did happen. Even making allowance
for the rate of infant mortality in those days, and the fact that no certain
remedy was available for many diseases that are no longer dangerous, it
would seem that James H.'s spermatozoa were poisoned and that
Patience's womb received too willingly the venom.

Patience bore James H. Nicholson eight children. Four of them
died before reaching the age of three. Years later, Walton was to see the
family plot in the old Stamford cemetery—see it under somber enough
circumstances and in a gray drizzling rain that required an awning over
the newly dug grave. Yet even then, in a mood of depression, he found
relief in the four small headstones—one marked "Josie," one "Patricia,"
and the other two simply "Nicholson infant," with dates. Relief, for
without giving them any careful attention he had an impression of carved
cherubs and a sort of hearts-and-flowers motif that lessened the bleakness of the scene and the occasion.

Yet their deaths had surely brought no measure of relief to Patience
Nicholson, and she must have suffered no less poignantly over at least
two of her four children who grew to adulthood.

The oldest, Cora, had all of her mother's sensitivity, without that counterweight of delicate toughness. She regularly regarded her father with a precarious sort of awe; she was actually known to turn as colorless as water when he raised his voice, and several times to crumple noiselessly to the floor, as though either to run or to utter a sound before fainting was at once too strenuous and too assertive. Walton, hearing a few stories of Cora's childhood, could only wonder how she had retained the required minimum of "sanity" as long as she had—or, rather, what heroic measures her mother had resorted to in order to effect this holding off of the inevitable.

But everyone who had really known Cora was as vague about her as she herself had been about making demands of life. All Walton really learned was that she had attended and been graduated from Miss Meecham's School, a select nearby seminary for young ladies, had made samplers, read poetry and consorted gently with other frightened and retiring girls through her twenties—having exercised most of the spirit she could muster in refusing to have anything to do with young men.

Then, at something like thirty, she had begun to "decline," as Walton's mother put it. There was apparently no sudden cause for this wasting away, but several physicians were of little use beyond lending official confirmation to her status as an invalid. Before long it was clear that she was not only sickly and losing weight, but that her mental faculties were impaired, as the genteel expression of the time went. Despite periods of perfect lucidity, there were times when she would abruptly begin to giggle and, if pressed—as she sometimes was by her father—babble half-childish nonsense.

With the passing of time, Cora became more and more the sort of family ghost who remained, unseen but whispered about, in an upper chamber, or who was glimpsed at a distance in the evening, walking somewhere in the orchards of the Nicholson estate, trailing a big straw hat in one hand. . . .

"Then they put her away." Again Marcia Herrick's words, uttered in one of her strange mixtures of sadness and inverted pride, all the while watching Walton sharply for the faintest indication of contempt, of a turning away from her because of the tragic vagaries of her family. She first told him about it long before the beginning of a period of Awful Secrets: there was a stretch of a year or two, when he was in his teens, during which he might be forced to listen to such a recital on an average of once a week. There were so many ghosts—not to be laid, alas, but to be pacified.

They put Cora away in a "nice sanatorium" some fifteen miles from Stamford, for the other children were growing up and finding her not only mildly disconcerting in her own right, but a vivid embarrassment to their friendships with others of their own age.

Thereafter she and her father never laid eyes on each other, but she wrote him voluminous letters. He would retire to the veranda to read these, staying out there alone so long every time that Marcia told Walton she believed he must have read each letter over and over again. Yet when he came in, to dinner or to the perusal of a legal brief, he never mentioned the letters, or even betrayed by the slightest expression or gesture how they affected him. Patience Nicholson would look up, search his face, and resume whatever she had been doing. And Marcia did not believe that her mother had ever seen one of these letters, or even learned whether or not he replied to them.

Meanwhile, Patience went to Heart's Haven, the sanatorium, every Saturday afternoon, always taking a little bouquet of flowers, tied around the stems with a pastel ribbon, or some carefully wrapped delicacy like guava jelly or freshly baked cup custards. She went quietly and undemonstratively, and returned as she had gone. Once in a while, at the dinner table, she would say, quite unexpectedly, something like, "Cora looks so young," or "Cora ate all the blancmange I took her"— firmly, clearly, to the momentarily bemused family, but without obvious emotion. And James H. would nod gravely to her, then go on talking about the previous topic of conversation as though there had been no interruption.

That was all. That was all Walton knew about his aunt, until, when he was fifteen, his mother was notified of Cora's death and he accompanied her to Stamford for the funeral. It was a quiet, decorously rustling affair, attended by some dozen ladies of middle age, friends of his mother's and—in one or two cases—of Cora's earlier days. Everything was hushed, but sensibly hushed, and marvelously free of the barbaric emotionalism which he later had reason to associate with funerals; under the circumstances, tears could be explained only as produced by aroused associations or by a general sentimentality about the tragedy of waste.

The only really striking thing about the occasion to Walton was the face of the corpse. He had been prepared for grotesqueness at the worst, inanity at the best. Instead, he found himself looking at thin, gentle features of a surprising tranquillity—features that brought back with startling clarity those of his grandmother—startlingly, since she had died when he was only six or seven. In view of his inexperience, he could not know it then, but in retrospect, when he had a basis for comparison, he realized that this had not been an artificially induced serenity, either— indeed, that for all the wonders of embalming there was no such thing.

No, he had a sudden disconcerting feeling, even at the funeral, that this woman must either have been, not only sane, but exceptionally sane— or else that she had found some ultra-rational peace through the knowledge that she had escaped and even outlasted the father who had both fascinated and terrified her.

This line of thought was uncomfortably heady for his age, yet he could neither shake it off nor disclose to his mother his sudden intimation that Cora must have, in deliberate self-preservation and with a sort of instinctive cunning, willed herself, however unconsciously, to revert back into a forbidden and hence inviolate childhood—only, perhaps, thereafter to leave it when she chose. The letters? He could at the time hardly bear the knowledge that he would never see even one of them, never know the slightest thing about their contents—for after James H. suffered his stroke Marcia had access to all his possessions, but never, she told Walton, had come across them.

Nor was he in fact ever to see one of Cora's letters to her father. But after Marcia's death in 1948, Walton went through an old trunk of hers containing many yellowed papers, tattered notebooks, and packets of letters. The faded-sweet smell, the delicate, almost colorless forgotten flowers, so brittle that a touch dissolved them into dust, the endless lines of poetry that Marcia had copied in her tall, dashing, spiked handwriting —all these brought him for the first time an almost overpowering sense of sadness. It was a sadness not for his mother, whom he had known, but the young woman whom he had never known, and who had hoped and dreamed and believed.

At last he took up a pile of uniform notebooks, with stiff board covers of a speckled red and white pattern. After opening a couple of them, it became evident that these had belonged to Jas. H., that he had used them for notes in preparing cases for trial—a separate case to each notebook. Walton also found the scrapbook containing clippings about the Lucas case in 1875, an apparently famous murder trial in which James H. had been the prosecutor, and about several others of which he had heard from Marcia.

Then, finally, examining a notebook dated 1893, he discovered a scrap of paper, a jagged segment of the first page of a letter in the thin, spidery script of his grandfather. A premonition of its significance set him feverishly to work checking the pertinent dates. This was dated 1893; Cora had been born in 1860 or thereabouts: it fitted together perfectly.

Walton read the fragment carefully, with a growing sense of discovery. After reading it a second time, he laid it gently on the desk before him and sat there quiet for a long time, staring at the wall.

August 20, 1893

DEAR CORA:

Daddy sends his little girl a kiss. Her last letter made him very happy, to know that

[*Part Two*]   **3**

WHEN the emotional sinews, the psychological tendons of a child are not strong and supple enough to bend and adjust to the warping pressures that all the dying life around them seems to direct against them—then the child may die. Or he may, more likely, survive, but sit out, as it were, his childhood, his growing time. A lonely and forlorn spectator, huddled against the cold in unidentified bleachers, he may gaze, eyes covered with a protective film, at the unedifying spectacle on the field before him. Precocious, conspiring, he will see everything and misinterpret most of it.

It took Walton Herrick years, decades, to realize fully that something like this had happened to him. But before he could apply this understanding to himself with any confidence, he had begun to perceive the nature of this process in others. He began to see how many of his friends and acquaintances, having missed their childhood, its unencumbered sense of self, its freedom to stretch and grow, to be—not just to exist—were now groping toward a childhood, a sprouting time, in middle life, though outwardly functioning with decorum in a recognizably adult pattern. There were mornings on a commuters' train to New York when he looked about him at faces, known and unfamiliar alike, and was sure that he could see in every one the lineaments of the lost child, now surreptitiously and incongruously peeking out through the physically adult features, above the buttoned-down collar, behind the morning newspaper.

And so, he thought, it was handed on. Groping for themselves, never willing it so, people prevented their children too from having their growing time.

This haunted pursuit leads ultimately, at its radical end, to an absolute retreat into childhood—or a grotesque, fantastic substitute for childhood. With old people, who have lasted most of the way, we speak of senility or "second childhood." But in terms of those who succumb earlier, we refer to pathological conditions, to psychopaths, to schizophrenics, or—in the vulgar version—insanity and crazy people.

Walton's family—indeed, his families—were full of all this, but it only came home to him with a terrible direct impact through his sister Elinor.

It seemed strange to Walton always—and sometimes with a frightening sense of unreality, as though she had never been there at all in actuality—that he could remember so little about his sister from the childhood they spent together. When he thought about Elinor, it was as a fixed entity in the scheme of things—not as a sister, not as a person at all. She was fastened there, somewhere on the nerve scale, and every time the finger of his memory touched her note, the sound that issued was dull and flat. He would feel a moment's acute pain, and then a dreary melancholy laced with guilt and self-contempt.

All this, of course, from the days of her illness and the slow disintegration of her nervous system and, eventually, personality. But when he forced himself past those twenty-five years of misery to the period when she must actually have been *there,* more or less fully, he still couldn't find her. A partial reason, he thought, must have been his preoccupation with himself, at least from the time of his own enforced period in bed. But not all. He remembered her presence once or twice in a childhood scene of some security, warmth and happiness: once before the family fireplace, eating supper with him on a cold winter night; another time, shouting joyously because she had found, in a field adjoining their home, a valued ring lost by a neighbor. But mostly he remembered his mother telling her, "No, Mother doesn't think it wise for you to do that."

Of course Marcia said this as often to him, but he learned to withdraw, to a large extent, out of her reach. He was in a way terribly dependent on her, and for a long time could not rebel actively against her; but while she could and did limit his life, elicit from him a full outward, however sullen, obedience, he was too wary for direct combat.

Elinor had more plain spunk, but she didn't have enough. She stamped her foot; she shouted; once or twice she flatly disobeyed. But she was no match (what child would have been?) for a woman whose horizon was ringed with overpowering fears, who felt herself the incarnation of protective motherhood, standing on a bluff, say, overlooking the windswept ocean under a lowering sky. So she saw herself, Walton was sure—whether or not in this particular image—erect, defiant, sheltering a child with either arm.

Elinor succumbed—in actuality, Walton supposed, little by little, but, it seemed to him then, in dramatic catastrophe. He remembered most vividly, when Elinor was a freshman in college and entertaining her first grown-up date in the living room, how he—at fifteen—called his mother insistently until she finally left them to find out what he wanted. He begged her not to return to them, to let Elinor have a date alone, the way any girl would. Marcia's face was at once amazed and angry.

"Why, I wouldn't think of it," she said. "She's only seventeen. Besides, he likes me. He enjoys having me there."

A year later, during the Christmas holidays, Elinor was one of thousands in Cleveland hit by an epidemic influenza. But in her case, as in a few others, this was followed by encephalitis lethargica, and it in turn by Parkinson's disease. Then twenty-five years (Walton was surprised to realize how long a stretch of time this was, even though he always thought of it as an endless desert waste of dreariness and hopelessness) —twenty-five years of slow deterioration, and finally death.

Even in so hideous a parody of life, even during this degenerative process, there were, for some years, astonishing spurts of the expression of a will to live in Elinor. But in the last five years of her existence all hope was gone; the muscular and over-all physical decay was followed by the psychological—to the point, if not of the extinction of personality, at least of its reduction to the terms of an early senility. In the final years of her life, Walton ceased thinking of Elinor's development as having ended at the age of eighteen, leaving her, so to speak, pinned there, emotionally and intellectually—for he realized that she was now regressing into childhood.

Here, at last, Walton came to believe, was her revenge on Marcia. The first stages of Elinor's disease after the initial weeks in bed were marked by an overwhelming inertia, a need for protracted sleep, and a tendency, when walking, to move as though she had never wakened. Her eyes were glazed, even glassy, and her movements were stiff, like those of a jointed doll. She lurched and even tottered, as though she had forgotten how to walk normally.

A sequence of several physicians followed, wholly baffled by her condition; they attributed it to what they called, in easy generalization, "a nervous breakdown." This diagnosis, it turned out, was accurate enough, although they had no really exact idea of what they were talking about.

It was clear that she had been working too hard at college, had set herself goals that she was not equipped to meet, since she was a good student only in the sense of conscientious but superficial application and mechanical mastery. The capacity for the rest—the imaginative grasp

of whatever materials—had been squashed out of her. The whole
family knew that she had overworked, and so informed the doctors, to
give ignorant support to the concept of a nervous breakdown. But it
was only after seven years, and the advent of Dr. Beardsley, a quiet,
sharp-but-kind-eyed, stoop-shouldered man in his middle thirties, that
they had a scientific diagnosis.

Patiently, and too dryly for Marcia's taste, he explained that this
particular form of encephalitis damaged incurably the motor part of
the nervous system, tore loose from their moorings the nerves that
enabled one to relax in or after muscular action—hence the jerkiness and
rigidity. There was no known cure—indeed, how could one repath
these nerves?—but there was relief, still in the experimental stage, in
the form of stramonium, the product of an herb which induced a partial
relaxation. It was believed that its constant use might shorten life, and
that it eventually lost its effectiveness, little by little. But there was nothing else.

The stramonium did help for some years, but it was not a question of
"nothing else." The therapy Dr. Beardsley introduced by stimulating
Elinor's interest in books, in music, in languages, and in typewriting for
the help it might bring in slowly regaining some use of weakened hand
or finger muscles—all this was tremendous. Implicit in the program was
an encouragement to independence, and when Marcia began to realize
this she fought it blindly, without knowing that she was. "Typewriting!"
she would snort. "As though she could or would be a stenographer!
Walton, there's something queer about that man. I think he has an evil
influence on Elinor."

The good doctor (a cliché, but for once, in Walton's opinion, holding a profound validity) could not in the end prevail against Marcia, time,
the slackening effects of the drug, and the years of apprenticeship to the
denial of life that Elinor had served. Yet he provided her with the
nearest thing she ever knew to happiness, in the anticipation of his visits
and the resultant quickened sense of her own importance as a human
being—no longer either a wooden doll or an alternately obedient and
frustrated child. And perhaps, Walton finally decided, Dr. Beardsley
would have at least half succeeded, had not the impulse in Elinor to get
even with Marcia been so strong.

Here the ultimate irony—and herein the essential story. Elinor's
childhood had been so constricted as to leave almost no room at all
for individual growth. Walton sometimes thought of the difference
between her childhood and his in this fashion: Marcia sent them both out
in the yard "to play." She tied a length of clothesline around Elinor's

waist, the other end fastened securely to the clothes pole. When she turned to Walton, he ran and squeezed through a hole in the boarding to hide under the back porch. Occasionally she could cajole him out, but more often gave up in angry despair when he stubbornly remained where he was. Thereby he kept for himself one thing—a relative freedom of movement, although within a drastically confined space, bereft of sunlight. Elinor had more apparent freedom, and in full light, but every time she moved spontaneously and with any real energy, she was jerked back and sent sprawling. She was trained in such a way as to become wholly subject to the arbitrarily fixed limits of the length of the maternal rope until, as she grew older, one could almost see her jerk back as she came, in whatever circumstance, to the borders of her conditioned experience. The new, the unknown and therefore dangerous, Walton would explore with considerable timidity and tentativeness, sometimes groping as though fearfully in the dark. But the same conditions induced in Elinor a convulsive epileptic dance of terror and revulsion.

The more hysterical her rebellion, as vagrant spurts of a will to life recurred from time to time, the more resolute Marcia's determination. And eventually Elinor came to indicate such impulses by nothing more than a twitch of spontaneity, an ache in the limbs denoting a migratory dream of the life that might have been. "Growing pains," Marcia might say.

But she did not know what she was saying, what she was doing. That, it seemed clear to Walton, must be acknowledged. Marcia Herrick was no monster—and she believed with all her heart that she hated cruelty and tyranny. But the lenses through which she experienced life were sufficiently distorted to have caused a person with normal eyes to dance in pain if he were forced to look through them. And the distinguishing character of her vision, it came to seem to Walton, was that, herself having been all but crushed by the overpowering will of old James H., she had retreated behind her copy of his mask—as her way to survive.

Behind the mask she was terrified—of everything. She had gone through life looking over her shoulder. Her addiction to cathartics and enemas; her so constant application of nitrate of silver to her throat that in old age her complexion turned a gray-blue from the poisoning; her incessant fear of fever ("Your head's hot" . . . "Let me feel your forehead" . . . "Is my head hot? Feel it . . ."), so interminable that both she and the children were as likely to be seen with thermometers in their mouths as not—these, among a legion of other symptoms, were sufficient proof of a life riddled with fear.

What she did to her children, then, in a world empty of her father, she did because she could not help it. And brooding on all this, and particularly on Marcia's acting in the image of her father, Walton finally thought he saw caverns of black fear in old James H. himself. However compulsively masochistic Patience's reception of his fury, as Walton had dreamed it, was it not possible that he must return, in one respect at least, to his original picture of her strength, and recognize at the least—and in however distorted and perverse a way—that she may well, no, *must* have known of the springs of fear at which her husband drank, and never feared him because of this, and because of this have been actually the stronger of the two?

At any rate, it became abundantly clear to Walton that, far from finding marriage to a crippled man abhorrent, Marcia would probably never have married anyone except a disabled man as truly gentle and kind in nature as William Herrick.

Thence, to *her* daughter's feeling for *her*—and ambivalence toward life and her own destruction. Elinor's revenge on Marcia was surely unconscious but nonetheless slyly deliberate. The nerves and sinews of body-mind decide and act without consulting conscious intent. Elinor was still, at eighteen, as much Mother's little girl as many children of eight—more so than healthy eight-year-olds. And when the disease filled her (invited unconsciously, Walton also came to believe, if only in the sense of her being run down and helpless through being exhausted by the discrepancy between the demands she made on herself and what she could actualize) she let go and knew the darkly negative satisfaction of, in effect, saying, "All right, you've kept me a child; now you take care of that child."

At first, of course, it was a question largely of caring for an invalid, one who did not need a wheelchair, but always the supporting hand, the partial supervision, the defiantly courageous companionship—courageous in the face of gaping or averted faces, curious or revolted by the spectacle of jerky movements, slack jaw, fixed and seemingly unfocused eyes. Walton accompanied Elinor many places in those days, even obediently had her up to college to a dance, did not complain but suffered excruciating torment, and avoided such assignments when and however he could. But Marcia bore it as her cross with a proud, even haughty demeanor. In fact, as always, she leapt into the breech from the beginning with an alacrity that an "outsider," observing, might have found surprisingly like the movements of joy.

From a post of sustained observation and supplied with the antecedents of the situation, would that observer have surmised that

Marcia, bemoaning the devilish cruelty of fate, nevertheless, when alone and not to be overheard even by her conscious self, was muttering that now her little girl was at last safe from the hostile world, to be guarded always by herself?

Walton did not know. And he did not want to trace the ambiguities implicit in her feeling this way and at the same time deafening blind Heaven at times with her outcries against his father, charging that his crippled condition was a communicable deformity, which might be inherited, even if in a delayed manifestation. And William, as Walton once overheard him in something between prayer and self-reproach, wondered in all earnestness what he had done that God had visited this reminder of his failings upon him, and sought the aid with which to endure this visitation!

At any rate, during those early years after Elinor had been struck down, she and Marcia were almost inseparable. Gladly consigned to the outskirts of their alliance, Walton nevertheless was close enough much of the time to overhear something of the terms in which they constructed their joint fantasy world. Elinor would recover; she would "grow strong and well"; she would marry and "have a normal life"—all in due time. (Marcia's unfailing proof for this last eventuality was her own marriage to William.) And meanwhile Mother would never desert her little girl; she had seen much sorrow and endured many calamities: she was strong enough to support many more.

So we huddle together in the darkness, Walton thought, if we are not persuaded that to be alone would still leave someone there.

If Marcia and Elinor were inseparable during these years, they were *one* in the later period. Between came the interlude of Dr. Beardsley and an enforced, if only intermittent and spasmodic, prying apart, to permit brief snatches of a private life to Elinor. But this was only in the nature of the appearance, two or three times in the course of a day spent under massive gray skies, of a pale and faintly glimmering sun. Mother and Elinor's revenge motif won out; and eventually, some fifteen years after Elinor's first illness, they moved away from Cleveland and Dr. Beardsley.

Thereafter, the drug slowly lost its potency; there was no interruption of the two women's intermingling, their merging into one strange, warped personality. The parasite vine climbed upward on the tree until the trunk disappeared, and the weaker growth so covered its support that almost all one saw of the tree was its dark nourishment of the vine. Marcia's life, in old age, consisted wholly of attending Elinor: from seventy-five to eighty she performed prodigies of care and attention before which one forty years younger might well have quailed. Common sense pleaded that each should be in some sort of home, separated from the other, cared for by competent people; yet they clung together, fought, made their peace like lovers, and Walton had not sufficient courage to tear them apart. So he bought them, when he could ill afford it, a little house in Ridgefield, over which Marcia presided.

Weighing ninety pounds, her once ample frame shrunken close to the skeleton, Marcia cooked, nursed, scolded, petted and telephoned the physician, groaning under the burden but finding in it the whole meaning of her life. And with William Herrick dead some five years, she would from time to time reverse her old complaint and lament, "I am paying for my sins; I did everything wrong for you children." But she would always conclude, "What *did* I do wrong, Walton? What did I do wrong?"

Withal, she survived Elinor by almost two years, her hauteur toward the world almost unbroken, and discovered in a quiet, informal old ladies' home enough to find fault with to insure the maintenance of some interest in life to the very end.

At any rate, in these last years, Elinor retrogressed to the point where she was exclusively obsessed with a few physical needs, chief among them her fear that she would not be able to urinate. The creeping disintegration of muscle and nerve and the resultant lack of voluntary control had long since rendered her close to helpless. With the thumb gone limp in each hand, she could not feed herself; her walk was all a tottering now; and when the sphincter muscle became affected, her days and nights were filled with terror. Whenever she was relieved, and knew a few minutes of security, her pleasure and interest were in childish things: she endured the amenities of alleged maturity for a little while when family or friends visited her, but she much preferred a bright color, a pretty pattern, a string of beads that might have been a toy.

So she went back, although racked with terrors and pain, into childhood—beyond, into the darkness in which one can only curl up in the original position, to seek and find the ultimate relief of nothingness. And so through all the years Marcia Nicholson had her little girl, and toiled for and defended her on past her own eightieth birthday.

Walton eventually made the inevitable comparison with Aunt Cora; there could be no doubt that Cora's was a much happier variant of this retrogression. She had known no such physical distress, and there was a removal from the overwhelming parent—even a reconciliation on a different basis, if one could trust the evidence of the fragmentary letter.

(Had it ever reached her? Why was it in James H.'s scrapbook?) At
any rate, the face Walton saw at the funeral knew some sort of peace
and a found refuge. Elinor's dead face wore an implacable expression of
hatred. Walton, alone of all who knew her, saw her dead; what he saw
was hatred. Several years later, he could tell himself that perhaps the
expression was caused by the rigid way the undertaker had set the lips
that had always, due to the shortness of the upper one, been opened a
little—but he knew he was talking to himself against the dark.

Elinor's story ended in 1946, only a year or two after she and
Marcia moved to Ridgefield. As the final regime of terror, the fear of
"bursting" as she called it, grew closer and closer to being unbearable,
the doctor, on call two or three times a day, warned Marcia that she must
send Elinor to a sanatorium. Then, late one November evening, Walton
was called in New York and told that the most severe attack of pain and
hysteria had resulted in her being taken to the hospital in Danbury.

He reached the hospital early the next morning, to find that Elinor
had been so irrational and screamed so much that she had been placed
temporarily in a room away from the regular patients. He found her in a
bed set amongst various pieces of hospital equipment; it was a room
through which nurses constantly moved, to carry off or bring back this
or that. Several young nurses were there now, half amused at Elinor—
or so it seemed to Walton then—and calling out to her such things as,
"Wassa matter? Want a date, babe?" and "For Christ's sake, stop yowling
like that; you're driving me nuts."

They were probably suffering from that almost universal embarrassment at the sight of derangement and physical atrophy, and filled with a
conscious need, as apprentices to their profession, not to be soft or
sentimental. Yet there was no room in Walton at the time for such
understanding. Elinor's hair was uncombed and matted with sweat; an
ill-fitting hospital nightshirt barely covered her; her eyes were literally
starting from her head in fright; and she was wailing a soft but insistent
low lament that conveyed no certain emotion but seemed rather the
mournful, mindless dirge of a homeless spirit lost beyond death.

She was not *there,* in any real sense, and this somehow at the
moment seemed more unbearable to Walton than it would have been
to see her desperately aware of the situation. He went over to her: for a
moment she stared at him blindly; then she shuddered, and recognition
came back into her eyes fearfully, sullenly, slyly—as though she were
afraid of the retribution it might bring with it.

She reached out a shaking hand, exploring the air between them,
and then burst into tears and clung to him. "I thought you would never

come," she said over and over, and "It was so awful."

In the ambulance that took her to a highly recommended sanatorium in Stamford, he sat beside her and held her hand. All the way she said little, only occasionally, "I want some water," and "Hello, Waltie" (a name she had used, to tease him, when they were little, but never since); she even made her first attempt in months at a smile. But by the time they reached their destination she was having another attack and screaming in a world he couldn't reach.

Walton was not reassured by the appearance of the assistant physician at this place, a gross man of enormous size and small, somnolent eyes. But he was due back in Ridgefield to tell Marcia what he had done and then return to New York. The head of the place seemed pleasant and competent, and, assuaging his guilt over the possible new terrors awaiting Elinor, Walton tried to persuade himself that she was not going to know where she was.

He was, it turned out, right about that. The next morning the head of the sanatorium called him at his office to tell him that she had not at any time since he left been fully conscious and that her temperature had now reached 104°. He urged him to come out to Stamford immediately if he wanted to see her alive again.

He went, with a good friend, a New York physician, and saw this time that the place was really run on a humane basis, saw many of the patients. Elinor lay in a coma, breathing slowly and heavily. Her fever, with some final reinfection of the whole cerebral system, had reached 106°. They had done what they could to make her presentable. At least, her hair was braided and her face washed, but her mouth was open, and with her all but destroyed teeth showing she was not pretty. Yet somehow, this once, at long last and for the last time, the lost sister came through to him and he saw there, blossoming from the broken mind and the racked body, the little girl with whom he had played, whom he had once loved and then, so strangely, long ago lost sight of.

He wept and, his friend the doctor later told him, though he remembered only vaguely, stroked her hair and spoke to her tenderly, so that she stirred a little, as though in some otherwise incommunicable comfort. And he wished later that he had not seen her the next day at the undertaker's, mouth set in that implacable, unyielding hatred, so that the eyes, covered, yet seemed to be staring at him unforgivingly. Even then it struck Walton how unfailingly, over a period of more than half a century, the Nicholsons had continued, here in Stamford, their somber drama of disintegration and death. The Nicholsons, but also "Alas, the whole place has fallen into degenerate hands," Cornelius Herrick had written in the very paragraph in which he had referred to the room in which he, his brother and sisters had been born as "the room given up to sickness."

Marcia visited in Walton's home in New York for several weeks after Elinor's death. Then she settled down again in the Ridgefield house with a local woman acting as companion, and spent occasional weekends in New York with Walton and Julie.

During the first half of that winter, it seemed to Walton that she was surprisingly docile, but little by little she regained her indomitable spirit and even, occasionally, resumed the *grande dame* manner that, in her prime, had caused much hostility and some amusement. To guests in Walton's apartment, for instance, she spoke of her "ancestral home" in Ridgefield. This was literally accurate, of course, in the sense that her father had grown up there, and several generations of Nicholsons behind him. Yet the manner in which she spoke conjured up a huge mansion and a vista of rolling lawns and terraces, rather than the tiny house she actually inhabited.

Late in February, Marcia spent one of these weekends in New York. On Sunday afternoon, Walton took her home by train. As usual, when they arrived at the little Branchville railroad station which served Ridge-field, they were met by Mr. Hornsby. He operated a taxi service of sorts; that is, he regularly ferried people to and from the station in his 1926 Chevrolet. This car was always in a high state of polish; and although it creaked and rattled and groaned, taking fully half the journey in second gear, a combination of Yankee thrift and caution kept it adequate to the occasion.

This was also true of its owner. Mr. Hornsby (he made one feel that he had no first name) was the most consistent and the least communicative of men. He was always dressed in a slightly shiny, but neatly pressed dark blue serge suit, a string tie and a stiff collar. So far he looked like the popular rendition of an undertaker. But he made the concession to informality of wearing a soft gray felt hat with a snap brim, and there was a weathered look to his otherwise small, meek grayish face that suggested that a decent reticence made him seem milder than he really was. And his conversation, unlike the professional facility of the funeral director, consisted entirely of "uh-do" and "guh-bye," with only a slight convulsive nod of the head to indicate his acceptance and appreciation of the fare.

When Marcia and Walton descended this time at her house, she sensed immediately that something was wrong. It sometimes seemed as though she could smell trouble before anyone else felt the faintest apprehensiveness, but Walton finally came to believe that she so confidently expected trouble, on all occasions, in all situations, that inevitably, when there really was something wrong, she was the first to spy it. The validity of this premise was confirmed in his mind by observing its reverse side: how slow she was to relax, to relinquish the last of her suspicions, when everything was clearly all right.

At any rate, what she noticed first on arriving home this time was that no smoke was rising from the chimney. As they advanced toward the house, leaving Mr. Hornsby to wait in the car to take Walton back to the station for his return trip to New York, her certainty of disaster increased.

"I knew it, I knew it!" she exclaimed, stiffening and tossing her head in scorn—for with her indignation always followed hard on the heels of fear, whether as a chain of cause and effect induced by pride, or as an antitoxin she injected to prevent the spread of the first emotion through her whole system. "Mrs. Lee has deserted me!"

Walton didn't answer. She was always given to melodramatic expressions, especially to ones that suggested a comparison of herself to a nation, a species, or some vast prototype such as Womanhood in Travail or The Mother at Bay. He was busy trying to insert the key in the front door lock; for some reason it stuck, and before he could turn it and open the door her voice issued forth again, with a resonance that it seemed impossible could come from so slight and frail and old a body.

"Don't move, Mr. Hornsby! Don't move an inch! We may need you. There's no fire in the hearth."

Her tone, her gesture (one arm raised commandingly and a finger pointed upward), suggested a general rallying his men at the crucial point of a battle in doubt—or, perhaps better, a militant angel or one of the more aggressive Old Testament prophets, exhorting the Forces of Light against the Host of Satan. She was so thin (really the incarnation of that tired phrase, "all skin and bones") that she suffered acutely from the cold, and therefore swathed herself in a huge old coat with squirrel collar and cuffs, under which she would wear a light summer coat, a padded jacket, and three or four layers that she considered proper house wear. Whenever Walton thought of this peculiar costume, which made her appear stout to the point of roly-polyness, and of the startling contrast provided by the thin, pointed old gray wrinkled face that peered out above it under an outmoded black felt cloche he realized again how really potent her personality was, how really bruising the impact of her will—that it should be able to overcome so easily the impulse to laugh.

And Mr. Hornsby, although he had had no intention of leaving, jammed his foot as hard upon the brake pedal as though he were playing with her an elderly version of "Still water, no more moving!"

The key grated in the lock, turned, and Walton pushed the door open, to be swept by what seemed, even to him, a glacial current of air. Marcia, peering over his shoulder, uttered a wail of lamentation not to be scorned by the Trojan women—a wail, however, that was almost immediately tinctured with anger.

"I knew it, Walton, I knew it!" Her eyes flashed balefully, in defiance of the event; her lips twisted in disdain for the offender. "I knew it! Mrs. Lee has deserted me, and the furnace is broken." Then, turning and descending the two steps of the doorway carefully, in gingerly fear of a fall, she reissued field orders to Mr. Hornsby.

"It's no use," she cried desolately. Walton experienced, as he had many times before, a realization of the intimate association, for her, between desolation and triumph. "It's no use, Mr. Hornsby. The furnace is broken and the house is like an icebox. I shall catch my death of pneumonia; there are icicles hanging from the chandelier."

Despite his forty-odd years of life with Marcia, Walton looked, half-credulous, at the chandelier. It swung idly in the breeze from the door, indubitably unencumbered brass. Then he winced, as Marcia's voice rose half an octave.

"Don't just sit there like a ninny. Go and find Mrs. Lee! There's no use just sitting there like a lump on a log. My son can't leave me now; he won't desert me."

Walton heard the grinding of gears in a car that had never known such an indignity before, and then a noise that suggested that the little Chevrolet was bucking and heaving like a recalcitrant pony. He did not look. He went over to the thermostat and, moving it from its minimal fifty degrees to seventy, heard the familiar starting lurch and steady beat of the oil burner. . . .

Mrs. Lee had indeed, for reasons that Walton forgot over the years despite Marcia's frequently reiterated summary of their callousness and irresponsibility, neglected to come over that noon and warm up the house, and she was indeed guilty of reporting back for duty a half hour later than the time scheduled. But after an hour or so of speculations about chills and pneumonia, the grim self-administering of a dose of two teaspoonsful of whiskey in a glass of hot water, and the thaw in relations with Mrs. Lee, who was sufficiently resourceful to know that if she matched Marcia's haughty reproachfulness with a resolute refusal to acknowledge guilt, she could induce fear and a more conciliatory attitude—after an hour devoted to the gradual restoration of that state of armed truce that passed for peace in Marcia's ménage, Walton was permitted to telephone Mr. Hornsby to take him to the next train.

"You are a good son," his mother assured him with the approximation of serenity. "You saw me through this terrible shock. You stood by me."

Walton was tired, and he didn't challenge her interpretation of what had happened. He was glad enough to climb into the Chevrolet beside Mr. Hornsby, grateful in anticipation of his silence throughout the five-mile run to the station.

But they had not gone more than one of those miles when Mr. Hornsby broke silence in a reedy but vehement voice.

It seemed to Walton that he had said, "She's the spittin' image of her father," but this seemed so unlikely that he asked Mr. Hornsby to repeat his words.

Mr. Hornsby cleared his throat.

"I said she's the spittin' image of her father. Old James H. Nicholson. The Honorable, as he called himself. And maybe he was honorable; I don't care to say as to that. The High and Mighty, we called him. The meanest and hardest old bastard I ever laid eyes on, if I am his cousin. Asking your pardon, since you're his grandson. I got no quarrel with you."

Walton stared at him.

"You mean—you knew my grandfather? You knew all along who my mother was? And you're her cousin—or his cousin? We're cousins— and you've never said anything about it? Why?"

Mr. Hornsby seemed to draw his head in, like a turtle. From under protective cover, he looked at Walton shrewdly, but in a not unkindly fashion.

"His mother, that was your great-grandmother, was my grandmother. Reckon that makes us second cousins, or first cousins once removed. Never could get that difference straight. And it was the Nicholsons that had the hard streak. My folks lost the name and the streak. Glad to say."

"But why haven't you ever told me?" Walton repeated.

Mr. Hornsby gulped: it was as though he had expended too much oxygen in all this talking.

"Saw no reason to. We never got along with the Nicholsons: they're too high and mighty. Had nothing against you folks, though. Till today. You heard her." He turned his eyes, suddenly flintlike hard and small, but not mean, simply intransigent, directly upon Walton. "You heard her. Raising high tantrabogus, giving me orders like I was a servant. You, too.

I don't see how you stand it, a nice quiet fellow like you. Suddenly she was the spittin' image of her old man."

It seemed to Walton that his expression was softening now, in contradiction of what he was saying.

"When you say he was the meanest old bastard you ever knew— what do you mean? What did he do?"

Mr. Hornsby shook his head.

" 'Tain't any one thing. He was a hard man—like he was made of stone. Proud and cold and—downright cruel, some folks thought. I tell you one thing (you know he was a lawyer, and a judge, too?): he prosecuted cases like he thought he was the Lord on Judgment Day. And so stiff-necked. My mother was his sister, you know. He treated her like she was the rubbish under his feet. I never forgave him for that."

They were almost to the station. Walton was suddenly intensely curious for details. This was the same old story; there was novelty to it, but no further real illumination. He asked abruptly, "But what did he do to your mother? I've heard this about him before, but very few stories of what he actually did—except for a few people he prosecuted, and his own immediate family, and—maybe one other."

Mr. Hornsby gave him a speculative look, and made some decision —whether to withhold or to tell him something particular, Walton didn't know.

" 'Twasn't a special thing he did to my mother; it was what he didn't do. Here he grew to be so rich and own a big house and a lot of land—and he never even gave her a Christmas present. I should say he never even gave her a smile. More right—for she didn't want money. We were poor but comfortable. But my mother was a woman full of Christian charity and love, and he had no feeling at all—no natural brotherly feeling. And her being younger, and respecting him so, it made her feel bad. Here we are."

His voice changed, left the range of a personal relationship, became the voice of Mr. Hornsby, private cab driver. Walton felt self-conscious about paying him; but Mr. Hornsby showed no flicker of embarrassment.

After a moment's silence, Walton held out his hand. Mr. Hornsby took it limply, suspiciously, as though he were forced to examine—and so hold—something wholly alien, perhaps even a little repulsive: an exotic bug? a wounded, fluttering bird? a garter snake?

Walton looked at him steadily; something different, new to him, was moving in Walton. Mr. Hornsby dropped his eyes.

"Perhaps he couldn't help it," Walton said, and walked over to the station platform.

Later, he didn't know just what he had meant; or why he had said it to Mr. Hornsby, to whom it was almost sure to be not only meaningless but ridiculous and perverse as well; or what the exact nature of the strange feeling within him was. But the two of them, during the remaining months of Marcia's stay in Ridgefield, never discussed family matters, and the only concession (if it was a concession) to this conversation that Mr. Hornsby ever made was to add to the words of greeting and good-bye an occasional, "Nice day." Nor did Walton ever tell Marcia of his talk with Mr. Hornsby.

[*Part Two*]   *4*

THE second of the four children of James H. and Patience Nicholson who survived infancy was the only son to reach manhood—Herbert. What an unenviable lot, Walton often thought: to be the only son of James H. Nicholson! Whenever he remembered this situation, he experienced a slight, but immediate, lifting of the load from his own shoulders.

Eventually, Walton came to know a good deal about Herbert Nicholson—more, in a sense, than his mother really wanted him to. Cora was an Awful Secret, but susceptible to Marcia's ennobling imagination —because she was remote, removed from the present scene. Herbert, on the other hand, turned up from time to time, at intervals crossed the horizon of Walton's childhood and adolescence, even came painfully close to him.

The difference to the Herrick family was marked in at least two respects. James H. had provided indefinitely for Cora, before his financial status suffered a severe reversal at the time of his stroke; Herbert he disinherited. Hence, frequently during the first twenty-odd years of his marriage, William Herrick was called upon to help Herbert with money —and though he was not ungenerous, money was not sufficiently plentiful to prevent family "scenes" on these occasions. In the second place, despite all Herbert's difficulties and vagaries, he was at large—not marked (with the easy confidence of the times in such distinctions) "insane" and stowed away.

It was, then, in terms of Herbert's periodical appearances—whether in person or through letters—that Walton measured the course of his life. He remembered him first (on a long visit to Cleveland) as a big, broad, stoop-shouldered, rather swarthy man in his late thirties or early forties—with an impenetrable shyness at all gatherings that included adults, but capable of surprisingly warm laughter and an easy way with children, as Walton and Elinor discovered on the few occasions on which he was allowed to be alone with them. He knew how to *do* things—that was the way Walton thought of it as a boy—and none of the Herricks did. He had a jackknife with which he could carve whistles that really blew, little figures that really stood up on their own feet, strong frames for kites that really flew. He told stories with people and animals in them that you really wanted to hear about; he built a sand box and a wooden platform on which Walton could run his toy trolleys and cars.

Yet the times during this long visit (some six months or so, and related, Walton eventually realized, to Uncle Herbert's lack of money) in which Herbert Nicholson was left with Walton and Elinor, unsupervised, were very few. This fact was never explained or discussed, but frequently, when it seemed that there was going to be a long, lazy, thrilling afternoon spent alone with this uncle whom Walton vaguely thought of as a sailor (perhaps partly because of his dark complexion; at any rate, the identification was related to the picture books again), Mother would appear and literally whisk one of them (the man or the boy) away. No amount of weeping, screaming or whining shook her purpose; if it was Walton she took with her, she would simply state, flatly though mysteriously, "There are some things you don't understand, dear; Mother knows what's *safe* for her boy," compress her lips, and stare fiercely off into the distance.

Then, about a month before Uncle Herbert finally left, there was a sudden flurry, one of those not unfamiliar but never clearly explained winds of anxiety in the house: Mother's voice raised, Father's groans, the slamming of a door and Uncle Herbert's banishment from meals with the family. Walton remembered most clearly Mother's getting out all the wooden toys that Uncle Herbert had made for him, and, wearing rubber gloves, scrubbing them with a colorless liquid, all the time muttering angrily to herself. But he also remembered being led into the bathroom, shown the toilet seat as though it were some rare and precious but poisonous flora, and being told that he must from now on always tell Mother when he wanted to sit down, so that she could sterilize it first—and that when he was standing up, he must on no account ever touch the bowl. Later, comparing notes with Elinor, he found that she had been subjected to the same discourse, with variations that interested and perplexed him a good deal.

During that stormy month, Walton actually saw Uncle Herbert only once or twice. Once, playing in the yard, he looked up by chance to see him standing at the window in his bedroom, hands flat against the upper pane, staring out. There was something frightening in the stance, menacing almost, and Walton scurried to a point in the yard from which he could not be seen. The other time, *he* was inside the house and saw Uncle Herbert slouching down the street, his hands deep in his pockets.

Then there came at last a day when the Herrick children were aware (as they had not infrequently been before) of momentous events, without being allowed to know their nature. They were led to the attic playroom, the door at the foot of the stairs was firmly closed, and they were told to stay there until called—told in a voice that meant disobedience would be rarely dangerous.

Walton spent more than an hour, however, standing at the foot of those stairs, with his ear pressed to the door. He heard a long conversation between his mother and his uncle, unable to make out many of the words, but understanding that she was urging, pleading, demanding, and that Herbert was answering her only in surly monosyllables. Until the end—when his voice suddenly rose, expanded, so that the words rested, swollen, hot and thick, upon the air of the house, long after he stopped shouting.

"You're just like him, that's the trouble with you. If you're generous it's on your terms. If you're friendly, it's only as long as anybody does what you want them to. For Christ's sake, I'm not the first man in the world to have gonorrhea and I won't be the last. And all your preaching won't prevent it, either. You can take your sanctified hospitality and you know what you can do with it. You'll never hear from me again. I spit on your help; do you understand?"

After the silence Walton heard his father painfully climbing the stairs from the first floor. Breathless, he listened, feeling that something even more portentous would follow. But when his father spoke in his clear, ringing voice (that was the first time Walton realized that a stranger, hearing the voice, without seeing the man, would envision a tall, stalwart figure), he said only, "Just want to wish you luck, Herbert. I hope the job turns out fine. Let us know how things go." Herbert's reply was again a sullen mutter. Then his footsteps down the stairs. Walton rushed to the window, almost knocking Elinor down, and she joined him with the intent of giving him a good slap.

Instead, they stood there, silent, motionless, watching Uncle Herbert go down the street, even more round-shouldered than usual under the weight of his sagging, lumpy old valise. There was a terrible disconsolateness in his figure, Walton thought even then; Elinor began to cry, though she hadn't really liked Uncle Herbert as much as he had, and some vague allusion (from where he did not know) to "those who descend into everlasting hellfire and damnation" settled sadly over his own mind.

Mother called them brightly, gave them a tea party which ended in tears and even a slap, because everyone felt frayed and tired. The years passed, and the next time Walton saw Herbert Nicholson was on the eve of Cora's funeral.

Between, there had been, despite Herbert's angry assertion, at least two calls for money. There had been an occasional Christmas package, about which Mother always said, "He made them himself! Don't make fun of them, children; he doesn't remember how much older you are. And it's the spirit that counts, anyway." It had not occurred to Walton to make fun of his gift—for the beautifully carved new whistle or soldier held a haunting, nostalgic appeal for him (his mother, incidentally, always opened Herbert's package in advance and disinfected everything in it). It was the twenty-five-cent pair of socks for his father, the messy, sticky box of candied fruit for his mother, that were really pathetic.

In a vague way, meanwhile, Walton had been aware that his uncle was making what living he could back in Stamford by acting as an agent for all sorts of magazines. But these were the crowded, self-obsessed years of adolescence, and he gave the whole matter little thought. He was, therefore, totally unprepared for the events of the night before Cora's funeral.

First, his mother engaged in a sharp telephone conversation with the hotel clerk.

"Certainly it's my brother, Mr. Herbert Nicholson." She enunciated the words in the cutting, haughty manner with which she always met condescension or snobbishness on the part of others. "You will please show my brother, Mr. Herbert Nicholson, to my room immediately."

Troubled, uneasy, sensing apprehensively an unpleasant scene to come, Walton looked at her as she replaced the receiver. Her eyes were snapping, her face set, her breast heaving a little. " 'There is a man down here,' " she repeated angrily. "Indeed! We'll show them."

And then, as abruptly as though she had disappeared and another person replaced her, her face became composed, almost expressionless, and she said quietly, "Your Uncle Herbert is coming up, dear. Let him know that you are glad to see him."

Why am I here, anyway? Walton later remembered having thought. Why had she dragged him, a boy in his early teens, five or six hundred miles for the funeral of someone who was only a name to him? Within a few minutes he was to be flushed with pride over her loyalty, her courage, her indomitable refusal to turn her back on the poor and outcast and miserable, her determination to face up with quiet grace to a real trial. Yet, if she had all these qualities, all this strength when she needed it, why did she need him too—making him miss a big party at home in the bargain?

He never knew fully until she was eighty years old. Oh, she'd told him often enough, "It means a great deal to me to have a tall, handsome boy of my own who cares enough about his mother to go out with her, who isn't so smitten by silly girls that he has no time for his mother. Especially when your father isn't able to do those things." But it was not until, in an extremity equaled only once before, he saw her old lady's eyes grow large with desperation and panic, her old lady's brittle hands clutch frantically at her lined but still soft old lady's face, actually breaking the skin with her nails, and heard her hoarse whisper, "I've always been afraid. So afraid. I don't know of what—or who. But I've never had a moment free from fear, this terrible, terrible, unbearable fear"—it was not until then that he knew with unmistakable clarity that the mantle of James H. Nicholson had rested upon his own twitching, unwilling shoulders. "You're so strong," she had murmured to him through the years, often at times when it seemed to him that his whole nervous system was screaming at the intolerable succession of demands made upon him. "It's such a comfort. You're so strong."

And so, while she had the courage and the nervous strength to greet her brother, when he knocked at the hotel room door, as though he were a prosperous, well-groomed and respected businessman, she could not do it alone—and she demanded insatiably of Walton that he be her companion knight-errant, that he share with her the morbid sequences resulting from her compulsive quixoticism—appealing, whenever he rebelled, to whatever was most likely to make him ashamed: his pride, his love, his honor, his duty—to everything he had been drilled to believe embodied the equipment of a virtuous gentleman, ever since he had been old enough to repeat the words after her.

And so, after ten or fifteen minutes of brightly affectionate and meaningless conversation with the shabby, stooped, semi-humpbacked and gnarled though burly gnome that Uncle Herbert had become, she said, nodding significantly to Walton, "Walton has several errands to do for me, Herbert, and he doesn't know how to find his way in Stamford. (It seems absurd, doesn't it?) Would you mind very much, dear, showing him around? Cassie Smith is coming to see me and we'll be having a chat—you know, about women's things. Gossip." And drawing in her breath sharply, she put her arms around Herbert, and kissed him warmly, tears in her eyes.

Tears in her eyes, Walton had thought, as the dismissed man and boy descended the stairs to the lobby. Tears in her eyes—but what about me? And instantly dismissed—no, tried to dismiss—as selfishness, as a lack of nobility, even of common decency, the cry of outrage that rose within him.

It was a bleak expedition. Later, Walton realized that his own sensitiveness to the situation—the high-pitched sensitiveness of his years to being thought ridiculous or queer, augmented by the rawness of his feelings about the way people stared at his father—had led him to exaggerate the number of pointing fingers and whispered comments, the smirks and outright laughs that their progress from errand to errand occasioned. Yet there were some in fact, certainly a sufficient number to warrant real discomfiture, and what pierced him even more deeply was the realization, from the greetings Uncle Herbert exchanged with a few people, that his uncle was the town character, the eccentric buffoon to whom the rest of the town spoke with half-amused, half-distasteful condescension.

They said little to each other, but near the end of the trip Herbert turned suddenly and looked squarely at Walton with a surprising direct shrewdness evident in his eyes.

"You're a bigger, stronger-looking feller than I thought you'd be," he said in a voice both hoarser and drier than the one Walton remembered. "But you'll need all of that. Don't you let her run your life."

That was all, but it was abrupt, and quite enough at any rate to discomfit Walton. He muttered something in reply—he was not quite sure what—feeling a sharp resentment, and they walked the rest of the way to the hotel in silence. A half block from the entrance, Uncle Herbert stopped short.

"There it is," he said, and added dryly, "I don't believe you'll have any trouble finding your way from here," and disappeared as suddenly, is seemed to Walton, as though he had vanished into thin air.

Here was one of the dilemmas that Walton found himself increasingly less able to deal with. His mother had been not only loyal, but even gracious to this—this clown. (Yet hadn't he himself, up there in the hotel room, resented the particular form that graciousness had taken, found in the way in which she had used him to effect it something specious and even selfish?) In return, this man, this brother, this town character, had spoken of her as he had, just now. (But wasn't it true, what he had said? Hadn't he spoken aloud the very thing that most worried Walton, most frustrated him?) It was one thing, he had slowly begun to realize, to have rebellious and skeptical thoughts oneself—quite another to have an outsider voice them.

He went up to the hotel room uneasy and troubled, but his mother introduced him to her old and unmistakably aristocratic friend, Cassie Smith, with the words, "This is my big boy, of whom I'm very proud." And through his superficial embarrassment he felt a returning warmth and loyalty. . . . Then, still later, when Miss Smith had gone, and they were saying good night, Marcia looked into his eyes and said simply, without apparent sentimentality or falseness, "That was a noble thing to do, son. In some ways you are already much stronger than I am." Replenished, reassured, almost exalted, he went to bed and slept tranquilly. . . .

Uncle Herbert did not attend the funeral. Walton saw him only once after that—some ten or twelve years later when he came on to Stamford alone to take charge of Uncle Herbert's own funeral. It was in May, and the Connecticut trees were unsheathing. Everywhere this feathery, soft green—and the melting yellow of the willows. In the young, dispassionate sunlight, the first day was not difficult. Walton went to the funeral parlor, identified himself and the shrunken, leathery corpse with a minimum of feeling. He did not even mind the overpunctilious politeness of the undertaker, unmistakably attributable to the latter's conviction that so seemly a young man must be experiencing considerable embarrassment at having to acknowledge his relationship to Quasimodo. He returned to the hotel, feeling at once free and depressed by the freedom (these were the years, after his first divorce, when he was living at home with his family, and had very little time to himself), had three cocktails and an expensive steak dinner, and found himself disinclined to continue the reading of *Axel's Castle*, which had so excited him on the train trip East.

And so he walked the streets of Stamford in the mild and fragrant spring evening, indulging in occasional unexpectant and almost sad fantasies about an attractive girl stepping up to him and saying, "I'm lonely. You must forgive me, but—"

He was as depressed as he had been untouched earlier in the day. In the first place, although he had volunteered to make the trip to spare his father, he now felt that once again too much was being demanded of him—that he was being burdened unfairly, as he had always been.

The second cause of his depression had to do with the undertaker's revelation that Uncle Herbert had taken out and maintained funeral insurance. Not much, to be sure—not enough to permit any but the simplest of coffins and burials. But this he had done, and when the undertaker rather unctuously suggested that Walton would hardly be satisfied with the rough pine coffin alone available under the meager budget, Walton had replied stiffly, coldly, "I respect his desire to take care of this himself."

Partially, then, his low spirits were caused by a feeling of guilt, of shame that he hadn't answered differently—but in part, also, in some strange way, simply by the fact that Herbert Nicholson had done this thing. This feeling he didn't understand, but it was perhaps the strongest part of the complex reaction he felt; he could not shake it off, and at last, just as it began to rain, he returned to the hotel, weary and disheartened, to shift and turn and twist on his bed until nearly three o'clock.

In the morning it was still raining, and he went through the ceremony at the cemetery grimly. In addition to himself, the undertaker and the minister, there were gathered under the awning only two other people, old friends (or retainers?) of the Nicholson family, gray and pinched, who shook hands dutifully, stared into the grave with a dazed absorption during the minister's reading, and fled precipitately the moment the service was over. The only relief Walton felt throughout was from his perusal of the infants' headstones.

There remained one task: going through Uncle Herbert's possessions. He had the address, and went directly from the cemetery. He was greeted by a rather sour-faced middle-aged woman with a prominent goiter, who said sharply, "Who? What? Oh, him," and took him to the head of stairs which apparently led to the basement; then, snapping on the light below, she left him with the words, "Nobody's touched a thing. We're all honest, God-fearing people here. Not that there's anything a decent person would want to touch."

The stairs did lead to the basement. Walton stood at the foot, bewildered and so filled with a strange, uncomfortable distaste that for a moment he considered running out of the house without examining anything. Then he heard footsteps descending, and was confronted with another middle-aged woman, half of whose face was covered with a dreary birthmark, but whose voice was cheerful, almost coquettish.

"You're his nephew? All his things are over there, on his bed. He hadn't much, poor soul." She clutched her sweater more tightly about her throat with one hand and extended the other to hold Walton by the arm. "He left me, you know. He got mad when I told him he'd simply have to wash his sheets once in a while, even down here. But he came back. Nobody else'd take him, he was that dirty. And he hadn't any money of course. That agency of his was just a joke the last couple of years. But I took him back, I'm that softhearted, and let him tend the furnace for his keep." Her voice changed, grew suddenly hard, suspicious and sharp. "He never had enough to eat. Even *that* I gave him—scraps from the table. I think he died from starvation, really. I didn't know he had any relatives; I was the one that took care of him—just me. It was charity."

Angina pectoris, the coroner had said. But Walton didn't mention this point. Instead, he said only, in a cold tight voice, "I'd like to look alone, if you don't mind."

She gave him an angry glare, turned around and started up the stairs. He could hear her talking to herself until she reached the floor above: "Oh, very well, my lord. Alone, indeed! It's small thanks you get in this world for a Christian deed. And him without even enough food and clothes!"

A greasy, threadbare overcoat, the pockets stuffed with notebooks, magazine price lists, five- and ten-year-old letters from customers. A battered valise—was it the one of twenty years before, on the ill-fated Cleveland visit? Within, a crumpled heap of dirty shirts with ragged collars, frayed neckties, a tattered sweater, some worn winter underwear with long legs. An old and empty brief case. And finally, here on the pillowless army cot with the dirty sheets and a single foul-smelling blanket, a cardboard carton, neatly bound and tied with cord.

Walton turned on the unshaded overhead light, hanging over the ten feet of floor between the cot and the furnace. He found an old rickety straight chair, dusted it with his handkerchief, and sat down directly under the light. Cutting the cord with his penknife, he discovered bundle after bundle of manuscripts.

Vaguely disappointed, he began to read. . . .

Two hours later, after the landlady had twice descended the stairs and twice been ignored, he stopped reading and sat there motionless, staring into the dim, cobwebbed corners of the cellar. He was aware at that moment, as he had never been before, and was not to be again for a long time, of the fundamental falsehood of his own life, of the gray and dismal defeat that he had characterized to himself as the pursuit of duty, of the timidities and inhibitions that he had called sacrifice or love, of the compensatory false pride that he had called sensitiveness. And he felt a despair so overwhelming that it did not seem to him that he could bear it.

At the same time, he knew that he could and would bear it, that he was by now so conditioned to hopelessness that he would go back to Cleveland and take up the familiar routine, strike the unchanging attitudes, and even—with a secret relish, although outwardly with grave reticence—tell the story of the poet in the furnace room: "A little like Blake," he would say, lying. "Nothing really that remarkable, you know, but with extraordinary flashes of insight, and occasional uncanny phrases and lines."

Lying, for it was quite mediocre poetry. Hundred and hundreds of poems, many only doggerel, the more pretentious ones actually inferior to the doggerel. And rejection slips, hundreds of these too, from every kind of magazine. Out of all this endless mass of rhymed lines, written in a childishly unformed, perfectly legible hand, only one contained anything beyond the banal and perfunctory. And even of this one, which was not good poetry, only four lines had struck Walton sufficiently to cause him to stop in his perversely continuing search—the inexplicable urge to which had made him persist, furiously turning page after page.

Only four unrhymed lines:

> I do not think in the furnace room
> To find a light, a star, a poem,
> That will repay the debt I owe
> For all the hate I've shed like sweat.

Only these four lines, and below them, written in a hand so hurried, so driven, so urgent that it lost all its customary round clarity, "The hate hate hate hate hate."

And so finally he folded this sheet of paper, put it in his pocket, dumped the rest of the manuscript pages into the trash can, and went up the stairs.

The two women were sitting in their living room, rocking ominously. Walton stopped at the entrance to the room. "You may destroy everything," he said. "There's nothing worth saving. And thank you for letting me look."

The woman with the goiter glared at him in silence, but the other said tartly, "Words of thanks are easy."

He hesitated; there flashed through his mind the possibility of at least giving them a few dollars; he dismissed it, more from the fear of being ridiculed over the sum than from prudence or parsimony; and left. It was still raining.

That night, he sat up on the train until late. Watching the solitary lights that blinked here and there in the dark night, somehow always before, on other trips, beacons of a warmer and more abundant life, he brooded over those four lines in alternate misery and unfamiliar hope.

In particular, he could not get out of his mind the words "I do not think . . . to find . . . that will repay the debt I owe for all the hate I've shed like sweat." It was as though they set in operation a monstrous telescope that, turned inward, opened to him his first clear vision of the constellation of himself. It was as though each part of what he now beheld were as different from the way he usually thought of himself as the actual appearance of a planet is from the twinkling pointed "star" it seems to be.

For a time he felt almost exhilarated over the discovery as discovery. But then, little by little, its meaning began to penetrate his excitement and to sober him. After a further half hour, he faced squarely for the first time in a long while the realization that if he did not soon make a break he would be trapped indefinitely, perhaps for life. Waves of a hysterical fever swept over him, successive and enervating tides of heat that nauseated him and even made him wonder if he was losing his mind.

Years later, looking back on that train ride, he could not remember just how old he had been: twenty-four, -five or -six. But, whatever his exact age, he had then repeated that number again and again to himself, realizing that, for most of that quarter of a century, he had done so little of what he had wanted to do as to constitute nothing. It had been as though there were some mechanic hidden within him who pulled the levers and pressed the buttons, who steered, and stopped, while he, his actual he, was only a passenger.

But what did he want to do? A new panic surged up in him at the realization that he didn't know—that when he had thought a moment before of never having done what he wanted to do, of desperately needing to break away, to escape, he had thought only in vague images of travel, beautiful women, achievement, above all else (although not specifically) of the freedom to decide what he would do any given evening.

But if he actually went home now, announced that he was quitting his job and leaving the family—where would he go? It was shocking to discover how alien the concrete possibility of setting out on an unfamiliar journey to an unknown destination was to him—worse than alien: frightening. There was no sense of adventure in him: the confinement he hated was still the set course of his life; he was conditioned by everything in his past not to leave that course.

Yet he must. His conviction of the applicability of the four lines of Herbert Nicholson's to himself, the sudden blinding illumination of the self-forbidden hatred and despair that were eating away the days of his youth demanded that he make the break. All sorts of tenuous promises, casual friendly suggestions of visits he might make, jobs he might be considered for, swarmed to his mind. He seized at each in turn, held it squirming under examination, and discarded it for what it had always been—a passing possibility, gone the moment after its appearance.

As each of these in turn faded out, his agonized sense of crisis grew.

At last he gave up the attempt to remember or think of an escape that could really be taken seriously. And, strangely, when he did, a calm settled over him. Very well, he knew of nothing specific. He would go all the same. It would be difficult, frightening; he would be open to the unending assaults of guilt and self-doubt. But he would do it. He would do it.

He slept fitfully, and in the morning he awoke feeling as though he were suffering from a hangover. (At that point in his life, he had experienced only one or two real ones.) By the time he was halfway home from the East Cleveland station in a taxi, he knew that he had given up. He had been drunk last night, drunk on words and on ideas that now seemed utterly fantastic—derived in all probability from the strain of his mission. He felt both security and shame as the taxi drew up before the house, and in the long talk with his mother that followed he skillfully re-created the sequence of the last several days, stressing the nobility of the hard-won insurance policy and the Blake-like quality of the poems until she burst out, weeping, "He was a true Nicholson, after all. And my boy had the sensitiveness and the fineness to see this through all the poverty and sadness! Oh, you don't know how I've suffered, how I've reproached myself!"

It was only after two days that she settled down to brass tacks sufficiently to ask about the disposition of the poems. Walton was hard put for a moment or two, but he finally confessed that he had exaggerated their quality; it was the spirit that mattered. The dream of a posthumous book had interested her only passingly; she accepted the explanation as a further proof of Walton's own generous spirit. He never showed her the one poem he had saved. . . .

[*Part Two*] **5**

MARCIA Nicholson was one of a pair of twins. Not identical twins: indeed, the two sisters were as unlike in their orientation to life as they were in details of physical appearance—having in common only the twin facts of their need to dominate (to be sure, in utterly different ways) whatever small circle they belonged to, and their sense of an implacable but indefinable doom incessantly peering at them from a corner. Yet, after the children who died as infants, and Cora and Herbert, they must have seemed paragons to their parents.

In the first place, they were the last of the Nicholson children. They were five or six years younger than Herbert; they arrived at a time when James H. was beginning to be embroiled in his determined fifteen-year effort to "make a man" of his only son. Secondly, and relatedly, they were girls, and as such to be awarded their smaller share of the special consideration he extended to their mother. This did not mean that he was never stern or severe with them; it did not mean that they were not afraid of him. But they had a more favorable opportunity than Cora, as the first child, to "survive," and Herbert, as the first son, to do a fair share of their own unhampered growing.

These were their initial advantages, and as time went on it became evident that they were both going to be more than ordinarily good-looking. They were referred to as "the beautiful Nicholson twins"; they were regularly eyed by the boys, and reasonably popular with the girls of their own age. After the tragic sequence of early deaths and clearly discernible aberrations among the Nicholson children, it was small wonder that Marcia and Lucia Nicholson (named by their mother) seemed for many years—to their parents, perhaps always—the final reward of God-fearing people who had endured great tribulation.

Yet they did not, of course, escape unscathed the family pattern of stern edict and hapless rebellion; the winds of fear and duty blew upon them too; the parent tree cast too heavy a shade and threw out too long roots for them to be uninhibited and straight in their growth. Substantially, Walton decided as he reviewed the whole tribe of Nicholsons —substantially, what happened to the twins was that through their various advantages over their brother and sister they escaped the category of grotesques and the charge of being "crazy"; they were able to function as "normal" human beings, which meant that they lived in a state of profound anxiety and uneasiness all their lives, coping with their innumerable emotional problems inadequately but with a sufficient superficial appearance of competence to "pass" in a society in which those who were really comfortable with themselves and their associates were so rare as to be thought a little queer anyway. They escaped with Marcia being called arrogant and vain and high-handed, and Lucia being considered soft and sentimental and helpless.

Striking differences between them were evident from the beginning. Marcia was always the "difficult" one. She was bolder—both in the sense of taking the initiative and in that of having more physical courage. But she was also the one to have tantrums—when there were any tantrums —the one to turn moody and sullen and, as they entered adolescence, to indulge in long melancholy reveries. Lucia sucked her finger and wet the bed much longer; she was also the one, and the only one, to win an affectionate nickname: Ludie. She was generally pliant and malleable, and she burst into tears at relatively slight provocation—but she was mostly sunny and smiling. She was to achieve her domination of people and situations much later in life through being helpless and appealing— through leaning.

By the time they were thirteen they rode horseback well (they had their own horses): Marcia like a man, Lucia side-saddle. At fifteen, on a dare, Marcia rowed out a long way in the Sound (their property went down to the shore) and sailed back in, using the shirtwaist she took off as a sail; Lucia, unable to bear the prospect of her sister drowning, had stayed on shore and notified their father, who was waiting grimly for the boat and the girl in her camisole. At eighteen, when both had been graduated from Miss Meecham's School, they sang in the church choir, went on sleigh rides (chaperoned) with young men from Yale, and had their debut in New York. Yet again the differences were marked. Lucia had a superb voice, Marcia only a fair one; yet Lucia did nothing with hers, while Marcia applied herself with almost fanatic intensity.

The divergences between the twins were in no way more apparent than in their relations with suitors—as young men who evinced any interest in a particular young woman were known in those days. Marcia, the more striking-looking, had one or two devoted young men over whose attentions she brooded, alternately endowing them with sentiments of a nobility that would have frightened them had they been aware of her expectations, and disdaining them for their lack of such ideals. Lucia's charms, if less distinctive, were more opulent, and enhanced by a temperamental disinclination—or, perhaps more fairly, inability—to say no that would probably have brought her to grief had it not been that Marcia kept a sharp eye on her. She was attended by easily ten young men to every one who pursued Marcia, was in love with all of them, and serious about none. Yet, oddly enough, at their debut, Marcia, flushed and graciously regal, carried away all the honors; she was borne from the arms of one importunate swain to those of another—while Lucia was, for some reason, less popular than usual.

Frank beyond her wont, whether from the unaccustomed champagne or the even headier wine of a triumph, Marcia confided to her sister later, as they were undressing, "It's the only time I've ever been more popular than you, and the only time I ever will be. I rise to only the grandest occasions, Ludie." And Lucia, instead of taking offense, shrugged her plump shoulders, smiled affectionately, and replied, "It's because you're really much more beautiful, darling, and you could do it any time you wanted to. Only, usually you're too fussy and particular. You aren't satisfied with the way things really are, so you're always disappointed in people and in parties, and then you're not friendly."

Prior to their father's stroke and the radical change in the family's fortunes, there were two incidents that served particularly to emphasize the distance between the twins' characters and ways of looking at things. The first occurred when they were fifteen, the second six years later. Walton heard his mother's version of each often, but he took the trouble, when in his forties he began brooding on the family record, to write to Aunt Ludie, by then eighty-four or -five, and ask for her account of them.

The first incident took place several weeks after Marcia's famous sailboat episode—famous because Lucia told all their young friends about it. At any rate, Marcia, dry-eyed and defiant, was still serving her one-month term of confinement at home every evening and being allowed no visitors. Otherwise, she would probably not have been in the house on the evening Herbert returned after being expelled from Yale; Ludie was at the home of a close friend, receiving a call there from one of her admirers.

Shortly after nine o'clock, Marcia, having finished her preparation for the next day's classes and begun an entry in her diary, heard the sound of a carriage drawing up before the house. She rose and ran to the window, peering out. She recognized Herbert in the lamplight, noted that the driver was helping him take down an unusually large amount of luggage and, remembering that it was the middle of May and a time when there were no college holidays, was immediately alarmed.

Alert and wondering, she continued to watch. After the carriage drove away, Herbert still stood there, surrounded by valises, portman-teaus and even a small trunk. He stood there, shadowy in the dim light from the house, obviously irresolute. From the dejected way his shoulders slumped it was clear that he was frightened. He looked the way he had when a boy of ten, awaiting terrifying punishment.

At last he moved, walked a few paces, but away from the house. After hesitating again, he disappeared down the path that led to the water.

Vague forebodings of wild and desperate actions, of catastrophes and tragic violences, crossed Marcia's uneasy romantic imagination. A hand to her throat, she considered for a moment disobeying her father's edict and slipping down the back stairs, through the servants' quarters, to follow Herbert. She anticipated the Gothic pathos of the scene that would ensue, the sad and lofty talk between her and Herbert under the willows, and the way in which she would strengthen him, there by the dark and whispering waters of the Sound. . . .

The tall figure of her father appeared below, casting a massive shadow across the rectangle of light thrown on the lawn and bushes from the living-room window. His commanding whistle shattered the night, silenced the soft, piping voices of the spring. One long, tremendous note, sustained without shrillness or apparent effort, it was the final, imperative summons to all the Nicholson children. And as Marcia watched, feeling a deadening, a conclusive hopelessness, Herbert reappeared, almost trotting.

The long shadow of a pointing hand now. In silence Herbert obedi-ently carried his luggage to the veranda directly under Marcia's window. His father helped him with the largest portmanteau and the trunk, but still silently, still without a word exchanged between them. Then they entered the house; listening, Marcia could tell that they were bound for the study, where all disciplinary sessions were held.

She hesitated only a moment longer; then she drew off her slippers and, lifting her skirts, with pounding heart raced silently down the back stairs, past Maggie the cook (who, being the twins' confidante, only grinned), and into the butler's pantry. There, crowding into the darkness beside the dumbwaiter, where an imperfect board left a chink in the wall separating her from the study, she listened.

When he finally spoke, James H.'s voice was grim, but no grimmer than the long silence that had preceded his words.

"A disgrace. A deserved disgrace. My son!" A pause. "I am satisfied that the men who administer the affairs of the Yale University would not expel a student unjustly." She could hear the sound of his heavy, measured tread, as he paced back and forth; she knew, without seeing, that his hands were clasped behind his back, and that his chin, his beard, was down on his chest. A cessation of the steps now, a pause. "What did you do?"

The ensuing silence was unbearable. Marcia knew the hot, cloudy look that would be in Herbert's eyes now, the way his head would be down, the way his sweet full sensitive mouth would be drooping. She prayed wildly, without words, for divine intervention.

"What—did—you—do?" Thunderous, overwhelming—the great judge of the last tribunal. Marcia clasped her hands together until they hurt; numbly, she was aware of a slightly salty taste where she had bitten her lower lip.

Again, the heavens splitting open: "What—did—you—do?"

There was a tortured, whispered answer . . . a silence . . . the sound of a blow—the dull, heavy sound of a blow struck with massive force. A terrible cry, not human in its agony.

Marcia fled through the kitchen, seeing fleetingly the white, stricken face of Maggie, a hand covering her opened mouth; she ran down the hall and flung open the door to the study, to stand there, panting, staring.

Hands clenched, breathing heavily, James H. Nicholson stood over the crumpled figure of Herbert. His back was to Marcia, and he was staring down at his son, so immersed in his own passion and wrath that he had not even heard the door open.

"You—are no son of mine. You—you unspeakable scoundrel." His voice was low, almost without inflection; the words somehow seemed the more final, the more terrible, for the fact that he was not shouting. "You leave this house tonight, and you never come back. I never want to lay eyes upon you again."

Herbert did not move. He lay where he had fallen, one knee drawn up as though protectively, his hands covering his face.

"You brute! You bully! I hate you!"

Marcia heard her own words with a curious detachment. She felt as though she had been split in half and—without consciously thinking of it that way—knew somehow that the split was permanent, that she would always hereafter be able to have one of those halves furiously engaged in indignation, in defiance, in whatever violent emotion, and yet the other completely withdrawn, uninvolved, watching and feeling nothing.

Her father swung around. Even in that moment Marcia noticed that there was more pain and astonishment in his eyes than anger. He swung around and stood there, staring at her, baffled at this new indignity, a wounded and heroic figure at bay, his great hands dangling at his sides, his fingers working.

"I hate you," Marcia repeated, somehow titillated by that strange division within her. "I despise you, using your big, ugly strength on us all the time." She had the most extraordinary feeling that in a moment, incongruously, she would smile.

Her mother slipped by her at this very moment, her face drawn, her dark eyes enormous and inconsolable. She moved past the colossal figure of her husband too, and, dropping on her knees beside Herbert, took his head in her lap and began stroking it. All in silence.

And in silence, James H. Nicholson, shaking his head from side to side like an infuriated agonized bull, strode to the window, threw it open and stood, his back to them, staring out at the black night.

As Marcia watched, motionless, her mother, whispering broken consolation to Herbert, began to sob. It was the first time any of them had ever known her to cry, and the effect upon them was immediate, beyond the power of all the preceding violence. Herbert stretched out a blind hand to comfort her; Marcia was conscious of a stirring within her, as though the circulation of her blood had previously ceased and only now begun again. Their father uttered a loud but muffled groan; then, drawing his head in from the window, moved with heavy strides toward the door.

But by now Ludie, having arrived home, had pushed in beside Marcia and, unaware that her hair was disarranged, her cheeks and eyes glowing with some secret warm knowledge, and that her slightly décolleté gown had slipped from a shoulder, exposing a little of her full young bosom—unaware of her own appearance—was staring, round-eyed, at the spectacle.

Their father paused before her, raked her with one wild, anguished look, and shouted, "Cover yourself up, you hussy! Take that wanton look from your eyes."

Ludie shrank aside, leaving Marcia to confront him. He hesitated and then said in a quieter voice, "As for you, young lady, you may hate me. You may call me bully. You may have no respect and love in you. But you have some spirit. I would to God you were my son."

They heard the heavy front door slam; the house trembled. And while they all, in a way, pulled themselves together, Marcia realized that the life was drained out of them; they were listless, without hope. Patience Nicholson took Herbert, nursing a great purple bruise on his face, off with her; the girls went to their room and undressed slowly, apathetically, saying little. When they heard the sound of their father's return, they only looked sadly at each other in silence. Their mother finally came to say good night. She made no further mention of the incident, but it was apparent to them from her manner that their father's disinheritance of Herbert had not been revoked.

When she had left, Ludie asked with a nervous giggle, "What on earth do you suppose he did?"

Marcia regarded her scornfully. "It's nothing to laugh at, for heaven's sake." And, stoutly, "I don't care what he did. Whatever it was, Papa drove him to it; he's always been hateful to him."

Ludie, combing her shining black hair, dreaming into the mirror, was indolently penitent.

"I didn't mean to laugh. It all scares me so. I don't know where in the world you get the courage to stand up to Papa like you do. I'd be terrified."

Marcia was about to tell her in detail how to deal with bullies, when there came a knock at the door. It was Herbert. Two suitcases stood beside him. He looked at them almost sullenly, and for a moment nobody spoke.

Then Ludie flung herself across the room and hugged him frantically, weeping, nuzzling her face in his neck.

"What'll you do? What'll you do?" she moaned softly.

Herbert patted her shoulder, looking past her to Marcia, with a curious expression on his face—almost of resentment, it seemed to her.

"Be a good son, Marcia," he said, still holding her eyes with that hot, smoldering look.

Marcia was hurt as she had seldom been. She said nothing in reply; turning away, she walked over to a window, to pluck at the curtain, eyes averted.

"Where are you going?" Ludie whispered persistently, and burst into a fresh shower of tears.

"I'm being sentenced to Uncle Jason's farm," Herbert answered. "But I'll get away. He says I'm not his son, and if I'm not he can't make me do something I don't want to. I don't care. Let *her* be his son." He put Ludie from him.

"Oh, be careful. Be careful," she whispered, as she watched him close the door finally. For several minutes she stood there, staring at the door, her fingers raised to her mouth.

"Let's go to bed," said Marcia dryly. . . .

Long after, when Marcia was still lying, rigid, staring into the darkness while hot, unbearable thoughts swarmed in her mind, she heard a rustling.

Ludie spoke, at first hesitantly, then with a rush.

"Do—you—like Frank Thatcher? Do you—think he's handsome? Oh, Marcia, he held my hand tonight, and I never felt that way before. As though all sorts of wings were brushing around inside me—just their tips, softly. And, oh, it was like some divine tickling." She giggled. "I know how silly that sounds, but it's true. And my hand was like needles; you know, the way it is when some of you's been asleep and wakes up. I'm scared of him, he's so sarcastic, and yet I—I think I love him." Dreamily: "I think I love him. . . . Marcia!"

Marcia lay rigid. What *had* he done? What could be so awful? Not, surely, even getting a girl in trouble.

"Oh, all right, if you don't want to answer, be mean. I let him kiss me, too, and it was just like melting. . . . Marcia! . . . Marcia?"

The fool, the silly, sentimental fool. She didn't know what real feeling was. She'd already forgotten all about Herbert, and yet—yet what love Herbert had to give was all for Ludie. Everybody liked soft, silly people; they cared nothing for character.

Ludie's breathing became soft and regular; she was already asleep. Like a baby. A baby's feeling and— But everybody loved her; she did, herself. While she, Marcia— She caught herself. Deep down inside, all along, she had been hearing the words, "I wish to God you were my son."

Poor Herbert, she thought. And again: poor Herbert. But she relaxed; turning on her side, she prepared for sleep.

The twins were twenty-one years old when what Walton regarded as the second key episode defining their character occurred. The awful nature of Herbert's passing attachment to a classmate at Yale had long since been learned, speculated upon (not without shudders) and pushed back into a cranny of the mind—along with Cora's insanity and other ghosts and goblins. From time to time, when Father was away, at the capital or upstate on a visit, Herbert would appear, spend a night deep in conversation with Mother, and depart. These visitations, if not so regular as Mother's visits to the sanatorium, were a part of the same marginal, half-real extension of the family's regular life.

The twins had both been graduated from Miss Meecham's School, had had their debuts, had continued their singing lessons, had become immersed in a round of sleighing parties, hay rides, church socials and voluntary work for charities. Marcia had had two emotionally violent but wholly uncarnal love affairs; Ludie had sipped at the chalice of a dozen less exalted romances, always shored up at the crucial moment of temptation or heartbreak by Marcia. Their father had withdrawn more and more into himself and into his public affairs; between Marcia and himself there was an armed truce, welded of mutual respect and a precarious, ambiguous kind of hostility. Their mother continued her familiar circuit, running an outwardly quiet and orderly house, accepting her husband's moods as they fell, tending equally to the needs of the official family and the outcasts.

It was Frank Thatcher who upset, this time, what passed for equilibrium in the family. The boy who had caused Ludie to feel "a divine tickling" when she was fifteen and he was seventeen was now a man of twenty-three—dark, dashing and dissipated. If there was any change in Ludie's feeling for him, it was that it was heightened. Yet she seldom saw him, for in this situation a strong alliance between her father and Marcia, born of a tacit understanding of the frailty of Ludie's capacity for self-discipline, stood between her and meetings with this generally acknowledged wastrel, the dissolute son of wealthy and dissolute parents.

Yet occasionally she slipped away from her guards, and one December Saturday evening, barely a month after their twenty-first birthday, Marcia went upstairs to speed Ludie's languid preparations for Fannie Armstrong's card party, to find their bedroom empty and a note, addressed to her, pinned to her pillow. She tore it open with unsteady fingers.

> DEAREST MARCIA,
> Its no use. By the time you read this, Frank and I will be many miles away. I cant help it I love him so. I havent your strength of will.
> Your weak and sining sister.
>   LUDIE

Marcia wasted no time. When George Cottrell, her escort, arrived to take her to Fannie's, she commandeered him and his sleigh immediately. Before he was really aware of more than the fact that he was being pressed into some sort of emergency service, he found himself driving wildly along the road to New Canaan.

Nor was he ever allowed to learn more about the particulars than his somewhat bugged-out eyes were able to perceive for themselves.

Marcia was playing a hunch; she knew that Frank Thatcher's equally wild and disreputable cousin, Sam Foss, owned a small house on the outskirts of New Canaan—a house he dedicated solely to the unrefined pleasures in which he and Frank indulged, since the rest of the time he lived with his parents. Ludie's mildly illiterate note could mean elopement or worse. If the former, Marcia knew that she could not hope to catch them—but, she reasoned, that would not be really catastrophic: a sorry, unwise marriage was at least a marriage. On the other hand, if the misspelt word "sining" was meant literally, there was a good chance that Frank was taking her to Sam's house.

Her guess was right. Leaving the still-gasping George to hold the reins, with the fierce injunction to "Stay there, be ready, and hold your tongue," she advanced from the sleigh to the cheerily-lit little house. The blinds were drawn in the front, but, wading heedlessly through the ankle-deep snow, she went around to the side and peered through the window.

What she saw stuck in her throat in a strange way. This Walton decided for himself through watching her closely as she told him the story, and his guess was innocently substantiated by Aunt Ludie in her old age when he risked confronting her with his mother's account and she, chuckling with the license of antiquity, added her impressions of Marcia's bearing throughout the incident. It was nothing so simple as anger or contempt or revulsion. And it could not, she reasoned further—if one considered Marcia's principles—have been envy or an induced excitement.

But whatever the emotion (or the complex of emotions), it paralyzed Marcia for a moment, suffused her body with a strange prickling kind of heat, at the same time that it left her mind and heart— so she put it once to Walton, placing one hand sententiously over her sixty-year-old heart—cold, empty, drained. For minutes she stood there on tiptoe in the wet, clinging snow, staring and trembling on the verge of acute vertigo.

On a thick white fur spread on the floor before a roaring fire lay her sister in her camisole, dark hair undone and tumbling over her shoulders, white arms and shoulders exposed—locked tightly, inextricably it seemed, in the embrace of Frank Thatcher. Fantastically, the thought came to Marcia, as she watched, that the most difficult problem of all would be the actual physical prying apart of them; grotesquely, she could already imagine herself tugging desperately at one, then the other, while they offered only passive resistance, each refusing to slacken his hold on the other. And Marcia was conscious, most of all, of the ridiculous figure she would cut, hauling and pulling at them: this filled her with fury.

It came to her then in a flash that this was the lot of those who did their duty—those who, as she was later to say again and again, "suffered from a New England conscience." Those who did their duty were always ridiculous to others; those who were weak and soft and conscienceless were always sprawled out looking beautiful and desirable. Two symbols, she found some time later, persisted out of the welter of impressions she had of the scene: Ludie's gay red dress lying crumpled beside the embracing couple—and the extension of herself, changed in some bizarre way into the likeness of a traditional witch with tall pointed black hat and long black cloak, pulling away at the interlocked figures, tugging and pointing and shouting at the nastiness of it—the nastiness that was yet somehow poignantly beautiful.

And the enigma of these symbols, of course, the painful paradox of them, was that she was right—was doing her duty—and Ludie was wrong, was (even as she had said herself) weak and sinning. It was an enigma and a paradox Marcia was never to solve; it haunted her all her life—as in the case of her husband's brother Lloyd. Yet there was never any doubt as to what she was to do, *must* do. It was as though God had reached out his long, prescient finger and touched her, saying, "*You* will do my will." And except when confronted directly with the sweet, wild disorder of the abandoned red dress, with the terrible poignancy of the straining, embracing figures, she was, of course, glad. No, perhaps not glad, but certainly proud . . .

She did not have to pry them apart. When she finally drew herself, trembling, away from the window and, running to the door, pounded upon it, they sprang apart convulsively. This she could see through the narrow window beside the door—see with a savage glee that in retrospect troubled her before she resolutely detached it from her memory. Then the door was opened and she confronted them.

Frank, after the first moment of surprise, was debonair, ironically courteous: "Why, Miss Marcia, I had no idea you wished to join us. Could I have anticipated your wishes, I should certainly—"

She was in no mood for his specious gallantry. According him briefly the most withering look she could summon, she advanced upon Ludie, who sat now upon the floor, eyes downcast, clutching to her bosom the red dress, her face as rosy a color as the dress and the fire.

Marcia spoke commandingly. "Put your things on."

Ludie hesitated, turned to Frank, who looked deeply at her for a moment, then spread out his hands deprecatingly and shrugged his shoulders. This was for Marcia Ludie's ultimate humiliation, suggesting eloquently as it did her initiative, her greater need and desire, in the whole matter. And, indeed, Ludie's color deepened still more; slowly, mechanically, she put on her dress and coat.

At the door Frank bowed.

"May I escort you to your conveyance?" he asked.

Marcia slammed the door in his face. In a spirit of fierce exultance, she propelled Ludie to the waiting, pop-eyed George, and they drove back to Stamford in a silence broken only by Ludie's sobs and whimpers.

At home, Marcia turned briefly to George. "Go to Fannie's," she said, "and tell them that Ludie was sick and we had to take her to the doctor's. Just that—and nothing more. Mind you: nothing more."

He nodded dumbly, and drove off. It was several days before Marcia, knowing from the nature of inquiries about Ludie that he had kept his word, deemed it an appropriate time to thank him briefly. . . .

These were the twins, it seemed to Walton; the copious rest was all elaboration.

JOURNAL: 4

from the journal of Walton Herrick . . .

June 28, 1953

I cannot remember where, in my reading, I first came across the phrase "timor mortis me conturbat." But I do remember, though not too clearly, that there is a philosophico-religious development of the idea in a book called *In Job's Balances,* by a Russian named Leo Chestov. I know little else about him, nor do I remember anything of his treatment of the idea and the phrase. Yet I know that I read it in my late twenties, a period in which I was much given to a high-falutin mysticism. I could expatiate, for example, for hours on the admirable soundness of Tertullian's "Certum est, quia impossibile est."

But there was another streak in my stubborn antirationalistic mysticism—a melancholy death-and-love-obsessed streak. My old glorification of defeat nobly endured reappeared, doubled in strength but softened and romanticized. Doubtless there were good and sufficient reasons for this morbidity; many men have built a systematic philosophy as a subtle and impersonalized justification of their own psychological misfortunes. At any rate, in these years I drowned in the "Liebestod"; I exulted sadly in Matthew Arnold's "Dover Beach"; I loved Keats and Shelley, and despised Pope and Dr. Johnson. So I believe that I can ascertain justly the fascination I felt for such phrases as "Give me my crown, put on my robe / I have immortal longings in me"; "O Ile leape up to my God"; "woman wailing for her daemon lover"—and, yes, "timor mortis me conturbat."

This last must have held a less obvious romantic appeal than most of the others I cherished; indeed, had it not been for the solemnity of the Roman consonants, I doubt if I should have admitted it to this anthology of mine. Yet I did, I remember, and I feel sure that I was wont to chant it to myself with a somber satisfaction.

The melancholy appeal of these quotations, the moods that induced them and those which, in turn, they induced—all this romantic and transcendental claptrap permeated those days of my life during which I had (without understanding it) given up on life. These were the years between my first brief, hurried marriage to Joanna and my meeting and marrying Lydia—the years that I devoted almost exclusively to my mother and father and Elinor, with my only holidays retreats in fantasy not, it seems to me now, much more mature than the comparable flights of my early adolescence. Those of my teens were compensatory for the rigid, conventional and uninspired routine of life in our family; so, too, were these later ones of my twenties, only bolstered now with literary and philosophical authority, and embroidered with a hundred fancies from my reading.

But of all this—some other time. With the advent of Lydia—and that's the right word, advent—little by little these substitutions for an engagement in the immediate world of empirical actuality slipped off, were left behind—and all my regressions since have been only partial.

Ill-equipped I was for living closely with anyone, and the astringent quality of Lydia's wit could make me writhe. But usually, after the passage of a few days, it cleansed too, and the one thing it made impossible was to hide back in that shadowland I had inhabited. I have consistently been fortunate in the women who have been important to me, after my mother. Fortunate, in that their chronology has been of such an order that I could learn from each and—it may seem a strange word in this context, but it's what I mean—survive. Clearly, not *with* them, however. Or have I inverted the meaning of this experience, reversed cause and effect?

But I grow impatient with my own digressions. What is it that I don't want to come to grips with? *Timor mortis*—the fear of death.

I can remember my mother's saying to me, not once but a number of times, "I feel so queer—as though nothing that is happening is real, as though it were all a dream and not even happening to me. When I'm doing some particular thing, it's as though I were simply watching it. Life is so unreal."

"Life is so unreal. . . ." My way of putting it, when I have felt my own version of this experience—I believe, less stringently than Mother—would be "Life is too real." For I think the sense of unreality resided in herself, rather than in the life around her: I believe that she felt literally that she was not there, a unique human being (as every live human being must be), Marcia Nicholson Herrick, not to be duplicated.

And here is where *timor mortis* enters—the fear of death, extinction, nothingness. First *timor vitae,* the fear of being torn apart by conflicting passions, desires, *instructions.* Or so it seems to the person who, not knowing, feeling, being his autonomous self, has a substitute persuasion that some force within him, or other people, are dictating to him. Above all, the fear of commitment, of involvement. And those who suffer from this fear of life, who like Ivan Karamazov "respectfully return their tickets to God," and resign from life, must then shove home bolt after bolt, bar the windows, inspect with wary flashlight and timid tread each dark corner of the house to which they have retreated, lest life, with its reaching fingers of light, its happy boisterous laughter and its tears, somehow have managed to invade this pale sanatorium, selected on one compulsive false premise: that it would be safe. It is a state of semi-animation that is, like purgatory, a halfway place— but not between human life and heaven: only between human life and hell.

I remember writing a single angry line, one day shortly after I began keeping this journal, after having sat idly at the desk for an hour: "I am a locker of doors." And so I am, though less than I was. A locker of doors, to insure privacy—lest one of the menagerie that inhabits me discover that another was acting counter to his own illusion of authority? A locker of doors, to see to it that incompatible, hostile, contradictory things might be done behind each such door without resultant chaos in this strangely empty-seeming house? A locker of doors, surely, to keep out the hurricanes, the furious mobs, the conflicting demands, the threat of violence implicit everywhere—in elemental nature, in people, in voices, voices clamoring outside every window. To shut out all these . . .

But it does not work. For these forces, these passions, these voices strident and hoarse with importunity, are within me. And I may, in averting my face, in turning away, in refusing the invitation to life and fleeing to this dark dwelling, mean to silence them forever, to curb and bridle any voice within me wanting, seeking, wishing—lest it be a *wrong,* hence frightening me—but I cannot. They will speak anyway— if not in conscious daytime, then in dreams, and the terrified child within me will awake, crying out, "O, o, nurse, o, my love is slain, / I saw him go, I, o'er the white Alpes alone." And the terror without will be the terror within, the monster trampling through life against whom one had locked and bolted the door will be lurking on the dark stair. So *timor vitae* leads to *timor mortis.* . . .

Until this summer, I have not lived alone for more than a week or ten days at any time in my life (where, except in the Herrick or

Nicholson family—or among those so poverty-stricken as never to afford privacy—could one find another such instance?)—and always before, at these brief, scattered times, in a small, compact house or an apartment.

The very first night here in our big house I found it unusually hard to go to sleep. I was uneasy, fearful; I listened tensely to every creaking sound, to the silence between each such pair of sounds. But I was so unwilling to probe the actuality of this feeling, so ashamed at even the flicker of such an unrealistic fear (this has also, I am sure, kept me from writing of it until now), that I frantically diverted my mind to all sorts of other matters. Surely a man in his middle forties, over six feet tall, weighing 190 pounds, father of four children, recognized and respected in his work, and nurtured on the American dream of rugged manhood, could not be afraid of being alone in his own house? It was an unbuttoned thought, and so it was not consciously thought.

But the uneasiness persisted, and after about two weeks of dreading, but not admitting dreading, the return each evening to a dark and empty house, I awoke, in the middle of the night, shaking with terror over what I had just dreamed.

In the dream, I had fled. I did not know, or could not remember, from what I had fled—but I remembered vividly and poignantly the ultimate moment of freedom. Panting, I stood somewhere in the darkness under a sky bursting with stars, exultant with the knowledge that I had won through a harrowing ordeal. Behind me lay a great battle: hand-to-hand combats under the lurid glare of shells exploding overhead; flight from overbearing numbers, pursuit, periods of hiding in swamps and marshes, discovery there by the enemy, more intrepid fighting, desperate fighting for survival and again escape.

And then I stood upon a little knoll and lifted my face to the infinite stars, breathed cold pure air and knew, within, the unmatchable human experience of having been greatly tried, having stood up to the trial and won my way through. My body, even in the pale light, glistened with sweat; my rags were caked with dirt; my chest heaved with long slow rasping breaths. But this was I; I filled myself—not to any superhuman dimensions, but to my own. This, I thought, was the measure of man, and neither exhaustion nor hunger or thirst could matter in the presence of this happiness.

And then, suddenly, in a new flurry of the glaring red and yellow light bursting far behind me, I was aware of a sudden motion, below and before me. First it was only a movement, blurred and indeterminate;

then it became a terribly purposeful action, though still not identifiable; finally I could make out that this was the enemy's panzer division, as light armored car after car wheeled into place and stopped, drawn up in line upon line at the foot of the small hill upon which I stood.

Men spilled from these cars and, moving with an inhuman precision, formed a solid ring around the foot of the hill, three or four deep. The whole action, from its inception, gave the impression of a single unitary *thing,* with each individual part of it a perfectly coordinated capillary, muscle, nerve: there was nothing human about it, none of that blessed, ragged diversity and unevenness of performance that makes for the separateness, the plurality, that are the hope and the joy of human life. These bore the likeness of men, but they were not men, for they were instinct with a mechanical perfection that was deadly.

My heart shrank. It became a cold blue shriveled core within me. All the joy, the sense of fulfillment, the feeling of having won my self— gone in this instant. Slowly I began to descend the hill, to deliver up what was left of me. As the talons of the Enemy gripped my wrists, my arms, I awoke.

Awoke—and lay there panting, trembling, feeling that in all this large house in which I lay there was no life—nothing animate, nothing that throbbed or palpitated with even an expiring twitch of sentience. All was cold and extinguished; this was that final glacial time, from which would come no thaw, no faintest stirring and trembling of hope.

Tentatively, with a feeling of great weariness and hopelessness, perhaps simply through a reflexive action, I moved a hand, a foot, an arm, a leg. It was not that I believed I could thereby prove the existence of life; I knew that this was impossible. I did have the power to move my limbs, but there was no resultant feeling in them; there was no *meaning* to the movement, since there was no life in it.

Then I heard them. Not as a noise, but as a presence—and yet it seems to me that the experience was one of hearing. And I instantly knew that it was the Enemy moving up those long stairs, to approach the room where I lay, half paralyzed, half dead.

That was a long moment, one that I should not like to experience again. I knew that I was helpless, even that I was nothing. And yet that nothingness could not shield me from the event. The bleakness of the terror that I felt then is something I cannot describe, beyond saying that its essential nature was the condition of knowing that it would not end; its very devilishness lay in this knowledge that the imminent awfulness was not going to end—unless (and I could not even imagine my capacity to do this) I found in myself the will and life to end it.

Somehow there came then a lull; I dared to move over onto my side. I could not look toward the door, knowing that the long black procession was still climbing the stairs, but I could and did push the full force of the fear from my conscious mind. I could and did think; my consciousness was no longer frozen.

I remember thinking miserably then that this was my precarious childhood revisited, that I was somehow being forced to return to and live through terrors that I had long ago escaped—at least in terms of full recognition and experiencing. I actually felt myself physically again a child, and there streaked through my mind the story a friend of mine had told me: how, suffering from shock after a tonsillectomy, the six-year-old boy whom she had adopted had relived, literally re-enacted, all the torments and fears of his first three brutally used years, and thereby purged himself of them. She had nursed him throughout this time, and her hair had turned white in a few months. I thought of her as the noblest and bravest of human beings; I longed for someone of like courage to be with me now—not even *that,* simply anyone human, the weakest and frailest of my fellows, anybody human. I screamed silently for any human presence, terrified at the same time lest this noiseless uproar further activate that horde swarming up the stairway.

And then, slowly, with infinite pain and terrible effort, I peered through a crack in my consciousness to a beginning glimmer of light. I—I myself—must help myself. I myself must act, must initiate a movement of some sort, any sort that would break this unbearable tension and bring me somewhere, out of this nowhere.

The thought was itself insupportable at first. It seemed to me that I heard a low metallic singing, like the noise made by vibrating wires. But I knew immediately that this was only the groaning wail within me at the realization of what I had conceived. And then I knew that this new burden I had placed upon myself somehow fortified and intensified my original dread. Having conceived this way of ending my torture, I must go through with it or extend the torture. And if I must go through with it, I must do it quickly.

And so I drew back the bolts, one by one, braced myself, and threw wide the door behind which the course of action was hidden. It was all clear in an instant, and I felt a partial relief already in the sense that I was going to present myself naked to my Enemy. Who was it who had said, "Give thyself to the destructive element, and it will bear thee up"?

I knew there was truth in these words and yet I sensed now that there was also a vein of trickery in them. The idea of exposing self to a course of action had been right, had been the only way leading to self-preservation. Yet this was not the way I could face the Enemy on the stair; it was a passive course, and for this conflict I must take an active one.

I just wrote that the course was all clear in an instant, and so it was. For I realized now that the host of the Enemy out there was not the mechanical men of the panzer division in the dream—or, at least, if still they, in different garb. These were tall, hooded figures with hideous masks above their long black gowns. And what I must do to destroy them and save myself was to tear off those masks, to disclose the true nature of the Enemy beneath them.

Again for a moment I shrank back and then, with a convulsive spring, attacked, hands trembling, arms jerking back each time in an ecstasy of revulsion. *Each* time, for I leaped and reached for the first creature and tore his thin papery mask from him with my shaking hands, only to disclose another, grinning, leering, more horrible. And after it, another—and another and another—and another. Shaking in my St. Vitus' dance of desperation, I tore mask after interminable, hideous mask away, finally to uncover the bald end of a long-handled broom.

There was nothing there! The robe had hidden an ordinary house broom, the succession of grotesque masks its handle end, such as is grasped by a housewife in the pursuit of her ordinary day's work. It was all a Halloween masque, a broomstick trick. With glee, I leaped and rushed amongst the other figures, ripping, rending, tearing at the ghoulish insubstantial masks, revealing always the inanimate, inoffensive broom-handle heads.

And at last, never having moved physically from the bed, I lay back, exhausted, sweating, but filled with the knowledge of having laid my ghosts. And thereafter, through these following weeks, although a solitary black-robed figure may steal up the stairs from time to time, I no longer need to resort to such violent action to destroy him. I find that I can exorcise him by learning to relax and induce back into me a sense of my mature self, a reassuring bone-and-sinew knowledge that I am there, a middle-aged man, no small boy. I no longer feel, for more than a minute at a time, the urgent need to dispel the night by turning on a lamp.

Yet it is not an unconditional surrender that the Enemy has granted me. Four nights out of five I awaken to find that the luminous face of the clock beside my bed records, within five minutes at the most, the hour of three. It may be two minutes to three or four minutes before or after, or even exactly three: it is always within the span of those ten minutes.

I do not understand this. I know just enough about the unconscious to be sure that this has a meaning which could be useful to me, perhaps even very illuminating, and I have entertained in my mind as many of the connotations that the number three might have for me as the associative process will summon—but to no avail. Concept after concept, symbol after symbol has flooded past—like a procession of river barges, or a series of floats in a parade of subconscious memories. But none of the possibilities thus suggested satisfies me; indeed, even as I write, the superficially fantastic idea comes to me that I should have grasped one of those brooms by the handle, and swept—swept down the stairs, headlong, impetuously and inclusively, all the rubble of figments and fantasies, mystic numbers and hallucinations—ghosts and goblins and weirds of my sick imagination. Swept them down and out—opened the door to hurl them into the darkness without, and thrown wide the windows of my mind to receive the cold dark air of the neutral night that I have found so hard to accept.

But I did not, of course, and up to now I must content myself with the partial victory I won that night. To me, it is considerable to know that while *he, it,* can still awaken me, I am not subject to blind terror upon awakening. . . .

The person who is afraid of life believes that he lives in a hostile world, a world of fang and claw in which *homo homini lupus.* My mother's constant anticipation of desertion, retribution wildly out of proportion to her trivial or even imaginary offenses, her ceaseless fear of burglars, thugs, white slave traders, etc.—her expectations of finding all these elements surrounding her on any given day, anticipating Death as it were on every corner—made of her an expert on the grotesque statistics of unreality. All these situations, these sorts of people, do exist, of course, but in numbers that would not total a fraction of one per cent of her private probability tables and—still more to the point— hardly ever touched even the suburbs of her sheltered life.

It comes to me as I write these words that an obsessive fear of death is actually a fear of the nothingness one feels if no clear sense of self has developed in one. So, too, when I fear being alone, it is because I feel this nothingness: there is *no one* there, because I cannot feel my I. I abhor the vacuum.

The person who is afraid of life is forced to live it wholly as strategy and maneuver. Lacking any autonomous sense of himself as an active creative agent, he cannot respond, react or initiate spontaneously; he is forced always to a countermove, the motivation of which is "safety," self-preservation. If such countermoves are unpleasant or even disastrous to other people (they are most likely to be of serious consequence to children toward whom he has a parental or otherwise authoritative relation), he may sincerely feel regret about this, yet also feel that he cannot help it. The regime of terror within him means that he must justify it by finding its original in his external environment, or concede that he approaches madness.

So he spends his days studying the logistics of fear and danger, often with no conscious computation—since even this he has deputized to a dark agency within him, which like some monstrous calculating machine shifts levers and ticks away, an outlandish metronome measuring risks and perils, accelerating its beat from time to time to warn him to say "no."

For he is an endless, a pitiful nay-sayer, ready, if necessary in the terms of his compulsion-haunted life, to immobilize himself into perpetuity in order to avoid the shock, the grinding impact of an active and spontaneous participation in human life. Lying excuses come to his lips as readily as ripe fruit falls from trees.

And yet, oddly enough—and this is what often causes the thoughtful compassionate observer to find him a touching figure—he is frequently wise and honest in his advice to other people; he can often help them in the very ways he cannot help himself. Again my mother comes to my mind, and I realize for the first time, I think, the full extent and meaning of her generosity and constructive kindness to many others, especially to those of humble situation—waifs and strays of all sorts. Although she did not consciously know this, I am sure that she felt herself to be of their company, and the only way in which she was able to help herself, take pity on herself, mitigate her despair, was through projecting herself into them and acting in the guise of one assisting another.

And, finally, this sort of person has often a terribly poignant sense of the beauty, the rich complexity potential in human lives, but always as of an almost unbearably beautiful spectacle of which he must remain only a spectator. I remember with acute pain such a realization coming to me one day a few years ago, as I sat at a table upstairs and, in a moment of idleness, heard below me the busy hum of household activity. A pervasive sadness filled me as I felt fully the promise and the fulfillment attainable, the plunging of one's whole self into life as a good swimmer runs down the beach and plunges headfirst into the breaker rolling, huge and proudly crested, toward him. Sadness permeated me as I knew for a transitory moment the deep satisfaction of life in this sense, yet knew at the same time that I was outside it, that it was not for me.

I think of moments like this, of people who consistently suffer from this crippling disability to meet life, in terms of the Face at the Window. I think of that face as pressed with constrained avidity against the pane, peering with the eyes of a hungry child at the scene within. He gazes with longing, in his mind pounds upon the glass, begs wordlessly to be admitted. His anguish is the greater for the knowledge that, once admitted, he could not really participate: no matter how great the kindness with which he might be received, how imaginative the understanding of his difficulty—the warmth, the freshness, the unpretentious vitality of that atmosphere would be unendurable to him.

In the Nicholson family heritage there are two such faces that I cannot forget—two such scenes in which the literal event and the symbolic significance are at odds, yet possess a genuine continuity of cause and effect. One of these is the face of James H. straining against the window pane of the Burgess living room, watching with burning eyes the ardent young minister and the lovely Emmy. The other is the face of his daughter Marcia, after she has brushed aside the heavy white thistles of snow to see her sister lying in the arms of a man before the roaring fire in the little New Canaan house.

What were they prying into so greedily, filled with so distasteful a self-appointed righteousness?

It no longer seems to me that this is the pertinent question—even that there is any pertinent question. What they did thereafter (and these were quite different actions) they did because they had to. In the one case, I cannot condone the course taken; I do not pretend to judge the other. But what I do understand at last is something of the desperation, longing and consequent anger that each felt as he pressed his face against the cold, comfortless glass.

And this of course. I realize now, I feel the more this Sunday night because of Julie's answer to my letter. For the first day or two, I tried to tell myself that I was not too disappointed, that I had not really expected her to tell me to come on, that her decision was sensible.

Then, only yesterday, I became angry at her for shutting me out. I consciously withheld more than the merest mention of her name in yesterday's journal entry. Had I conceived then of the Face at the Window image, I would have thought of it differently—as being locked out.

But tonight I know better, and know that it is my inability to endure the warmth and friendliness, the give-and-take, the rough-and-tumble of life in the room behind the window that has caused the break between Julie and me, and caused the trouble I have always had in living closely with anyone. I must explore all this further in these months.

[*Part Two*]   *6*

IT surprised no one that shortly after James H. Nicholson suffered his stroke Ludie was married. This was a different Frank—Frank Howe— who was also sarcastic, but a promising, sober young lawyer whose ardor exceeded her own. Weeping tears of affection and grief over the state of things at home, she moved with him to Columbus, Ohio. Nor would it have been hard to predict that Marcia would stay home, refuse two proposals for marriage, including one from a man by the name of Tom Sherry, who more nearly fulfilled her own romantic dreams than anyone else she had met—stay home to replace her paralyzed father as the head of the house, and, when his fortunes, due to the collapse of the market, crashed about his stricken head, dismiss all the servants save one, sell all the property except the fringe around the house, and grimly, but without complaint, bring the remnants of the proud estate to a greatly reduced but secure financial equilibrium.

There she stayed, until her father's death. They had little or nothing to say to each other, and there was evidence in his eyes that he found it more painful to be subject to her ministrations than to those of anyone else. Yet he accepted the situation with granite passiveness, and once in a while a flicker in his eyes conveyed to her his enduring if reluctant respect and admiration.

After his death, for more than a year Marcia and her mother were alone together. Walton tried once or twice to elicit from his mother some clearer picture of Patience Nicholson in these days. But she did not—perhaps could not—satisfy his curiosity. She always replied, in a set manner if not the identical words, "Mother was very quiet. She grieved for Father, but she never mentioned him."

Poking around among the possibilities, Walton realized that he had naïvely, even sentimentally, envisioned a whole new order on the old estate: the strayed lambs, Cora and Herbert, would be brought back and so lovingly tended as to enable them to know the salvation of peace, if not a restoration of their full faculties and a seminormal life.

Nothing of the sort happened; indeed, nothing of the sort could have happened, for he knew perfectly well about the disposition of the rest of those two lives. So he was left with conjecture only about this period after the death of James H. What he pictured was Patience going quietly about the house by day, ordering its course in a general way but leaving the particulars to Marcia, while passing her afternoons tatting, reading uplifting books, writing and painting water colors— one or two uninspiring examples of which he had seen. As for Marcia, he thought of her conducting the details of the household with her head held high, enduring her lot with her familiarly perverse and melancholy sense of triumphant defeat and deprivation, doing the marketing with her armor buckled on against the thrusts of neighbors who must certainly, she would have believed, rejoice maliciously over the downfall of the proud Nicholsons.

But he thought of the nights as times when each woman retired early to her chamber, Marcia probably to relax her militant vigilance and indulge genuine despair for an hour or two before invoking again Duty, that "Stern Daughter of the Voice of God." Patience, he was equally confident, bewailed in the privacy of her room the loss of her real life—gone forever with her dark, daemonic lover. Walton was himself surprised that, once he had conjured up the fantasy of the bedroom scene between James H. and Patience, this scene so obstinately remained the hub, as he saw it, the symbolic axis of their lives, that regardless of the ravages and mutilations of time, these two were always first of all, for him, trapped in, and dependent upon, the net of their passion.

And so, for this part of the family chronicle, he was forced to rely upon these suppositions, these more than half-imagined generalities. Until one day in Marcia's old age in Ridgefield, a day unusually relaxed for this equally strange small household—an almost unique day among those set aside for Walton's bi-weekly visit to his mother and sister. For Elinor was enjoying a special and unaccountable dispensation that day from her regular routine of fear and anguish, and Marcia, for once anticipating a happy deliverance for the future as facilely as she usually foresaw doom and desolation, talked more freely than in a long time. She talked so freely, in fact, that Walton remained persuaded that she neither realized how much she was telling, nor comprehended the full significance of what she said.

It all began with a reference to a trivial event of the day before.

Settled on this small street at the edge of town, Marcia and Elinor saw
little of others, except the doctor and delivery boys. Their perspective
on human intercourse, Walton often thought, had become so distorted
as to make each routine appearance of the baker, the milkman, the
Fuller brush man loom as vast on the day's horizon as a human figure
must bulk in the awareness of an ant or a spider. And since Marcia's
tabulation of events always involved a partisan aspect—each person
encountered was good or bad, for her or against her—anyone outside
the family would have been astounded at the number of daily skirmishes,
full battles, triumphs and tragedies that occurred.

In this particular case, it was the arrival of a stranger at the front
door on the previous afternoon that had filled the day with an alarm
and scurrying guards. (In all justice to his poor mother, Walton reflected, it was no wonder that she dreaded the ringing of the doorbell,
since it might come at a moment when Elinor was in the midst of an
"attack" and in a panic verging on hysteria.)

A quick, staccato punching of the bell had been followed, without
intermission, by several insistent knocks on the door. Marcia had approached the vantage point of an overlooking window by sliding along
the wall, hands spread, palms flat against the nubbly wallpaper, which
seemed to afford her a support to which to cling. Peering out at last,
she saw only a pair of masculine shoes: she explained earnestly to
Walton, "The biggest in the world." Then the bell resumed its clamor;
the stranger impatiently shifted his position and she had a direct view
of his face in profile. "Hard," she told Walton. "Hard, angry and
unrelenting."

She made her decision not to answer—not, Walton was sure, without soul-shaking tremors: *for who could be sure it was not a detective,
or at least someone with authority?* After several more knocks and a
moment of silence, the man "stamped off" to a neighbor's house—
where he could soon be observed engaged in lively conversation with the
housewife who emerged on her porch, pointed, shook her head, pointed
again and even swung her arm in emphasis, and in the opposite direction from Marcia's house.

At this point in the account, both Marcia and Elinor burst into
laughter, laughed until tears were near. Walton joined in—not so
heartily, but with some relish. If he didn't wholly understand the thin
line of saving humor that enabled his mother and sister, having conjured up horrors that would affright a Sherlock Holmes or Arsène
Lupin, to relax into shrieks of laughter over the absurdity of having
taken a man who simply sought directions for a criminal of the first

magnitude or a dangerous (*sic*) officer of the law—he at least welcomed it.

The laughter diminished, subsided to intermittent chuckles, a spasmodic hiccough or two. Then Elinor looked up, thoughtfully, and remarked with a certain grave defiance, "Well, he did look like a confidence man, all the same!"

Marcia wiped her eyes and said suddenly, "Remember Cousin Gertrude and the Confidence Man?" And she and Elinor were off again, shaking convulsively.

What did it remind him of? Walton wondered—and almost immediately answered himself with a vision of his father and Mrs. Harris, caught up in Dickensian reminiscence. Quite different, and yet this world of dreads and drolls also healed, assuaged, brought blessed relief.

"Cou-sin Ger-trude!" Marcia spluttered and choked, but persisted. "And the Con-fi-dence Man!"

Among the unfortunates of the Nicholson line had been a first cousin of Marcia's with the unlikely name of Gertrude Faustus. She carried the awesome connotations of her surname awkwardly. She was a tall, thin, pigeon-breasted spinster (in her late thirties when Walton knew her) with prominent front teeth, a fatuous giggle, and a languishingly romantic view of life so incongruous to her appearance as to provoke horrified mirth in the most casual acquaintance.

Cousin Gertrude spent several years in Cleveland when Walton was at the edge of adolescence, and he had a vivid, if not particularly edifying, recollection of her. She often came to the Herricks' modest Sunday evening open house, ogled any male over ten and under eighty, and went away as unattached as she had arrived.

Then came the Sunday of her triumph—the one on which she arrived with an escort. She gushingly introduced this gray-haired, solid, unexceptional-looking man of fifty-five or so, as Mr. Parker—and Mr. Parker he remained for the Herricks, until after a number of visits William tried futilely one evening to discover his occupation.

Having forgotten much else of the period, Walton could still remember the blandness with which Mr. Parker parried, evaded, fell silent. William never found out, but when—after the guests departed—he remarked on the peculiar qualities of the whole incident, Marcia said decisively, "Well, *I* think he's a confidence man!"

Mr. Parker (henceforth "the Confidence Man") came less often after that evening, and one Thursday night, after a prolonged and obviously tearful talk on the telephone with Marcia, Cousin Gertrude appeared to spend the night. Her eyes were swollen, her plump cheeks (which, together with her outsized teeth, had always reminded Walton of a chipmunk hoarding nuts in his mouth) tear-swept. Her lamentations went on into the night, but the only words Walton could remember with certainty were "He was married all the time. He just thought I was an heiress!"

Waiting now for Marcia and Elinor to subside, Walton suddenly wondered just why this pathetic if commonplace story had always so tickled the risibilities of his mother and sister. Was it in a way a catharsis for their own fears, their own appalling ignorance and yet suspicion of all the world around them? Were they unconsciously making fun of themselves? Just what did they really think a confidence man was, anyway?

And so he asked.

"Mother," he said, "what do the words 'confidence man' mean to you? Do you have any idea of what one really is?"

She straightened up, flung him a look of amused indulgence.

"Of course I do," she said. "I once had an experience . . ."

And so, rarely relaxed, Marcia told, for the first and last time, the story of Mr. Remington. Some eight or nine months after the death of James H., she had come home one afternoon from a long and heavy-hearted walk, to observe, even from down the street, that her mother was entertaining a caller on the veranda. Her first impulse, in the mood she was enduring, was to slip into the small grove of trees between her and them, and gain the back entrance without being observed. But at the very moment she had decided to do this the man stood up, walked to the railing of the veranda, and stared with an apparent absent-mindedness directly at her. This aroused Patience Nicholson's interest in turn, and it became impossible for Marcia to avoid walking directly up to them.

So it was that she had already begun to nurse an irritable resentment against this man before she even met him. Then, when she reached the steps of the veranda, she felt the full impact of his eyes "like a physical wound."

Those were the words she used; and, for all her flair for the histrionic, they were so unlike her, Walton reflected later, that they constituted an immediate signal that what was to follow would be out of the ordinary.

"His eyes made me feel as though he had given me a physical wound. They were very black, so that you couldn't see any little spots and flecks in them, the way you can in most eyes. That was one queer thing about them, and another was that they never blinked or turned

away, but kept looking at you endlessly. I don't know, I've often wondered, but perhaps he was a hypnotist. When I learned that Mother
had already agreed to rent him a room, I was terribly frightened."

To Marcia it was abundantly clear that he had already hypnotized
her mother. The very idea of the Nicholsons' accepting a roomer! That
night she talked more harshly to Patience Nicholson than she ever had
before or ever was to again. This was the final board in the casket of
the Nicholsons' fortunes. They didn't need the extra money: weren't
they getting along all right, even if they did have to consider the smallest
expenditure carefully? Now they could have no privacy. Besides, her
mother had no right to make such a decision without consulting her,
after the way she had taken charge of the family affairs ever since
James H.'s stroke. And worst of all, this particular man! He was queer,
frightening; there was something evil about him.

All to no avail. Marcia began to understand how her mother had
been able through the years to remain undaunted and undominated by
her formidable spouse. Patience Nicholson would not argue. She spoke
only once in reply, to explain, very quietly, that Mr. Remington had
just arrived in Stamford to hold a responsible position with the largest
local industrial concern, that he had the best credentials (she would
not elaborate, despite Marcia's insistence), that he was an active,
practicing Presbyterian, and that the amount he was willing to pay for
the convenience of the location of their house (the new industrial elements in Stamford were now steadily encroaching upon this once
proudly residential section) would greatly ease their situation. Besides,
he was clearly a gentleman, and she, a lady, had given her word to him.
Would Marcia have her break it?

That was all. Marcia went to bed, angry and defeated, and the next
day, after work, Mr. Remington moved in. For the following week or
two, Marcia saw him regularly twice a day, always in one of two
attitudes.

These contrasted so strangely, each with the other, as to constitute
a paradox. For one of these scenes was an epitome of the genteel life,
and the other so shockingly coarse, vulgar, as to send Marcia scurrying
downstairs with cheeks flushed with indignation and all kinds of vaguely
suggestive images tingling within her. She did not literally, this morning
long after, so describe her experience to Walton and to Elinor, who
listened drowsily, content in this hard-won moment of security, but this
was the feeling Walton entertained as he listened to her.

"I'd see him every afternoon at four-thirty, when Mama served
tea. He'd come back from work about four every day, rush upstairs to

his room and change his clothes. When he came back down to the library for tea, he'd always have on a black suit, freshly polished black shoes, and a new collar that glistened. And his hair! It was very black, and he'd plaster it down on his head in the most sickening way."

"Did you have tea with them?" Walton asked.

His mother shook her head with vigor. No, despite her mother's pleas, she never did. But something that displeased her in herself forced her to find errands that would take her past the open door, to steal surreptitious glances at them. He would sit with such precise, finicky straightness, holding the cup and saucer as though they were the precious elements of some esoteric sacrament—and his head was so persistently tilted at a slight angle of deference that Marcia always wondered how he managed to straighten it again. It seemed that Patience Nicholson did most of the talking, and Mr. Remington remained silent, the soul of discreet attentiveness.

The other, the contrasting scene that recurred with a regularity that haunted and frightened Marcia, took place every morning. There were on the second floor two bathrooms, and since one of these, at the end of the hall, adjoined Mr. Remington's bedroom, Patience had assigned it to him for exclusive use. This arrangement was convenient for him, but not for Marcia, who had to cross the same hall, at half its length from Mr. Remington's bathroom, to reach the other bathroom through her mother's room, which provided its only entrance. And now, it turned out, no matter what time of the morning she made this trip, Mr. Remington was always in his bathroom, shaving, with the door wide open.

She would arise an hour before her wont, at six-thirty; she would dally in bed, trying to awaken at least a minimal interest in a book or thoughts about the chores before her: it made no difference. It was as though he were truly the clairvoyant she had fearfully suspected him to be, and at the same time holding so important an executive post at his place of business that he could arrive there in the morning at whatever time he chose.

For once or twice, in desperation, she waited until nine or after before leaving her room, only to find the usual tableau awaiting her. He made her so uneasy that she took to dressing fully before crossing the hall, with the resultant nuisance of having to remove her shirtwaist in order to bathe properly. She felt exasperated, harried, persecuted. Yet her mother, who breakfasted in bed and did not leave her room until ten o'clock, never, of course, witnessed this predicament, and Marcia felt a strange reluctance to tell her of it. She didn't know, she said in answer to Walton's cross-examination; she couldn't say now just why she so disliked the idea of complaining to Patience.

But what was there, anyway, Walton wanted to know, that was so dreadful about the spectacle of Mr. Remington shaving? Did he speak to her, say something rude or obscene? Did he come out and accost her? Marcia had used the words "coarse" and "vulgar"; just what did she mean by them?

Marcia paused, hesitated, averted her eyes. At last, slowly, with reluctance, she said, "I don't know. It's hard to explain. He'd be standing in his undershirt, and it was yellow, as though it hadn't been washed enough. He was all hairy; it sprouted out above the round collar of his undershirt and under its short sleeves. Ugh!" She shivered, and went on abstractedly, almost as though she had no idea of what she was going to say next, and was curious, bemused, herself, as to what it might be.

At any rate, he never said anything to her. Hand raised, razor motionless against his lathered cheek, suspenders drooping obscenely over his dark trousers, he would simply stare at her with those hypnotic eyes and a half-smile on his lips. What was insulting, she supposed, what so angered and humiliated her, was implicit in the open door, the half-dressed condition, the insolent silence and staring, and, especially, the recurrence regardless of the time. . . . Marcia's voice trailed off, and they all sat in stillness.

Walton roused himself first.

"What happened to him?" he asked.

Marcia looked directly at him, with an apparent candor he had seldom seen in her eyes.

"I don't remember," she said. "Isn't that funny? I haven't thought of him for years, and all this comes back so clearly this morning and yet I can't remember what really did finally happen." There was a peculiar sort of sweetness in her voice that Walton found unnatural; it was almost honeyed, yet the eyes were clear, direct and unwavering. Then, as though with a great effort, she roused herself vigorously. "Oh, he went away, of course. But I can't remember whether I persuaded Mama to get rid of him, or he left of his own free will, or she decided that it had been a mistake." She turned to Elinor. "How's my baby? Would you like some soup now?"

The interview was over, the story told. But Walton knew with sureness that there was more left untold—something that interested him far more than the obvious fact that his mother had hardly proved her point about a definitive understanding of the term "confidence man." Swiftly computing the statistics with which he was acquainted, he knew that, no longer than a year after the time of Mr. Remington's arrival, Marcia had been threatened with a nervous collapse. All sorts of conjectures crossed his mind, but he could summon no master scene of the kind he had for his grandparents—nothing beyond a central persuasion that in one fashion or another the image of Mr. Remington had long reinforced his mother's persistent and unremitting fear of life, her obsession with the officers of retribution who would one day knock at the door that sheltered her.

Was it guilt over the commission of some act, the nature of some final scene with Mr. Remington? Was it simply her original fear of him and the threatening symbol he had been for her from the first, with those implacably seeing eyes? Or was it a sense of sin and shame at what transpired only in her consciousness over this daily meeting— wild and unwilled imaginings?

Walton had no idea. But he had been told often enough about how, within a few months, Marcia had finally broken under the strain of those last years. He had often heard the conclusion of that story in another sense. She had gone around for several weeks as though there were no thoughts behind the blankness of her eyes, stalking the house and grounds like a grim and comfortless spirit. Her mother had waited and watched; then, sensing the imminence of a real collapse, dispatched her to visit Ludie, who had moved with her husband to Cleveland. And there occurred the one event that it would have been most difficult to predict—her meeting with, and her eventual marriage to, William Herrick.

[*Part Two*] 7

By the time he was in his mid-twenties, William Herrick, having already disproved all fears and predictions of his permanent inability to support himself, had been graduated from college and the Auburn Theological Seminary and installed at the new College for Women of Western Reserve University as an instructor in Biblical literature, succeeding his father, who had taught the course while acting as president.

Now, having also found the successor to the presidency whom he had promised the other trustees, Cornelius Herrick retired from the University and returned to his pastorate. He did not even need to propose William for the courses in the Bible; his grateful colleagues, many of whom admired the refusal of the crippled son to accept invalidism, arranged for the line of succession.

At first, William was disappointed, for, being now an ordained minister, he had dreamed of having a church of his own. But he found no church willing to take on so handicapped a pastor and, with his customary fortitude, accepted the second-best opportunity and plunged into teaching with all the vigor and passion he possessed.

Among the parishioners of Cornelius Herrick at this time were Frank and Ludie Howe, who had recently moved from Columbus to Cleveland. In his casual way, Lloyd Herrick paid easy court to Ludie, whom marriage had brought into full bloom. Her soft, warm beauty had reached maturity, and Lloyd described her to his sister Rosalind, in a rather more poetic (though not very original) vein than was his wont, as "a heavy-headed poppy, nodding and begging to be picked." Rosalind's adoration of Lloyd did not keep her, remembering Ludie's bust and shoulders, from asking sarcastically, "Are you sure you mean heavy-*headed?*"

But Lloyd was discreet. There were plenty of other nodding flowers and he had no desire to run afoul of Frank Howe's cutting tongue and perhaps even a physical fight—for Frank was desperately possessive, for all his apparent laconic indifference. Then, too, Ludie had caught Cornelius Herrick's eye and was one of his favorite young ladies. So Lloyd tempered his compliments, made eyes at Ludie but never for a dangerously long time, and refrained from even holding her hand. The result was that when, after James H. Nicholson's death, Marcia came on for a visit, Ludie invited Lloyd to be her sister's escort to a band concert.

Lloyd was not at home when the invitation came, and his father promptly accepted for him, without consulting his plans. Two days later, and only three days before the concert, Lloyd came, late in the evening, to William's room.

"You've got to help me out, Old Integrity," he said abruptly.

William was pleased, as he always was when his older brother appealed to him.

"Of course," he replied. "What is it?"

But his expression of anticipation changed to one of horror when Lloyd explained the situation.

"I couldn't do it," William groaned. "You know we've heard that she's not only beautiful, but a very sophisticated young lady who made her debut in New York. Why—why, she'd just refuse to go." He spread his hands out in a gesture of quite impersonal disgust, indicating his legs. "Why, it would be like Beauty and the Beast. Besides, I've never even called on a woman in my life, except an old one. I wouldn't know what to say or do."

Lloyd studied him shrewdly.

"You've got to stop running yourself down, Reverend," he said at last. "You're right that you don't know much about girls. If you did, and if you weren't so confounded modest, you'd know a few things that you don't even dream of. I'm going to tell them to you right now; you won't believe me, but they're true. So think about them."

He dropped into a chair, threw one leg with careless grace over its padded arm, and lighted one of the small thin cigars he affected, gazing thoughtfully at the uninspired color prints with Biblical subjects that adorned the walls of William's small attic bedroom.

"First of all," he went on slowly, "you're much better-looking than you realize. Those liquid eyes of yours would melt the coldest dame on record. And there's many a fine-feathered deb who's sick to death of the jaded bloods and sparks, and aching for an honest young fellow who means what he says. They're all after marriage, and the only thing you ought to be afraid of is being caught. No—now wait a minute. I'm not going to listen to you run yourself down, and there's one more thing I want to say."

He paused to relight his cigar, which had gone out through his failure to puff at it during his earnest discourse. Then he pointed it at William.

"Don't get me wrong. Don't let this bother you or make you draw into your shell. But women can't resist—what does our revered father call it—your affliction. Or anyone's, if it's endured with guts. Even my addiction to drink. I'm talking about women now, however, not the kind of hussies I like to play with. Your crippled legs are irresistible to a lot of women, since you're also good-looking and *good*. You shut up and listen. You are good, in a way Father couldn't be if he lived to be a thousand. Don't shake your head. I don't expect you to agree with me. But think about it—I mean about the appeal I say you have for many women. I've seen it down at church, time and again."

William was struggling to keep the pleasure he took in Lloyd's words (the most appreciative ones he had ever received from him) from turning his head.

"She'd find me repulsive," he cried, "and, besides, Father would never consent to such a shift."

Lloyd shrugged his shoulders and waved the cigar contemptuously.

"Father won't have anything to say about it," he declared. "I'll get at the whole thing through Mother. She'll fix it. Now let's consider it settled. I warn you, if you back out, I'll run out on the whole thing anyway. I've promised Becky Wolf, and I wouldn't miss the chance to snuggle with her if it meant being disinherited all over again."

William didn't quite see how it could be a question of his backing out if he hadn't as yet agreed, but secretly Lloyd's proposition had fired his blood, and he was too confused to answer further. The upshot was, of course, that Lloyd went ahead with his plan and, as he had predicted, Catherine Herrick (stirred, on her part, by her conviction that William must begin making the acquaintance of young women, and fully convinced that he could marry, and make the right sort of wife happy through his very lack of the traditional male egotism) disposed of her husband's objections in short order.

Ludie, to be sure, was much disappointed on what she believed to be Marcia's account, but she was softhearted and also confident that this was the kind of situation that Marcia would eagerly arise to. She could not help thinking to herself that the right words were "revel in." At any rate, she accepted the change gracefully, and it was arranged that William should meet them at their reserved seats in the park, to avoid the necessity of his making the longer trip. One ticket was dispatched to the Herrick residence, through the agency of a Negro woman who did Ludie's washing.

William, after two largely sleepless nights, appeared, dressed in a brand-new suit, a straw skimmer and a tie borrowed from Lloyd, which he fondly believed to be modish. As a result, he looked much more awkward and gauche than usual, and his collar was as stiff and uncomfortable as his manner. When he finally spotted them as he shuffled down the grass aisle after the usher, he almost turned around and fled. For Marcia Nicholson, in evening décolletage, was more beautiful by far than any Dickensian heroine over whom he had ever mooned.

Somehow, blushing and stammering, he stumbled to his seat and tried to overcome his agony of embarrassment by fixing a painful smile on his face as a substitute for conversation. He smiled so long and so hard that his jaws and cheeks ached. He listened as diligently as he could to Ludie's chatter on his left and Marcia's slower-paced comments on his right, but he could not find his tongue. He felt Marcia's eloquent brown eyes searching him, and wondered, in ultimate distress, whether she found him too repulsive to bear. His head swam from the proximity of bare white shoulders and the delicious fragrance of these two terribly real, terribly female creatures.

The music saved him. It spared him the necessity of finding something to say; it diverted the attention of the others; finally, it gave him something to talk about. He felt the tension in him lessen; he began to enjoy himself—even without realizing it, to hum a particularly rollicking air the band played and to tap his fingers on his knee in time. Then, again, he felt Marcia examining him, and his hand hesitated, lay still.

At intermission time, Ludie and Frank decided to stroll. With an effort, William turned to Marcia.

"Wouldn't you—"

She shook her head and smiled deeply, dazzlingly.

"I'd much rather sit and talk."

And, miraculously, they were talking. He could not remember afterward just how they had come to speak of her father's death, but with a startling suddenness, it seemed to him, she was telling of her dream of the river and the boat and the great chorus of voices singing, "Washed in the blood of the Lamb. . . ."

He listened, entranced—by the sound of the voice, so clear and soft; by the familiar symbolism transformed by new romantic touches; by the single brown curl that escaped the cluster of upgathered ones and rested, swaying, on the graceful curve of her white neck; by the tears that he thought he could see in the lustrous eyes. From somewhere, some undetected, unknown cranny of himself, came the boldness to reach out and touch her hand.

"Such a dream," he said simply and directly, "is the child of a great faith."

Ludie's voice broke in on them; she was holding daintily aloft two clouds of pink cotton candy. Their hands leapt apart, but several years later Marcia told him that the phrase he had used was written in her daily book that very night: "Such a dream is the child of a great faith."

William never knew what the next two numbers on the program were. He heard music as one might hear distant surf, but the center of his being lay in his hand, in those fingers that still tingled with the recollection of her soft, smooth skin. Only when, near the end of the program, the band broke into "After the Ball Is Over" did he dare look at her again—and found her smiling, with a faintly rosy tinge to her cheeks that he did not remember having been there before.

And when they all stood while the band played "The Star-Spangled Banner," she slipped a hand in his arm.

Frank turned to William.

"I've hired a carriage," he said. "Let us drive you home first."

William took a firmer hold on his cane and straightened his shoulders.

"No, thank you," he replied. "I'll see Miss Marcia home."

And, while the carriage waited out front, he and she sat alone on the porch for a few minutes, he urging her to read Browning. As he took her hand to say good night, aware that the impatient hansom cabby was muttering more loudly to himself, he looked into her eyes and quoted: " 'Ah, but a man's reach should exceed his grasp, Or what's a heaven for?' "

She said softly, "I shall always remember this night," and went in.

Riding home in triumphant solitude, he chanted Browning to himself:

> And the sin I impute to each frustrate ghost
> Is—the unlit lamp and the ungirt loin,
> Though the end in sight was a vice—

before he suddenly caught himself and thought, What am I saying? And indeed, what had that to do with so gracious and lovely a woman?

When he finally climbed into bed, he remembered that he had not asked her when he could see her again. Here, so far from her, it all seemed once more quite impossible, and his courage lagged. Lloyd could tell him what to do, and how to do it, but he did not want to confide to Lloyd about this—or to anyone else. What should he do?

At the end of an hour the whole evening seemed so unreal that he was in despair. He finally lighted the candle he kept by his bed, and in the flickering light reached into the pocket of the coat that hung beside him, needing to see the stub of the concert ticket as proof that it had all really happened. Instead, he pulled out a delicate lacy handkerchief!

He remembered then, as he inhaled that same ethereal fragrance, the moment when her fingers had stolen into the crook of his elbow, and that he had fancied (instantly to dismiss the whole thing as nonsense) that the hand had slipped lower, touched his side pocket. Clutching the handkerchief, he blew out the candle. "Dear God," he prayed, "I thank Thee for all Thy manifold wonders," and fell into a long and tranquil sleep. . . .

It was not, of course, quite so serene a course as that. Walton never heard many of the details, but he knew at least that Marcia found it difficult to make up her mind. She blew hot and cold; she was alternately ravishingly receptive, gentle and affectionate—and cool, aloof, remote.

But something new possessed William Herrick: he refused to be hurt or rebuffed; he pursued her with a wholly new confidence; he laid siege to her soul with Browning, Keats, Tennyson, the Bible, James M. Barrie's story of *Tommy and Grizel*. He sent her flowers, ices, small books of verse, copies of the sermons he was beginning to write. When her visit ended, he wrote her every day, chastely ardent letters in which he compared her to all the respectable beauties of history and legend. In a few months, he took the trip to Stamford, where he newly endeared himself to her by his thoughtfulness for her mother and by sitting up all night with their old St. Bernard, nursing him through to health again.

The rest of the Herricks watched in some amazement. Only his mother was sure of the outcome. "He'll get her," she announced at dinner one evening while William was in Stamford. "My only doubt is whether he won't be sorry he did after a few years. She's high-handed."

It was Rosalind who was present at the decisive scene. About to be graduated from Smith, she was the only member of the family in the East, and she wrote to Marcia, proposing that they meet at a little lake near Hartford and the ancestral Herrick home, which she had visited before, and spend the day on an outing.

"It was a gorgeous day," she told Walton many years later, after his father's death. "We canoed and had a picnic on an island and spent most of the time in chatter of the sort that was supposed to be fashionable in those days. We were both a little wary at first, but warmed to each other as time passed. Your mother, you know, can be perfectly charming when she wants to be."

Walton nodded, thought about the phrasing, and nodded again. He knew what she meant, though he didn't think that volition had much to do with it.

"On our way back to the mainland, she talked to me about William. She said that she loved him, but she was not sure that their marriage would work out. She had been through a great deal with her father, and something, she said, made her want to change the direction of her life. Sometimes she felt that she needed terribly a person so strong, physically as well as spiritually, she said, that she would not have another responsibility in her life. She was awfully in earnest—in fact," Aunt Rosalind made the grimace of distaste that always accompanied her driest tone, "I realized later that she had no sense of humor at all. But then, being young, I only thought how beautiful and tragic she was, and felt torn between wanting her for William and being afraid that it *was* all wrong. . . . Finally, just before we reached shore, she turned to me with her face all lighted up and said, 'You've helped me so much.' (I'd hardly said two words.) 'I feel sure now that it's right. He has the only kind of strength that matters—the strength of gentleness and goodness.' And then she became very solemn and said, 'I'll be a good wife to him, Rosalind, faithful and true.' "

So much only, until Walton took his Aunt Rosalind to lunch in New York in honor of her seventieth birthday. She had become a resilient, humorous, wise older woman. For you could not truthfully call her *old* at seventy, Walton thought, listening to her gay, relishing laughter, and observing the bloom, the faint rosiness that lent a youthful vitality to her undeniably wrinkled and lived-in face. A late-bloomer, he added to himself. But weren't all the Herricks, who ever bloomed at all?

"I don't want to hear any more denials from you about your achievements," she was saying. "You're a true Herrick, unable to take to yourself and enjoy what you've fought so hard to win. One of the few joys of getting old is that you feel free to say just what you mean, and want to say. And those who have ears to hear listen. The rest don't matter." She made an airy gesture, so airy that she caught herself in it and giggled. "Stupid sheep," she intoned with an attempt at vindictiveness that convinced neither of them. "Don't belittle what you've done,

Walton. When I think of how your mother would make you wear rubbers if just one solitary little cloud appeared in the sky, that sums it all up. We used to say that you'd never had a chance, that you were licked before you started. Yes, that's the way we used to talk.

"And just look at you! You're the best of the bunch. I'm including your grandfather and *both* my brothers. I don't care what you've done wrong. I don't even care any more if you treated both your dear little first wife and Lydia badly—I don't say you did, and I don't care to know. I've done lots of wrongs myself, but now I content myself with the knowledge that most of the time I did the best I could.

"But whatever you've done wrong, you're a man. You've fought for what you've got, against terrible odds. And you've both been faithful to your burdens and still kept yourself alive. I know what you did for your mother and Elinor, when anyone else would simply have had them put away. And after what Marcia did to you! And your father told me before he died what you meant to him."

Walton could think of no appropriate answer, but he did feel a warm, relaxing glow, for it was true: in his stumbling, confused, aching way, he had kept that faith.

"Marcia . . ." Aunt Rosalind was musing. "One thing I'll say for her: she was the most genuine aristocrat I ever knew."

Walton looked at her blankly.

"Aren't you just buying her own appraisal?" he asked. "Because if you're not, it's the epitaph she'd most have liked for herself."

Rosalind shook her head vigorously.

"No," she said. "No, I'm not. And I don't mean what she meant: the Nicholson family. For look at her twin sister. She didn't have this quality. And I can't define it, beyond saying that while Marcia was the most wrongheaded person I ever knew she had principles and lived by them. And this gave her a dignity even when she was most foolish."

Walton was silent for a moment. Then, looking at her directly, he said, "I love these talks with you. You're a wonderful woman."

Rosalind drew into her shell for a moment.

"Pshaw!" she said. "Don't talk like that. You don't know what you're saying. You don't know me at all." But he observed that her eyes were suddenly wet.

"And your mother took some mean whacks," Rosalind went on determinedly. "You know how I loved William, but it wasn't easy to be married to him. Or to *get* married to him," she interjected, her voice abruptly fierce. "I suppose I shouldn't tell you this, even now, but I've kept this secret ever since it happened, and I don't see how it can hurt you. You remember I once told you about meeting your mother up at a lake near Hartford, just before she finally decided to marry your father? Well, I was sent there—by *my* father and mother.

"Now listen to this," she went on, and her voice bristled with indignation. "A week before, your Aunt Lucia, your mother's twin, had come to Mother and Father, to beg them not to let William marry Marcia, because she'd ruin his life. Oh, I can just see her, all sweetness and treacle, shedding tears over this sad, sad duty she had to perform! What a mealy-mouth! So I was delegated to find out what Marcia really felt for William.

"And I'll tell you what I found out," she continued urgently, leaning forward in emphasis. "I found out she *did* love him and really *was* concerned as to whether or not their marriage could work out. Oh, she was impossible to live with, all right, and bad for you and Elinor— and often I couldn't get along with her at all—but she *didn't* ruin his life, no matter how unhappy they became; in some ways she saved it."

Sisters . . . twins . . . Shock was a strange feeling, Walton thought: it was a long time since he had been shocked.

"I'm starved," said Rosalind. "Let's order"—and it was clear that the time for reminiscence was over. Though not without its valedictory. "I'll have the fruit salad. Oh, we were such babes in the woods!"

Babes in the woods William and Marcia had certainly been, Walton reflected. With that unerring instinct of the newly-married for making things as difficult for themselves as possible, they went to a camp in the Adirondacks for their honeymoon. It was cold and rainy. At the wedding, William had eaten something that disagreed with him and was sick for three days. Or possibly there was a psychological twist to his illness, confronting as he now did at last a final great fear related to his physical handicap and his resultant ingrained sense of inferiority as a male.

They were both sexually inexperienced and as ignorant as all virtuous young people in 1900. This Walton pieced together, without much desire to, from the revelations of Marcia on one of the several occasions in her eighty-odd years when she became hysterical. He could picture fairly easily the ardor of which she would have been capable— the almost overwhelming ardor of the romantic idealist who imbues the marital relation with majestic colors and a lofty poetry that would frighten the true sensualist to death. This, combined with Willam's fear of incompetence, made the honeymoon something less than a success; they returned to Cleveland shaken, sobered, but determined to present a good front.

From the moment she arrived in Cleveland as a bride, Marcia

was aware of watching eyes—cold eyes, greedy, predatory eyes, bright inquisitive ones. Probably a good many people were actually curious, if only because of William's being crippled. But the chances were, Walton reflected, that the things she interpreted as cruel and malicious were often only tactless and ordinarily thoughtless. At any rate, she heard things that struck at her heart, and imagined others. She heard the remark about Beauty and the Beast that William had himself been the first to make (to Lloyd before they had even met). She overheard criticism of her respecting William's request that she board a trolley car before him and in other ways ignore his lameness. She discovered that the Herricks were not really feted and sought after, but—with the exception of Cornelius himself—were marginal participants in "society" life. But she did not interpret it that way; with the peculiar distortion that suited her own needs of pride and self-pity, she continued to insist that everyone thought the Herricks were "so wonderful," while snubbing her.

She resented deeply every suggestion, piece of advice, or criticism that Catherine Herrick offered. To be sure, William's mother had had her doubts about the marriage from the beginning, and she probably was quite acid on occasion. Yet Walton felt sure that Marcia so expected hostility that she found it even when it was not there.

Given the circumstances and the individuals, it was probably inevitable that the marriage of Marcia and William should deteriorate into that American middle-class version of the institution that presents a more or less solid front to the world, while within, the walls actually shake from the friction, the tumultuous outbursts, the recriminations and tentative reconciliations and renewed complaints.

William was of course not nearly so romantic as his courtship had seemed to make him out. He really preferred Dickens to Browning and Keats. His gentle strength was not impervious to arrogantly conceived and utilized charge accounts at department stores, or to constant indictments of his family. For all his victorious struggle to become his own man, he had cherished secret dreams of being babied by a wife who adored him, and he was not equipped to take "all responsibility" off his wife's shoulders.

Nor did she really want him to. Marriage itself, for all her difficulties, meant a new security, and she began to assert herself in a way that was not too unlike old James H. There were, indeed, times when she chafed over the fact that she was not a man (if she could have gone out into this man's world, she'd have shown them); this probably led, in a way characteristic of her emotional logic, to her violent stand against suffragettes. And to her the greatest indignity of all was William's devotion to books, and the way in which he would look contented to the point of bliss if she were off to spend an evening with Ludie—until the Howes moved to Detroit two years after Marcia's marriage.

Yet there were, to be sure, compensations. There were evenings when they both recaptured the early glow, and with a waning of his extravagant gratitude over her having accepted him, and his consequent gain in ordinary self-respect, William found it easier to play his part as a lover. Actually, the core of that gratitude remained in him, a constant to the day of his death. He often told Walton, "Your mother made a man of me. No matter what our troubles, I can never forget that."

Their common grief over two miscarriages drew them together, but their mutual consolation was flawed by the thought that perhaps there was something wrong with William that would prevent their having healthy children. William introduced the possibility himself the first time, with Marcia stoutly, if falsely, refusing to listen. The second time, she did not protest so much, but wept more. Then at last, after five years of marriage, Elinor was born in 1905, Walton two years later.

Marcia gave birth to both children at home, in the house on the street next to Cornelius Herrick's, with the aid of a sponge dipped in chloroform. William was thirty-five when Walton was born, Marcia forty. This discrepancy in age was one of several forbidden topics. It was only in his maturity that Walton was allowed even to know that the difference existed. But by the time he was five years old it contributed substantially to an overt and basically final division between his father and mother. For childbearing and the additional years made his mother seem much older than his father, and William little by little ceased to take the reasonable pleasure in his marriage bed that he had hitherto. At the same time, he acquired a new secretary, a pretty brunette who became passionately devoted to him.

Walton never knew the rights of the matter, but, knowing his father, could only believe that at most what happened in his office was a mild flirtation. Nevertheless, Marcia viewed it differently and, after a month or two of proud silence, finally screamed to high heaven. The children, wide-eyed, witnessed open violent scenes, in which their mother, pride now flung to the winds, hair unkempt and dress awry, shouted insults and imprecations. "Dirty little Jewess!" she would hiss as a final shot before grabbing a child with each hand and leaving the room. Upstairs, both children would plead with her: "Mother, please forgive him" . . . "He didn't mean to do anything, Mother" . . . "Please."

William tried to weather the storm alone. He confided in no one. But five months later he broke down and spent the summer in a sanatorium. He returned for the fall term, pale and reserved, and from that time on withdrew more and more to the periphery of family life. Marcia quieted down; there were no more scenes, but her hypochondriac tendencies grew unceasingly. They affected her attitude both toward herself and toward her children. And since Walton was not so strong as Elinor, he received most of her attention. In a short time he began his year and a half in bed.

Marcia nursed her wrong in comparative quiet now. But by the time Walton was ten, and in a period when her neurotic fears were so intense that she would not permit her ten- and twelve-year-old children to play in their own front yard unattended, and tasted every can of food in the house to make sure that it was not poisoned, she uncovered the old wound to Walton.

"I was still a young woman," she said dramatically, "and he refused to share a bed with me. It's unnatural."

It was a long time before Walton wondered about the compatibility of this complaint with her frequent comment, "That's a true love—spiritual—nothing nasty and sexual in it." But it bothered him sufficiently as it was. All sorts of unbidden, disgusting images floated in his mind. . . .

And so it was that life seemed to him to be composed of armed camps—his mother's, the Herrick family's, the big one belonging to The Outside World, his father's lonely tent pitched by itself. Even when there was peace, it was not peace but a sort of suspended war, and active hostilities threatened to begin again at any time. There was nothing to do but to placate or withdraw, as the occasion seemed to indicate wisest. Active fighting for himself got him nowhere; the only warfare he could wage successfully was indirect—the use of guile. So he practiced being the perfect son and precocious gentleman that he gathered *they* wanted him to be, until he came to believe that he was it—so unquestionably it that he was almost relieved of the necessity of making his actions adhere to the standards of *it*. Until he finally went to school—and lived through days of terror and shame.

But as he grew older somehow he found his way back more and more often to a region inhabited only by himself and the creatures of his fancy—into a fantasy world in which he rested, inviolate and perfect, quite safe from his detractors and persecutors at school and in the neighborhood, and able to accept his mother's adulatory possessiveness and loving tyranny without either consciously valuing it or putting up more than a passive resistance to it. He ceased wondering who he was or what he wanted.

1953

Postcards . . .

Dear Dad,
Timmy and I have lerned
to sail. We ride twise a week.
both of us. I can do the jackknife dive. Come as soon as
you can.
                    peter

DEAR DADDY
  I MISS YOU LOTS
CANT YOU PLEASE COME
SOON MY BIG
                    TIMMY

JENNY

and a note . . .

DEAR WALTON—
   The children are sending you postcards, so I'll just write a line too
to thank you for the check. I think this summer continues to be very good
for them—and for Father. But I've worried because you haven't written
since I answered your letter. I think a lot about you and me. Do write
me—even just a postcard.

Love,
JULIE

July 7, 8

THE heat was brutal and insistent. For the third consecutive day—ever since the bright, clear Fourth—the official temperature had reached ninety-five before the morning was half over, and even at bedtime was over eighty-five. Walton had slept only fitfully for the past two nights, and now, at eleven, he lay wide awake, staring up at the cumulus blanket of stifling air between him and the ceiling. It was so heavy and static that it seemed visible, almost tangible.

Miserable, listless, he thought of it as a darker element, alien to the humid air filling the rest of the room; he found himself personifying it, attributing to it a malign character that had chosen to hover there simply to torment him. He kicked the covering sheet fiercely down to the foot of the bed.

In his state of sticky, itching discomfort, he tried to distract himself by thinking of tomorrow's birthday lunch with Maria, but this was a mistake: he found himself remembering his unhappier passages with Lydia; the days when Maria, four, with her honey-colored hair piled in curls on the top of her head, would ride her tricycle up and down the sidewalk before their house, singing ecstatically. And then—guilt and regrets and self-justification; a sudden poignant sense of the accretion of unfulfilled promises for all the tomorrows that were gone, the procession of Joanna and Lydia and now Julie, and voices calling in the distance—he strained to hear what they were saying, but could not. And suddenly it seemed that he was a boy again, in rare daring hidden in the tall wind-swept grasses, lying close-packed to the earth, hidden, digging into the ground with his fingers between the clumps of thick stalky grass and pressing his cheek angrily against the unyielding earth, secret and hidden, answering no summons, declaring himself. The voice of the child's blood crying yet, *Who hath remembered me? who hath forgotten?*

327

And the loneliness of time, the whole sweep of the plains of time through which we move, assailed him now unbearably. Sequester Meadow. Where did that come from? He could not remember, but there it was—a vision of a sun-drenched field with wild grasses and yellow-eyed daisies and blue flowers whose name he did not know, and the singing of the bees was peace. Somewhere outside of time, in an island meadow he lay inviolate, and over him the great blue empire of space, flecked here and there by streamers and delicate arabesques of white cloud. To return—no, he had never been there: to find it and lie down, finally at peace.

Walton sighed, groaned, shifted his position. He became aware of similar sighs and groans that were the character of the house itself—that, only a month or so before, in that strange regression, had invoked in him nameless childhood terrors, phantoms of the secret branches and tributaries of his life down whose banks he would not wander unless forced: forced by a series of anonymous compulsions that without warning (but thank God, rarely) plucked him by the sleeve and summoned him, a series culminating in the masked figures on the staircase. Tonight, however, the structural sounds of the house did not dismay him—rather reminded him, ironically, of the pride he had felt when they had moved into the house: a place, his own, with land—several acres, their home. And now his own, alone.

He tried to induce reluctant sleep by lying now on his right side, now on his left, by turning on his back, by switching pillows (this derisive double bed!), by placing one pillow upon the other. At last the slightest shiver of a breeze stirred the curtains at the window by his side, and the faintest soft breath of air passed over him. He sighed, somehow reassured, and shortly after drowsed into a semicomatose state in which images and fantastic, disconnected episodes drifted through his mind—Lydia and Julie riding a tandem bicycle; Lydia's red hair growing stiffly, like spiked grasses, in a meadow; Julie, only with Maria's face, pleading with him (for what? for what? if he could only know!); and some grotesque carnival in which familiar faces bobbed up and down above the painted horses of the carousel.

But through all this, somewhere in his psychic cellarage, a single thought or emotion, a dark something, kept pounding a muffled, barely audible drum beat. Vaguely he realized that its reiterated message had to do with that earlier mass of steaming dark air over him where he lay. And both of them, now, in this drowsy passiveness, connoted that presence of which he had become increasingly aware during the past few weeks. For a moment he could not differentiate: had the presence been there endlessly, behind him, and he dreamed all the conventional events of these days? Or had he lived *them,* and was this vision rather a wholly new experience, disguising itself, in some ambiguous intent, as familiar? He did not know, but he was aware of a tightening of his muscles, a band across his diaphragm, and the pervasive almost suffocating presence of a corrupt, despotic trinity: vapor, drum beat and the Presence, manifest in the other two.

It was the real—and he did not mean his familiar fellow traveler, the Spoiler. Vividly now he saw himself during these past weeks—on the commuters' train, in the office, ascending these stairs to bed at night. Clearly, almost clairvoyantly now, he could *see* how often he had turned swiftly around, to catch *it* off guard, to discover, in a quick maneuver, its surely frightening lineaments.

Of course he had never seen it. But often, when hurrying with fellow commuters (his fellows?) through Grand Central to catch the 5:23, he had dodged, ducked his head, to avoid the blow he felt coming toward him. (And was this why Abe Fortune kept his head constantly cocked to the side? Had the great strokes of the Invisible Hammer driven it there in admonition?)

No blow had ever actually fallen, yet Walton had never been able to avoid flinching, or wincing, or even actually dodging.

And now, at last, half dreaming, half paralyzed-awake, Walton did make *it* out in the returning cloud of hot air—dimly, imperfectly, but surely as one perceives a familiar but undesired object from a window when the morning mists begin to resolve themselves and swirl into disintegration. No, perhaps he could not see it—but feel it: certainly.

And soon he also felt terror. It was in part, he knew numbly, a terror of his own insubstantiality. But it was a curious mixed feeling: the threat of that mass of closing dark air was claustrophobic; yet, contradictorily, it seemed to him that his wispy, transparent and insubstantial self was in danger of being wholly lost in the vast plains of space.

Sweating, trembling, he lay there, praying for extinction, oblivion of any sort. Let it be terrible, if it would only be instant. Existence, consciousness, was despair. But having thought this—or sensed it—he realized suddenly that he was fully awake. It is life I cannot bear, he thought. It is life that weighs inexorably upon me, that hovers smotheringly over me, that pursues me.

He was comforted. He lay serenely still, in a convalescent quiescence, for a long time. Those incessant commentators on summer heat, the cicadas, filled the emptiness with their sawing chatter, but through the sound they made Walton seemed to hear first one, then another of his children cry out or murmur softly or turn restlessly upon their wrinkled sheets. It seemed to him that all four of them were there, nearby; he could even distinguish the groaned protests of the boys, reliving the strident, tumbling minutes of the playground; the feverish, reaching murmurs of the adolescent girl, troubled over the life into which she was growing; and the shrill, insistent tone of the little one, half prattle and half precocious conversation.

It seemed, too, that he had but to turn to watch, through the darkness, the sleep-softened face of Julie. Drowsy and content, even in some peculiar fashion exalted, he felt a poignant sweetness in the voices of the children; he longed to touch the repose of his wife's face, to wake her gently and tell her.

Tell her what? He could not have said. Tell her that he had worn the Nessus shirt of contrition and terror and despair; that he had exorcised his guilt and anguish by charging life with the responsibility! Stammer out his mystical sense of peace, his recovery of his self— indeed, of a self? Expect her to believe that all the leaden days of misunderstanding and silent reproach, of hopelessness, of wooden, dragging silences and automatic existing, were over? And with them, too, the bitter arguments, the recriminations? That he had brought himself to a vigorous and serene life by admitting that he could not endure life?

He had a swift vision of those recurring times he and Julie had approached each other—tentatively, wryly, stretching out a cautious, exploratory word here, making an oblique gesture there, testing each other like competitors warily circling about and waiting for the exposure of a vulnerable spot before striking. Then the thrust, the cry: blood. And the anguished pounding at each other, the incessant beating of mortal fists until flesh was indistinguishable from own flesh, the beloved enemy oneself.

Was this over, then, because of one midnight's terror-stricken watch and exhausted relief?

No. The hand he had lifted, as though toward a Julie he would find beside him, dropped—it seemed by its own separate power, its own autonomous animation. The leitmotif of this fledgling happiness, the substance and meaning of this baptism into a new life, was the keeping of silence, the maintenance of an inner condition. Let it speak for itself.

He was aware that there were tears in his eyes, and that they were not from self-pity. There was a wonderful looseness, a relaxed peace in his whole body. It was real, he repeated to himself; it had actually happened. And for now, it was sufficient. Clasping it to himself, he fell asleep. . . .

To awaken, staring, wide-eyed, with no sense of this tranquillity, no knowledge of how long he had slept or where he was, no awareness of anything but the bleak gray light that filled the room, and its counterpart within him, chilling him, telling him that he had experienced a dream whose beauty had no counterpart in his life.

He felt chilled and inconsolable; he shivered uncontrollably. The warmth that he wanted, needed desperately now, was the warmth of a mother: he wanted to wrap himself around Julie, to tug at her, to curl up, Timmylike, in her arms, let her absolve him with her hands— no matter that she could not really forgive him. Really? What was more real than this need and its assuagement?

His teeth were chattering, his shoulders shaking. The chill that was on him was more than illness—this wintry blight. It was his soul that was congealed, and its mortal teeth that chattered. And so, because there was no Julie there, he lay back, rigid, until the cold in him became so absolute that it had no course but to diminish.

Then, finally, he saw that it was daylight, felt that the insufferable heat of the night before had barely lessened, and rose—to shave, bathe and dress for the forthcoming day.

To Maria on Her Fifteenth Birthday

When the winds have blown away,
The sun will bring another day.
What you've lost is left behind;
What your heart wills, you will find.
Therefore on this birth-starred day,
Look ahead: be glad, be gay.

Waiting at the entrance to the restaurant, Walton reread the verse on the birthday card for the fifth or sixth time, frowned, wondered whether it would seem too rhymed, too simple, too *young*, to Maria, shifted the small square box to his other hand, ground out his cigarette in the ashtray beside him, and resumed his nervous watching of the door.

He did not know whether she would appear alone—whether Lydia would come in with her, or whether he would simply catch a glimpse of her tall slender figure out on the sidewalk as she said good-bye to their child. He did know that his head ached, that his eyes felt as though there were grit in them, that his shirt stuck uncomfortably to his back, and that he had not recovered from the irritable anger that had flared in him when Dennis Byrnes had attempted, an hour before, to reopen their discussion of the Asiatic Studies program.

Walton lighted another cigarette, but found the taste so unpleasant that he moved quickly to the door and opened it, to fling the cigarette away. And there was Maria, alone, with sun glints in her light brown hair, her brown eyes smiling, flinging herself into his arms.

"Oh, Daddy, Daddy! What do you think has happened? Julie's invited me to spend all August with her and the kids on Martha's Vineyard and Mummy says I can go! Isn't it marvelous? Isn't it simply *super!*"

Kissing her, Walton disengaged himself gently, but kept his arm around her shoulder.

"Hey, hey! Wait a minute. What's all this? Come on in where it's cool."

He cast a last look down the sidewalk, but there was no sign of Lydia. Then, with Maria still bubbling excitedly, they moved on into the dark, cool restaurant and were led to the table he had reserved in the far corner.

Two feelings were circling in him, opposed and contending for dominance: pride and hurt. The source of the first was easy to identify; people on all sides were looking and smiling at Maria's eager, happy face, at the way she wrung her hands to express her joy (a curious and endearing habit that conveyed a full sense of the intensity, almost the fierceness of her feelings; when she had been little, this had always been accompanied by a hopping step)—but there was admiration in the glances, too: the gawky girl of thirteen and fourteen was slowly changing into a woman and, Walton knew suddenly with a sharp thrust of pride, into what promised to be a beautiful woman.

And the hurt? With a fierceness of his own, he pushed it aside.

"Now tell me slowly, baby," he said, unfolding his napkin. "What's all this about Julie—and August? But first, happy birthday." He extended the small square package.

Her eyes shone as she read the verse, and she looked up at him in so luminous and direct a response that he could not bear its full impact and dropped his eyes.

"Open it," he said almost sheepishly.

"I will," she said softly, "but, Daddy, I love the poem."

This time he managed to meet the ardor of her gaze and to say,

"I'm glad, baby." Something, both in the ceremonious way she untied
the white satin ribbon, instead of ripping the package open, and in the
brilliance of her eyes, touched him so sharply that he felt the imminence
of tears himself, and was relieved to see the waiter approach them.

"Maria," he asked, "do you think your mother would mind if you
had a glass of birthday sherry?"

She stopped full in the act of unwrapping the paper, and said with
a comical air of impatient worldliness, "Daddy, how silly! Of course not.
I've had *wine*—" she underlined it as though *wine* were some childish
beverage beneath sophisticated contempt—"and loads and loads of sips
from Mummy's cocktails. And I've smoked two cigarettes. But I don't
like drinks. I'd rather have fruit juice while you have your cocktail. Do
you have Honolulu Fruit Punch?" She impaled the waiter on a sharp,
commanding look—almost as much as to say, "If you don't, you're not
of much account," and seeing his perplexity, dismissed the whole matter.
"I'll take pineapple juice, then," she said and seemed to subside into a
reverie that ignored the two attendant men, murmuring, "It's a simply
yummy drink of all sorts of juices put together with simulated rum. But
of course it's *new*," and fell to opening her package.

Walton, feeling somehow subdued, ordered a dry martini and asked
reflectively, "How do you simulate rum? I've never heard of that."

But she didn't hear him. She had opened the box and was staring
raptly at the bracelet resting on the satin lining—a dull silver set with
a single garnet. When she lifted it with reverent fingers, still without
saying a word, Walton knew suddenly that he had bought her exactly
the right thing. All the gestures, the words, the looks of this child-
woman in the last few minutes came back to him in confirmation now,
and thinking how nearly—tired, hot and discouraged as he had been
the day before—he had given in to the impulse to end his search quickly
by choosing some conventional, uninspired thing to hand: handker-
chiefs, an overnight bag, a red pocketbook, he felt a surge of happy
relief. He had half expected her to toss aside her napkin and come
dashing around the table to hug him. But instead she extended the
bracelet to him with an unmistakable woman look.

A little clumsily he took the bracelet and slipped it over her hand
and wrist. Her hand was large, capable (though beginning now to taper,
to gain proportion, he thought, remembering how, only a couple of
years before, he had secretly shared her despair over the size of her
hands and feet), and he had to tug a little at its broadest point. But
then the bracelet was on, snugly fitting her forearm.

She held her arm up, (unconsciously?) turning it slowly in the immemorial fashion of women admiring themselves in new finery, and again Walton felt a warming filling of his throat. Hurriedly, he took a sip of his drink.

"Now—" he began, but she interrupted him.

"Daddy," she said gravely, shaking her head in wonder, slowly, "it is *very* beautiful. It is my first grown bracelet and I'm glad you gave it to me. I've been hoping for some time now that you would make such a gesture."

Choked somewhere between mirth and a deeper happiness, Walton managed to order. Maria was very explicit, deliberating for several minutes between asparagus and broccoli. Then, abruptly, her mood and manner changed, and she shoved the menu at the waiter as though it were some distasteful object, the touch of which she could not bear.

"Oh, I don't care," she announced happily. "I feel so wonderful I could eat hop toads. Oh, I just love my bracelet. Thank you, Daddy, thank you, thank you." And now she did rise and gave him an enthusiastic kiss. "It is time," she declared, "that we talk about serious matters. Well, anyway, I had this letter from Julie, saying that she and the kids would be at her father's place on the Vineyard all summer and why couldn't I spend all August with them? She said how the kids loved and respected me so—and Daddy they really do, you know; they have the utmost respect for me. Well, anyway—" and this time she interrupted herself with such clear and happy laughter that several people at nearby tables turned again to look and smile—"I am funny, aren't I, Daddy? I feel so dignified and hasn't my vocabulary really improved a great deal? Mummy thinks so. And then I use some expression that is too dignified for what I want to say, and I think that's very funny. Well, anyway— Mummy says I can't say anything without starting out, 'Well, anyway'— well, anyway," and now she collapsed into helpless laughter in which Walton joined.

Then, wiping her eyes, she tried again, her discourse punctuated now only by occasional giggles. "Mummy says I can go and it's going to be the most wonderful month I've never been to the Vineyard—oh you know that—and I hear it's perfectly beautiful and Julie says beside swimming and sailing I can ride her father's horse I've never met him but I can imagine him as very elegant and white-haired and smoking cigars in amber holders and the only thing I wish was that you could come up then. Don't you get *any* vacation at all?"

Feeling again the pain that had pricked him when Maria had first told him about the plan for August, Walton identified it. The left-outness, the aloneness again. And somehow a resentment of Julie's invitation. He knew that this wholly irrational feeling would subside, and that he would eventually be glad and grateful, as he was already for the clear indication that Maria—and surely Lydia too—knew nothing of the reasons for the summer's separation. Julie, as always, was warm and generous in this invitation, and a part of his petty resentment was, he understood now, that Maria should be going when he could not. He felt ashamed.

He heard himself saying mildly, "No, honey. I can't get away. We're having a complicated time at the Foundation, and it isn't like other summers, when everything is cleaned up in June. But I don't mind —especially if you can have this month there."

He was aware that she was again regarding him gravely, thoughtfully.

"Daddy," she said finally, putting down her fork, "I have two very serious things to say to you. I've been thinking about them for some time, and it seems to me that my birthday is an appropriate time to tell you. One of them—" and now she became a little breathless, slightly low-voiced—"one of them is that it's so much more fun to be with you since you stopped feeling guilty over me. I don't know just when it happened, but sometime in the last year. You used to make me unhappy because you felt so guilty—I remember times—but you haven't for ever so long, and I think that's why I've come to appreciate you. It's a very wonderful thing for a girl when she comes to the age where she can appreciate her father." There was a subtle change in her voice now, and a new merriment in her expression. "Provided he's ready to be appreciated. And you are. Now. I think. And I'm glad." Again she broke into that chuckle she reserved for good-humored amusement at herself. "There. That's that," she said, and held up her arm to admire the bracelet. "The other thing, Daddy, is that I can't thank you enough—" she leaned forward earnestly—"for naming me Mar-eye-ah, instead of Mar-ee-ah. Mummy's told me that the name was all your idea and I just love it. Of course I don't mean that there was any idea of using that other name—Mar-ee-ah—but anyway I just love my own name, and that's a happy thing to have. It's so distinguished, somehow, and now I've gotten old enough so that the kids have quit calling me 'Mare,' and that's a comfort." She chuckled again and picked up her fork. "My food's getting cold," she observed, "and anyway, I'm through. But thank goodness, when you had the idea, you didn't go and spoil it by calling it that other thing, that horrid Mar-ee-ah."

Walton was enchanted. The whole meal was enchanted: the small cake with the candles, the attention of the other tables, the successful blowing out of the candles—every detail was to Maria's eminent delight, and as they reached the climax of the cutting of the cake, it seemed to Walton that, in this enchanted birthday, the many failures and heartbreaking disappointments of the preceding years were obliterated, both for him and for his daughter.

At this moment there was a distraction in the room. At the buzzing sound of raised and appraising voices, Walton looked up, to see a woman and two men being seated at a nearby table by the headwaiter and a small cluster of obsequious attendant waiters. For a moment he stared at the slim, elegant figure of the woman in black, her wheat-colored hair, cropped like a boy's, her prominent cheekbones, and the bare arm lifted indolently to accept a menu—and then recognition tapped him with a commanding finger. He leaned across the table.

"That's an old friend of mine who just came in," he said to Maria in what he realized was, strangely, almost a whisper, "an actress named Karen Kodály. I haven't seen her for several years. Will you wait here just a minute while I go over and speak to her?"

Maria's eyes achieved what he would have thought impossible: they became larger.

"Daddy! You mean the *famous* Karen Kodály? You *know* her! You really do? Oh, Daddy, I want to meet her. You mean the one who was so brave in the war and all—and married to a senator? Oh, I think she's the *most* glamorous—even more than Marlene Dietrich—and the most beautiful woman in the world. She's Hungarian, isn't she? And you know her! You never told me."

Walton sounded somehow prim to himself.

"You never asked me. And she's not the most beautiful woman in the world, in my opinion, though very attractive. And I don't believe she's married to Senator Bradford any more; I read that they were—divorced. But you let me go over and speak to her, and then, if I signal you, you come over and join us. All right?"

Maria nodded. A shrewd look had crept into her eyes.

"Perhaps not the most beautiful," she murmured, "though I think so. But the sexiest, anyway."

A little jarred, Walton crossed to the other table and stood a moment behind one of the men until Karen Kodály looked up. He watched, with confident expectation, the rather wearied lifting of her eyebrows, the widening of the eyes, the undiluted pleasure of recognition. She stretched out her arms.

"Walton!" she said, giving the "W" a faint trill that made it almost a "V," almost a dashing name. "Valton Herrick!"

Through the first rush of her words, through the act of bending to kiss her soft and perfumed cheek, through the introductions, Walton was so flushed with pleasure and—yes, pride—that he had only a confused sense of what was actually being said. But after a few hurried and interrupted exchanges of "wheres" and "whens" and "whys," he remembered and asked, "May I bring my daughter over for a minute? You are her favorite celebrity."

"But of course. Please. Where is she? That lovely tall girl. Oh, Valton, how time runs away from us."

Then Maria was there, blushing and bright-eyed, and Karen was saying in her most charming and cordial way (what a lamb she really was, Walton thought, how always perceptive and understanding), "This is very happy for me to meet you, Maria—" she even managed to pronounce it right. "Your father is one of my best friends." And she extended—in a gesture that seemed quite simple and direct, wholly untheatrical—her right hand to Maria, while reaching for Walton's with her left.

"I guess," said Maria clearly, in a voice that rang over the room, "that this is the greatest moment of my life."

Before they returned to their own table, Walton had promised that he would come to see Karen on Sunday evening. "I go," she said, "to Deer Isle for a rest on Monday, and I must see you. Please."

As they left the restaurant, Maria said with awe, "You kissed her. She must like you very much." And when they parted at the corner, she said shyly, "You're a big man, Daddy."

DEPOSITION: 6

A letter to Senator Jonathan Coates Bradford, of Massachusetts, dated July 9, 1953, from Karen Kodály, formerly his wife . . .

DEAREST JON,

I shall go to Deer Isle this Sunday for a rest. I shall take only little Carla (you remember Carla Levy?) and Pépé; of these, as you know, I do not tire. And we shall stay, I think, until September, when I return to Europe, perhaps to the house near Cannes.

The picture was very fatiguing. Jodelle is excellent but difficult; to work with him one must have a rubber soul. And I do not like the moving picture any more. This is *un rien.* I have two scenes which permit of acting. The rest are disposed to portray the Kodály legs and—once upon a while—the Puckish face with the *sensibilité.*

I am a wisp. I shall lie and lie in the sun naked and sleep and watch Carla and Pépé splash in the water. *Ça va, ce ménage à trois.* You shock, dearest Jon? For that is what it is—and I find it so simple and natural. Young flesh and *élan*—pagan souls: this I am easy with. As you know, not that fierce wrestling between man and woman. Ah, you are so dear to me, *mon petit ours,* at a remove! For the writing of letters.

And it no longer hurts you that I write thus, for example? I think not. You know that I love you, and that we have tried the impossible. But an impossibility so *outrée* as to be heroic! Racine.

Perhaps, Jon (I dream tonight), I could not endure the circus of marriage (*quel brouhaha!*) because of a mother who is Hungarian, and a gypsy *au fond,* and a Norwegian sea captain for father. This is fashionable to think now, but I do not say it for fashion. They never stopped for fighting unless it was the time to make love. Oh, I knew, I knew, when I was but eight.

But you know all this. I bore you. And so I prefer to play at love with Carla and Pépé, and we do not care too much who is male and female. *Nous écoutons les pipes de Pan.* All is permitted except the anger and jealousy.

Most often our letters seem to me natural and loving. You tell me in full verity what you cannot tell others of the great false world in which you live, and I tell you of my little world of make-believe pastoral. I do not answer you about yours, nor you me about mine. Yet we write and listen and love—from far away.

One thing I do not tell you, ever. But now, like this, why not? For always you say, "Why? Why? Why not?" And below all the *politique,* you are too sensitive to accept only that I cannot live the wife (I meant to say "life" but this is better) of *un homme d'affaires.* You are just: I could so live, with difficulty, but *live* it, if that were all that afflicted me.

You worshiped me. *Toi, fou d'amour.* As actress, as glamour doll, I am worshiped. Everywhere men kiss my feet. So I kick them. But your husband you cannot kick. You must scratch, bite, scream. I cannot live so. Dear, dear Jon, you are so big without me; you—how does one say—shrink with me. I smother. I am not a goddess, but a woman, though a very strange one.

Perhaps you will not like what I write just now, and what more I want to say. But I hope. It is so long now since the divorce—horrid stupid word and law!—that I must do as I can to set you all, all free. For you have not married, and you, you dear Jon, of all should marry and have Bradford sons and a wife who waits at the home for her good and strong man. But all the Americans are romantical, and I think you sometimes dream that it all may begin again.

No—*et tant mieux pour toi.* So I will tell you that one time, before our marriage, there was a man, one man, who did not worship me, and whom I did worship. It returns to me because I have just recountered him in a restaurant. This will not recur; one does not stand still in the river of time. And I am too enervated, too—old? But it remembers me.

You know his name—Walton Herrick—from me and from the matter in the Congress in December. But you do not know him or this about him.

I do not think it would always have been like this between us. But he had then been married twice and twice divorced. Now again married, and it seems this endures. But for two years between we were lovers and it was good. He overwhelmed me, he ravished me, and this I died of thirst for.

It was then that I was *toute femme*—and then only. After all the adoration, a man who took me *sans politesse*, without even the asking. You would not believe it to see him. He is American—to madness —as you are American. He will be everything at the one time: good and successful, just but competitive, honest and self-deceiving, popular yet strict to his aristocratic beliefs, democratic and intolerant, a hedonist and a Puritan. But *you* choose, you elect, and do not receive the other side of yourself. He must keep all these together in him; it is not possible: he is Saint Vitus.

But not to me. You are strong, in control. He is wild, a paradox on two legs. But you are weak with me; he is strong with me.

I do not know why, my dear one. Perhaps it is only in love you do not trust yourself. (But you will, you will—find her.) And he never doubted himself with me. With other women, I think yes. It may be that my fear (yes, my deep, lifelong fear) of closeness, of being caught, so that I may bear intimacy only if it does not mean responsibility, made him the more free, and that he feared something of this *de son côté*.

I do not know. But my fear was gone, I was mad with love, I kissed his feet. And the power he held over me, this he softened with poetry, so that, in those times, I was his possession, but so prized, so tenderly cherished, that I wished only to be possessed.

Yet it ended? *Ça va sans dire.* Something else happened—I do not know—but to him the first. He became *sombre, ténébreux*, remote. I said good-bye. I took a knife—I do not exaggerate—and cut out my heart.

And it is gone, dearest Jon. Perhaps he could present it to me again, take it from his pocket and bow. Even so, we could not be lovers. He has gone on and away, and had he not I could not bear so much of joy and giving again.

Now go, dear Jon, I am tired. Go, dear one, and be closed of me. *Toujours.* But do not dislove me. You I love still—in my way.

K.

SO-CALLED "STUDY OF A FRIEND"
BY D. FOOTE
Notes, continued. July 9 . . .

One thing is clearer to me. I'm not trying to write a novel—or even to take notes for one. I'm studying Walton, partly, I suppose, because of that spectator side of me. But there are other reasons, too. At my age, I'm beginning to take stock: why did thus-and-so happen to me, something else to him; what's the meaning of many things we take for granted; who's who is for what. Then too, I want to write, and I can't seem to get myself organized for writing in an established structural form. But finally—and related to these matters—I have the feeling that if I can understand Walton better I'll understand myself better, and especially why I've always found it so hard to pull myself together and push ahead, break new ground.

Sunday night Cyn and I had dinner at Lydia Herrick's. I've often wondered why she hasn't remarried. She's a striking-looking woman, tall, with gingery-red hair, full-breasted, broad-shouldered, very graceful. And she's a strong woman, a little sharp-tongued but very perceptive, bright and interesting. I guess she does very well at her editorial job with *Compass*, and she certainly must not lack attentive men. She's probably just over forty, but could easily pass for thirty-five. And until Sunday night I'd never had a hint as to why she hasn't married again.

There. I've just reread that paragraph, and it's a flat indication of why I'll never be a novelist. I describe Lydia's looks: color of hair, figure, etc.; I speak of her mind and a little of her style. Would anyone know her from what I said? It's an old critical saw that one "brings characters to life" by striking particularities, a few specific traits either of appearance or manner or expression. I'll try again.

When I think of Lydia, I think of her hands first, I guess. No, that's a lie—hands second. Legs first: most beautifully proportioned legs I've ever seen. Marvelous taperings and curvings, swellings and diminishings, at all the right places to make for an unusual combination of the aristocratic and the sensual. Especially her knees. But I can't describe them. I've always been a little reticent about lingering, even in spoken words, over the female shape—so here goes Inhibition 1—but how does one say that a knee is rounded perfectly, without the slightest semblance of boniness, and yet that its ultimate charm is in the central vertical lines of the lozenge-shaped hinge?

That way, I guess. But what does it sound like? Some kind of jointed doll made of candy. Ugh.

I've mentioned her hands. Long, tapered in their own ways as the legs are—a quality of fineness and proportion. And her skin. She's keen on the outdoors, and the result, with her coloring, is freckles. But what enchanting freckles! Pale gold, ranging in size from little dots to pennies—and appearing in the most unlikely places (Whoa. I don't really know many of them.) It's as though they give her her vitality. With her fine bones, the carving of her face, her coloring and her long clean lines, she would otherwise be too perfected, too cool, too unlived. But she's been weathered by her freckles, and so she has her share of human imperfection. When very young, she must have been frighteningly perfected. But now she's rusted a little (I'm just remembering that Walton's name for her, when they were first married, was Rusty!), and become a woman.

What else do I most remember? Her smile. It's genuine, lights her eyes too, but very quick. It flashes like a sword, and is gone. She is not leaving it around for anyone to examine. And she has a gesture like that, when she's making a point. Slash! and her arm slices straight down, cuts the air and subsides in her lap.

Finally: I'm a little scared of her. Not just the sharp tongue. Cynthia has one too. But Lydia gives me the feeling that there's something cold at her center—that her judgments on anything that really mattered to her would be just, but tempered with little mercy—to herself or anyone else. She'd never scream, like Cyn; she'd never play tricks on her side; she wouldn't sulk; but if a man cheated on her she'd slice him like a potato—and probably cut out her own heart in the process. I seem to remember she's from New England.

I'm not going to read this back for a few days. I'll give it a chance to simmer.

Anyway, Cyn and Lydia had exchanged telephone calls several

times; I never saw Cyn so eager to renew an old acquaintance—"friend," she insists, though how a long weekend together years ago and a "Christmas letter" once a year make a friendship is beyond me. But apparently Lydia feels the same way, because when we arrived Sunday we found that she had invited no one else with us. There were just the three of us —and Maria, her and Walton's daughter, for a few minutes. She's a lovely girl—fresh and direct and honest, and just at the age where she utters philosophical platitudes with the air of a vigorous, original mind, and then in the next breath says something very naïve and childlike. I don't know which is more delightful—the heavy, serious assumption of adulthood or the freedom from being self-conscious over still being partly a child. She was much excited over the prospect of a birthday lunch with Walton (they must have had it yesterday) and over spending all of August with Julie and the kids. But she was on her way to have dinner with a friend in the same building, so we didn't see much of her.

All through our dinner we talked about the theater, schools and colleges, living in the suburbs as against living in New York—Cyn and Lydia doing most of the talking. But when we got to the point of sitting over our coffee, we fell silent for so long that it got embarrassing. It seemed as though we were all in that state of desperately fishing for something to say, but when we pulled up our lines, there was nothing at the end but seaweed.

At last Lydia looked up (she'd been staring at her coffee with her head bent) and straight at me, with those handsome gray eyes intent and serious.

"Well," she said, a little too briskly, "how's Walton?"

I remember actually sighing with relief.

"He's pretty well," I said. "No, he really isn't, I guess."

Now Cyn fixed *her* pretty blue eyes on me. I was really sweating over being the only one who knew about him and Julie, and I made up my mind then to tell Cyn later that night.

Cyn said, "What do you mean, Dudley? I didn't know anything was the matter with him."

I threw up my hands.

"He isn't sick. Nothing's wrong with him physically. He's just so tight and tense and drives himself so hard at work that I worry about him sometimes."

Lydia nodded.

"Tell me, Dudley, how well did you know Walton in those early days? He always spoke of you as a particularly good friend, but with Walton that doesn't necessarily mean that you were intimate."

"Good friends," I replied, "but I'd say not intimate. That was as much my doing as his. I like the shallows, where I can splash around, do a little straight swimming now and then, but also rest. And I'd rather stay on the surface."

"You *do* hate a fight." Cyn was musing out loud, and there was something so pensive and almost wistful in her tone that both Lydia and I laughed. "You're so damned good-natured that you let a lot of no-goods use you till I could scream." She wound up indignant.

"Hey, now," I said. "You quit that. I can take care of myself."

Cyn said something about no, I couldn't, though I took very good care of her and the kids. But Lydia wasn't letting go of the subject of the conversation.

"But you're open, Dudley," she went on, "and Walton isn't. It may have suited you to have that kind of relation, but he *had to*."

"You know," Cyn broke in, "I've seen Walton only once, at the office, since I got here."

"He's coming to dinner next week," I said.

"Don't get touchy," Cyn said, squeezing my arm. "I'm not attacking him."

There. Stop. How do people write dialogue, anyway? Just isolate it: "Cyn said, squeezing my arm." If that doesn't sound like a second-rate story in a ladies' magazine, I'm six feet tall. And stopping and biting the pencil, trying to think of synonyms for "said" that won't sound affected. It's too much for me.

I wanted to set this conversation down as exactly as I can remember it, so that I could come back to it, and especially study the things Lydia said about Walton. That's one reason. Another is that without as yet any definite conclusions about Lydia's remarks (including the ones only Cyn heard), I'm going at it just the way I described myself—staying on the surface. But it doesn't work.

Let me begin with how I've felt about Walton these last weeks, and then go on to find out (literally) how I felt and feel about Lydia's points of view on him.

I've been feeling very ambivalent about him. And that, I realize now, is what Cyn sensed but didn't express directly, at Lydia's. I can't get over that business about Gail and then, in a few days, Sonia. And after what he said to me about Julie. And now this evening with Lydia. All these women! What is he, a male nymphomaniac—whatever the hell you call it?

And both these wives are fine women. He can win them, but either he can't or doesn't want to hold them. I could never feel as warmly about

Lydia as I do about Julie, but I like and respect her. And while I mildly dote on Gail, there's something a little silly about her. Sonia, no. Terribly sexy, but no real feeling, I'd guess.

Anyway, it isn't just the women. Take Dennis Byrnes. He's a highly elusive young man, but I'm sure there is some justification for his being hurt over Walton's dropping him. It's evident that Walton made a lot of him when he first came to the Foundation, and it's hardly surprising that Dennis resents his fall from grace.

But on the other hand, when I begin to think that Walton has no real feelings for other people, only uses people as extensions of his own needs and conflicts, up pops evidence on the other side. His Evelyn has told me not only how good and thoughtful he is to her but how he helped her out when her mother had a heart attack. And she told me how he gave her a letter to a man in Cleveland and enclosed a check for several hundred dollars. It seems (he told her) that this man worked for his father years ago, and was very good to him. And now he's old and in financial trouble, and Walton not only helped him out but wrote him a letter telling him how well he remembered all he had done for his father and how *proud* he was that he had turned to him. It made Evelyn cry, she said, and she had felt as though Walton somehow felt this was an expiation. "Only he hasn't done anything he needs to expiate," she insisted. "He's a wonderful man."

Or just take me. There was nothing in what he did for me that could remotely be construed as using me. And whenever I remember what he did do for me, I realize further that the amazing thing about it is that he did it in such a way that I haven't felt any of the resentment one usually does just over being in debt. "Don't be angry at me," someone said the other day. "I haven't done you a favor." And he really hasn't done any of what worried me most—tried to dominate or absorb me.

Yet I am uneasy with him. It's not like the old days. Maybe I'm envious of the power in him, both to accomplish things and to win people. I honestly don't think so; I'd never want to pay the price he pays.

Lydia. At the point in the conversation where Cyn was squeezing my arm (it ought to hurt by now) I had an inspiration. A woman will talk more freely with another woman when there's no man around. So I began plotting how to get out and leave them alone for a while. At the same time, I didn't want to be crude about it—and Lydia *was* addressing her questions to me.

"Does he still sit in some kind of black study as though he were all alone, and then suddenly burst out in a rage?" she asked.

Suddenly now I was aware of the intensity in her eyes, and of how tightly she held herself.

I made a face.

"Yes," I said.

"And at a party does he still corner one person and ignore everybody else?"

"Well—" I hesitated. "I guess so. I'm not so sure about that."

"And at work, does he still find it upsetting if someone or something he doesn't expect breaks into his routine?"

I was on the hot seat. She was throwing these questions at me like a fast-ball pitcher who wouldn't let up, and I felt as though I couldn't get my bat off my shoulder. But, even worse than that, there was such a burning inquisitorial tone to the whole thing that it was—it had to be —even more embarrassing to her than to me or Cyn. She was all wound up and she couldn't stop. And with her fine sense of decorum and her usual civilized control of herself and the situation, she must really have been mutilating herself.

I hadn't answered this time, but she kept right on.

"Does he still assure you, with his wonderful rationalizing deep voice, that he knows perfectly what you're talking about and agrees with you, when you know all the time that he has no more idea of what you're talking about than if—if—" her voice was breaking now—"than if you were talking moon language?"

It was awful. I hadn't felt like this since my sixth-grade teacher broke down in class. And just as I thought that, Lydia, that proud woman, broke down and began sobbing.

I stood up, grabbing wildly at an invisible straw.

"I've got to go find a cigar," I said, and rushed out.

I'd forgotten how hot it was, but even that didn't drive me back. I walked and walked the still, muggy Sunday streets of the East Side, till I left the fashionable part and found myself, even at this late hour, in a neighborhood of shirt sleeves, ragged children, screams and shouts and scuffling—a neighborhood where the darkness came alive, into hot, sweaty, bickering, good-natured, dirty life. Then I felt I could really breathe again.

I don't know how long I was gone, but when I got back Cyn was waiting for me, looking all soft and shaken up, and there was no sign of Lydia or Maria. On the late train back to Northport Cyn told me the rest of it.

How Lydia had sobbed and sobbed, and only finally become quiet and just sat there, breathing exhaustedly and drying her eyes.

"She didn't apologize," Cyn told me. "I liked that. When she finally spoke, she just said, 'That's been coming for a long time.' And little by little, while we had some brandy, she told me how and why she would never get over him."

How and why. How she had "bought" Walton at his own evaluation, felt that she was marrying a strong, vigorous and wise man, been proud of this marriage of true minds, only little by little, as the years went by (there were in all six of them), to discover that what she had seen was there only as a potential. She insisted on that: the stature, the strength, the generosity reappeared from time to time—even the tenderness and the wisdom. But these were only flashes, lights in an otherwise total darkness; they flickered and went out after a day or two, an hour or two. "That was the awful part," she told Cyn. "If all that richness, that potential, weren't there, it wouldn't have been painful, but possible to make up my mind and break off cleanly. But there it was, though lost and hidden, and I couldn't give up hope without a fight. I loved him even when I hated him for what he did to me and to himself."

The first unforgettable and unforgivable incident, for her, occurred after Maria's birth. He had sat up all night in the hospital, waiting. And as long as he had been allowed to stay with her, he had been tender, thoughtful, reassuring.

When he returned to her after the birth, this was still true. Tired, almost haggard, he had still seemed to her to have grown overnight to his full mature stature: her happiness was complete. Yet the very next day, watching her nursing Maria, he broke the intimate silence with the words, "One thing, Rusty, I ought to tell you now. I'm not much of a family man."

Cyn's eyes flashed as she told this. Her funny little uptilted nose wrinkled in rage, and she said fiercely, "It's dreadful. I don't even care what he's done for you. He is—he has to be—a dreadful man."

She wouldn't listen to my defense when I tried to explain that I thought I knew how he would have said it—that I had even heard him say things that reminded me of this one—and that his crazy kind of thinking about honesty and candor would have led him to it, so that in his mind it was a matter of thinking, "I ought to get this straight with Lydia now, not mislead her."

Cyn replied so angrily that people two or three seats ahead of us turned around.

"*That's* no answer. It doesn't make any difference. It's unforgivable."

And then Walton's father died, and there was a whole new sequence of problems, with constant pressure on him from his mother and his invalid sister Elinor. Lydia told Cyn that she grew to hate them for the demands they made on Walton, and partly because it kept her saner—that was the word she used—to hate them, rather than Walton. But now she had someone to fight for besides herself, and she would not be reconciled so easily as before Maria had been born. And in the fourth and fifth years of marriage, bad turned to worse: battles of bickering and frozen silences lasting days; he stayed away from home more and more, and she was sure he was having affairs—having "indiscriminate poultices" applied to his wounded, sulking ego. So finally she summoned the strength to act, and made the break.

Cyn was worn out with all the emotion, and at this point she just put her head on my shoulder, and we didn't talk any more till we reached Northport. But in the car she sat up very straight and said, "And she hasn't married again because he killed something in her. She didn't say *that*, but I know it. She's had four or five proposals in these ten years, but even with the one man she felt enough for to consider marrying, she found she was constantly thinking that of course she didn't really know him as he would be to live with, and she didn't dare trust herself, her own judgment and feeling.

"You see, that's what I mean. He's wrecked her life, because he's taken away from her her womanness. And what's worse: in a funny way, I think, she still loves him, hideous black warts and all. She's only met Julie once and really likes her, but feels, I guess, that Julie's going to have to go through her own version of what she did herself. She's surprised that it's lasted so long this time, and she's just beginning to wonder if there isn't something drastically wrong with her *herself*, whether Julie hasn't proved that Walton could be all right with a woman sufficiently understanding and sound."

I swallowed hard. And I'm not proud of the fact that as I told Cyn in the kitchen about Julie and Walton some kind of mean elation kept creeping into my account. It was partly, I think, the satisfaction of corroborating what Cyn already felt, partly the chance to tell a "dreadful secret," but what bothers me most was the hint that I resented something in Walton so much that I was also satisfying some spite in me—despite what I've written above about my feelings for him. Anyway, I felt so ashamed that I didn't tell Cyn about my suspicions concerning Gail and Sonia. I had that crumb of comfort. It hardly filled me.

July 11

JANE FORTUNE, Walton decided as he sank comfortably down on the couch that commanded a clear view of the dining room, was an even more attractive woman than her husband had suggested. Stuffing his pipe, he remembered several of the phrases Abe had used: "forty-seven but still trim"; "a tongue like a needle"; "great sweeping, swooping pictures"—and realized that he had not seen a single picture of hers, at least not to know it was hers. No, here in the large, comfortable living room with the huge picture window overlooking the waterfall far below this modern house perched on the edge of an abyss (or so it had seemed to him when, on arrival, he had first looked down the giddy drop)—here in the living room there were a Picasso print, a reproduction of something he could identify as Breughel's, though it was one he had never seen before, and another of a familiar Rouault.

Soothed by homely, comfortable things—the fragrance of his pipe, the satisfying sense of a superb but not heavy dinner, and the sound of Abe's creaking footsteps over his head (What could he be doing? He kept limping back and forth)—Walton returned to his contemplation of Jane Fortune. "Trim," Abe had said, but "compact" seemed more apt. The other word held connotations of a slenderness that not even the most uxorious eye could attribute to Jane. Yet, short as she was ("Five foot one," Abe had said), and solid, there was not a single line to her that seemed superfluous or heavy. An eminently womanly figure, Walton decided with approval—and topped with a cap of silver hair that was so marvelously cropped, in some mysterious way, as to give no effect of boyishness at all—but rather to increase that of femininity.

That was an interesting thing about short haircuts for women, Walton mused—and interrupted his pleasant and now slightly drowsy absorption to respond to a wave of the hand from Jane, who was whisking back and forth between dining room and kitchen, having dismissed sharply the idea of help. "A tongue like a needle," Abe had said. Yet all that Walton had observed so far as relevant to this statement was that she was quick and bright, and any possible sting in her comments was softened by the lowering of lids over what were usually termed "sloe eyes," and a smile that was lazily provocative. But the domestic human animal, he reflected, differed from the social one by a complicated and enigmatic system of heightened and lessened emphases. What was witty and charmingly provocative in a gathering of people could be shrewish and wounding alone with the mate; what was distinctively individual abroad might seem, in close daily contact, to be eccentric and infuriatingly irrational.

"Hurry up," he called. He was fully aware of his almost domineering insistence and confident that she would find it flattering. "I want to talk to you."

She flapped her small hand at him derisively, meaning, he decided happily, any unascertainable one of a number of things. And when she reappeared briefly to set a snifter of cognac beside his coffee ("There," she said)—not so much flirtatiously as indulgently—his contentment was complete. He half sensed now why this whole business was delighting him so, but he resolutely pushed the partially formed thought off the conscious level of his mind.

Where had he been? he wondered lazily, lifting the balloon glass and sniffing the aroma. Yes—short haircuts for women. They were a marvelous innovation, for they introduced so many new variants in beauty, charm, poignancy. Jane's silver cap was somehow womanly though saucy, and suited the whole style of her compactness. As though she were able to read his thoughts, there was a sudden heightened clatter of dishes in the kitchen, submerging the uneven sound of Abe's persistent footsteps. Walton smiled and spent several desultory minutes in futilely trying to whittle out a sharper definition than "compactness."

No matter, he thought lazily. Julie—Julie's was not that short, but cut almost in the style of what had once been called a "Dutch bob." Yet those words suggested a boyishness that was no part of Julie. The very gleaming straightness of her fine black hair conveyed a sense of silkiness that required some severity to keep from being almost uncomfortably exotic. It, and her sensual mouth, he thought, the little pad of flesh below her thumb, the crease in her elbow, her delicate feet . . .

"Wow," he muttered half aloud, "the Song of Solomon." But it was Solomon in Exile: Walton amidst the alien corn. He wondered why he still felt so content—knew a contentment beyond the power of a royal dinner with an excellent Chablis, even beyond that of good company and two slugs of his favorite bourbon on the narrow porch perched over the foaming waterfall.

And Sonia, he resumed. Sonia . . . He could not avoid her altogether, and once he had received Julie's reply he had again begun seeking opportunities to visit P.H.'s office, though he had little to say to her when he saw her—and despite his feeling of contempt for his retracing of this route as soon as Julie wrote him not to come to the Vineyard. Sonia's hair was soft, and cut in lops and loops that fell over each other in an artfully tangled way. What detail! he thought, and again grinned comfortably at himself. Like a boy with a secret, he thought.

Then there was Karen. Immediately everything fell into place. He recognized, and saluted, the importance of his anticipation of to-morrow evening, and while he thought calmly, rationally, "That is absurd, and I must keep it absurd. As things stand, the last thing that I want now is to resume with Karen Kodály"—he knew in his bones that the thought, full-minded, was less than halfhearted.

Rolling the brandy on his tongue and then swallowing it and taking a sip of coffee, he obstinately continued his reverie. Karen's wheat-colored hair was as close-cropped as Jane's, but with a completely different effect. It was Puckish, Ariel-like, conveying the sense of a charming raggedness. This was, perhaps, the essence of real boyishness —but, again, had nothing to do with boys. Rather, perhaps, it was, in the purest sense, epicene. And people misused the word when, almost always, they employed it about men in a derogatory way. Her figure, too, in its delicately rounded slenderness, partook of this quality. She was a subtler Peter Pan, perhaps, as knowing and as finally restless—but far less afraid of giving herself.

And her true boyishness lay in her intimate manner, in her private gestures (unknown to her public) with their careless, angular indifference to traditional grace, yet invested with a wild and slaphappy grace of their own. Then, making love, she was suddenly all softened, vulnerable woman.

Hearing dimly sounds from the kitchen that suggested the completion of Jane's tasks, Walton deliberately hurried his dalliance, wanting a lapse between the subsiding of his now inflamed imagination and the intrusion of a present personality.

His vision now was of Karen's nipples. Her breasts were slight, no more really than faint, rounded curves, hardly breaking the adolescent delicacy of her body. Yet those nipples were so knowing, so responsive, so charged with concentrate life, that they assumed the dignity of breasts, the full burden of rapture.

The sounds from the kitchen were now all indicative of putting away. Cupboard doors were slammed; there was a jangle of pots and pans, the unmistakable sound of a torrent of water, then shut off. But before Walton had fully roused himself from daydreaming, he heard approaching footsteps.

It was not Jane, however, who entered the room first. It was Abe, carrying an old-fashioned glass filled to the brim with his beloved pink gin. As he grunted a greeting to Walton and painfully crossed the room, some of the liquid slopped over the edge of the glass and fell to the floor with a faint splash.

"Abe the Phoenician," said Walton, before he realized that he was speaking aloud.

Abe stood for a moment, regarding the small pool of gin on the floor and cursing mildly. Then he dropped into the nearest chair and considered Walton as near to sourly as Walton had seen him look. "Well," he remarked in a voice incongruously gentle. "What's that for?"

"What's what for?" Jane inquired from the doorway. "That puddle of your damned gin? That's for cleaning up, my good man. It awaits your ministrations."

Abe cocked his head a little farther to leeward. To Walton's still not very alert gaze, it seemed in danger of toppling off his neck altogether.

"No. Good for the floor—gives it a tone. The name—" he pointed with his chin toward Walton—"he called me."

"What name?" Jane demanded. "I won't have you calling my husband names unless I can put my imprimatur on them."

Walton shrugged.

"I called him Abe the Phoenician. I don't think I can explain it, but it's what came to my mind when we met several weeks ago, and I just said it aloud now, without realizing that I was. Let's see. It has to do with the whole cast of his looks, his darkness, and the— well, the sort of inscrutability I feel about him. He's perfectly willing to answer a question if I ask him one, but I have the feeling that there are extensions to every answer that it would take a lifetime to fill out. As though he'd been everywhere, seen everything, weighed it, connected it with other, entirely different parts of his experience and tucked it away for some future use." He paused, took another sip of brandy, aware that he had their full attention. "The Phoenicians, of course, were the first great sea-going merchants that we know much about. Only"—he chuckled—"that's all I know about them, so I'm free to assume that in their very wise and businesslike voyages (that's part of the resemblance) they had—at least the best of them—while at sea plenty of time to absorb the implications of explorations. For, however hardheadedly useful these expeditions, they really were explorations too, as surely as the ones that first brought Europeans over here. And so I see the best Phoenicians, the master Phoenicians, as philosophizing merchants—eminently sane and sound, but exposed to so many exotic and alien encounters as to feel the need to include these matters too, to bring strange and even mystical and romantic attitudes, customs and sights to heel, to synthesize the familiar and the unfamiliar."

Abe was studying him closely, his gin forgotten, but when Walton fell silent, he said nothing—though his peculiar warming smile appeared briefly.

Jane, however, let out so formidable a whoop that Walton turned to her—turned and recognized instantly her expression. This combination of amusement and pride—this was patently the Wife's look.

"Phoenician, yet!" she exclaimed. "The trouble with you, Walton Herrick, is that you're so properly, Midwesternly Anglo-Saxon that you can't recognize a Lower East Side Jew when you see one. Abraham Gelbstein, please!" She grinned happily at her husband.

For a moment Walton was not sure what she meant. Then, by the time he did understand, Abe was already speaking.

"Why not?" His shrug was eloquent. "Who wants Gelbstein in this world? Have I cut my mother's throat? You can put it all in the obituary column—you know those adjectival ones: Gelbstein, Abraham, beloved husband of Jane Sherry, dear brother of Sophie, loving uncle of Morris and Sol, devoted great-uncle of Isidor. . . . And where the births are recorded, just Abe Fortune . . . Well. Maybe *in vacuo*." He paused reflectively. "Maybe everybody should rename himself when he's grown up." Suddenly, unexpectedly, he put up a defensive hand. "Well. I kept the Abe."

Walton was delighted.

"You see," he said. "It all fits together. It fits what I had to say much better that he should choose the name 'Fortune' than that he should be born with it. I wish I knew how you came to choose *it,* though, instead of any one of a thousand other names."

Jane grinned and looked at Abe.

"Easy," he said. "Wanted to make one. Name for luck, mostly."

Walton thought he understood the "mostly." Abe would not pretend, would tell the truth—but felt no compulsion to tell all the truth.

"And he did make one," Jane stated, suddenly stroking Abe's head with, it seemed to Walton, an almost fierce tenderness.

Abe straightened his head to nod.

"Right. And that's my business." He turned to Walton and smiled, to indicate that no rudeness was intended. "Not so interesting. Not vulgar or sensational. No garter belts or contraceptives."

His smile grew cryptic. Walton realized he was not going to learn any more about it—tonight, anyway. He looked thoughtfully at Jane.

"Abe told me about your painting," he said. "May I see some of them?"

Abe broke in.

"Damnedest fellow. Whole acquaintance based on my learning about him. But spend all our time learning about me. And now you. No pictures tonight. Tomorrow."

"I have to go back to town tomorrow," Walton explained. "I have a date for dinner."

Abe waved the whole matter aside.

"Plenty of time. You two'll be alone in the morning."

Jane observed Walton's surprise. "He sits up most of the night," she remarked. "Maybe that's when he practices looking enigmatic. So, anyway, he sleeps most of the morning. You know, I've been meaning to say how much I wish you'd been able to bring your wife. Abe told me that your family's away for the whole summer."

"I'm sorry, too," Walton said. "You and Julie would like each other."

Jane nodded. "What's she like?" she asked, and there was a new expression, somehow, of expectation, it seemed to Walton, who now, for the first time, was fully aware of how much the mobility of her face accounted for her attractiveness.

"She's quiet," he said in reply. "Though in meeting people she seems—is—very animated. But mostly, I think, through her attentiveness—because she doesn't talk a great deal. She's got enormous sense, yet almost always strikes people as somehow, well, poetic. She's marvelous with the kids, without ever particularly seeming to be. I mean she doesn't talk a lot about or to them, and she's not particularly demonstrative. But when there's a row or a problem, she sets it straight so fast I haven't caught up with it before it's over—and all without raising her voice or seeming to be at all upset."

The silence seemed eloquent to him. Looking up, he realized the intentness of his audience, and wondered about its significance.

"Sounds blue ribbon," said Abe. "Is she younger?"

Walton knew that he was flushing, and was, as always, annoyed that he should become self-conscious at this question.

"Yes," he said, almost shortly. "About eleven years."

Jane's smile was persuasively friendly.

"You haven't told us what she looks like."

"Beautiful," said Walton, and joined in their laughter. "Well, I find it's hardest to describe someone—that close." That was, he thought, a stiff way to say it. "She looks a little the way I think of Pocahontas looking, though her hair's short and she hasn't any Indian blood."

"College graduate?" Abe asked, and smiled. "Professional question."

"Yes," said Walton. "Swarthmore."

Abe pushed himself up.

"Need some gin. How about you? Recess."

"No, thanks," Walton replied, and was aware that he was both alert and uneasy. Alert because, in however friendly a fashion, these questions had to do with *the issue*. Uneasy—not for the same reason. No. He knew only too well: uneasy from guilt—the too close juxtaposition of his meditation on Karen Kodály and the need to describe Julie.

Jane spoke softly. He observed what he had thought of as her heavy-lidded look, and decided from her new question that, at least in terms of the usual connotation, his description of the expression wouldn't do.

"*Is* she a poet? I mean, really a poet—not just in personality."

"Yes," said Walton. "I'm interested that you ask. She's had a lot published—no book yet, though; that's hard to get in our times, for a poet. She uses her maiden name, Julie Norton."

Jane seemed lost in contemplation. "Julie Norton," she repeated and shook her head. "No."

Walton wondered what meaning the "no" had beyond the obvious one of not having heard of Julie or read any of her poetry. It was, perhaps, entirely unjustified to assume that it had any other significance —and yet he did. However, he reminded himself, he'd been seeing double meanings and hidden intimations and oblique allusions all evening.

Abe stopped in the doorway.

"What does Connecticut need?" he asked abruptly.

Walton pulled himself erect in his chair.

"It's time I came clean," he said. "Actually I'm only here because I wanted to see more of you—and to meet Jane. I'm no candidate for the nomination—and by now you must know that as well as I do. There are many reasons why I can't answer your question intelligently. In the first place, I'm a commuter. Except for one term on the Northport Board of Education, I've had nothing to do even with local civic matters. I've had little time and, honestly, little inclination to get mixed up with things at home when I've got so much on my hands in New York. So, even on the city or town scale, I'm an ignoramus about Connecticut. Far more so, when you're thinking about the state as a whole." He paused, to relight his pipe. "Besides—and Leon Goodman could verify this—I haven't had any of the right training. I know little about economics, little about political science, less about the law. I'm essentially an unpolitical man—not a nonpolitical one, if you get the distinction. I haven't even had very much business training, in the usual sense. I simply don't qualify, pleased though I am to be thought of."

Jane's expression conveyed, in some obscure fashion, admiration. Abe's was unreadable. But he limped to his seat, saying as he went, "Perhaps. Well. But that's not what Anna Manges thinks."

Walton was flatly astonished.

"Anna Manges!" he exclaimed. "Do you know Anna?"

Abe allowed himself a loud chuckle.

"Bull's eye. Anna worked with me back before you knew her at your teaching post. She's still there. Maybe you know."

"Yes," said Walton. "I saw her a couple of years ago. You know, I've always figured Anna belonged in politics, not teaching the academic variety. But what a mind! Like a razor. And it's so damned unusual for a woman to be that sharp and yet—so amiable, so uncontentious, such a good companion."

Jane's eyes were bright.

"Do you think most smart women are contentious?" she asked.

Abe waved her away.

"Leading question. Dismissed. Irrelevant. Well. Wrote Anna about you and possibility. Valiant answer. Written her again. Asked for fewer laurel wreaths, more critical judgment. No answer, must have got huffy.

"But Anna—and Leon too—think you have the qualifications. He only doubts whether good for you. As for my question, nobody else knows—with any clarity—how to answer. Someone says roads, someone schools, someone industry. And so on. Wind. Problems present themselves, suggest others not obviously connected. If you have the brains and stuff, play it by ear."

Walton shook his head.

"Whatever Leon and Anna have told you, I'm really convinced that I'm right. Within the limits of my particular job, I don't believe that I'm a bad administrator. Yet that part of the work isn't what appeals to me most. I'm really a book man, a humanities man. And while I don't believe that I have all the limitations that are regular with my tribe, I have some of them. I'm honestly more interested in abstract ideas, and in their expression in the arts, and in the psychology of the individual than I am in practical measures, in the social sciences, and the problems of the state."

"Sounds good," said Abe, who had produced an ivory toothpick and was putting it to use, "but Wilbur Cross wasn't a bad governor."

"I'm sure he wasn't," Walton agreed, "but although his name was associated with the humanities, and he edited the *Yale Review,* I'm sure he must always have shown a far more natural inclination to the political scene than I have."

Abe sipped gin.

"Abstract vs. practical, arts and social sciences, the individual and the state." He counted them off on his fingers. "All artificial. Can't handle state unless you can handle people. State without people abstraction. Abstract gets awfully practical. Read Aristotle."

Walton grinned.

"Abe," he said, "how did you get to talk that way? That kind of—personal shorthand? With no adjectives or articles, and sometimes no verbs? It's like a telegram—especially tonight. You can't have come by it naturally."

Abe gave him a long, thoughtful look. Walton was suddenly aware that Jane looked as intently expectant as he himself felt.

"Why not? Depends on what you mean by natural. I think it's because the older I get the harder it is to talk. It tires me. I don't want to waste effort on those extra words. Besides—" grinning in his turn— "it always throws the other fellow off balance a little."

Walton nodded, watching Jane, who looked as though, still skeptical, she was weighing evidence. But surely *she* must know.

Abe shifted his weight in his chair.

"How about your appearance before the Congressional Committee?" he went on as though uninterrupted. "Nothing ivory tower about that . . . Arts and social sciences: words. Arbitrary division for teachers. All one big spider web. I don't believe in evolution."

Walton caught at the words.

"Look here. You said that before. What do you mean?"

Abe gazed into space.

"Everything moves crabwise—not in any straight line, vertical *or* horizontal. Spirals, if you like. Ape into man too simple. Bad man growing good fantastically oversimplied. Progress an absurd rationalization. Barely know enough biology to make Jane happy wife—" he ignored her snort of disgust—"but am sure Darwinism as incomplete as all other evolutionary and semi-evolutionary concepts. Spider web —crossing and crisscrossing. Variation one key, and variation brings variety. Aristotle great thinker—but only half right in his A is A. A is A but more because connected with B and C and square root of ampersand. Every A is. Always can learn more—new knowledge doesn't supplant as often as we think. Supplements. When you see x and y, fine. Then somebody discovers z; everybody says y no longer true and x different. Wrong often. Wait for q and y re-emerges. New combination. Get me? Not relativist. Absolutist, but awed by enormous complexity. Possible to know all? Yes. Now? No. When? Don't know. But your argument's irrelevant."

Jane's eyes were shining with obvious pride. Walton looked from her back to Abe.

"I'll digest that over the next few weeks. Or try to. But one more question: why did you say, when you left last time, 'Leave the cigar store Indians alone'?"

Abe gave him his smile, but this time was willing to footnote it.

"Highly relevant. Consider the cigar store Indian; it neither sows nor reaps. Wooden abstractions as bad as no abstractions. Leave them alone."

"But what had I said—" Walton began, a little ruffled.

Abe raised a hand.

"Your problem," he said. "But maybe nothing. Maybe just my general fatuous advice." His manner changed; he pulled his head up, fastened Walton with the most earnest expression he had yet seen him wear. "Well. Look. Next time we talk with Armour Ward. He wants it. The county chairman here. I'll pass on your reluctance. Let him talk like politician to you. Let it simmer. Watched pot. Good thing here. No commitment by you, but no absolute no yet either. That much you'll give, right? Good. Now let's forget it. Poor Jane—ignorant woman. Impatient all this hifalutin talk. Time for music. Like Vivaldi?"

Abe's taste was eclectic. After Vivaldi, Sibelius; then Bach and Bartók. When he switched the record player off, Jane brought in a tray with highballs, cheese and crackers, and Abe's bottle of Beefeater gin. They talked in a desultory fashion for a few minutes; then Jane finished her drink, stood up and said good night, repeating her promise to show Walton her paintings in the morning.

Something in Abe's expression caught Walton's attention now.

Abe put his hand under Jane's chin and lifted her face to kiss her good night. One of the most familiar of domestic scenes—yet Abe gave it a different accent, it seemed to Walton, through the searching way in which he looked into his wife's eyes.

When Jane had left, Walton turned to Abe.

"It's getting late," he said. "You must want to go to bed, too."

Abe shook his head and poured another gin, dropped in ice cubes, gave the bitters bottle a quick shake, and waved Walton over to the tray.

"Have another bourbon. She told you: I don't go to bed. Sleep's a bore. Men who who drink bourbon are passionate, serious, but lack flexibility."

Walton paused in the act of pouring, and grinned.

"Do you really believe that?"

Abe waved a paw in the air.

"Sure. Half sensualists who aren't comfortable with their sensuality. Opposite of gin—comfortable with sensuality, but no passion. Scotch neither one. Except women: then rules off."

Walton stirred his ice with his forefinger.

"Vodka?" he asked. "Rye?"

"Let's not hammer it into the ground."

They fell silent, and for some reason, with the only sound the incessant music of the waterfall, Walton found himself remembering the pacing footsteps overhead earlier.

"Was thinking about you upstairs tonight." Walton started in surprise. "Wish I knew why such a conviction about you. Anna and Leon have given me plenty of reasons, but something else—" He paused again, and then asked, "Your family been in this country a long time? Mayflower?"

Walton nodded, a little embarrassed.

"Not the Mayflower, thank God. But early; 1630 one side, 1636 the other. The Herricks were always in Connecticut until my great-grandfather, who started west. The generations since went from upper New York State to Ohio, and now I've brought my family back to Connecticut."

Abe looked interested.

"Good. Not first importance, but good. I mean more—want to account for feeling you give me. Not talking about governorship now—but sense of clue to something—don't know, something American."

Walton shrugged to indicate his own perplexity. Abe muttered to himself for a moment, then stood up, and began pacing, gin once again slopping over the edge of his glass. At last he paused in his limping progress around the room and stood over Walton, looking down at him intently, his brow furrowed.

"Look," he said. "Do you mind? Tell me about your family—no, families."

After a moment's hesitation, Walton set to. He told him what he knew about the Great Original, William Herrick I, the Pequot War and William's memorable tripping "over a dead Indian"; his move to Hartford and Windsor; the memorial stone; and about the mysterious fright and death of William's wife, an account of which Walton had read in his father's book of the Herrick genealogy.

This book set forth that on the records of the Criminal Court at Hartford (one of the courts at which Jas. H. prosecuted more than two hundred years later) under the date of September 6, 1655, "James Stiles, Thomas Jessup, and Henry Drake, all for their riotous misdemeanor in William Herrick's family, and thereby frightening his wife: the court adjudgeth that each find securities in £20 for their good behavior to the next court, and then make their appearance, and James Stiles is adjudged to pay 20s. to the common treasure." So the notice read (Walton paraphrased it for Abe); William Herrick's wife had died on the preceding July 17. Apparently the connection between the two events could not be established; but it was known that the three men cited were neighbors, young married men with no other criminal record. . . .

Walton told Abe of his vision of Sequester Meadow, of Peletiah Herri'k, who spelled his name in this eccentric fashion to renounce his kinsmen, and again paraphrasing, gave him Cornelius' account of Peletiah in his old age:

> It must be said, not because it is a pleasant thing to speak of, but as being part of the environment of my life, that my grandfather Herri'k was given to strong drink, and often came home the worse for liquor, his beautiful and faithful gray mare knowing much better than her master how to order her steps. It was often remarked that the horse seemed to know when her master was off his base, and to extricate herself wisely from predicaments of unstable equilibrium into which he had forced her. Oh, that a poor dumb beast should show more of God-given reason than its master!
>
> As we children matured, this weakness of our ancestor

was the occasion of great mortification, humiliating us often in the presence of those with whom we desired to stand well, and as he lived to be almost ninety years of age, the discipline was long drawn out.

At this point, Abe declared solemnly that it was time for another drink. A little self-consciously, Walton made sure that he was not boring him, before going on to give Cornelius' account of the nature and frustrations of his father, Aaron; to tell of Cornelius himself, of Lloyd and William, and his own early life.

He did not take so long over the Nicholsons, since he was not so familiar with the ancient record. But Abe exclaimed over James H., confident that he had heard many old-timers mention him, with more admiration than Mr. Hornsby had accorded him in the Ridgefield incident. Even in this shorter account, however, Walton stressed the Gothic elements in the Nicholsons' story. At last he stopped, drew a deep sigh, and said, "Amen. I won't thank you for your patience, because I could tell you were really interested."

Abe nodded.

"What stories! My head's whirling." He looked sharply at Walton. "What do you make of all this? It's yours, and you've studied it."

Walton hesitated, stared at the swirling liquid in his glass.

"I think it *is* American. The elements may be present elsewhere, but that would be in different combinations. And having only come to be interested in the last few years, I've been full of it—really so much so that I've thought of all these people, these stories, these conflicts as mine, somehow inside me *physically*. Especially my two grandfathers. I can't get them out of my craw. I know intellectually that I'm using them as symbols, yet they feel more immediate to me than that."

Abe looked thoughtful.

"Symbols?"

"Well," said Walton, scratching his head, "personal symbols to me. But in a larger sense, symbols, too, of two great lines in American life and thinking. The one line stretching from Jefferson down through the men who opened the frontiers, who became abolitionists, who were at various points in our history idealistic political radicals—the Optimists, I call them. In various forms this line has always believed in what I'd call relationalism and pluralism, been consistently liberal and progressive, had some confidence, if not in the perfectibility of man, at least in the possibility of his improvement and his potential to live cooperatively with others, believed in individualism, individuality, and the value of dissent, and had more faith in the power of environment than in that of heredity. I've grossly oversimplified, but unavoidably so, I think."

He paused and gulped some of his drink.

"And the other?"

"The other, to simplify again, extends from Alexander Hamilton. Or more truly, to go farther back, from Jonathan Edwards—as against Roger Williams. Politics and theology provide different illustrations of the same world view. At any rate, these are the Pessimists, distrusting human nature, invoking Hobbes, inclining to absolutism and fatalism, conservatives in politics, filled with the sense of original sin (whether Calvinistic or Freudian) and—at worst—total depravity, persuaded that heredity—whether literal genetic or theological or even national—is dominant in development."

"Puritanism vs. American optimism," suggested Abe.

"Not quite." Walton set his glass down and began lighting his pipe. "Both lines stem partly from Puritanism—or at least Calvinism. Don't forget that individual free enterprise came in with the Reformation. If, as Calvin and Luther variously believed, man's good works were irrelevant to his salvation, and God in his inscrutable and arbitrary way chose his own Elect, they at least paved the way for a freedom to concentrate on one's own material welfare, and eventually it even came to be believed that material success might well be an evidence of God's favor, a hint of membership in the Elect. So both the optimistic and vigorous American drive and individualism, and the pessimistic view of human nature may derive from Puritanism. But even that's oversimplifying. There were the Quakers in Pennsylvania, the Dutch in New York, the Catholics in Maryland, and a different British element in Virginia. Among still others."

Abe's head had slowly become uncocked. His current pink gin rested beside him, untouched.

"All right, then. The Optimists vs. the Pessimists. The Herricks vs. the Nicholsons?"

Walton nodded.

"It's something like that. The ebullient, expansive pioneer vs. the puritanical, constrictive or contracting theocrat-standpatter. And the Herricks vs. the Nicholsons. But that's too simple too. The dark stream runs through the Herricks. That first wife, our first mother (I think of William as a kind of Adam in America) was frightened to death. Or may have been. And her son, though I haven't been able to get precise information yet, seems to have been mixed up in witchcraft trials. Or take Grandfather Herrick's journal. He opens it by saying that his first three memories are the death of his little brother, the death of an aunt, and his grandmother cutting a currant switch to take to him on a Sunday! And, in between, I see many of the line as like Aaron— dark and tormented and frustrated."

"But they kept on going," Abe commented. "Maybe not every generation. But old Peletiah—and your grandfather. Any bright ones in the Nicholsons?"

Walton shook his head.

"I'm not sure. Some, I think, farther back. From the little I know, my maternal grandmother's father, a Colonel Walton in the Civil War, was a man of action, and outgoing. But when you come to my grand-fathers—or at least the way I think of them—the two lines are very marked."

They fell silent again, Abe's steady gaze speculative, even inquisitive. Walton broke in again abruptly.

"Crudely, that's the American version as I see it. But the line goes way back, in similar terms, at least to Plato and Aristotle. Sometimes there are attempts at a reconciliation, a mingling of opposites— in fact, I think, at least sometimes, that that attempt is the secret to fulfillment, to a rich life. If there is any secret.

"For you see, I've presented it as though the Optimists, the Herricks, were life and the other side death. But that's wrong. Intellectually, I'm a liberal, a humanist, and an affirmer. But liberalism-optimism *in action* can become very shallow, very do-gooderish, and, instead of invoking a realistic positive, simply put on blinders. While the old dark conservative pessimistic stream, invoked by a real thinker or artist, cuts deeper, into richer soil, may result in a genuinely and authentically tragic view of life. Then it's a cello against the liberal fife. But if one can blend these elements—" He flung his hands wide and stood up. "I've kept you up too long."

Abe ignored this last. He took a sip of what must have become lukewarm gin.

"And you?" he said suddenly. "Where do you stand?"

Walton winced. He meant it as a comic gesture, but he was sure the real pain must show through.

"Right in the middle," he said quietly. "Sometimes I believe they're all alive in me, half of them dancing the dance of life, and half the dance of death. I try to affirm the one and deny the other— but since I can't, sometimes I try to freeze them both."

"Bad," said Abe. "What about the attempt at reconciliation?"

Walton shook his head.

"One thing to understand and say, another to live in your own bones. Abe—when do I hear your story?"

Abe rose now.

"Another time, Walton. I'm going to let *you* sleep, at least. Man with all that in him needs rest. You know the way."

A handclasp. Undressing upstairs, Walton felt its warmth still on his palm. He felt plainer, simpler, more honest than in months, he thought sleepily—with none of his usual retrospective regret at having talked so openly. He felt clean and quiet.

The Unmoved Mover

stir.

down by the river, in the marshes, the fitful fires were flickering, dervish—stir, touch and stretch. sluggish, the whispering blood. thick, stirring. i. (ces barbares marchent tous nus, et nous, nous marchons inconnus, fardés, masqués . . .)

stir.

whisper flicker rustle. and moving. i. dark but the marsh fires stir rustle shift. lick. licking. low glow. whisper.

sweep sweeping up. the drum. the throb. i. move. lift. the drum.

i shall arise and go down where the willows blow in the steam of the smoky swamp. smoky dervish eyes devil dance. thump.

the drum. throb pulse drum. i: down where the dancers go. down where the golden . . . golden? gilded (nous marchons inconnus, fardés, masqués)

parting the branches, cutting a switch. willow wand switch. drum. switch. throb. noiselessly treading. lick. dark dervish devil dance whirling, corrupt flashes of white, flickering shadows, come. come drum. drum. drum. throb. swelling.

mask. eyes agleam. a shudder. drum. come. weaving through the thickets, parting the branches. a shuddering shoulder, a lifted knee. by the fire. come. come. drum.

and wilt thou worship at the great womb-ear that listens while it opens and receives. dance. parting the branches, i come. drum. drum. thump.

and in the clearing, down by the river where the marsh fires burn, they dance. i. with the switch, the little silver whip with the bell on the end. switch. thrash. whip. and the drum. throb. the drum drum drum. swollen.

dance. they i. toss, sway. dance. dance to the drum.

whistle the whips. dance to the whistle of the silver switch. i wield.
wild. shuddering gold-licked flesh. thump.

rumplesilkskin was her name. the heaving breasts, the throat thrown
back, the firelit flanks. whistle, dervish, whistle at the delicate rounded
rump. (tous nus)

the eyes atwitch, the nerves ashudder. the convulsive nodding of
the head (fardés, masqués). we come. drum. we come. bursting.

together. i come to the throb of the drum. together. work at the
dervish dance, thrust and spin. lock and couple to the throb of the drum.
together apart together. drum. drum. drum drum drum. i come. (leave
thy mask)

heave and wrestle, struggle struggle. drum. we come. together.

faster faster. flicker dervish swirl and whirl. strike and thrust to the
throb of the drum. shiny glisten strain and drive. thump! i come. drum.
drum. drum drum. we come. together. (inconnus) drum drum drum
drum drum.

and still. still. the thump.
stir?

The starres moove stil, time runs, the clocke wil strike,
The divel will come, and Faustus must be damnd.

July 12

SUNDAY turned hot again and almost insufferably humid. Especially after his lazy, comfortable stay in Stamford with the Fortunes, Walton found the steamy, airless train (the air-conditioning was broken) and the great, panting city (it seemed as though the heat pulsated in visible shafts over the streets and sidewalks) depressing. But of course—as always—it was not simply the weather that so affected him. He found himself wishing that he had not been required by circumstance to juxtapose his visit to the Fortunes and his meeting with Karen. But, he reflected ironically, this meant only that he felt sure he was doing wrong in seeing Karen again—and *that,* in turn, that he had hopes for this meeting he was unwilling to admit openly to himself.

In the taxi that carried him to the Foundation's building, he forced himself to face up to the issues that had been irritating him because he had determined not to let them bubble to the surface. The Fortunes had, in their warm camaraderie, reinvigorated him in his lifelong conscious conviction that a good life meant participation—the sharing of thoughts and feelings and experiences with family and friends and colleagues, the sense of living with, not merely existing in proximity to, other people: in warm, close, sometimes painful, sometimes rapturous, sometimes comradely intimacy. Not smothering or being smothered, not absorbing or being absorbed, but not being afraid, either, of cleaving one to another—in whatever fashion.

A lifelong conviction. He smiled bitterly. Yet a conviction that had had very little fulfillment. For what did his broken marriages, his frequent conflicts at work, and the lack of close friends that made him so value this new association—what did the unadorned record of his life mean except that he found it painfully difficult to live in the way he envisioned so optimistically. What he had written in his journal about the Face at the Window applied to himself with a force he had never

367

before felt so urgently and so painfully. He was seldom comfortable in groups—and, with even rarer exceptions, then only by consciously directed and controlled reminders to himself of those tendencies in him which led to the creating of friction: the claim to special attention, the need for a position in the center of the ring, his susceptibility to offense where none was intended, the confusion and self-consciousness attendant upon being in a group containing people who, *he felt,* expected different and even conflicting things from him.

Ordinarily, then, to avoid these difficulties, he would withdraw to the outskirts of a gathering and engage just one person in conversation, not trusting himself with more. And usually it must be someone he knew well—someone who, he felt positive, was fond of him or respected him. Then he felt comparatively safe.

Safe? Safe! Why safe? There was so endlessly much to probe if, in this brief summer, he was even to approximate a strong enough elementary knowledge of himself to bring it to a favorable conclusion. Words! "Favorable conclusion": he snorted to himself. Realizing that the sweat was pouring down his face, he took out his handkerchief.

But safety was pre-eminently important in his scheme of things, he thought, as he paid off the cab driver and entered the dark, empty building. Going up in the lone Sunday elevator, he noticed that he had felt the slightest reflexive twitch at the realization that the operator was unfamiliar. And, as he fitted his key into the outer office door lock, he caught at another element in the pattern of anxiety in which he lived his days. Anyone, anything, wholly new and strange, bothered him. This, too, was a part of his aversion to social gatherings. When he came into a room of strangers or slight acquaintances, he was always uneasy and stiff.

He dropped his small valise on his desk, took from it his shaving equipment, and went into the adjoining bathroom. As he stripped off his wet, clinging shirt and began to lather his face, he realized that, all the way from Grand Central, he had been digressing, however informatively. He paused, brush aloft, and stared intensely at the half-lathered face in the mirror.

"The problem," he said aloud, "is simply this. You began this summer determined to dig in, to devote all your time, your energy, your resources, to one thing: a sufficient understanding of yourself to enable you to resume your life with your wife and kids. You know that this purpose faltered, broke down that evening with Sonia, and again when you met Karen. Then you went to the Fortunes', and they reminded you of everything you would like to be true of your own home.

You don't have the guts to choose. You won't call Karen and tell her you can't come. And you won't or can't say to yourself, 'I don't care enough about Julie and our life together—or about the values I think of as my values—to offset my need to go to Karen and my hope that she will let me make love to her again.' You lack guts, and all your achievements (not world-shaking at that) and principles and professed determination can't conceal *that*."

But wasn't it simply human, the Face in the Mirror was replying, to have a desire to possess a beautiful woman—especially when you have possessed her many times before and know the delights of the act? Especially when you also know that there are no mundane consequences beyond—that this woman will never make further trouble for you? Especially when your wife has withdrawn herself from you—has put herself beyond your reach? And is the fault in that situation exclusively yours? And under the circumstances what man who is a man could fail to take a woman beloved of two continents, the sweetheart of thousands, perhaps hundreds of thousands, of anonymous men—especially at a time when his ego has been under siege, has been savagely attacked and is in imminent danger of being reduced to rubble? And are your self-reproaches really the promptings of conscience and honor and self-respect? Are these really ever the motivating forces of human conduct? Or is it not rather the fear of being found out, the fear of the guilt you will feel when next you see Julie, or even the subrational obedience to early dictates that shaped you, twisted you, warped you, so that you respond to the present with the nerves and muscles and reflexes of thirty-five and forty years ago? Isn't the voice of virtue simply the voice of timid expediency? Don't you simply lack the courage to act as you really want to, in the face of a reality that includes Julie *as she is* and Karen *as she is,* and raise all these bugaboos and scaremen simply to enable you to be less ashamed of yourself, simply to put a noble face on it?

Walton realized with surprise that he was completely shaved and was now drying his face with a towel. He peered at the Face in the Mirror—friend, sage counselor, devil's advocate?

"I know this," he said, again aloud. "I know that only a man who has nothing to hide, nothing to be secretly ashamed of—only such a man can live at peace with himself and others."

But this time his voice sounded weak and unconvincing to both of them, and that other voice resumed with a discourse on peace. Was peace so wonderful, then? Wasn't peace more consonant with the state of death than that of life? Was peace perhaps simply a hypocritical synonym, a euphemism, for timid do-nothingness?

On and on went the voice, master of an unparalleled facility. And as Walton showered and dressed he became slowly aware, throughout his mind and body, of an accelerated pace, a feverishness of activity that suggested to him dimly that he was now running away from this colloquy, rushing to Karen, hurrying to make sure that nothing now intervened between him and the consummation of which, hidden from himself, he had been dreaming all the time.

Outside again, he saw that great black clouds were gathering overhead, and the west was a solid wall of angry gray. He caught another taxi and gave the driver the address Karen had told him—that of a friend's apartment in the East Sixties. She had told him to come to dinner, he remembered now, rather than speaking of going out to dinner together. He hoped feverishly that the friend would be away—that he and Karen might be alone together.

During the short ride, his mood swung him from exuberant anticipation to a gloomy presentiment of finding in the apartment a large gathering of "theater types," then back to excitement. Arriving, he paid the driver and ducked under the canopy of the apartment just as thunder growled ominously and the first great drops of rain slapped solidly against the pavement. . . .

She was alone—alone in a dim, cool world entirely remote from that out of which Walton had come. And almost immediately, even before he was aware of this marvelous chilled air—almost immediately he was aware of the gross injustice, the indelicate, almost insulting depersonalization that his heated imagination had committed against her.

For she was Karen, his friend, his love that had been—and as soon as he saw her welcoming smile, the warmth of her pleasure that it was Walton Herrick who was here to see her, not just a man, not a male, but this particular individual man, he felt a deep shame. And, before he could even say a word, a flood of withheld memory brought back all the happiness of knowing her cool, just intelligence, her tenderness, her undemanding affection.

"Here iss Valton Herrick," he announced, drawing himself exaggeratedly erect and saluting in the manner of a Prussian soldier.

She said nothing, only smiled and held out her arms. As he put his around her and drew her close, he was aware, to his humble astonishment, of that very feeling of deep, flooding peace that he had believed the antithesis of this meeting. And with his arms encircling her, his one hand flat, spread on her back, feeling the delicate articulation of her shoulder blade; the other, clasping her warm side where waist curved into hip—with this close holding, it was still peace, a simple, undiluted happiness that he felt most.

She sighed, moved her head from under his cheek, looked up, smiled and, slowly releasing him, was released.

"Sit down," she said, "over there—" pointing to a window seat, beyond which loomed the black sky, split in the distance at this moment by the terrifyingly incisive passage of a knife of lightning—"and let me just look at you for a little."

Walton obeyed, suddenly reminded that Jane Fortune had posed a man so, against a great window with a gray-black sky behind him. Through the rents in the darkness of this background peered minute heads, painfully alive with the lineaments of terror and grief and supplication—each bearing, despite its tininess, the vivid and unmistakable evidence of some almost insupportable pain. Only the large head of the man in the window, admirably drawn, showed comfort, optimism, ease. Looking from it to the small, demon-ridden faces in the clouds, and then to Jane, he had shaken his head.

"The longer I live," he had said, "the more astonished I become over the difference between what people seem to be and what they are." He was, of course, thinking of her—but perhaps even more of Abe, who had spoken of her "sweeping, swooping" canvases, while all the ones Walton had seen were like this one: half sardonic, half wistful, filled with juxtapositions of conflicting elements, grotesqueries out of some antic Walpurgisnacht lolling or sprawling in a scene of conventional calm; poetic fancies peeping over the heads of mean and ugly realities.

Jane had nodded.

"You rarely see more than one aspect of any person at a time," she had replied. And Walton could not forget the cryptic expression that accompanied the words: pain? fear? combined with an element that in another woman he might have taken as a subtle sexual invitation. Intimacy of some kind, at any rate . . .

Across the room, Karen stirred from her position of almost trance-like stillness and flapped her arms, like some improbably lovely rooster. Peter Pan, Walton thought triumphantly.

"All right," she said. "You may now do anything you want. Walton, do you remember that last lunch we had, over three years ago, at the little restaurant on Fifty-fifth Street? I have not seen you since. I wanted now to see how different you are from what I said then."

"But you can see only one aspect of any person at a time," he said, rising, and then—as thunder crashed around the corner—starting a little.

Karen shook her head.

"No, with you, I almost always see more than one. I often wonder whether it is because you are so seldom *one,* or because your—do you call it complexness—is closer to the skin than most people's." She advanced a little toward him, and spread her hands, to indicate the room. "Is it not nice? Every time I come back to America, I realize that I am really still the bank clerk's daughter, finding more pleasure in comfort like this air-conditioning, this luxurious room, the view of the city and the storm, than in all the wonders and antiquity of Europe. Then, after a while, the air turns bad. I feel smothered and glutted and lazy and fat— and I go back. Will you make us a drink?"

Walton went over to the huge sideboard, and made the drinks. Then he joined her by the window. Together they stood for a few minutes, watching while the full fury of the storm mounted, struck and abated. The lightning, after one shattering thrust that seemed to leap the length of a nearby skyscraper, retreated, stroke after stroke, as though in gigantic promenade from section to section of the city; the thunder rolls, which had seemed to shake the building they were in, became distant growls, the minor rumbles of a celestial intestine. The rain slackened, dwindled and ceased. And in a little while a pale yellowish sun winked low through the spectral western sky, and light once more spilled over the city—gleaming dully on spires, softening roof tops that had stood out starkly in the black air of the storm, bringing to the glistening dark streets far below a metallic luster.

"What are you thinking of?" Karen asked softly.

He looked down at the charmingly ragged, cropped head and remembered his private discourse of the night before.

"Just now? Before, of the storm, but now of you. Of how almost any other woman I have known would either have lighted up over the fireworks, or been frightened and made capital of her sex. But you were really interested in the storm as storm; you didn't confuse it with your own feelings."

"No. How could I?" She laughed. "You make everyone more— wonderful?—no, more more than they are. I looked at the storm as a storm, but not as a scientist would. Very much as a woman. I was glad I was watching it with you. This is not detachment."

Walton rested his hand on her shoulder for a moment.

"No, it isn't. And I felt that, too. But I don't believe what you said contradicts what I said. You were glad we were watching together, but you don't confuse that feeling with some romantic notion about the storm itself."

She gave him a long, searching look in which there was something of humorous appraisal.

"Good," she said. "But you were not always so classical in spirit. Are you off on another wild duck chase, trying to find, this time in the opposite direction, the absolute good? I remember so many."

What was the association that brought the long-dissolved sound of his Uncle Lloyd's husky voice (*there* was one thing: disparate though they were in every other respect, Abe Fortune's and Lloyd Herrick's voices were alike, although only one sounded like a whisper) back to mind? He could not find the exact words of the echo drifting in his memory, but during one of those long, discursive accounts Lloyd had quoted someone: "Which is it this time—girls or gambling or God?" Something like that, long ago . . .

"You're far away. Come back."

He looked down at Karen's upturned face and smiled.

"Yes," he said. "Yes, I guess I am. Both. Far away and off on a wild goose chase. And that's not new."

"No," she said and settled herself on the window seat. "No. But what *is* new?"

Walton did not misunderstand her question. Settling down beside her, he murmured, "Vanity, vanity . . ."

She pointed her glass at him, and the affection in her eyes drew out the sting from what she said. "Yes, you say that. But you do not believe it. Or you believe it, but all the time live as though it were not true. I have never said very much about the Puritan in you, but that is because I love you and because this is balanced by the Buffalo Hunter in you. You are so Puritan to yourself; but without believing in God, that is unbearable, and so you are driven to hunt some beast, like the old whaling captains we hear about in Martha's Vineyard and Nantucket, as though there were some final prize to win, some dragon to kill, some golden fleece in life. I would suppose that every so often, not finding it, and not yet able to believe in some new place where it may exist, you come home with a little scalp on your belt and expect your wife to pretend it is ambergris from the White Whale or the shaggy hair of the buffalo. Is it so?"

Walton felt a little foolish and a little hurt; so he grinned.

"You didn't use to be so analytical. Yes, I guess it's so—sometimes anyway."

"Oh, ho," she said, her eyes dancing, "I have drawn fresh red blood. Walton, why are you not happy? Three years ago you were happy—

happy for you. Now at last you have a good marriage, children, a good success—even in Europe I heard about your defense of freedom in the Congress. You have always been fated to be a great man— *un homme d'estime*. Now you are one. Why are you not happy, then?"

Walton smiled lugubriously, rubbed his head, stood up.

"You used to be so gentle, so unprobing," he said, only half joking. "Well, I'll tell you, but I'll need another drink first. You?"

She set down her empty glass, drew her knees up before her, and clasped her hands about them.

"No. Never. You remember. It is that one drink that makes me so free to talk. But only one—or I dissolve. And soon there will be others. I have asked Jodelle, the director, and Vladimir Pinsky—you remember? you liked him. And the little Levy, Carla with the nun's face. And Pépé— Pépé de Vega. Only those. We will have another drink and then go out to dinner. But they will not come for a half hour—more."

Walton poured a good stiff drink for himself and returned. He looked at her now in a sidelong, sardonic glance.

"Why do you look so?" She reached out and caressed his hand. "You know I do not probe to hurt you. Or is it you do not want the other people? I thought you would."

He withdrew his hand.

"I do not want the other people. I wanted to be alone with you. And while I like these people—the ones I know—I simply can't stand being with so many tonight. You'll have to forgive me, Karen. I won't stay."

She looked at him speculatively for a little, then said quietly, "Yes, all right. I will forgive you. But they do not come yet—I promise you. Now tell me what is hurting you?"

He hesitated, took a deep breath.

"Julie's left me," he said. "Not, perhaps, for good. But for the whole summer, with the children. To see if we can learn apart how to live together."

The silence hung between them. Then Karen rose in her turn, walked over to a table nearby, and from an inlaid box drew one of her infrequent cigarettes. Walton morosely watched her tap it thoughtfully on the box, gloomily observed the perfection of her slender legs as she turned her back to him. Why should this exact curve or arch, this swelling or that depression, be so achingly beautiful, when an inch or less of alteration would elicit no response at all? Why should the fine modeling —he was remembering now—of the hollows behind only one pair of knees in the world be so memorable, worthy of Catullus' pen?

In a swift, graceful movement now, Karen struck a match, and he watched the blossoming of her face as the light flared briefly through the gathering dusk. She turned then and looked at him, her eyebrows raised, but not in amusement—rather in some concern, the nature of which Walton could not identify.

"No one can learn to live with someone else by being away from him," she said. "What I was thinking, though, was how strange that expression 'for good' is. Why should 'forever' mean 'for *good*'? And here you meant 'forever *not*,' which is not good." She walked slowly back to him and said, looking down at him tenderly, 'You do not smoke your pipe any more?"

He felt himself relaxing as he pulled out the pipe.

"Yes. Here."

"Good," she said, and sitting down beside him took his hand again. "You are not unhappy because she has left you, Valton; she has left you because you are unhappy. Because you are always unhappy, except for very short times. And this is because you always expect more than there is to find. You are very spoiled, in a strange way, for someone—or some little bug in your genes—led you to think everything should be just the way you would like it, and you never seem to realize that the rest of us have our dreams too." She began stroking his fingers softly, as though to heal while cauterizing. (For these words did burn, he thought.) "No, that is not true, perhaps, but for you the dreams of the rest of us do not have the reality of your own. That is somewhat true for everybody, but not to the degree it is for you. What do you think is the reason your Julie is gone?"

"I can't seem to live closely with anyone," Walton said disconsolately. "Perhaps I do demand too much from people, but I think I demand even more from myself. Sometimes it seems to me that I am so aware of what I *should be* as a husband, a father, the head of a house, that what I might enjoy if I could feel that I was doing it voluntarily becomes drudgery because of this sense of obligation. And it makes me short-tempered, even impossible to live with. And then—I'm sure I'm right about this—Julie had her own expectations and partly, I believe, because I am much older than she, expected me to be wiser and stronger and decisive in a way that I can't. That's why you're wrong about your Buffalo Hunter. I'm not like that, Karen—adventurous and strong and unafraid."

She shook her head.

"Poor silly Valton," she said. "You do not know—and when I tell you, you will not believe. But there are no more physical frontiers, except perhaps Antarctica and the space up there. All the frontiers now, when *we* live, are inside. And into those you go, when most of us would hide our heads under the bed covers and pretend there is no such place to go. You forget that you told me all about your childhood, and how you were taught to be afraid of everything. Yet there you go again out into that—*in;* into that darkness there inside. You are very foolish, but you are very brave, my Buffalo Hunter."

This glow, he thought, was vanity, and he must not let it turn him fatuously pleased. He waited in silence.

"Yet much of what you said is true. Did you ever wonder," she asked softly, "why we could be lovers, much of the time live together for two years, and almost never quarrel?"

He looked her full in the eyes.

"Because you're so wonderful. Because you are so much a woman."

She smiled and squeezed his hand.

"I like to hear this, but I do not think it true. I think I am somewhat wonderful, yes—but also somewhat silly. And I am a woman, yes, but I am as independent as the American women who are always described now as so dominating. No, I think it was because I never made you feel this obligation you talk of. And was that because I am wiser or kinder than Julie? No. It is because I always want to be free myself. This is why I divorced Jonathan. He is not so good a lover as you, but he is a kind man, a good man, and he has much sense. Yet I felt always, married to him, that I could not be my free self and still do what his wife should do. I knew this before we married, I wanted not to marry—but I gave in. He is public and New England—an affair is not good for him. And so we, who might have been such good friends and lovers, are unhappy whenever we hear each other's name. It is not good. But, Valton—I do not know your Julie, but if she wanted to marry, to have children, to be your wife, to live the life of a wife and mother—then she is different from me, and what she wants is that husband and father to live with. What else?"

He puffed on his pipe, regarding her steadily, but saying nothing.

"One thing," she said reflectively, "that you can do alone is to try to find out how much you want to stay with her. Always you tell me that your wife has left you—you remember your *Lydie*? but always I feel that you left first. How is it alone now? this summer, for example? How much do you miss her? In what ways do you miss her? How often do you think of your children? What do you think about them? I am so glad I met your Maria. She is lovely, and I know that you do love her.

Yet you go long times and do not see her, perhaps do not even think about her. How do you feel about that?"

They were both silent for a long time, she stroking the back of his hand almost absent-mindedly, he sipping from his glass and smoking.

"You see," she said suddenly, "I believe you can learn things like that. Not know all about yourself with your head, but learn how you feel, listen to it and learn. You want to know *why*. But it is not so important. I do not understand much about psychoanalysis. I know it is not for me, and I do not think it is for you. You think too much about yourself anyway. Yet the last time I saw you, you had been going to such a man, and for that time the pursuit of your psyche was the Great Hunt. Do you go still?"

Walton shook his head.

"I went for a couple of years. I don't think that it did me much good while I was actually going; I was too secretive to open up. Or too suspicious. But I learned technique from it—ways of getting at my feelings—and that has helped me some since."

She nodded, but as though still preoccupied.

"You see, Valton, I believe that to go too deep is not good. You know I hate the insensitive, but I pity the person who must go deep underground. Yet you must. I feel it. You may agree with me now— you nod your head—but you will go on doing just what you have done before. Perhaps, sometime, not. But I think always. So I say only this. You can know about Julie and the little children and what they mean to you if you only listen to your feelings, as I listened to them when you came tonight. I do not know what it was, but you came and looked at me and then something changed in you. Do *you* know?"

Walton looked down at the floor.

"Yes," he said, poking at the rug with the toe of his shoe. "I came to see you all in a fever, hoping—no, needing you so much and wanting it all to be the way it used to be. And then, when I saw you, I realized that I hadn't really remembered how it used to be, how much I really loved you, but only instead had been thinking in terms of sex, so that it wasn't you I had been wanting, but—I don't know how else to put it— the beautiful Karen Kodály, the—the . . ."

She placed her soft hand over his mouth.

"Yes," she said. "But why is that so wrong? Why do you say *only* sex? Sometimes I think I go mad with American thinking about sex. Everybody makes jokes about it; everybody is ashamed of it; everybody is obsessed with it; and everybody talks as though it was some little machine or box that you plug in and out of the rest of you. My God, it is so stupid!" Her voice, so indignant, softened now. "Listen, Valton. Your need was your need. You remembered the act. Your pride has been hurt by your wife and you remembered me as a giving woman, who always wanted you to make love to her. It is what I said about your reality alone. But I do not mind: that is *some* of me, what you thought about. I thought of this, too, and gladly—if it could now be right for you.

"But you are very sweet, very good. When you came to the door, at the first minute, you saw Karen your friend. The rest of me. But still, what you felt before you had to feel. You did not want to; you had to, and so you did. Perhaps if you could accept that and not hate yourself for the necessities that all of us feel, you would feel no necessity where you could be free."

It seemed to him that her eyes were shining with some new and marvelous fire, and the perfume of her hand still lingered on his lips, long after the hand had been withdrawn.

"And now," he said, "after all, what I want is you. Karen, tell the others not to come."

She stood up and moved away a little from him.

"Now, yes, you want me. But, Valton, afterward, tomorrow, next month you will be thinking only that you were untrue to Julie. You will forget how good your feeling for me now is—and think it bad. I can say yes now and not feel bad later. And not only because I do not know Julie. I know you and I have loved you and so I can feel for Julie. For me, this would not harm her, or me. But you, yes—and because you, then Julie too, and perhaps even me. No, I shall let the others come and I shall hope you will stay too."

He stood up.

"No, I can't," he said in a strained voice. "I can't do that tonight. But I know you're right. We must not. Only I want you so much; I need you so much."

For a moment longer, his eyes burned into hers. Then he took her in his arms and held her as close as he could for a long minute before abruptly releasing her and striding out of the apartment.

Walton never knew just how long he sat in the darkest corner of the Swazey Bar, gradually numbing his anger with bourbon. Yes, anger, anger, anger. With his first drink, he told himself to remember the wise things Karen had said, to acknowledge that through what she had done and refused to do she had given every evidence of the depths of her feeling for him. He tried to remind himself of the shame he had felt upon arrival, when suddenly relieved of his blind hungry need by his realization of his feeling for *her*.

But it was no use. Now, finally, he thought, clenching and un-clenching his fist on the table, he was sick of being rejected: Julie, Gail, Sonia, Karen. He was sick of being told that he must be rejected because of how he would feel later, sick of feeling that way later. He was sick of leaving them, closing the door behind himself, alone. And he could not think; something was numbing his thoughts. So when he realized that it was anger—that was its name, there! he thought incoherently, there!—he savagely gunned the motor of his rage, let it roar.

And drank—drank to numb *it,* as it had numbed everything else in him. And in time he was quieter: there followed a sudden despair. He was lost, quite lost. Alone, adrift, spent. And nothing would save him, nothing could bring him back but a woman—to hold and be held.

He thought of Jane Fortune—and was shocked. But he didn't care, he thought doggedly; he had covered his desperate need too long, too often, with elaborate rationalizations. He didn't know why he should be cursed with this need: he was.

"You did not want to; you had to, and so you did," Karen had said.

And he had to. It came to him then, and he stood up.

In the telephone booth, when he heard Sonia's soft, lazy voice, he said thickly, "Walton Herrick. I'm coming to see you. I wanted to warn you."

There was a long breathing silence. Then she said, "Yes."

When she closed the door behind him, they stood for a while as they had the other time, locked in a dark appraisal. Then at last she sighed and lifted her shoulders in that indolent restless motion.

Soon, they were raging at each other in the close, hot darkness, still separate in hunger and loneliness.

Part Three

CHILDHOOD
IN
AMBER

[*Part Three*]   *1*

CORNELIUS Walton Herrick was named for his paternal grandfather, with his middle name a sop thrown to his mother. When William Herrick proposed that the boy's middle name be Nicholson, he secretly hoped that Marcia would, carrying out the formal steps of a psychological Virginia reel, bow in reciprocation and suggest that the baby be named wholly for his grandfather: Cornelius Butler Herrick II. But she did not. She remarked that "Nicholson" had too many syllables, and countered with "Walton," her own mother's maiden name.

Although she never admitted it to William, he had reason in time to suspect that she had in mind from the beginning that this name would eventually supersede the boy's legal first name. Who, after all, would want to call, even from the back door, "Cor-nee-lee-us"? And the potential nickname, "Corny," was hideous. Walton became Walton early, and—except for a few miscellaneous friends who tried gallantly but ineffectually, by referring to him as Walt, to give him a lighter tone than he could carry—he was never called anything else.

"What's in a name?" Quite a good deal, Walton sometimes thought. His, at least, lent itself all too easily to severe intonations. "Wal-tón" for example, suggests immediately a harsher vision of guilt and punishment than does, say, "Har-ry!" which becomes shrill and cannot be made really menacing. And "Walton," used quietly, matter-of-factly, in ordinary direct address, sounded sober, reserved, gray—at least to its owner. It could only come out of New England.

At any rate he acquired a distaste for it. "Walton Herrick," pronounced unexpectedly by anybody, at any time, had a wry twist for him; he would feel suddenly as if he were wearing a stiff collar a size too tight for him or —what was to become to him a recurring symbol of all that was restricted and inhibiting in his life—as though on a sunny, beguiling day, he were moving along a beach flowering in bronzed, supple flesh, while himself fully dressed and stiff, effete, awkward.

Frequently, throughout his life, hearing his name or, once in a while, seeing it in print, he would try to catch hold of the individual it represented—reach through the deceptively solid flesh and bone, to apprehend the elusive self that must be there, crouching chained and hidden in some corner, behind the creature who had usurped the authority to respond to the name: the creature who stiffened in reaction to depreciation, modestly (sometimes even contemptuously) accepted homage as his due, and alternately placated, withdrew to Olympian detachment, and shouted impotent puerile defiance at the world, ringed round with bristling hostility, that he thought he saw *out there*.

And so when Walton finally tried, in a more serious and sustained way than ever before, to go back into the fatherland of the past and learn exactly where and how he had lost sight of that "original self" and begun to accept identification with the bogus self that moved and spoke, acted and reacted without any convincing sense of inner consent—he found the task bewildering. Where should he find the ruined lot of his childhood, and—even if he found it—where dig for the treasure? The road signs were down, lying moldy and obliterated in the tall, rank grass of the years; the familiar figures of childhood placed hands behind deaf ears and shook uncomprehending heads. What he found, digging alone at random, what he recaptured, were scenes, moments, decisive relationships—decisive, he supposed, because they were either the ones that sprang to mind quickly or those, buried deep in the loam of the unconscious, that resisted, like fast-embedded stones, the intruding curious spade.

One that recurred most quickly to him was not, properly speaking, a memory at all. Yet he was told the story of his birth so often that he sometimes felt it was an event that he had witnessed as an observer. His grandfather, who died when Walton was only six, had told him the story several times; his mother, modestly stressing the hardships and courage of maternity at home with the only alleviation of pain the occasional application of a towel soaked in ether, told it once or twice, despite the fact that it was rather more a Herrick story than a Nicholson one; his father reveled in it.

On the face of it, what had happened hardly seemed to warrant such celebration. Walton's parents then lived within sight of his grandfather's house, and the old man, knowing that the child was to be named for him if it were a boy, requested that, if the birth occurred at night, a lantern be hung in an upstairs window to signify a boy, a candle set there for a girl baby. To be sure, the larger, brighter light for a boy did not testify solely to the advent of a namesake, or even merely to the subordinate position of women at the time: there had been, up to this point, no male child in Walton's generation to carry on the Herrick name.

Yet, even when one made sufficient allowance for this factor, and the further consideration that Grandfather Herrick also thought of the occasion as a matter of rivalry with an old friend who was in a similar manner awaiting the arrival of a (he hoped, male) grandchild, there was something overwrought about the recital to which Walton listened so often. A disinterested observer, not hearing the beginning of the story, might have believed that he had chanced upon the middle of an account of the birth of Arthur, or, say, Orestes or Roland—to avoid an even more hazardous comparison.

Walton was born before the dawn of November 3, 1907, and his father acknowledged that his hands had trembled so badly that it had taken him several minutes to light the lantern. All three versions attested to the fact that Grandfather Herrick, without thought to the prestige of his distinguished position in the life of Cleveland, arrived, running, in less than two minutes, with his greatcoat thrown over a nightshirt. Labor having begun before midnight, he had sat out the night in prayer. But what capped the effect of the story, at least as Walton's father told it, was the sense of his own worth that came to William Herrick as he faced *his* father in the dimly lit hall, bowed his head in confirmation of the news the lantern had conveyed, then raised it to look into the old man's proud and triumphant eyes, wet with tears, and knew, as he put it, that despite all his own handicaps and failings he had been responsible for this crowning satisfaction. That leonine head was held erect again, and William saw, above the ruffled nightshirt collar, and the black, snow-spotted overcoat, not just his father, but a fiery old prophet winning at the end the favor of God that had somehow always just eluded him.

It was, in short, presented to Walton as no ordinary birth, and he was given no ordinary sense of his own value. To one man, the lantern signified a final fulfillment, to another, the vindication of himself; to Walton it was to mean, more often than not, a garland of lead. . . .

[*Part Three*] 2

OF all the scenes that Walton could actually remember from his child-hood, the most reassuring, the warmest and the happiest, was the first in time. He could recall only the low children's table and the little chairs before the open fire in the living room—his sister and he sitting there, eating milk toast out of their large white bowls. His sister Elinor's had a wide ring of yellow chickens encircling it, his own a wreath of benevo-lent bears. That was all there was to it—except that the voices were low-pitched and happy, even his mother's, and the firelight flickered tenderly over all of them.

This was not so much the memory of a scene as of a feeling—warmth, security, tranquillity. There had been the sense of everything being in place, the rarely recaptured sense that there was, reassuringly, a regular and benign order to things, after all, and that this order was being observed.

This scene was in direct contrast to a frequently enacted ceremony which began before Walton was eight, and continued throughout the period during which he was kept home because of his "heart condition," but no longer confined to bed. His interest in history and histories led to his decision to write one of his own, and feeling that, since histories had been written about every epoch of the past, it would be dull to retrace ground already covered, he began a history of the future, which gave him free scope for improvisation, a happy release from discipline, and the chance to bestow the presidency of the United States, in turn, upon various friends of the family whom he admired.

Walton's *History of the Future* came up in the conversation quite spontaneously one Sunday afternoon after dinner; a comfortably stuffed guest amiably expressed the desire to hear some of the master-piece. Thereafter, this was an almost regular Sunday custom. With varying degrees of adroitness, Walton's mother would succeed in making someone feel that he had asked to have a chapter read aloud. When she handled the matter with real finesse, as she sometimes did, the guest would even wonder later what had got into him to prompt him to make such a suggestion.

Walton shuddered when he recalled those occasions, seeing in retrospect the indulgent, half-amused, half-horrified circle of adults, and this precocious boy, with a smile of self-satisfaction evident above his Eton collar, standing there and reading aloud, pausing when the laughter became too loud, but only half offended, because he took a curiously perverse pleasure in being able to detach from himself a semi-adult extension of that self that stood off, observed, and was proud of "the boy phenom." Here, he once thought, was not the beginning but the first overt public occasion of a knowing, fatuous self-love that was to milk his character insatiably for many years.

The light had been set in the window by his father to honor his grandfather, but it was his mother who kept it burning like the lamp of the Vestal Virgins. Marcia Nicholson Herrick tended the sacred fire; she regularly prepared the appropriate sacrifices, and Walton failed to recognize that fine gray ash as the residue of his autonomy.

It was not, of course, until much later that he thought consciously of his childhood as a prison term, served under the wardenship of his mother. He had been cut off from the free activities of other children, forbidden to run, to swim, to visit other houses—and had sworn a long-range vengeance: *Wait until I grow up.* He had been miserable, but persuaded by the force of Marcia's personality that the regime he suffered under was *right*, those of others grossly negligent, *wrong*, however pleasant.

It had been a prison in one sense. Yet, in another, a better analogy was that of a boy king, biding his time under a vigilant regency, with the understanding that he could not be freed to do what other children did, no—but he could do and have many things beyond the reach of other children. If he accepted these terms of his responsibility and privilege (how often his mother spoke of "finer stock"), everything he wanted in a material way was justly his. In vain his father pleaded and stormed over bills. Moreover, it was enunciated again and again (as long as there was no complaint about what he could *not* do) that he was indeed a remarkable boy, the very best of boys, brilliant and handsome and altogether exceptional.

The fact that Walton was more often sick than well during the first eight years of his life not only provided the bedrock for his mother's domination of him, but also meant that during most of that period he was the recipient of the greater part of her smothering, if supporting, love and attention, while the rest of the family, notably William Herrick, was accorded the irritability.

Walton suffered successively from diphtheria, a bout of pneumonia and, finally, a severe streptococcus infection; there were grounds in reality for Marcia's apprehensiveness about him. But her protectiveness was so extravagant that, combined with the indiscriminate enthusiasm of Walton's uncle-physician, Dr. Edgar Briffault, for cardiac disorders, it kept Walton from school until he was nine, and in bed because of the alleged "valvular leakage" for a year and a half of that time. Those who failed to be properly deferential to the boy king were dismissed by his mother as "lacking in fine feeling"—whether they were tutors, servants or physicians. All save Dr. Briffault, Walton's third doctor, who had to be endured because of the family connection (until there came a blowup at the end of this period), and William Herrick, who could not be dismissed because he was the boy's father.

Not that William was unkind, of course. But in his mild way he thought there was the possibility that Walton was being spoiled, and that he would be due for some rude bumps when he got out into the world, still expecting to be flattered and waited on. He even said so once or twice, to be squelched promptly by Marcia's haughty toss of the head and a reminder that he was welcome to spend more of his time with the children—for a change—to help a little in "bringing them up."

William had reason to dislike combat with Marcia, and after one or two attempts he took the easiest and quietest course, and stopped discussing the matter. He confined himself to efforts limited to his own sessions alone with Walton, trying, with a sound enough instinct but without much skill, to keep him interested on a fairly simple level of reality.

The result was that Walton supposed that he loved his father but did not place him even close to the exalted level occupied by his mother, Robert E. Lee, and Father Damien, in whose sacrificial work among the lepers—as reported in the *Book of Knowledge*—he took a peculiar nervous pleasure.

There was, for instance, the time—after eight months of confinement in bed—when Walton, filled with ennui and bitterness over his lot, was unable longer to absorb himself in books and imaginative games. (Games played partially for the pleasure he took in them, but equally for the praise his self-reliance would bring from his mother: "That little boy is a saint, I tell you; he's a reproach to all of us, a lesson. He never complains, just plays by himself, or reads all day long.")

The inhibited Walton hidden deep under this mask of perfection broke loose, erupted in a fury of sobs and kicks and shouts until Marcia, filled with an unaccustomed despair, came downstairs to William and announced, "I'm going to call the doctor. I don't know what's the matter with him; he never acts like this."

For once William snorted.

"Doctor!" he exclaimed, pulling himself up from his chair with an effort. "He doesn't need a doctor. He's just sick and tired of lying in bed. You let me have a try with him."

But when he reached Walton's bedroom and was confronted with the boy's screaming, thrashing hysteria (he told Walton years later), his confidence wavered and for some minutes he just stood there, waiting.

This was apparently the best approach, however accidentally stumbled upon. Accustomed to an unending solicitude, Walton's frenzy subsided and he finally lay there in silence, staring at his father.

"Well," said William at last. "Feel better?"

The dark eyes turned malevolent. This was not William's word, but Walton, too, could remember the incident clearly.

"I'm sick," the boy said sullenly.

William remembered that he had felt a lurch inside him suddenly, as though his heart had turned over. We're all sick, he had thought in an unexpected, undesired flash of illumination; we're all hopelessly, finally sick. And had as quickly sought refuge in God—had reached out an inner supplicating hand for that great immemorial hand which reassured him that in honest prayer there was no need for words.

"Sonny," said William, "did I ever tell you about all the years when I was—sick. Before I could walk at all?"

Walton twisted petulantly onto his side. Something in him didn't want to hear, didn't want his father to confess about himself in this solemn way. But he couldn't think of anything to say that would cut him off effectively.

"No," he muttered at last.

William told him, hesitating now and then in his search for the best way to reach the unreceptive boy, watching him attentively for some indication of awakened interest. He told him of his own long years of confinement to bed or a wheel chair, being careful to show his realization that Walton, like himself, had learned patience and endurance. He told him of the lonely wait in Philadelphia for his first operation and his joyful discovery of Dickens—again making a point of establishing a parallel between this and Walton's devotion to bird guides and Ridpath's illustrated *History of the World* and Guerber's *Myths of Greece and*

Rome. He told him of his further struggles and of the glorious day on which he took his first steps alone, aided by a crutch and a cane.

And all the while Walton lay there, quiet, passive, a resentment that he did not understand himself glowing in the eyes made much larger by his pallor and the thinness of his face.

That there was some justification for the resentment William Herrick freely admitted long years later. For he told his own story so seldom that, when he did, the self-pity and sentimentality that he had quietly disciplined away were apt to reassert themselves. But when he had finished, and when he finally broke the ensuing silence, there was no self-interest in either the tone or the substance of what he had to say.

"It's just this, sonny. You've learned very bravely how to accept your trouble without complaining. But now you've also got to learn how to beat it, how to fight against just accepting it and staying in bed. For after a while, I know, it seems as though there isn't any use in trying to hope any more. You even come to take a pleasure in giving up the fight. You don't realize it, but it's true—and it's dangerous."

Walton's expression had changed. He was not won, but he was interested.

"Dangerous?" he asked.

"Dangerous," William repeated slowly, aware of the crucial importance of what he was saying now. "Dangerous, I mean, because it might keep you from growing up into the fine man you can be. For it takes a lot of courage, boy, to keep on fighting when it's so easy to lie back and say 'I can't' and let other people do everything for you. Courage—and faith."

"Indeed," said Marcia, sniffing.

She was standing in the doorway, and despite the quietness of her sarcasm her eyes were blazing. Immediately her voice rose. "What do you mean by coming up here and frightening him? Talking about danger and courage to a sick little boy who's always so brave and good!" She crossed swiftly to the bed. "Mother's boy has nothing to be afraid of, ever. Mother will stand by him."

Walton shook off her hold petulantly, but William could see that he was hers, for all that. In the quietness now of his despair, he did not argue. He left the room.

And he never mentioned the subject again until the break between Marcia and Edgar Briffault, some ten months later. The physician arrived one day in an ugly, harassed mood, and revoked his verdict of eighteen months' standing in two sentences.

"His heart's all right now, and he's turning into a sissy. You're overprotecting him."

Marcia turned white.

"*I'm* overprotecting him! It's you who've kept him in bed. Only last week you said—"

And they exchanged estimates of each other: hers regally acid, not quite aimed at the right spots, a little overemotional for all her rigid control; his adroit, low-voiced, malicious, accurate. And Walton squirmed on the bed, half frightened but secretly delighted to be the center, the subject of such a controversy.

Dr. Billings followed—a genial, thickset, red-cheeked, white-haired, old-fashioned family doctor. On his first visit, after an extensive use of his stethoscope and a good many benevolent nods and grunts, he said to Walton, "If you're up and dressed tomorrow morning at seven-thirty, I'll take you in my car on all my calls."

On a snowy January day! Marcia was torn by conflicting impulses and fears. It seemed daring, dangerous. Yet, if Dr. Billings were right, this would be a dramatic triumph over Edgar Briffault and his eighteen-month regime of bed and valvular leakage of the heart. And his barked words about Walton's becoming a sissy had struck fear to her heart, too. Reluctantly, and with many anguished reservations, she decided to support the new physician.

And Walton? There was a real appeal in this invitation, with its promise of an end to the sameness and boredom of his days. He was challenged, thrilled, by confronting an adventure in all its unlikely immediacy. But he shrank from it, too; what his father had warned him of, months before, had slowly been taking place. By ten o'clock that night he had a slight fever and was unable to sleep.

While Marcia was downstairs, telephoning Dr. Billings, William shuffled into Walton's room and sat down on his bed. He placed his broad hand on the boy's forehead and looked into his eyes.

"It's a big rough world out there," he said quietly. "But it's also a beautiful one. It's more beautiful than anything we can read in our books. And once you've done it, once you've gone, you'll have a fine feeling. You'll think, 'I did it. *I* did it.' And way down inside you, you'll be the happiest you've ever been."

Walton looked into those large, dark eyes, so shining and tender, looked at the broad, prominently-boned face which (as usual, through allegiance to his mother's standards: "fineness of breeding and character shows in delicacy of features") he had come to think of as coarse and awkward, and was impressed and comforted.

His fever abated, and the next morning he was ready, despite a new snowstorm, an hour ahead of time. He returned late in the afternoon with more color in his cheeks than they had known in two years. . . .

[*Part Three*]   *3*

THE shores of childhood are littered with symbols. Any child will stoop and examine some of those he finds; he will pick up one or another, finger it, perhaps store it away in his pocket—something to live with. But there are others that he will not seem to notice: only a flicker of the eye or the faintest hesitation in his step will betray the event even to the most solicitous observer. At such times the child has not performed an act of conscious recognition at all. But in some long later moment of sleep or half-consciousness the tides of association, spilling in darkness over the reefs of his now unprotected memory, will wash these up to lie there, finally unmistakable in exposure.

No one is without his own particular set of symbols of this sort— even though he fail to record them for what they are: cryptic remnants and reminders, signs to the soul, dried by the winds of adversity, crystallized by the sea of experience, whitened by the great perpetual sun of all our days.

No one is without them; and no one fails, sometime, somewhere, to pause and—in a sudden moment of silence, seeing his own shadow long under the sinking sun—to observe that they are still there, lying in full-dimensional clarity along his lonely strand. If he may see them then and be able to consider them in peace of mind, know that they are his, take the pleasure of retrospect in their contours and texture—not without sadness and regret, but free from terror and from guilt alike, free from the melancholy wish to return and somehow to replace them with others of their kind—then all is well. If, standing there, he does not suddenly become aware of alien shadows athwart his own and, startled, turn to find the pterodactyls of anxiety, hysterical and predatory, swooping down upon him in leathery flight—then all is well with him. . . .

The fear-dominated world to which Marcia Nicholson introduced her children was the only world Walton knew more than marginally during his first nine years. His sister Elinor, two years older and not bedridden, at least attended school regularly. But Walton's education, until he was nine, was conducted by a series of governesses.

His father groaned and threw up his hands in a gesture which expressed both despair over expenses mounting so rapidly that he did not have the heart to study his financial records and frustration over the perpetual warfare between Marcia and the women she hired—all to no avail. These women came and went with devastating regularity: they found Walton's now well-established conviction of his specially privileged status in life almost as hard to put up with as his mother's arrogant supervision. It made their task no easier that the boy learned to read with infuriating ease before he was six years old, while refusing, throughout the next three years, to apply himself at all to the simplest arithmetic, persuaded by some higher logic of royal prerogative that the menial *(sic)* nature of figuring rendered it an inappropriate task for him.

For the most part, these governesses were a timid crew. There was one early and striking exception—a German woman named Fräulein Hess. She was stout and red-faced, and wore her hair in seemingly endless braids, coiled with meticulous precision around her head. She had a way of saying, "Yes. Thank you, good Mrs. Herrick," at moments when the words seemed to have no reasonable application at all—for instance, when she had been reprimanded or rebuffed—and this perplexed the children and their mother equally. The fräulein was also an ardent devotee of the Spartan life; at least she propounded it to anyone who would listen to her. She could become rapturous over cold baths, long walks and a spare diet; she would snort with relish over the memory of the sting of icy water or the delicious lassitude of tired muscles. Yet the children soon became aware that her favorite way of spending a holiday was to lock herself in her room with a box of candy and some magazines.

Walton was five and Elinor seven at this time, and Marcia was still prone to supervise every movement they made. Perhaps the greatest source of dissatisfaction to Fräulein Hess (at least so she often said, with apparent indignation) was that she was always expected to be with the children, but seldom allowed to be alone with them.

Yet one Saturday afternoon, when Marcia reluctantly agreed to accompany William to a Herrick family function, leaving Walton and

Elinor with the governess, there was little evidence that the fräulein was eager to use her opportunity. The parents had been gone only twenty minutes when she called the children to her room. She had removed her dress and put on a heavy woolen wrapper: clearly this was to be a holiday.

"I want you to go up in the playroom," she said with a good deal more asperity than she had ever used in the presence of their mother, "and be quiet. Not a noise."

Elinor had considerably more spunk than Walton.

"Mother said you were to take us to Wade Park to see the bears," she said. "If you don't I'll tell her when she comes back."

The governess grunted irritably and settled back on her bed, re-arranging her wrapper more comfortably and propping up the pillows behind her.

"You go to the playroom," she said, "or I'll put you in the dark closet."

This was a place used for storage, located on the landing halfway between the second floor and the third. The children, disbelieving and shaken, withdrew to the playroom and held a whispered consultation. Elinor was indignant, Walton terrified.

"When Mother comes back, I'll tell her just what she said, and she'll fire her," said Elinor. "You just wait and see if I don't."

Walton begged her to be quiet.

"She said no noise," he kept repeating in an almost hysterical whisper. "Don't make her mad."

After a time they grew less apprehensive and even played house with some semblance of content. But Walton finally complained that it was no "house" if they couldn't have something to eat, and Elinor agreed to go down to the kitchen for bread and jam. He raced after her down the stairs.

As he pounded down the second-floor hall, he was caught and held by fat, pudgy arms and glared at by fiercely hostile eyes that seemed to be popping out of a bright red face.

"I said no noise. You go in the dark closet."

Elinor came back, kicked, scratched and bit, but to no avail. Indeed, she only aroused the governess' fury to the point where she cuffed Walton freely and finally flung him into the storage space and bolted the door. Then, he could tell with what degree of clarity was left him, she made a lunge for Elinor and, missing, ran face on into the wall. Her howls and curses froze Walton's blood. As he heard her plunging down-stairs after the fleeing Elinor, he envisioned a composite of all the monsters he had ever seen in picture books, brandishing a carving knife with which she would cut off his sister's head. His face in his hands, he sobbed uncontrollably.

But this terror was mild compared to that he felt some ten minutes later, when he heard a door slam and heavy steps ascend the stairs. Elinor was dead, he knew, and now it was his turn. He screamed himself to the verge of a convulsion.

The bolt was drawn back, the door opened, and the monstrous goblin face appeared.

"You shut up," it snarled, "or I will eat you. I will cut you in small pieces and eat you." The door slammed again, the bolt was thrust home, and all was blackness.

Walton, hitherto so sheltered and insulated against the slightest rough treatment, experienced with a shocking impact this first taste of the world's brutality. By the time Elinor and the neighbors to whom she had run for help arrived and freed him, he had been reduced to a hysteria that lasted, in a slow diminuendo, for two hours, bubbling up again, time after time, when it seemed that it must have exhausted itself.

The governess left the house within fifteen minutes of Marcia Herrick's return and, needless to say, the children were not left at home without one of their parents for the next several years. Yet the inroad had been made, the insertion in the airtight compartment had been cut, and Walton's confidence in the safety that the world extended to one who did as he was told, his belief in the inherent fairness of the powers that be, once someone had consummated a deal with them, was never fully restored. There was, he still knew, a world in which he could with certainty expect cuddling and even adulation if he didn't ask to be allowed to have and to do what coarse people wanted and did. But that was Mother's world, and there were other worlds.

To be sure, during these early years spent so largely at home, and for the most part isolated from other children, Fräulein Hess's was not the only goblin face to confront Walton, and the dark storage room not the only frightening place of confinement. Empirical reality and fantasy were not always easy to disentangle in the Herrick household; Walton still found them indistinguishable in certain respects, years later, whether in dealing with the tangible and perceptible present or, retrospectively, with his childhood. As a child, he found the lonely evening ascent to his bedroom an ordeal. There at the head of the stairs, on the second floor, was a door to his left, always closed, that led up to the attic and, incidentally, the storage space.

But this door—or, rather, what he imagined behind it—frightened him long before the advent of Fräulein Hess. He was sure that there was a figure standing pressed against the other side—most often, he envisioned it as Hawkshaw the Detective, a comic strip favorite of the time. To be sure, in this particular comic (a sufficiently scary predecessor of the brutal and sadistic "comics" of the mid-century), Hawkshaw was a benevolent enough figure, a sort of elongated Sherlock Holmes, who was always on the side of law and order, and sported a long curved pipe, a checked hunting cap with an enormous visor and a large button set conspicuously on the top. He was much given to elaborate disguises, was prone at the moment of solving a crime to laying his finger portentously alongside his nose, and generally behaved himself admirably while pursuing that notorious and dangerous criminal, the Professor.

Yet, through some vagary of the imagination, Walton found the Professor an amiable person, even rather jolly, while Hawkshaw, tall, dark, beak-nosed, seemed to him the epitome of the sinister. So it was Hawkshaw, a sort of archetypal truant officer, who was responsible for Walton's journeys to bed so often being dismal, stiff-legged marches.

And it was from these days that Walton acquired one of his two superficially contradictory master fears, even obsessions. He was always to find a closed door significant. If he was behind the door, within the enclosure to which it was the entrance and egress, it signified the ultimate in safety, even in pleasure. But there must be company, a pleasant, familiar companion or two—and the room must not be too small. If he was alone, and the enclosure small, claustrophobia would assail him with terrifying vividness; only after checking the door two or three times to make certain that he was not locked in would he know even a semblance of composure. And conversely, if he was *without* the door and it was locked—or even if he had reason to believe that it might be locked—then he knew, with equal sharpness, the fear of exposure, or rejection, or both.

All this didn't leave him many places in which to be comfortable, he thought with amusement in later life—but of course these fears were hidden deeply enough, much of the time, to cause him no more than a vague sense of uneasiness. And perhaps those psychologists who maintain that most habit and behavior patterns are set in the first year or two of life are right, yet Walton was sure that he had no excessive fear of being left to take care of himself in the large, strange world, even in the dark, when he was five years old.

For he was just that age when one evening, as he was returning home with his parents and sister from some friends' house, he found himself more completely on his own than at any other time in his short life. They waited together in the early dark of a winter evening for the trolley car that would take them on the short ten-minute ride to their own house. When the big yellow trolley finally loomed up, a group of some ten or twelve people was gathered to board it. In the subsequent push, Marcia Herrick, with a (however independent) lame husband to watch out for, as well as two children, somehow lost her hold on Walton's hand. Small as he was, he was crowded back, unnoticed by the others, and the big folding doors closed, leaving him outside. The trolley started up, clanging its bell and emitting sparks from the wire overhead, and there he was, standing alone on a dark and empty street.

He felt no panic at all. Here at last was an adventure worthy of the heroes he had begun to admire in story books and in overheard casual adult conversation. He knew the name of his own street, and, when the next trolley opened hospitable doors to him, explained to a friendly and amused motorman how he had been left behind, where he wanted to go, and how sorry he was to have no money. The sang-froid of this small explorer with the high, piping voice delighted the passengers on the car; they at once laughed heartily and praised him for his courage. He, in turn, was so exhilarated by his evident popularity that he began to laugh uproariously—though not quite sure why.

At his own street, he descended, shouting a happy good-bye and confidently expecting to be met by an equally proud family. No one was there. This puzzled him, but he was now in familiar territory, and so he loitered by the trolley stop, hugging to himself with great pleasure the knowledge that he was quite an extraordinary fellow. . . .

Several minutes had passed, and the trolley had left a second stop before Marcia had discovered Walton's absence. Frenzied inquiries, as she grasped William and Elinor fearfully, were followed by a scream. She demanded that the trolley back up; she finally shook the motorman by the shoulder at the imminent risk of making him lose his grip on the controls; she assailed him, her husband and any passenger foolish enough to try to calm her. She herded the other Herricks off the trolley at the next stop and spent so much time there on the curb conjuring up the horrors that Walton must have encountered that the next car going in either direction had passed before she realized it. Then William prevailed upon her to let them climb on the third car headed for home, on the correct premise that Walton had undoubtedly been a passenger on the second one.

When they finally disembarked a second time, at their own stop, Marcia smothered the astonished Walton in her arms. Her wails of confused grief, terror and relief swept over his protests; rolling and tossing in her own emotions, she had no time for his story. And so he learned that, only by the grace of God, he had passed through radical peril, and what had seemed so much fun had seemed so only because of his ignorance. By the time he was allowed to give his own account to the single person interested in it, his father, he was capable only of a much diluted version. And he went to bed still pondering gravely, ominously, his mother's anguished cry, "Oh, my boy, my boy, I thought you were dead. Mother will never forgive herself, and she will never, never let go your hand again."

Yet there was always present an example of the very opposite attitude toward the dangers of life. If William Herrick had been the dominant figure in the family, Walton's first reaction to the trolley incident might have been his only one. For William's daily progress through the streets of a great city, crippled as he was, was beset with real dangers, his return each night the completion of a truly courageous, if unheralded, expedition.

Walton sensed this before he could have articulated it, as he sensed the rare quality of the tenderness and serenity in his father— for all of his allegiance to his mother. The daily event of the home-coming (once Walton was up on his feet at Dr. Billings' urging, and outdoors to stay) communicated to the boy a sense of William Herrick's great warmth and that triumphant life of his which—for all its mistakes and frailties and despairs and humiliations—was in itself an affirmation of the vast and unpredictable resources of the human spirit.

Walton would wait in the front yard, feeling a curious expectancy beyond what the moment semed to warrant. He would watch one long banana-like yellow trolley car after another move on up Euclid Avenue —tense and eager only when he could tell from the slowness with which the trolley passed the end of his own street that it had just stopped around the corner. Then, at last, the familiar figure would appear.

Or perhaps Walton would have been delayed within the house, and would only realize that his father was approaching through hearing the sound of the cane—tap, tap, tap—a regular metallic sound like no other. In either case, Walton would start to run, and when his father stopped and flourished his cane in the air as a salute, the boy always then understood fleetingly for what he had been waiting with such expectancy. A warm gush of feeling would flow through him, making him shy, tongue-tied, by the time he finally reached his father's side.

There were these times, these flashes of love and pride, these moments when his father was to him heroic—although always his unpretentiousness made the word seem embarrassingly inappropriate, even when not uttered. But there were also the ways in which his father accepted submissively his mother's dominance, her sarcasm and faultfinding, or brushed them aside with what seemed to Walton an inadequate laughter. These encounters did much to substantiate in the boy's mind his mother's repeated assertion (usually a veiled one, but clear enough) of superiority. And when, therefore, as he sometimes did, William Herrick exploded over the wild extravagance with which, in the face of their modest income, Marcia allowed charge accounts to mount, the icy ironies with which she would answer his hopeless anger seemed further confirmation of this conviction.

And, finally—though, as it were, against Walton's will—the boy could not help being affected in his feeling for his father by the acutely painful incidents that occurred when he accompanied William Herrick into the big outside world. William wore plain clothes, mostly black and dark blue suits and ties, and white shirts. But, like many men of his generation, in October he exchanged his summer straw hat for a derby. And on one walk Walton took with him, several tough little boys ran alongside them, shouting, "Charlie Chaplin! Yah, yah, it's Charlie Chaplin! It's the funny man! What's the matter with your legs, mister?"

For days afterwards, there danced obscenely in Walton's mind the grimy, grinning faces of these urchins, pointing and snickering, imitating his father and capering grotesquely. He knew well enough how he *ought* to feel (his mother, he realized, had made it perfectly clear how he ought to feel about everything), but that was not the way he did feel. He felt ashamed of his father, of himself, and of his shame.

There was a consequent ambivalence in Walton's attitude toward his father, throughout his boyhood and into his adolescence. He felt a determined loyalty to him and would never seek to avoid outings with him that were bound to lead to more incidents of the sort that had so upset him. But he was also resentful, and unhappily, though secretly, convinced of his father's inferiority to most normal people. To escape his consequent confusion and pain, he tried consciously to erect a model of his father's nobility in his mind, which ended by flattening his true feelings of affection.

It was only long after, in the last ten years of William Herrick's life, that Walton, little by little slipping the bonds of his mother's hold, turned to his father, at first as a maneuver in his war with Marcia, but eventually with the full directness of honest feeling. This final close friendship with his father was the deepest tie of the first thirty years of Walton's life. And the sure knowledge that his father, patient and uncomplaining throughout Walton's long servitude to Marcia, had eventually had a full assurance of his love and appreciation sustained Walton through the difficult years after William's death. He was adamant about the inscription to go on the tombstone: "Be of good cheer; you have overcome the world"; every time he went to the family lot and read it he could see the shuffling, grotesque, beloved figure stop far down the street, balance himself, and wave his cane, signaling love for others and fulfillment to himself. . . .

[*Part Three*] *4*

I<small>T</small> was with understandable reluctance that Walton finally gave in and accepted the frightening fact that he must go to school. The public school principal, completely bewildered by this pale, skinny, dark-haired boy who read with eighth-grade comprehension and knew more history than he did himself, yet could not do the simplest problems in subtraction, finally assigned him to Grade 3A, with the understanding that he was to skip 4B if he brought his arithmetic up to grade level by the end of the term. Here began an erratic sequence during which Walton attended 3A, 4A, 5A, 6A, and skipped 4B, 5B, and 6B.

Walton's first day at school fulfilled his apprehensive expectations. His teacher, a certain Miss Hazleton, lived only a few doors from the Herricks, and had always seemed a pleasant enough woman; he felt some reassurance in the very fact that she was to be his teacher. But not for long. He made one mistake in a spelling test on that first day (he had missed the first three weeks of the second term) for which the other students—but not he—had had some preparation. When Miss Hazleton read aloud the names of those who had missed and must therefore stay after school, he felt first an uncontrollable fury, then an inconsolable despair.

But neither rage nor tears had any effect beyond amusing the other children. Only long years later did he come to believe that he finally understood what the teacher's reasoning had been. While it was manifestly unfair, under the circumstances, that he be so punished, Miss Hazleton had probably felt that he was in for enough trouble without immediately being labeled "teacher's pet." But the effect for Walton at the time had been a confirmation of his darkest suspicions on his very first day of school.

There was worse to come. His mother had requested that he remain in the classroom during recess periods, pleading that he was not strong enough to participate in rough play. The teacher and principal had been courteous but adamant. Such an exception was granted only by instruction of the family physician. "Very well," she replied, and tossed her head.

But to her undisguised horror, and hence to Walton's augmented dread, Dr. Billings was firm. Walton was perfectly well: to "keep him out of things" this way was the very worst thing she could do. There was no recourse to any further authority; she solaced herself with injunctions to the boy and the teacher about being "well wrapped up" and staying away from "the rough boys."

All this would have been bad enough; but Marcia, with her customary certainty of her infallible rectitude, made no effort to discuss any detail of the matter in privacy; various children in Walton's class overheard the talk, and gleefully, with the impersonal collective malice of children, passed it on to all the rest.

Through some miracle, Walton escaped unscathed the first recess period. But at the very outset of the second one, as he stood huddled like some forlorn chicken in a corner of the playground, shifting from one foot to the other and praying for the bell to end these frightening ten minutes, five or six boys in his class came up to him.

For a moment they stood there, staring at him with what seemed to him the implacable insolence of the self-assured. Then one said slowly, "Hi, sissy!" He gave Walton a push in the chest with the flat of his hand, careening him into another boy. "Watch your step, sissy!" and he was catapulted to a third—and a fourth, and a fifth. Head rocking on his neck, eyes bulging in fright, too hopeless to try to fight, too proud to cry out, he was pushed roughly back and forth, batted from boy to boy like some animate shuttlecock, until finally one of the biggest boys grabbed him with both hands by the coat front, and thrust his scowling face close to Walton's.

"You scared to fight?" he demanded.

A pale, bespectacled boy, whom Walton, in his innocence, could not recognize as the most recent victim before himself, stepped forward, eyes gleaming feverishly, and said, "You've got to fight, sissy, you know, or we'll do this to you every recess."

Walton gulped miserably.

"All right," he stammered.

The big scowling boy landed a blow on his chest that knocked him flat on his back. He lay there, the sobs smothered somehow inside him, feeling no longer so much terrified as abysmally humiliated. He didn't want to get up ever; he didn't want to look at anybody and see the scorn in their eyes; he wanted to die, to sink into the earth where he lay, and disappear forever.

"Get up, sis. What's the matter? Are you yellow? Get up and fight."

He got up. Jagged streaks of red and black suddenly danced in his head, before his eyes, in his very brain. With a scream of sudden desperate rage, with arms flailing, he lunged at his assailant, kicking, gouging, biting. The very abruptness of his charge caught the other boy off guard and he went down before the assault. Walton leaped on him, pounding him, scratching his face, hammering at him like a maniac. He had already raised a lump on the boy's forehead and brought a trickle of blood from his nose, when a strong hand grasped him by the collar and hauled him off.

A particularly big sixth-grade boy shook him as though he were a sack. "You nasty little punk, don't you know how to fight fair?"

Dazed, lost, deeply ashamed, Walton endured the rest of the term—the long, unbearable recesses and the route to and from school. His primitive prowess when aroused kept many of the boys from trying to maul him physically, but they continued to taunt him unmercifully about the way he fought—"like a girl"—and the huskier ones continued to pommel him when not busy with more important matters. And while Walton held off for a month, he finally told his mother the whole story, thereby bringing a further catastrophe upon himself.

"Mother's poor, dear boy!" she exclaimed, clasping him uncomfortably in her arms and rocking back and forth. A further indignant talk with the principal followed. The harassed man could do little except offer to keep a sharp eye on the playground—and the chances were, Walton reflected later, that Marcia, with her haughty manner, made the principal feel antagonistic, rather than sympathetic, to Walton. Moreover, to add to his discomfort, Marcia decided that he must have protection between home and school. Under her instruction, the English governess of the period, who had stayed on with the Herricks as a sort of housekeeper, now took Walton to school in the morning and waited for him in the afternoon outside the building.

This, of course, was for the other children the last straw. They gathered in bands, one near the school exit, one halfway to his home, one at the very end of his own street, to accost him with insults, sly darting lunges and kicks, even—on occasion—stones. In vain Walton—with all his inexperience with this horrible world, already better versed in its ways than his mother—pleaded to be allowed to go home alone, like the others. There was no solution to the situation until the family—at the end of Walton's first year in public school—moved away, to East Cleveland.

Whenever Walton looked back to this period of his life, it seemed to him astonishing that he had survived these years at all. With the gang terrorism he suffered at school; with a doting, all-protective incubus of a mother; with a father who was physically unable to participate in many activities with him and temperamentally unfitted to counsel and support him through his new trials—with such a cycle of suffocation at home and exposure abroad, how did he survive?

He said as much one day twenty or more years later to an acquaintance who had remarked that it must have helped in the early years to have been so big. Walton went into detail on his childhood. The other man, somewhat to Walton's surprise and annoyance, shrugged. "So?" he said. "One survives." They separated and Walton continued to brood on his early miseries, doubtless the more for the "rebuke." Daydreaming, he conjured up two surrealistic pictures.

The one, of home, showed him, tiny and content, curled in the voracious lap of his mother, while a sort of dotted-line extension of himself, somewhat like the disappearing series of Cheshire cats, lay curled within the womb within that lap—only this embryo self, frustrated and bitter, was struggling to escape, kicking furiously at the walls of its prison.

Near them stood his sister, regarding them wistfully, her finger in her mouth, one foot turned in, the toe of her shoe stubbing the other one. And in a corner sat his father, engrossed in a book, with his feet stretched higher than his head, to indicate the comfort of detachment—while at the same time his large and bony hand, at the end of a thirty-foot arm, was extended in blessing, like a nimbus, over Marcia's head.

In the other picture, Walton, again small, sat in a posture of dejection and helplessness in the midst of a barren Daliesque desert. In the distant background was the haven of the school building, shaped round and concave like a sheltering lap. Around him lay scattered the whole or partial skeletons of other schoolboy victims, and advancing upon him from all directions were schoolboy tormentors with the assorted heads of ghouls, goblins and jungle animals, all grinning in predatory anticipation. But what was most remarkable in this picture was that Walton had removed his own head from his neck and held it in his hands. It was a strikingly handsome head—and, curiously, there was no fear on the face of this disembodied head, rather a smile of some guile and cunning.

It was only after the fantasy of these two pictures that Walton finally perceived the distortion of his estimate of those years. What he symbolized in this way was true enough. But there were, he discovered, two important considerations that he was prone not to consider. One was the grin on the face of the precious disembodied head, the other that he looked at the family picture from only one angle—his own.

Of course he had always conceded—a little too glibly, as a matter of fact—that his parents had had their struggles too: that they had done their best to do the right thing for their children, had held and attempted to practice sound ideals, to perpetuate a decent and virtuous family tradition, to prepare their children to meet life not wholly unarmed. He had always conceded this, but he had conceded it, really, as a sort of dismissal, and had gone on feeling resentful at what (he maintained) they had *done* to him.

Especially his mother, of course. For what his father had done to him was of a negative sort, constituted acts of *omission*. But Marcia Herrick was not one to omit. Her style was always explicit, her course one of overdoing. Even after her death, when her name was mentioned or he turned, through whatever association, to thoughts of her, the substance of what came to his mind was: why couldn't she ever leave anything alone?

Yet, when, in those years, he said as much frankly to certain people who had known her well and were fond of her, he was rebuked —mildly but firmly. When he pondered this reaction, he realized that these people had only one thing in common that he could perceive: they were all (all? they were not *that* numerous)—for whatever reason of background or caste—of that segment of American society that played subordinate roles, of whatever denomination. It was Marcia the Champion whom they remembered so faithfully. And—most important —it was not merely a question of their being timid or lacking self-respect.

Her championship of the exploited and the defenseless, to be sure, led to a series of attachments (rather than simply relationships) on the domestic scale. Here, as always, she simplified the possibilities. There were, for the most part, only two kinds of maids: good ones and insolent ones.

Yet even in this situation there was some confusion, for there were several family retainers who did not fit these classifications, were not "good" in the limited sense of properly subservient, and yet were devoted to Marcia.

Chief among them was Sarah Jane Metheny, a tiny British woman (not over four foot ten), known to the Herricks for thirty-five years only as Janie. Janie was British; she came to the United States at thirty-five, and directly to Cleveland because this was the city to which several of her brothers and sisters had migrated. She began working for the Herricks as a sort of combination governess and housekeeper; when the expense made it out of the question for them to retain both someone in this capacity and a maid, she became a free-lance seamstress. That is, while Marcia had her in two or three times a week to sew for her, she also introduced her into the homes of friends, and Janie worked a regular full six-day week in this manner for many years.

This resulted, it seemed to Walton, in the one unshakable, intimate friendship of Marcia's life. Janie was soft-spoken, kind, brave and unfailingly cheerful. She knew her blessings, which were modest enough, aside from her endowment of character, and she counted them. She knew her lacks and disappointments and misfortunes with equal realism, but she did not choose to count them. In the three and a half decades that Walton knew her, he actually never—not once—heard her complain or indulge in even the most trivial self-pity.

Like most people so sane and independent, Janie refused to be patronized or condescended to. When, in the early years, Marcia occasionally got on her high horse, and only then, Janie's voice would rise in indignation, and the Cockney which, no doubt as a part of her honest middle-class aspirations, she otherwise suppressed with some care would bestrew the room with misplaced h's. "Mrs. Errick," she would say, "Hi don't ave to put hup with such talk from no one, Hi don't."

Marcia would subside and apologize. And little by little such differences dwindled and disappeared. The two women traveled into old age together, sewing and talking and drinking tea, and when, at seventy-five, Marcia finally left Cleveland and said an all but final good-bye to Janie, now seventy, they clasped each other with love and grief and gratitude, and with a silent admonition from each to the other to endure the final years with fortitude, in remembrance of the time they had passed together.

Janie supported Marcia through sickness and fear and loneliness, stood by her patiently through her hypochondria, through Elinor's terrible illness, through William's death (it was evident to everyone that Janie was a little "soft" on William), through the whole lifelong procession of a family, for better and for worse. She supported Marcia, and she made her laugh. She alone could make her laugh. Despite the somewhat conventional aspirations to be ladylike that formed the core of Janie's orientation, she had a wide bawdy streak in her. And the same Marcia who would show only repugnance and contempt for an off-color allusion from anyone else would laugh at one of Janie's sallies, stories or puns until the tears flowed down her cheeks. . . .

Walton also came to realize that there was a great magnetism about his mother—one that her protective sovereignty over him frequently prevented him from seeing. When in a good mood, she had an entertaining idiom, marked by flashes of highly original insight and wit. Time and again he was reminded of this by some friend, his own contemporary, who would say to him after a first meeting with Marcia, "My God, Walton, your mother is wonderful. When you first meet her, you think she's the Duchess of Marlborough. But what a sense of humor! And she's so wonderfully tolerant. I've never met anybody her age who can understand and sympathize with young people's points of view the way she can."

The truth was, Walton reflected, that she put on a special show, and (if you hadn't seen it fifty times before) a good one, too, for the younger generation. She championed them as she did the sick, the weak and the unfortunate, and she desperately wanted them to like her and confide in her.

But she was more often grim and depressed than gay, and her "independence" was too often employed in the service of being outrageously rude, under the sanction of refusing "to lie." Unquestionably, the magnetism went deeper than that—had much to do with the strength of fiber that suffered her to endure more than eighty years of the grotesque misapplication of that strength, of perverse waste and consequent pain. Her "speaking up" was not exclusively motivated by perversity. There was, to be sure, a steep moral list—whether to starboard or port, Walton could not say—that disabled her from running a straight course. But she displayed frequently a moral courage that was not the less potent for its probably compensatory source, or for the ridiculous extremes to which she would carry it.

One of her favorite battles was over the way in which human beings treated animals. She abhorred hunting and even fishing; she pampered the Herricks' badly-trained and annoying dog at the expense of guests; for a stretch of ten years she forbade anyone in the household to swat a fly, but insisted on screens' being opened to permit the fly's escape.

Don Quixote himself would have blanched at one of her later exploits. She discovered a stray alley cat in the back yard one day— thin, dirty, half-starved. Three days of feeding and petting followed, and the clear realization that the cat was pregnant. With a contentious dog, Prince, in charge of the household, there was no sanctuary to offer the cat but the front vestibule. Walton was pressed into service to provide a comfortable bed, and for three weeks before delivery and for several thereafter the cat was comfortably ensconced, while guests went to the rear door and reached the living room via the kitchen. . . .

Here, then, was an important aspect of his mother, seen objectively, though more tolerantly than Walton could usually manage. And such a picture of her was important to any understanding of the balancing positive elements in the Herrick household of his childhood. But beyond these at once lovable and exasperating traits and attitudes of Marcia's, there were, of course, other favorable auspices.

Two events were so regularly recurrent in the family as to warrant calling them institutions. One was the trek that Walton and his father regularly took to League Park to watch and to shout for the Cleveland Indians; the other Walton designated as the Family Sunday.

William Herrick loved professional baseball with a passion he accorded few other things. How this devotion had begun Walton did not know; if William had ever told him, he did not remember. But from that day in the late summer of 1915, when Walton went to the park at Lexington Avenue and Sixty-sixth Street for the first time (his father had waited impatiently but determinedly until he felt sure that Walton was no longer too young to be really interested) and saw Walter Johnson toy with the Indians as though they were a team of schoolboys, baseball became the strongest link between the man and the boy. Summer after summer, day after day, they boarded the trolley, disembarked at East 118th Street, transferred to the Wade Park line, and rode for another half hour, engrossed in conversation about the pitching choices for the day, the possibility of Cleveland's breaking its annual tailspin, the foolishness of the manager's shifting of his lineup.

They were alike in their fantastic optimism, alike in their inconsolable depression after the loss of a game that could have been won with superior strategy. (In later years, Walton could laugh uproariously over the extremes to which his father carried his identification with the Indians: it was literally true that, when they lost a game through errors, he would often go home in grim despair, lock himself in his room and refuse all attempts to lure him to dinner! But at the time this seemed to Walton an entirely justified attitude.) They shared a vociferous loyalty, rare among fans who had so often been disappointed in a team that annually promised mighty deeds, only to peter out ignominiously when the chips were really down; they ached when some favorite, in a temporary slump, was roundly booed by a majority of the spectators. Walton developed calliope lungs that were always at the service of even the most tentative rally, while his father pounded the iron ferule of his cane on the concrete flooring and brandished his straw hat.

During the first years that they went to the ball park together, the Indians promised fairly often, but never really fulfilled the promise. Then came the golden regime of Tris Speaker, purchased from the Boston Red Sox and made manager, and in 1920 at last the first pennant ever won by a Cleveland team. Speaker the Gray Eagle, Jim Bagby, Stanley Covaleskie, Ray Caldwell, Larry Gardner, Elmer Smith, Charlie Jamieson, Joe Wood—those were names to conjure with: they assumed a legendary brilliance for Walton, and his room was literally papered with their pictures and records. He spent evenings, even recess periods, figuring all the changes in pitching and batting averages as each new day's box score altered the players' individual records. At bedtime, he would lie in the dark, waiting for sleep and going back over an inning-by-inning recital of the day's game.

Then followed the long drought that lasted until 1948, ten years after William Herrick's death. Time and again the Indians would begin a season like champions, only to falter and wilt. Just as the shadow of the ill-fated Chicago Black Sox had once briefly lain across all American League parks, so first the New York Yankees, with Ruth and Gehrig, later the Philadelphia Athletics, then finally once more the Yankees dominated the league.

But although, during the nearly two decades after 1920 that the two Herricks continued to go to games together, the Indians never won the pennant, they were frequently stormy contenders for at least part of the season; and William and Walton never gave up on them until it was a mathematical impossibility for the team to finish the season in first place. They always awaited the miracle that never occurred.

Looking back on this shared fanaticism, Walton remembered a midsummer early evening much later—in 1932 or 1933, when he was in his mid-twenties. They attended a long extra-inning game between the Indians and the Yankees. It was a game of no special importance, for the Indians were not doing at all well at the time; but it was a good game, and after the twelfth inning the teams were still tied, 3-3. Dusk was beginning to settle; it was a certainty (this was before the advent of night games and lighted parks) that the game would be called at the end of the thirteenth inning, even if the tie was unbroken. Walton was dispatched to the nearest telephone booth to assure his almost certainly irate mother that they would be leaving before long, and that they would be content with a cold supper.

On his way back, he stopped at the top of the steps leading down to his seat, and looked at his father, and beyond him, at the field. Their seats were in the upper deck of the grandstand, behind first base, and the whole vast velvety greenness of the field was spread before him. The infield, shaded by the grandstand, was in deep blue shadow now, but the rays of the sun, setting behind him, spread a mist of golden light over the outer stretches of left and center fields.

As the Cleveland pitcher finished his warm-up and the first Yankee batter dug in at home plate, the large crowd was suddenly silent. Walton studied his father's profile, set and intense, the way in which he sat hunched forward in rapt absorption; then he shifted his gaze to others, to all the rest sitting in this section, each demonstrating in some individual special way his participation in this common experience.

It was suddenly, blindingly clear to Walton that this was beautiful. Not the sentimentalities of shared emotion, or the dramatic climax of the game itself, but the scene, and the vision that the scene induced. The fading light brought everything into sharp, clean focus, lent a clarity of outline to the small figures in white uniforms down there far below, added another dimension to the stands themselves, to the multitudinous and multicolored figures in them; it emphasized the bold whiteness of the baselines, released, it seemed, primary colors that had remained latent all afternoon—released them in some mysterious way despite (or could it be because of?) the smoky lavender haze enveloping the outfield and sections of the stands.

It was beautiful, and so were the clean sweep of the pitcher's motion, the swing of the bat, the sharp, clear crack of a line drive through the hole between short and third, the puff of dust made by the shortstop's dive as he missed the ball, the left fielder's single-motion scooping of the ball and throw to second, the batter's easy rounding of first and return to the base to stand, hands on hips, on the bag.

It was all beautiful, and, descending the steps, Walton knew with sudden sureness that, beyond the partisanship which he and his father shared, they had in common a deep affiliation to this vision: that what brought them back here, again and again, was the same secret and inarticulate love for the perhaps indefinite but certainly communicable quality of this scene—the sense that somehow in its ritual and peculiarly unostentatious and subtle symbolism it was a sort of celebration of life that held a beauty and commemorative power far beyond its obvious appeal.

This was the dance of life—life itself with all its assertions and circumventions, its desperate hopes, its futile but brave and graceful gestures, its desperate remedies. And Walton suddenly felt a premonitory sadness touch him, as one is fleetingly chilled when, standing in the sunlight, the passage of an unobserved cloud between one and the source of warmth and light abruptly absorbs one into shadow. This was the dance of life, he had thought, recognizing it from the books he had read, the music he had heard, the dreams he had entertained—but, while feeling the intensity of his own response, he knew that the longing within him to participate would not be realized, that he was doomed by the inexorable decree of some authority he could not identify to remain a spectator.

But, at the same time, it was as though this sadness, his very exclusion from participation, intensified and heightened the quality of his appreciation. He was at any rate the poet, the minstrel, the troubadour who could invoke and celebrate the depths and shallows of human experience.

And there was much to celebrate here. When an outfielder made a hopeless but gallant throw in an attempt to catch a runner at the plate; when coaches and base runners hurled concerted obscenities at a pitcher; when a batter who had just struck out began the walk back to the dugout, head down, feet kicking up imprecations of dust; when a whirlwind double play, as swift and beautiful as the climactic passage of a ballet, cut off an apparently irresistible rally; when a baserunner stole second, sliding in to defy a formidable arm; when the manager, standing on the mound, took the ball from a tired pitcher, signaled to the bullpen for relief, and the new pitcher began his long journey to the box, jacket slung over his shoulder—when any of these familiar events occurred, what was it but the traditional pantomime of life, its aspirations and defeats, its generosities and petty competitions, its heroic accomplishments and its humiliations?

And sure enough, even as Walton turned in at the row in which his father was sitting, he saw William Herrick shift from his intense, even desperate absorption in the immediate peril to the Cleveland cause, to look out to where the late golden light flooded deep center field; look and draw a deep breath, sighing happily and, in a sudden swift gesture, spread out his hands as though to say, "Who can describe it? Who can do it justice?"

The fellowship with his father over baseball was a consistent source of happiness to Walton; the Family Sunday was for some time the well-spring of what security he knew, aside from that occasional and precarious sort engendered by his retreat into a private world of fantasy. The rest of any given week might be a haphazard sequence of ups and downs, mostly dependent upon the graph of his mother's emotions: her prevailing psychic weather could affect but never destroy the institution of Sunday, just as her persistent, but surely not consciously determined, tendency to get hurt, angry and withdrawn on holidays could injure but never wholly ruin his father's manifest delight in such celebrations. Hence Sundays gave to Walton as much of a sense of continuity as he knew.

In the first place, the loyalty to William Herrick that Marcia always displayed to the world outside the family was for once, on Sundays, exhibited directly to William for no one's benefit but his own. It was as though she at once eased her conscience and freed herself of further obligation to him by a strenuous effort to see that this one day a week was ordered as he would have it. This included, until the children reached their teens, going to church herself, except for the duration of Walton's protracted stay in bed; she even refrained for the most part from comments on the stultifying congregation of pusillanimous souls she found there, and from airing the sort of aristocratic pantheism that she and God found most truly religious.

Probably this concession of Marcia's was responsible for the way Sundays began. Walton never forgot the feeling of warm benevolence he would experience on being awakened by the sound of his father's heroic whistling in the bathroom. William Herrick always commanded a most melodious whistle, but on Sundays he outdid himself with prolonged trills, arpeggios and bravura passages. Walton sometimes wondered whether he did not render all the hymns in the order of the Presbyterian hymnal used in the First Church—such a stream of sacred song emerged. But this was idle curiosity: what mattered was the sense that his father was gloriously happy, would be jolly and interested all day, without any inclination to withdraw behind a book, would tell stories at meals—would, in short, be *there* all the time. What mattered still more was the promise of ultimate victory. Walton was not quite sure what he meant by this thought, but he knew that he felt a comforting assurance that God was in His heaven, that good would be rewarded, and that nothing unpleasant *could get at him.*

And then, after he had spent a few minutes of quiet, dreamy listening, stretching out relaxed in the warm hollow of his bed, his mother would come in, her face somehow softer and brighter than on other days, and say quietly, with what seemed to Walton a reassuring pride, "How's my big boy today?"

Breakfast was always especially elegant: griddle cakes and sausages or crisp codfish balls and fried hominy. Then, although being dressed in starchy Sunday clothes and—from the age of six on—having to shine one's own black shoes were chores, there was a pleasant bustle and stir, a vague but exciting sense of the portentous, in getting dressed for church.

It was a long ride on the big yellow trolley car down Euclid Avenue to First Church, but there were compensations. First, there was the rush to see if they could get facing seats, so that the whole family of four was encased in a private little island, which was the more easily transformed, in Walton's imagination, to an automobile or the officers' compartment on a troop train. Then, if this palled, there were—especially after he was seven years old, and before he served his sentence in bed—the games to be made out of what could be seen through the window: computing the number of people dressed in particular ways or the number of cars of each make that they passed.

Church was, in those days, solemn and satisfying. Walton could not remember his grandfather in the pulpit, but he liked Dr. Barclay, and the service was so arranged that the part preceding the leaving of children for Little Church, as it was called, was colorful, including a short, simple sermon for the children and a good deal of music.

Then came Walton's favorite moment, when he and Elinor, together with perhaps thirty other children, would leave their family pew, march up the aisle and pass before the benevolent gaze of the minister through the door beside the baptismal font at the front of the church. To be observed by this huge adult audience filled Walton with a sense both of importance and of dedication. He felt at one with the Biblical heroes of the stories read to him in Little Church; he accorded these a concentrated attention which he gave to nothing else.

The trolley ride home was tiring after such a morning, but Mother had usually hidden small picture books and several hard candies in her voluminous pocketbook, and at the worst the children fell asleep. There followed, about one-thirty, a big Sunday dinner, with roast chicken or roast lamb with mint sauce, and always a special dessert, with three helpings allowed.

In the afternoon, the family scattered. In good weather Mother might take the children for a walk. Walton preferred the rainy Sundays, on which he could hide away in his own room with, first, a cluster of picture books, and then, once he could read, every kind of book on which he could lay his hands.

From October to April, as dusk approached, a fire was lighted in the living room. Usually two or three of Marcia's and William's friends came in and supper was served on a tea wagon before the fireplace. Both before and after supper, everyone, large and small alike, gathered around the piano to sing, even William drawing up a straight chair to sit beside Marcia, who played.

At such times Walton was entranced with his mother. As though by magic, she took on a gaiety and charm she never displayed at other times; her voice, usually the best in the company, enchanted him, filled him with pride—and when, at the end of some song, she would reach out and stroke his hair, looking at him with a rich happiness in her eyes that he so rarely saw there, he would feel that he was bursting with repletion. And afterward, he and Elinor were allowed to stretch out on the rug before the fire and watch the pictures they could find in it until their heads drooped with sleepiness. Then with the tenderness of his father's good night enveloping him in a drowsy glow, he would take Elinor's hand—for once willingly—and follow Marcia upstairs, to be undressed and tucked blissfully into bed, falling asleep warm and serene, to the comfortable hum of voices below.

Where had it fled, the certainty and the love, the warmth and the security?

JOURNAL: 5

from the journal of Walton Herrick . . .

July 18, 1953

This morning it finally happened. I was barely awake—still in that pleasant state of realizing that it was Saturday and I could stay in bed as long as I wanted—when things began to fall into place. There is no other way to put it; suddenly I knew that x and y were related, l and m—all sorts of combinations of my nature and the events of my life. I felt cool, refreshed, clearheaded; I found myself thinking, "Then, if that is so, this . . ." and "Of course. If I did that, it was because . . ." And I knew with certainty that the name of this relaxation, this marvelous freedom from tension throughout my whole body—was hope.

Last night, home and determined to spend the weekend *alone and at home,* I looked at this journal and asked myself how, in the face of having made so desperate a muddle of my life—and then almost every day compounding the mistakes—I could pursue at a leisurely pace those speculations about my forefathers. How could I engage in the literary exercise about my grandfathers-in-me when my marriage, my family, my present work and my whole future were at stake? Was I really so remote from reality that, expecting a miracle to solve my problems, I felt I could sit and indulge in dilettantish, desultory meditation? How could I write my minor-league pensées while my life lay in fragments on the floor?

But now I see that there was no other way in which I could have gone effectively at the understanding of myself. I had a real flash of prescience when I wrote, in that first entry: "I must not analyze, describe, report . . . but invoke." By setting down, however indirectly, my meditations on this and that, whatever moved through my mind, I established a kind of ferment out of which has come now, after two months, a beginning comprehension.

Just how much I understand, even now, I am not sure. The almost incredible peace and clarity of mind I felt lying in bed has ended; my calculations were almost too rapid: now I must learn what I have been able to retain.

First of all, I see clearly that my nature is as demanding as Julie said it was—and I see at least some of the reasons for it, something of how I unconsciously lay claims upon other people: what they should think of me; what they should do for me; what they should grant me *as my due*. In this connection, I am suddenly aware of how often, and how righteously, I have used the words "entitled to" and "deserve." ("I'm entitled to some consideration" . . . "He deserved what he got" . . . "You aren't entitled to it.") Today it seems very clear to me that anyone (barring accidents, catastrophes—"acts of God," if you will) *in the long run* deserves what he gets and gets what he deserves. I am not thinking in theological or even conventional ethical terms, but in those of the simple neutral morality of cause and effect—nature's morality.

The reward and punishment system is deeply engrained in all of us. Though it has multitudinous forms; differing supernatural, national and local sanctions; and is applied variously, and even contradictorily, from region to region of the world—there is a real (whether conscious or not) *consensus gentium* on the subject. But the claims for payment of tribute that I (and, I must suppose, a good many others) have made have been of an entirely different—though perhaps analogical—order. The key to the difference, it now seems clear to me, is in the falseness of the *basis* of my claims, from which comes their unilateral recognition.

I am suddenly sure of this, but let me see if I can extend and clarify what I mean. If no one else—or almost no one else—sees my claims as valid, recognizes them as applications of tacit common laws of human nature and relations—then I must re-examine them. What are some of them?

Put crudely, the first that comes to mind—and it astonishes me— is that I am extraordinary, superior. Have I really believed this all along? Extraordinary in what way? Superior to whom?

The whole structure breaks down with embarrassing rapidity. I hear myself saying weakly, "Why, *extraordinary*. In all sorts of ways. And superior—" I am suddenly aware (have I actually always been convinced of this?)—superior to everybody else! Faced with the absurdity of this reply, I am forced to be specific. Well, I am not a genius, but I am extremely intelligent; I am loyal, honorable, courageous; I am possessed of a really unusual (chemical?) attractiveness to women. . . .

What a pitiful ragbag of half truths, lies, and evasive and fatuous generalizations! A good many people are extremely intelligent. Do I really believe that I am not a genius? Or do I mean by that, secretly, that genius is a magician's act, half charlatanry, half supernaturalism, and I am that better thing—a wise and talented man, a many-sided man?

Wise? After what happened to me two months ago? Talented? Again, how many others are talented! Many-sided? Count the sides—soberly. Am I talking about multiple aspects of my personality—or am I "covering" what amounts to a vacillating inconsistency that comes from the lack of a coherent, individual *center* to myself?

Loyal? Or stubbornly prejudiced, obstinate? What's the whole complex truth about my insistence on Kiefer? Honorable? Yet capable of lying, day after day, to myself! And also, dedicating the summer to working things out with myself so that Julie and I may come together— only to succumb immediately to my yen for Sonia. Courageous? Yet that dream, those figures on the stair? My phobia about airplanes? My timidity, stepping onto new terrain—whether physical or mental?

I have literally stopped in bewilderment. I have not written these paragraphs in self-abuse, but in simple, if limited, honesty. I have long laid claim, I now understand, to being a *hero,* the leader, perhaps, of an elite of one. Yet I can find very little in myself that is heroic; this morning I find it impossible to substantiate the idea of belonging to *any* elite.

Enough of this. How did I come to so ridiculous a conclusion? What has given me the conviction of being entitled to special privilege, so vast and vague as to encompass all human situations and relations? Why do I want to be honored for qualities I don't possess?

It is easiest to answer the last question. Surely because these seem to me the most desirable and honorable qualities. Let me look at them again. Intelligence—and/or wisdom—loyalty, honor, courage, attractiveness for women. Surely these are traditionally respected and admired qualities. Except the last—which is envied and desired. Yet there is something about the combination that stresses *I* lopsidedly. Take loyalty. Why not steadfastness, constancy—primarily, consistency? Loyalty suggests to me now a partisanship, and hints that I consider myself superior to the person to whom I am loyal, that I cleave to an ideal simply because it is mine, without examining rationally the merits of each case. This is an individualizing extension of "My country, right or wrong," which itself clearly italicizes "my": the phrase loses all meaning without the use of the first person pronoun.

Again, honor? Why not honesty? The plainer word suggests fairness, decency, realism. I cannot be a medieval knight, pursuing an artificial, archaic code of behavior, to whatever lengths. Or can I, secretly?

Attractiveness to women? Being loved, to put it simply. Walton the Well-Beloved. And as for *loving?* It is pleasant and satisfying to be wanted; it is almost unbearably bitter to admit that one cannot continue to satisfy and be satisfied in a close, prolonged human relation.

What conglomeration of Gothic concepts from my mother's romantic bower of idealism, and my own early reading and fantasies, has nourished such an unrealistic picture of self? To what extent did her expression of hopes for me, riding out as it were to redeem the dust-trailed banner, the shattered standard of the Nicholsons, lead me to the conviction that I was not wanted the way I was, and must develop a bogus self of this sort to fulfill my highest possibilities? Certainly she was the dominant figure of my childhood.

And the assertion of the right to special privilege? Did she not tell me again and again how remarkable I was, in the very terms I have been describing—so long as I accepted her vision of life and its curtailment of any spontaneous development of one of my own? And during that year and a half in bed, in a world exclusively governed by her, wasn't my destiny (too grand a word) pretty thoroughly nailed down? However many barnacles, exclusively my own, have in time adhered to this original craft—is not the craft my mother's, or at least my mother-in-me's?

I am aware now of a feeling of weakness, a fullness in my head, a queasiness in my stomach. I know why. And, I suppose for the first time in my entire life, I am also sweating from the full impact of an understanding of the fearful responsibility of parenthood. I am going to stop, take a walk, have lunch. But I must not lose this trail; I have really made only a beginning. . . .

Let me come at it another way. If I early became convinced, however unconsciously, that I must attain to this grandiose condition—that I must be at once, to oversimplify, whatever were my childish equivalents of Sir Launcelot and Socrates—then I must have ceased (if I had ever begun) the exploration of my own nature, apart from this self that my mother and I collaborated in superimposing upon me. Who am I? Who am I really? takes on a fresh and urgent meaning again. And since I have insisted—futilely, angrily, despairingly—on being what I am not, the only assistance I have ever had in this endless war of attrition based on the discrepancy between what I believed fanatically I should, even must be, and what I was (what I felt and did and couldn't feel and do)—my only assistance has come from others who have accepted the self I wanted them to believe in; who have been willing, so to speak, to service this bogus self.

There have been surprisingly many of them—whether because I am more persuasive than I find it easy to believe, or because it serves their own ends. But why should I need so badly to maintain the masquerade? My mother is dead.

But my mother *is* dead. And since (what am I thinking?) I have never grown up (a small boy in man's clothing?), it is no wonder that I am desperate and terrified. Am I? Can one really be so unaware, on the smiling or dignified surface, of the internal war, pillage and strafing and fire by night?

Is that what I really wanted in my marriages? Another mother— with one difference? A concubine-mother? Poor Joanna! Is that what Lydia meant? And is Julie staking everything—home, children, all— on the possibility that I may find myself and grow up to the status of an authentic husband and father?

Karen. When we were constant lovers. If there was any such maternal servicing given by her or demanded by me, I cannot find proof of it. Perhaps it has something to do with its being what people call an illicit love affair. "A mother's place is in the home. . . ." Perhaps *home* is forever jinxed for me by the nature of my early one. *It mustn't be.* I mustn't let it.

One thing, anyway, I do see clearly. Having accepted in general Mother's vision of manhood or latter-day knighthood, and then added to it certain elements which, in however tainted a form, were really mine and quite incompatible with some of hers, I finally demanded of myself so impossible and contradictory an amalgam of characteristics as to constitute none at all.

Incapable, then, of a coherent philosophy and course of life for myself, I have defaulted, handed over my sovereignty to a many-headed regent: *others.* Whomever. Thinking of myself as a many-sided man, I have simply tried to be all things to all people. Not knowing who I was, I have silently implored them to tell me. I tried to give them all what I decided they wanted. Not being able really to look in and see, I have thought I was looking out to discover. But did all these people really think what I attributed to them? Did they actually have such expectations of me?

I have desperately needed approval, not having my own. How

could I, when there was no one I could reach *in there* to give approval? Knowing instinctively that I must have a self, I have meant by approval that I wanted others to endorse the best self I could scrape together— wanted this so desperately as to demand it.

The incredible range of this insistence illustrates what I meant when I wrote of my invoking special privilege. As clearly as though it happened yesterday, I remember reading in the morning newspaper, some three or four years ago, that General Eisenhower was receiving some special citation. It was ten minutes before I realized that the irritability I had been feeling thereafter was caused by the fact that he— and not *I*—had been so honored!

That says it all. It is funny, but it is also shatteringly pitiful. I wonder how many people, seemingly functioning effectively in the life of their time and community, have lived so deeply—so perilously and ridiculously—in fantasy. For that is the meaning of this incident to me. So often decorated in daydreams, so wholly wedded to the bogus omnipotent self, so deeply bedded in the concept of special privilege that I am persuaded that cause and effect should be set aside for me—I could resent Eisenhower's precedence over me!

On such occasions as this, one's grandiose trumped-up image of self comes slap up against hard-grained reality. Yet I wrote, and meant, that my "loved image" must be "fertilized fully by others"! The modest twofold task I have unconsciously set my wives, friends and associates is at once to assure me that I am all the paradoxical and contradictory things I claim for myself, and at the same time themselves to set the pace, to initiate the particular course at a particular time that I can, should follow—since I have myself so little autonomous initiative. What an assignment this would be, if it were fully evident to them! But of course often all that comes to the surface is my tension, my irritability, my tendency to quick and seemingly inexplicable shifts in mood.

The exception is in working alone. When there is no impact of another personality, no question of looking to someone else for a hint of procedure—when there is nothing before me except the job to be done in solitude—all this drops away. Then I am confident, able, honest and objective.

More light. The dream about leaving the group on the grass—the sunlit, laughing group—and going out to sit on the pavement with tin cup and dark glasses, to beg for tribute. That's the word: tribute. With the group back on the grass, all was give-and-take, mutuality. But in that sense I had nothing to give, nor could I value what I might take.

Without a real me, how could I give? Without values of my own, how could I appraise what I wanted to take?

More—nobody was acknowledging my sovereignty. I remember that I looked over my shoulder as I was walking away, thinking that if someone made a *special* plea to me to return, then I could come back without detriment to my dignity. But no one did: my claims were denied, and so great was my need that I was reduced to begging for the pitiful sustenance without which I cannot live.

Live? Retain my dead existence: for that is what it is. And perhaps that explains the terrible ennui, the seemingly endless boredom and emptiness that I sometimes experience. I am a zombie. And yet, writing that, I feel no horror. It seems to me almost as though I take a melancholy relish in it.

So I turned my back on the voluntary exchange, the intercourse that is possible between live human beings, and preferred, with my pitiful false pride in the dumb show I have invented, to invoke, however desperately in this instance, the special privilege, the empty deference on which I am condemned to feed.

But the emperor has no clothes. . . .

I must take another rest. This is exhausting.

Some echo in my head led me back, after supper, to Grandfather Herrick's autobiography, and I found what I was looking for on its second page:

> It should be said that my father . . . was not an easy man to get on with, either for my mother or for us children. His government was capricious and his demands often unreasonable, and enforced with severity. It is not pleasant to say these things, but as he was allowed to grow up self-willed, he never realized but that everything on the premises should revolve about himself. He was easily elated over trifling successes and depressed by little misfortunes. . . .

And a few lines further on, Grandfather tells how he rebelled "against the unreason of parental control."

This was Aaron Herrick, of whom I have written before. This strikes home. Will my children say something of this sort about me? I am on the verge of making a new connection—between the frustration of these demands, these claims I have been writing about, and the sudden and violent rages to which I am given, my general touchiness, and the periods of black sulking I undergo—yes, *undergo:* not *indulge*. But after all that has opened up today, I shall wait for another time—now that I have marked the spot. I'm tired.

Certainly almost all of what I've put down today is related to what I called, two months ago, "the ambiguity of personality." But particularly that part about trying to be all things to all people, gauging only half consicously what they might, in any single case, want me to be—and trying to be it. I remember that I have said before that there are two elements in this ambiguity: the *tonal lying* within the person himself, and the differing reactions of those others who know him. I can now add a further step. It seemed to me before—and still does —that the half-conscious misrepresentation that I call tonal lying is the dominant factor of the two, cause to the reactive effect; but I now also see that it is effect as well, since the person (I, at least) looks out to others for his direction, to acquire that tonal shading.

Perhaps it is an endless series of complementing cycles. Anyway, it explains to my satisfaction what I was thinking about not long ago: how difficult I find it to be simultaneously with two or more people with whom I have markedly dissimilar relations. . . .

Enough enough enough. I'm running down; I've lost the sharp edge. I feel good, but I'm glad I've resisted the temptation to write Julie about some of this. I'm not ready yet for a quit-claim deed. . . .

Pause. And during the pause—from an undiscovered direction —all that business about the figures swarming up the stairs came back. And then how I wake so often anywhere from five minutes to three, in the morning, to five minutes after three. And the sudden resolve to lay a trap, to invite this very waking that makes me so uneasy—to open myself to it, until I can find out what it means.

The Buffalo Hunter . . . I'm glad Karen said no, and I wish I could tell her how often I've thought since of things she said that evening.

Back again after preparing for bed. I watched the newscast, and for a few minutes after it, the beginning of a movie. About an astrologer! Which led me to think—

Coming as I do from the Herrick family and the Nicholson family, it is inevitable that the constellations of my astrology should inhabit remote and irrelevant heavens. The signs and symbols I read in them provide me with an elaborate misinformation about myself and the actuality in which I must live. This, then, is the problem of my life. Having, so to speak, read my destiny in the stars from a post of observation on Sirius, I must experience it, piece it out painfully and differently on the earth. Having spoken in strange tongues, I must learn to speak in that naturally my own. Having been trained, and having accustomed myself in the darkness of my soul to another atmosphere, I must learn to breathe the true air that surrounds me.

Again, after a sleepless hour in bed. I reread the last paragraph above, and I think, "Brave words, bud. What about Sonia?"

[*Part Three*]   **5**

WHERE had it fled, the certainty and the love, the warmth and the security? Walton did not know, except long afterward through what he learned of the rift growing between his father and mother, and their subsequent courses. For himself, the long enforced stay in bed ended his full pleasure in the Family Sunday—or, rather, driving him inward and leading him to self-indulgence as his due, at least changed the whole direction of his enjoyment of the day. He began to derive a great deal of satisfaction from lying in his freshly remade bed on Sunday morning, listening to the peculiar hum and knowing that he need not lift a finger, that he could play all morning with his paper-doll baseball men, read or simply daydream—and that his mother would be there to heed his every whim.

After the end of this era, with the advent of Dr. Billings and especially the beginning of school, Walton began to have Sunday headaches. Marcia countered William's every impatient move, and Walton did not attend Sunday school or church. He found a perverse satisfaction in thwarting his father's cheerful attempts to persuade him to try venturing out; it was as though he was determined to have his way on Sunday to make up for his unhappy days at school during the week.

For even the move to East Cleveland after Walton's first miserable year in school was a solution only in the sense of his being thrown in with a different group of boys and girls. The scars were on him, there to be seen, obvious enough to an entirely new set of children. He still hated school, still suffered real or imagined indignities almost every day.

He continued to skip half grades erratically, to be far in advance of his class in certain subjects, barely at the norm in others. He was no longer subjected to the ignominy of having his mother try to have him excused from recess, but she now fought a similar battle about gymnasium and athletic periods, incurring the animosity of almost all the teachers. Moreover, when the class took a hike, held a picnic, camped overnight, Walton was excused. He was still a marked individual, still tagged a sissy.

An occasional understanding classroom teacher would be interested in him for the ability he showed spasmodically, or for the sheer tenacity with which he refused to hide behind her or make use of specious excuses to escape, in his own interest, the parts of school life in which he was sure to suffer some sort of defeat or humiliation—or simply because she recognized the dilemma forced on him by his mother.

During this period, on through his graduation from grammar school, it was the men who conducted the athletic program who, however unwittingly, made Walton most miserable. Exponents of the sturdy American male tradition, they were impatient with physical awkwardness; though probably not unkindly, they were overworked and their classes were too large to permit individual attention: consequently, after one or two attempts, they "gave up" on Walton or—in the case of one man—used his ineptness as a release valve for festering irritability. During the last of these years, the depths of humiliation for Walton were the gymnasium classes in which the students climbed ropes.

First they stood in a line and "counted off": One-two-three-four; one-two-three-four. Then the instructor would blow his whistle and shout "twos." The students who had counted off "two" would rush to the swinging ropes and start to climb. . . . Then would come the turn of, say, the "fours."

Walton would wait with lead in his heart. When his number was called, he would run out of line valiantly with the others, grab his rope firmly, and make strange abortive leaps upward, as though to convince himself and the rest that he was actually climbing.

But what he was doing was sitting—sitting on the big knot at the bottom of the rope and clasping and unclasping his hands over it, high above his head. He would stay there, doing this static dance wildly, automatically, like some idiot doll, while the others with varying degrees of skill—some like monkeys, some laboriously—made their way upward, to touch at last the ceiling and slide triumphantly down.

He would sit there, feeling the rope against his genitals, knowing a kind of frantic pleasure-pain over this rough contact, feeling a crazy confusion in his mind of one kind of excitement with another, one kind of shame with another—while the instructor would shout well-meant, if irritated, instructions over the raucous laughs and jeers. Then, when all the rest were back down, Walton would climb heavily off the knot and, head bent, flushed and guilty and self-scorned, walk slowly back to the line.

Looking back painfully long years later, he realized that it was literally true that no one helped him with any of the matters that most perplexed, frightened or humiliated him. Was it because his pride was so raw, so fearfully sensitive, that he could not accept help? Where was his father all the time?

Not there. In any real sense, not there. Always kindly, always receptive (whenever Walton came up to him and said hesitantly, "Daddy?" he would look up, push his spectacles up on his forehead or take them off and hold them in his hand, saying "Yes, sonny, what is it?")—he still was not there. Very early in his life, Walton realized that his father always turned to the book he was reading, or to the papers he was marking, with a guarded look of relief. True, he had helped Walton when it was a question of the will to get well; it was not that he lacked either the requisite imagination or the concern. But he had come to accept, as had the rest of them, Marcia's domination of the family; it was as though he had determined (once he knew how differently she conceived of the way to bring up children from the way he did, and yet gave in to her) that the best thing he could do would be to stay out of the way—friendly but remote.

Yet there certainly had been another important element in his withdrawal: his physical disability made it impossible for him to help Walton in athletics, or in the rough-and-tumble of boys' life, and his own separateness from this experience in his boyhood had undoubtedly made him tender on the subject. He did what little he could, sometimes sitting on the top step of the front porch to play catch with Walton, but this was not very successful. Perhaps, too, the very loneliness of so much of William's early life had made him uncomfortable about intimacy. At any rate, when, a year or two after the worst of the gymnasium trials for Walton, the boy entered puberty, William Herrick was wholly inadequate to the task with which he was confronted.

He asked Walton to come up to his room and then to close the door behind him. This had never happened before, and Walton was sure only that something bad was about to ensue.

His father avoided his eyes.

"Walton," he said finally, with an obvious effort, "your mother tells me that you have become a man."

Walton stared at him in stupefaction.

"What?" he said.

"Your mother tells me that you are now a man. You know that

there is a certain part of your—body that performs two functions: one ever since you were a baby, the other only now that you have grown into manhood?"

It was a question. The silence was so long that his father at last looked up, directly at him, and the pleading in his eyes was so bare, so potent, that Walton was deeply embarrassed for him.

"Yes, Dad. Sure," he said and nodded his head emphatically several times.

His father drew a long breath, looked away again, looked back.

"I would be glad to tell you anything that you don't understand, sonny," he said, looking a little less scared.

But not sufficiently less. It was a hopeless muddle, Walton thought; he hardly knew what his father was talking about, but anything was better than prolonging this conversation.

"No, Dad," he said. "I guess I understand everything O.K."

As he left the room, his father called after him, "Keep yourself clean, son. You'll be glad, when you're older, that you did."

Actually, from the time he had entered public school, Walton had heard all sorts of references (the details of which he had never understood) that had made clear to him only that boys and girls, or rather men and women, did something together that had to do with the differences in the ways they were physically made. (He had never been allowed to see his mother or his sister naked.) But the fact that he was growing hair, while meaning to him that he was getting older, bore no relation in his mind to this matter of a distinct change from boy into man. The only thing he felt reasonably sure of when he thought over this painful and abortive conversation was that what had happened to him at night had not meant that he had begun to wet the bed again. He was greatly relieved to learn this. . . .

At any rate, there was, in a quite precise sense, no one to help him. His father's inclination, for whatever combination of reasons, and however unconsciously, to discourage a discussion of those problems which most baffled Walton disqualified him, and contributed to the strengthening of Walton's already existing tendency to accept his mother's somewhat condescending estimate of William Herrick.

Nor, of course, could Walton turn to his mother for help with the problems of making a more accepted place for himself in his life at school. The once or twice he had discussed them with her, he had found reason to regret it bitterly. Still less could he ask her questions about sex, to which she usually referred only as "nasty." So he presented as impassive a front to the outside world as he could, determined to let no one know—so far as possible—of either his ignorance or his fears.

Two tendencies which had their roots in the jeers of the street urchins aping his father and in his first frightening and bewildering days at school spread and grew in him. One was the facing of the world with a kind of arrogance—a pride reflected more in his bearing, in the way he held his head, stiffly erect but a little to one side, and in the expression of his eyes, cold and wary, than in anything so overt as to be called properly a manner. This was his protection, superficially effective (because repelling any sort of comment), but actually of course pitifully inadequate, in its false defensive basis, its will-imposed motivation, to bring any comfort or even much conviction to himself.

The other tendency so intensified was to hide from everyone else his true feelings. And this eventually, of course, led him to hide them from himself too, although he could not realize this. In both of these tendencies he was following the course of his mother and, in turn, with however different an emphasis, that of her father. She had tried for years to hide behind the mask of Jas. H., and now Walton pursued his version of the same course.

Meanwhile, however, he had to live somewhere, if he were not to wither away altogether. So he went underground. He burrowed more and more deeply into himself; there, and there alone, he found satisfaction, comfort and even delight.

He first entered the caverns of fantasy during the time of his incarceration in bed. Reading Ridpath's *History of the World* and Guerber's *Myths of Greece and Rome*, he lingered over the pictures. Heroic men and gods, beautiful and preferably unclothed women and goddesses, pleased and perplexed him. When the lights were extinguished for the night, he would lie there in the darkness, and all sorts of enchanting and garbled figures of legend and history would float before him, mingling in strange combinations and groups, as he wove a story that he sometimes did not understand himself.

He was nothing if not eclectic. While these two books were his favorites, he drew materials for his daydreams also from the pictorial children's Bible which his father had given him on his fifth birthday, and from the Sunday comic pages. Hawkshaw the detective cohabited with Dido; Frederick Barbarossa shared imaginary expeditions with David and Jonathan.

Then came school, and although he looked forward all the more eagerly to the time he could spend alone at home, he was no longer so safely immured within the walls of fantasy. It was only much later that he guessed that this was because, without consciously thinking about it, he had himself participated as one or another "character" in these reveries, and now that he was playing so sorry a role (at least by his standards) in the world he found at school, the discrepancy between dream and actuality was too painful to endure.

Perhaps this fact in turn led to the next variety of fantasy-life that he developed. Despite his general loneliness among his contemporaries, he did come to have several very close friends with whom he played almost every afternoon. His favorite among these, after the Herricks moved out to East Cleveland, was a tow-headed, sturdy youngster named Bill Corwin, who lived in a house that backed onto the Herricks'.

Bill was three years Walton's junior, a much better balanced boy, who had no marked difficulties of any sort with other children. But Bill was fascinated, if a little bewildered, by the fertility of Walton's imagination. Actually courted by other boys his own age, he preferred playing one of Walton's fantastic games of imagined adventure in the Herricks' attic.

These games involved a variety of characters from Walton's comprehensive collection. One day they might cross the Alps with Hannibal, the next be tied on the railroad tracks with Hairbreadth Harry, on a third occasion help Odysseus sack Troy. But in all these variants, there was a constant that vastly appealed to Bill. He could always be The Hero.

Many years later, Walton found it of consuming interest to try to probe the origins of this arrangement. It was not so uncomplicated as to be simply a matter of keeping Bill contented; Walton's own infatuation with the secondary role of the Hero's Friend was equally decisive. He suffered wounds; Bill avenged them. He was captured and tortured; Bill saved him. He handed the secret message to Bill as he fell on the trail; Bill carried it safely to headquarters. He played the decoy and lured the enemy in the wrong direction, that they might not follow Bill. He surrendered the girl they both loved (this they played rarely, with blushes and giggles, but also intense enjoyment) to Bill's superior prowess.

Without any laborious analysis, Walton was eventually able to abstract from this attitude two decisive contributing factors. One was the glorification of defeat derived from his mother—those inverted values manifest in his own version of the Confederacy and the North, the Nicholsons and the Herricks. The other was an unconscious desire to draw some gratification, some source of self-respect, out of his current humiliations and defeats in school. Perhaps a further element was that in some peculiar way he did not dare to be on top; it was as though he felt this would make him unbearably vulnerable. Or was it because he suspected and dreaded the elements in his nature that would be exposed if he were to assume the role of power?

These games with Bill Corwin were played most regularly from the time Walton was ten until he was twelve; with the approach of puberty and the acquisition of some elementary skills in such games as baseball and basketball, the two of them gave most of their attention to organized sports, which Walton attacked with the fanatical tenacity he was to devote thereafter to every goal he really set himself as important.

This change drove his life of fantasy back underground. In conjunction with his growing interest in girls (whom, until now, he had rejected as a species, excluding from this segregation only two or three whom he had timorously worshiped from a distance), he began writing a book about the adventures of a hero (his name did not matter; he was Walton, capable of all those things he could not command in actuality) who traveled in a jaunty space car to other planets.

These adventures, written down laboriously in a lined notebook, were dominantly though naïvely erotic. The hero killed a few exotic Martian beasts, overcame enemies, threats to his power, and indulged in other manly exploits, but the bulk of the narrative concerned his encounters with an endless sequence of beautiful women—princesses of Venus, Saturnian adventuresses, charming waifs of interstellar space.

The notebook was hidden behind a loose board in the attic, and finally destroyed in a panic the night his mother announced her intention of cleaning out the attic, preparatory to moving to a house they had just bought.

It was not the text that he feared her discovering; it was the illustrations. Indeed, his sexual ignorance was so comprehensive that he was incapable of pornography; nor had he any real inclination in that direction. Even when he understood a particular dirty word (which was seldom), he had no strong desire to use it. The inhibitions of his childhood had such force that he was never to develop any public boldness about these matters, and even his intense private sensuality was jealously concealed and limited to fantasy for a long time.

Moreover, he conceived and maintained an inordinate emphasis upon beauty. Pure physical beauty was his precocious ideal; that he correlated it with sex was superficially surprising, in the face of his mother's expression of alternate disgust and fierce complaint and of his school companions' bald scatology, which should have been associated, it seemed to him in retrospect, with everything that was painful to him—the daily physical and psychological buffeting they gave him. Yet deep below, he supposed, this alliance of beauty and sexuality was to him an expression of rebellion against the puritanical order he found at home and abroad: a determined groping toward an ideal order—however twisted, misshapen and confused the motivation and the result.

At any rate, the text of his secret book was highly inconclusive, going no further in sexual detail than necessarily limited physical descriptions. The pictures he cut from current movie magazines, of which, around 1920, there was a plethora, copiously illustrated with lightly draped beauties; from gaudy Sunday supplements; from old calendars. His allowance of the period was disproportionately large; he would go to the corner candy and magazine store, sacrifice ten cents of his precious money to buy *Collier's*, because it was large enough to conceal the movie magazines rolled within it, and return, going directly to his room to hide his purchases under the mattress.

After supper, he would excuse himself with the announcement that he was going to write and did not want to be disturbed, go upstairs and shut himself in. His parents would smile indulgently over their young genius: he had been writing books ever since he was seven; they had read or listened to the contents of many of them, and could indulge this need for privacy without any feeling of concern.

So, up in his room, with a chair barricading the door despite his confidence of being uninterrupted, Walton sat cross-legged on his bed, wielding scissors and paste more often than his pencil.

Just as he had divided the individuals whose pictures he found in his Civil War history into good and bad on the basis of their appearance, so now he chose his good beautiful girls and his evil beautiful women (*this* was his distinction) on the basis of their figures. The actresses and models who were slender and willowy were the heroines of his fantasy world; they loved him and he honored all of them with marriage on some polygamous planet. The ones with more mature bodies and richer curves were the sirens with whom he fought long battles, opposing female guile and witchcraft with male honor and courage. Here his reading of Odysseus' episodes with Circe and Calypso provided him with models.

Finally, however, he came upon a picture of a minor actress (he was never to see her in a movie, and she probably appeared in only one or two) who completely captivated him. Thereafter, she dominated the narrative he wrote, and he and she together underwent all the adventures that his jumbled reading and precocious imagination could combine to produce.

More important to him, poised as he was on the verge of adolescence, and secretive as he had become, his restless erotic preoccupation centered now upon this figure who began to fill his daytime fantasies and dreams. She had ash-blond hair falling onto her shoulders, was tall and slim, but with large round breasts and full, tapering thighs. Unconsciously, he began to seek her realization in the world of actuality—among the little half-budded girls who were his contemporaries, among the college students who came to the house when his father and mother held their annual Christmas party for the college choir, among the younger married women who were occasional guests at the Herricks'. He sought her counterpart and several times believed he had found her, only to discover, after a close and absorbed study, that there was some characteristic wanting—whether a physical one or one of personality.

Occasionally, sitting in a corner, away from the adults and watching this or that girl's every move—the gestures of her hands, the way she smiled, the way she swung her body as she turned to speak to someone—the half-formed thought would cross his mind that adults were very stupid; that the girl in question, and everyone else in the room, for that matter, would be first astonished and then horrified to know what was going on in his mind. This confirmed his determination never to reveal his secret thoughts.

And all the time, whether in the classroom, in the living room at home, or on his own bed, hovering deliciously between consciousness and sleep, the white, full-breasted girl of his fantasy life would haunt him. She might be lying on a warm bed of leaves (he had not developed far his study of interplanetary botany) in a Martian subterranean cavern, her soft hair framing her face as she lay in slumber, or be running toward him, arms flung out to welcome him, her lone companion on a remote satellite. Most often, however, he saw her coming from the water, dripping, a rounded knee breaking the surface of the pool and the light of Saturn's moons shining on her wet shoulders and breasts. Around her, the savage, squat scenery of the alien planet, and in the distance its conical mountains.

She, dripping . . . He did not understand his obsession with water any more than his love for exotic landscapes, but this was the picture that most disturbed and excited him—and was most likely to cause that new phenomenon which his father had half explained to him. Scrupulously Walton avoided conscious masturbation; his mother's recurrent expression of disgust and exclamation of "nasty!" had left its mark. So instead he had happily tumescent dreams of gleaming beauty, white knee breaking the water, swelling breasts and uplifted arms. Nymph, witch, beloved . . . He never named her; she was forever She, mysterious and unending source of delight. . . .

Throughout this period, Walton took particular pride and comfort from the fact that all these bewitching creatures of his fantasy, including She, loved him without his so much as raising a finger in an effort to attract them. Even the evil sorceresses, trying their strength against his, did so as under the influence of a malevolent fate; they were driven by the furies to try to outwit him, but it was abundantly obvious that they, too, were sorely smitten with him and yearned to have him overcome them.

It was only after his adolescence had advanced, and he had destroyed the illustrated adventure book, that his bland dreams of smoothly paced love gave way to more sadistic fantasies. By the time he was thirteen he had still never so much as kissed a girl, but he had some time since transferred his dreams of desire to actual girls of his acquaintance—girls who seemed totally unaware of his existence, while they giggled and made eyes at the other boys, who seemed to him, in his secret arrogance, so many louts.

In revenge, he took to fantasies of a harem. He was absolute ruler of an extensive ménage, a luxurious sort of prison, and into a beautifully appointed cell was thrust any schoolgirl who had, that particular day, incurred his desire or anger. Little Jane Mecom, with the enchanting freckles; tall, dark, snobbish Felicia Harrington; Nancy Seasons, whose early physical opulence and easy tolerance made her the prevalent favorite with whom to wander out from a class dance— all these and others took their turns in Walton Herrick's harem-prison— and even an occasional teacher, as well.

Lying awake often until close to midnight, he would visit cell after cell, enjoying perhaps most of all the moment when he would unlock the door, step in, and turn the key again, shutting himself in with the cowering girl. He used the lash freely, with an imagination kindled to a fine heat by movies and books (it was the age of *The Sheik* and Elinor Glyn) over which no parental censorship, curiously enough, was exercised; he was brutal and vindictive, and enjoyed it. Yet the outcome was always the same. Whether in a particular case he finally flung the girl in question into a corner—used, dominated, possessed— or there was a happier ending, the result was identical: she was filled with a groveling, hysterical love for him.

At times he thought dimly that there was something wrong about this process, so alien both to the actualities of his relation with girls and the general principles which he had inherited and professed. But he could not give it up; he might resolutely swear to discontinue these dreams, especially after a particularly forbidding sermon in church, which he again regularly attended at this time with his father—but it was useless. Unbidden, even forbidden, the procession of girls, white and slender as willow wands, would rise up before him, and all his oaths of reformation were blown away like so much dust. He burned, and he found no other way to quench the flame.

BEFORE he was fourteen, Walton finally encountered in class a girl who seemed to him exotically beautiful—one who, unlike the rest, evinced an immediate interest in him. The first day they were in class together—she had just entered the school—she tucked a note into his hand at recess. "I like you," it said. "You are more mature looking than the other boys. My name is Carol Seixas. Do you want to walk home with me?"

Poor Walton was overwhelmed. He wavered between hot, feverish visions of actual adventures matching those of his imaginings, and a dread that induced panic. He could not bring himself to write an answering note and give it to her. He was so dazed that he performed badly at his studies all day. He would, with a strong effort, bring his eyes around to look slyly at her; if she, in turn, was watching him, he would drop his eyes and feel a hot color staining his face. Once she was smiling, and his discomfiture was complete: he was sure she was making fun of him for not being brave enough to write her any answer. "Mature looking!" She must think him a fool, a baby.

But, when the last class was over and Walton loitered in his seat, she came directly to him and smiled again, unmistakably not in ridicule.

"Well?" she asked.

He stumbled over the iron support of his desk, trying to get to his feet. He cleared his throat, which felt hot and dry, looked up shyly at last, and said, "Yes, I would."

Now she seemed really amused.

"It's not so terrible, you know," she said dryly. "I only asked you if you'd like to walk home with me. I live near you, on Claymore Street. I know you live on Dalton, because I asked Lucy Jordan."

The knowledge that she had boldy spoken to someone else about him completed his astonishment. But it also gave him a confidence greater than any he had ever before felt with a girl—sufficient even to enable him to offer to carry her books.

The walk home with this dark Egyptian princess was the most intoxicating experience of his thirteen years. Even the amazed look on his sister Elinor's face when she saw them left him undisturbed; he smiled at her with Olympian grandeur.

Carol talked easily all the way—about Latin and music, her favorite subjects; about the school she had been attending until her family had recently moved; about favorite movie stars. She was sophisticated; Walton had all he could do to keep from gaping. She fascinated him, and yet his predominant emotion was one of sadness.

Sadness—because he knew that when they reached Carol's house their relation would be over. Elinor would be sure to tell Marcia about seeing the two of them walking home together, and his mother would forbid him to do it again until she had investigated Carol's family. The thought of disobedience did not even occur to him; he felt hopeless about the matter, tasted already the futile rage he would know more poignantly when the edict was issued.

But at the front door to Carol's house, a modest two-family affair, she smiled and said simply, "Come on in and keep me company. Mother doesn't get home from work till six."

To fail to come directly home from school was a flagrant indiscretion; the once or twice he had done this, Marcia had barely stopped short of summoning the police. Yet the smile was too much for him. It was half a pout: Carol's full lower lip drooped even while she was smiling, and there was some shadowy, mysterious expression in her eyes that he found irresistible. He was in the house and sitting on the shabby mohair couch so soon that he felt as though he had been propelled there by an invisible force.

Carol brought grape juice; she showed him family pictures in a large ornate album, explaining about the father who had disappeared eight years before; she told him of her ambition to be either an actress or a ballerina; she admitted to being fifteen, which seemed to him an overwhelming age.

Walton was largely silent. He did shyly and awkwardly confide his own determination to be a writer, and managed to make what seemed to satisfy Carol as adequate answers to other questions. But mostly he sat there spellbound, enchanted by her smile, her chatter, the glimpses of her shapely legs as she whisked about the room, her short skirt whirling above her knees—and most of all by the way in which she would reach out and touch him (his hand, his knee, his arm) whenever she was speaking of something that excited her.

It seemed as though he had been with her only a few minutes when her mother appeared, confirming his worst fears. For Mrs. Seixas was the sort of woman he had long since learned that his mother considered common. She wore a good deal of makeup, and earrings. Her dress was tight, her skirt fashionably short. She had a somewhat brassy voice, and even her obvious kindness and cheerfulness didn't make Walton feel any better. At first look his mother would, he knew, say with scorn, "Common Jewess!" Mournfully, he took his leave and went home to face the worst.

His mother surprised him. He was met with a long, inquiring look, but her "Hello, son, you're almost late to supper" was in her most serene voice. When he mumbled, "I'm sorry," she went on, "Elinor told me that you went to a classmate's house. Is she a nice girl?"

Again the disguised look of close inquiry. Walton was not sure that this wasn't more discomfiting than the reception he had expected. Reluctantly, he looked up and directly at her.

"Yes," he said, and was surprised at the degree of confidence he gained from having answered the question.

"That's nice," said Marcia. "What is her name? Cohen?"

Her voice was dangerously quiet, but Walton felt a new courage.

"Seixas," he said flatly. "Carol Seixas."

His mother pursed her lips and frowned in innocent bewilderment.

"Say-shuss? Say-shuss? Is that Mexican?" And when he did not answer, "Well, in the future, when you plan to go to her house instead of coming directly home, please let Mother know."

The case was dismissed, leaving Walton wholly perplexed. But the way was clear, and day after day he took advantage of this fact, jubilant over the new freedom that enabled him to say, as he set out to school after breakfast, "I'm going to study with Carol this afternoon, Mother," without fear of reprisal or prohibition. Yet at the same time he felt uneasy: something was wrong; this was not the way things happened. To be sure, he eavesdropped one night and heard his mother say to his father, ". . . a decent, hard-working Jewish woman, supporting her little girl. The best way to handle this is to let it wear itself out. I have enough faith in the way I've brought up my boy not to worry about it." But he could not quite believe that matters would rest on this basis.

Meanwhile, he and Carol actually did study together on many of these afternoons. Side by side on the sofa, knees and shoulders touching, they would do their Latin, their math, their history. And since they were both bright and quick, they would finish by five o'clock and still have an hour together of desultory talk before Mrs. Seixas, wearing an amused smile, appeared and Walton would hurry home.

Increasingly, a lazy enchantment fell over this final hour. Carol was quieter than she had been at first; often they would sit in silence for ten minutes at a stretch, holding hands and staring dreamily off into secret vistas. By the third week, Walton, after hundreds of such ventures in imagination, finally kissed her. He leaned forward abruptly, awkwardly, and reached the corner of her mouth. She turned, gave him her most dazzling smile, and placed a finger where his lips had touched her.

"I was just thinking about that," she said softly, and looked candidly into his eyes. "Now give me one right here." She touched the center of her lips.

He kissed her ardently, but she pushed him away and frowned. "No," she said, "softly, like this."

It was the touch of a butterfly. Walton felt a strange and delightful itching on his lips; he reached out for her but, laughing, she was already across the room.

"That's all," she said. "It's not nice, you know." Then, thoughtfully, her sulky lip thrust out. "But it *is* nice, isn't it?"

That was all that day. Walton was easily put in his place. And he couldn't understand the swift, contradictory changes in mood in Carol during the following afternoons. Sometimes she would not only let him kiss her, but would cuddle complacently in his arms there on the sofa, her head on his shoulder, and once even let him slip his hand under her blouse and stroke the soft curve of her shoulder. But in a moment or two she might spring up, say crossly, "Stop it! What kind of a girl do you think I am?" and, putting on a phonograph record, sit down in a chair on the other side of the room and begin to sing to herself as though he were not even there.

He continued to grope his way, easily excited, easily dejected. He was sure of only one thing—that in some incomprehensible way their relation had changed. They no longer talked at length about their interests and hopes and ambitions; they either fell into long, sullen silences or chattered loudly and nonsensically, indulged in gusts of wild laughter. But while he didn't fully understand this change, he did know that it meant they were closer, on a more intimate basis than before, despite the loss of their warm, casual rapport.

Then, one unseasonably hot afternoon in late April, there came a far more decisive change.

When they entered the living room that day, Carol slammed her books down on a chair and said moodily, "I'm so hot and sticky. I'm going up and change, Walton, and have a bath. You do the math while I'm gone." Halfway up the stairs, she called back more pleasantly, "There are apples in the basket in the kitchen."

Walton dutifully began the homework in math, but after finishing two problems felt so drowsy that he dropped the book and dozed off on the couch. . . .

What wakened him he did not know, but he came back to consciousness regretfully, protestingly. The room was unbearably hot; even with his coat off and his tie loosened, he was sweating. For several minutes he lay there, listening to the shrill sounds of the younger children on the street shouting at their play and wishing he could go back to sleep. He had no precise sense of where he was.

Then, abruptly, he remembered and sat up, looking at his watch. Four-thirty! He had been there for more than an hour. And now he became conscious of silence—silence so absolute that it seemed as though it were eating into the room, actually cutting a wedge through the space around him.

For several minutes more he sat there, waiting—for what he was not quite sure—and listening. As the silence remained unbroken, he became aware of a new tenseness in him, of his quickened pulse, of a sense of unfamiliar excitement. Slowly, he rose and made his way to the stairs.

He had never been upstairs in this house, but he did not call. He climbed the stairs as slowly and as quietly as though he were on the most furtive of errands. At the top he paused and waited, holding his breath as he listened. Then, at last, he heard a faint humming sound from the last of the three doors that opened on the narrow hall, and tiptoed toward it.

Carol lay naked on the small bed in one corner of a square, rose-colored room: a frilly room in which curtains, bedspread, rugs, lampshade—everything was a rosy pink. Her black hair was gathered together and tied with a narrow blue ribbon; she was lying on her back, one leg crossed over her other knee, and she was humming softly to herself, gazing out the window. Her head rested on the palms of her hands, which were linked on the pillow.

For just a minute he stared in silence at the slim white body, the little pink-nippled breasts—stared, dizzy and unbelieving, his throat dry and constricted. Then she turned her head and looked at him sweetly, her eyes wide in what seemed to him the purest and most loving expression he had ever seen.

He knew that he uttered a strange sound, but he could not have said what it meant, or even exactly what the nature of the emotion he felt was. Then he almost hurled himself across the room and buried his face in the soft young flesh of her belly.

He didn't know how long he knelt there, his face hidden in this alien, fragrant flesh, feeling her fingers stroke his head gently, almost protectively. But it was a long time—a long time during which he did not dare to look up, did not dare to move, and slowly came to have no desire to do so, as the wild animal elation that had first filled him slackened and he felt himself given over to a peace transcending any he had ever known.

Then, at last, he felt her stir, knew, half expectant and half dreading, that she had sat up, felt her fingers lift his chin, and faced her searching eyes, suddenly so adult, so wise, that he felt he had become a little boy again.

Still searing him with this strange woman look, she took one of his hands and placed it on her breast, gravely watching him as he felt its sudden tensile strength, the straining to life of its nipple.

He was flooded with an agony of shame and excitement. This was at once more wonderful than his wildest fantasies, and humiliating —humiliating because, beyond the fact that he did not know the secret that she certainly knew, he was aware of being tried and, it seemed to him, condemned.

So sure was he of this that, when she gently pushed him away and rose, he did not try to detain her. Dully, defeatedly, he watched her, felt the ebbing of hope and desire within him, as she crossed the room and pulled a plain pink dress over her head. Then, still without a word, she came back to the bed, took his head in her lap, and began stroking it again.

After a while she stopped and stood up.

"You'll have to go now," she said softly, and there was once again in her eyes that luminous sweet look. "Don't feel bad, Walton."

But he did. Lying in bed that night, he remembered nothing of the peace and gentleness; he was consumed by a sense of failure and ignorance. He realized now that he had not been so much *condemned,* in that moment he had thought of as one of trial, as rejected for being too young, too innocent—and in the hurt to his pride his only thought of Carol was one almost of hatred. He thought of her body quite apart from her, remembered as though he had not really seen it until now the surprising soft curly black hair that he had not known would be there, made of it an obscure obscene symbol. Defined with astonishing clarity, a sentence swept into his brain: "I hate women." He repeated it to himself several times, once aloud, though quietly, and felt some satisfaction. He finally fell asleep, temporarily calmed by a sense of congenital male superiority.

In the morning he felt only self-hatred and emptiness. He avoided Carol during the day, and after school went home alone through back streets. His mother greeted his unwonted early arrival without comment. But when, just before supper, she told him of a plan to have a dancing party for Elinor and him the following week, and asked if he wanted Carol to come, he detected a peculiar anticipation in her expression. His reaction led him to say in simple defiance, "Yes," and despite her control he knew that she was disappointed. Yet later that evening, when she had finished her telephone calls to the mothers of those who were invited (Elinor had pleaded in vain, "But nobody else's mother calls the mothers"), she told him calmly and pleasantly, "Carol's mother says she will be very pleased to come."

He fell asleep wondering how Carol really felt about coming, and the next day he waited for her after school as though nothing unusual had happened between them. He caught her watching him with an occasional speculative look, but she also was silent about what had happened, and they studied together in their customary way. The only difference was in their avoiding touching each other, and even that wore off in two or three days.

The party was on a Friday night. Walton's first sense of anything ominous came when he called for Carol. She was overdressed. Not by his standards, he realized after several minutes—not, indeed, by those of anyone specific, except his mother. But her blouse was sheer, and her slip and shoulder straps showed clearly through it; her skirt was short, and her stockings were real silk. Worst of all, she was wearing lipstick. She had not been ready when he arrived, but had called out the window upstairs for him to come in and wait. When she finally appeared, he had immediately a curious sense of being divided in his loyalties. Half of him protested that she would look too sophisticated beside his sister and Ellie Clark and Jodie Reynolds. Half of him was excited as he had not been since the afternoon in her bedroom.

It seemed to him too that she stood there in the doorway waiting for something, but he was so involved in his own complicated reaction that he made no move. Then she crossed the room to where he sat and, looking down at him, said lightly, "Mother's in Toledo for two days. I'm going to be all alone tonight."

The full import of her words didn't come to him until halfway to his house. Then he reheard them, in his mind, with a shocking impact. Whatever chance there had been of his facing the evening with a fair degree of poise vanished. He was abruptly and unhappily yanked back to the very first afternoon he had spent with Carol; he was possessed of the identical feeling of hopelessness. She was going to be alone, but his mother would be counting the minutes until he returned from taking Carol home—if she permitted him to take her home. He had a sudden bold desire to run away from the whole thing, from both of them.

It was a miserable evening for Walton. He had his first formal lesson in female strategy applied to another female. His mother was scrupulously polite to Carol; she showered more attention on her than she was accustomed to accord her most distinguished adult guests. But this very politeness segregated Carol from all the other boys and girls. To Jodie Reynolds and Frank Cramer, for instance, Marcia was tonight a casual intimate, almost a conspiratorial crony. She winked at them; she spoke to them with a most uncharacteristic rough camaraderie: "You'd better go up and comb your hair, Jodie; it's all mussed up. You know the way," and "Don't look so sad, Frank. Everybody knows you hate to dance." And then, in contrast, "Walton has so much enjoyed studying with you, Carol. You've been very kind to him."

For she never left the party. And despite his miserable preoccupation with his own plight Walton could not help observing, in however blunted a way, Carol's unusual maturity and stature. If Marcia Herrick made her feel isolated and even unwanted, she gave no sign of it. She was entirely and unself-consciously herself, as Walton knew her. She wasted no time on the other girls; she flirted a little with the other boys but reserved all special favors for Walton; she was comfortably courteous, in her turn, to Marcia. And when Marcia finally put on the victrola the record of "Good Night, Ladies," at eleven-thirty, Carol said in a clear voice, addressing him across the room, "Time to get my coat, Walton. You know, the pink one."

As the other boys and girls crowded out the front door, calling good night and their thanks, Marcia intercepted Walton and Carol.

"That's an awfully dark street at night, son," she said. "I think you'd better let Frank go with you. Since he lives right next door, he's not taking anybody home."

Walton stared at her in bitterness. Carol said nothing, but placed

her hand lightly on his elbow. He felt a sudden surge of independence.
"No," he said. "I don't need Frank."

Marcia looked at him for a long minute, held his gaze with her
most imperative private command. Then she swung around.

"Frank," she called, "you won't mind walking over to Carol's
with Walton, will you? Then come back for some cake and milk."

Walton's mouth opened for a rejoinder, but Carol gave a sudden
strong pressure to his arm. He said nothing as the reluctant Frank
shambled down the steps beside them.

But at the corner, out of sight of the house, he was filled with a
fierce resolve.

"Frank," he said. "You go on home. You know how Mother is.
But go the back way; don't let her see you."

The relieved Frank disappeared; Walton and Carol walked on in
silence. They had almost reached her house before she spoke.

"That's all I meant," she said, squeezing his arm. "My gracious,
you don't want to fight about it."

A sudden reversal of feeling assailed him. To speak up for himself
had been difficult, an achievement; to have Carol imply that he and she
were allied against his mother caused him an acute pang. He felt disloyal, almost dishonorable. And with this feeling came a resentment
against Carol as strong as his reaction the night after she had sent him
home with the admonition not to "feel bad." He walked on to her house
in unhappy silence.

She opened the door and swung around, moving closer to him, so
close that her face almost touched his.

"Well, Walton," she said so softly that it was almost a whisper. "You
can come in and—stay a while, if you want to."

The images of ugliness and hatred swarmed suddenly in his mind.
Against their background, he saw his mother sitting at the window in
the darkened living room at home, and felt a rush of sentiment for her.
He summoned—did he summon them, or did they come unbidden?—a
set of arraignments against Carol. The very sentence she had just spoken,
which had seemed so provocative to him in some book he had read
secretly, meant that she was really a bad girl, one who did the vague
bad thing. His father's voice came out of nowhere: "Keep yourself
clean, son." But the need to humiliate Carol blotted out all the other
conflicting desires he felt.

"No," he blurted. "I don't want to." And he ran rapidly down the
steps. . . .

They said no more to each other thereafter than a frozen hello or two. But a month later, Bob Baker, a popular boy in his class whom Walton knew only slightly, accosted him in the hall at school one day. Scratching his head in some embarrassment, Bob said slowly, "I don't quite know what this is all about, but Carol said to tell you that all your worst suspicions were right. That's what she said, and that's all I know."

And for several years Walton returned to his former bitter, half-suspicious, half-timid removal from any connection with girls. At the same time, his harem fantasies regained their lost intensity. . . .

THEN there was Red Stewart. Walton's friendship with Red was one of those crucial relationships that turn a course hitherto so despairingly regular as to seem inevitable and unending. What Carol Seixas meant to Walton, long after and far beyond the immediate failure and consequences of their attachment, in terms of his relation to women, Red Stewart meant in the world of men. Between them, Walton came to realize, they had almost literally salvaged him from the desolate and water-logged raft of his origins—or, perhaps more accurately, from the island of fantasy on which he had cast himself away. They were to him a new breed; because they were not afraid, they felt little or no need for hatred, envy, scorn. They could love without fear of deception; they could give without calculating returns.

All this, of course, filtered very slowly through Walton's consciousness. When he and Carol broke up, he thought as badly of her as her message through Bob Baker implied that he did and should. And even when he came to a more just appreciation of her, and of what she had done for him, he was not sure that she really approximated this *free* kind of person: there remained an ambiguity to the quality and motivation of her relation to him.

On the other hand, insofar as he knew him, Red Stewart was this sort of person. Yet, after the single year of his friendship with Red, and despite his superficial gratitude, Walton was left with a sense of superiority to Red, who was, he reasoned, his inferior in brains, looks and background. It was only with the slow attrition between himself and the world of external reality that Walton came to understand the essential decency of these two friends and to estimate more accurately Red's stature.

By the time he was twelve, Walton had learned to play basketball with fair success, baseball and football with less, but some. In each case, he played with fanatic intensity. In basketball, he became a better than average shot through practicing alone in his own back yard, hour after hour. Yet even with his growing ability, he was not really accepted by most of the other boys. And in baseball, where the ball was so hard; in football, with its more decisive and brutally direct bodily contact— he was still timid. Playing on his street football team when he was eleven (he had hidden his football gear in the back yard so that he could leave the house without incurring his mother's suspicion), he dreaded seeing the opposing ball carrier coming his way. Yet he continued to show up for the games, and his pride so far exceeded his fear that in at least one game he made several excellent tackles, drawing praise from his idol, fifteen-year-old Tim Collins.

But, despite all this advancement, he had no real confidence in his own physical prowess and, being slow-footed and not very well co-ordinated, he was a barely mediocre athlete. Moreover, he still felt shy and uncomfortable with boys his own age; he saw in every hostile eye a potential recurrence of his early recess days, heard in every jeering voice taunts and slurs directed at himself. Fist fights frightened him beyond anything else; there was something terrible and primitive in another, even smaller, boy advancing toward him with fists doubled.

Add to this state of mind the conviction born of his mother's warn-ings and his first school experiences—that every stranger was inimical— and you had an approximation, Walton thought, of reasons for his feel-ing of panic when he was told, at fourteen (the year after the incidents centering around Carol), that his mother's health required a winter in a drier climate and a higher altitude, and that he and his sister were to go with her to a small town in the western part of New York State, where they would attend the local high school. True, he had never been happy at his present school, but he preferred familiar woes to imagined ones.

The first several weeks at the new school, located in the outskirts of this little New York State town, were a pleasant surprise. Both boys and girls seemed simpler, kinder, less sharp to detect aberrations and vulnerabilities than the city ones to whom he was accustomed. When he was promptly admitted to membership in the Hi-Y Club, which in Cleveland he associated only with the popular leaders of his school, he began to believe that he had been transported to a wholly different social order; for the first time in some years, he awoke each morning looking forward to the day ahead.

But this new state of happiness lasted less than three weeks. One morning, a big boy who lived on a farm four or five miles from town (many of the students were farmers' children, and the boys came to school wearing hipboots smelling of manure) slouched over to him during recess.

"I challenge you," he said.

Walton felt no reaction beyond a vague uneasiness: he did not understand the words. But as this boy, Carl Barbour, continued to stand there in silence, grinning knowingly down at him, he began to hear a familiar sound inside himself. It was fear knocking.

"What do you mean?" he asked finally, in the flat, neutral, tinny voice of dread.

Carl Barbour lounged comfortably against the wall.

"You belong to the Hi-Y, don't you?" he demanded lazily.

Walton nodded, his mouth too dry to answer. Besides, he didn't want to hear that voice again—the voice that spoke for him without his permission, even against his orders.

"Well, we have fights—boxing—every week before meetings. Three-round bouts." His voice suddenly lost its laconic drawling quality, became harsh. "I challenge you."

He said "yuh." He actually said, "I challunge yuh," which somehow added to Walton's conviction that the bells of doomsday were ringing.

"Well?" demanded Carl, thrusting his face forward, close to Walton's. Later in the year, when they were friendly, if not actually friends, Walton realized that it was a pleasant enough face, even a rather attractive one. But at that moment it seemed to him tough and threatening. "Well?" repeated Carl. "How about it, you—a week from Wednesday?"

"O.K.," said Walton in a leaden voice, no longer even attempting to conceal his fear.

"I'll beat the tar out of you" was Carl's concluding comment.

The day passed in dreary, subdued anguish. At such times, when the dreaded fear was a certainty, Walton experienced no sharp emotion. But between him and others, even objects, there hung a thin gray veil that exterminated brightness, reduced the color in everything to a dead somberness. He knew that a week from Wednesday he would be torn to shreds. But there was nothing to be done about it; these were the relentless approaching steps of doom.

As he left the school building that afternoon, he was so saturated in hopelessness that he only turned indifferently when someone slapped him on the back.

It was Red Stewart, whose lean, freckled face was grinning.

"I heard Barbour talking to you," said Red. "You going to fight him?"

"Yes," said Walton listlessly.

Red's shrewd but kindly eyes appraised him.

"You know how to box?" he asked.

Walton shook his head, confident of the contempt to follow, but not really caring. He stared at the ground.

"Want to learn?"

The voice was warm, friendly, even somehow eager. It was that as much as the unlikely words that made Walton so slow to understand. But he listened for some refutation of what had been said, and, since there was none, finally looked up again, and directly at Red.

That was the moment, not what followed. That was the moment that came back to him, one steely November dusk long years later, as he dropped his rake and stared into the smoldering, smoky fire under the maples in his yard in Connecticut. For the level blue eyes were saying, simply and unmistakably: "I mean it; I'll teach you." It was, he supposed, a kind of tenderness no less central than that in Carol's eyes when she had held his forlorn head and stroked it. But it was also easier, somehow, to accept from Red than it had been from her—perhaps because he had already experienced it from her. At any rate, what was decisive was that Red Stewart, football quarterback, baseball and basketball star, class president, was offering to teach him—and offering with no contempt manifest in either his eyes or his voice.

Shame dropped from Walton almost physically. He felt, to be sure, a residue of suspiciousness; he felt more than a little shyness. But he found himself abruptly, incredulously, able to smile and look Red firmly in the eye.

"O.K.," he said.

"Come on, then, fellah," said Red. "There's no football practice today, and we've got almost two hours before I got to cover my paper route. Carl said a week from Wednesday, didn't he? That don't give us too much time."

Up in Red's dusty attic, clumsily drawing on the gloves under the bare rafters, Walton felt a heightened suspicion. Was this a new, delayed form of torture—a refined version of the bullying to which he was accustomed? But this new fear was almost immediately dispelled by the businesslike briskness of Red's tone.

"The first thing you gotta learn," he said, "is that you use your left hand—you're right-handed, ain't you?—out here in front, see, to protect yourself. You keep jabbing with it this way, see, and you hold your right back to punch with. And all the time you're jabbing and leading and feinting, you're protecting yourself, too. You catch everything the other guy throws at you with this left fist and arm. Get it?"

Walton got it, in more respects than one. Somehow, in some miraculous way, Red found time every day, for the next nine days, to save out an hour or an hour and a half for him. Sometimes it was before school in the mornings, sometimes after, even once or twice in the evening. But, whenever it was, Walton said yes and came. Marcia stormed at him, pleaded with him, wept over the bruise on his cheek, forbade him to go back, threatened to call Mr. Barnes, the school principal, promised to get Mr. Barnes to let him out of the bout with Carl Barbour. In vain. Walton said doggedly, "I'm going. Red's teaching me how to take care of myself. I'm going, Mother."

Red barked at him, roughed him up, hit him hard, jolted him, knocked him down once or twice, then cursed him out for letting his guard down. But Red also praised him, picked him up, dusted him off, slung an arm around his shoulders, said, grinning, "Attaboy, Walt."

Walton would control his pride, his downright happiness, each time until he left Red's house. Then, his new bruises stinging in the sharp October air, he would want to dance, to skip and shout and sing. And the times when they had had an evening session he did: he gave open expression to the joy and hope that filled him. He didn't care what the few passersby might think of him, capering grotesquely along the sidewalk and singing loudly off key.

Red's final gift was presented with his characteristic offhandedness. After their last practice, the afternoon before the match, he drew off his gloves, slapped Walton on the bottom, and said, "I'll be in your corner tomorrow night, kid. That way I can keep an eye on Barbour, size him up, and tell you what you're doing wrong. You'll beat him. He ain't got much, the big old hulk, but this way we'll play it safe."

That was the second important moment. The words "You'll beat him," spoken with such easy confidence, rang triumphantly in Walton's ears all the way home. He realized that the daring concept of victory had never crossed his mind, or—if it had—that he had sternly dismissed it at inception. What, he asked himself now in astonishment, had he been learning for? To take care of himself, he had told his mother. And that was true, of course: crucially true. It went well beyond boxing Carl Barbour. Yet that was the immediate objective and, realizing that he had not *dared* to consider the possibility of winning, he understood for the first time how savagely low and hopeless an estimate of himself, under the mask of his false egotism, he had really entertained.

It was too sudden, too new a possibility—that of actually winning over Carl Barbour—for him to conceive of effecting it, alone and unaided. But he was not alone—and with Red, he felt sure, he could do anything.

That was the second moment; the third, of course, was the fight itself. Red's low, calm voice in his ear, Red's strong hands on his shoulders kept the nervousness engendered by the bare glaring light, the pushing bodies of the other boys crowded around the ring, and the shouts and yells (among them, "Kill the city dude, Carl") from being unbearable. Walton entered the first of three rounds a little dazed but clearheaded enough to approximate what Red had told him to do.

It was a slow round, with some booing from the spectators. Neither boy was quick on his feet; neither was aggressive in taking the initiative. Walton took one solid punch from Carl on the side of his head, discovered that Carl did not hit so hard as Red. He landed two himself— one on Carl's cheek, a more solid blow to the stomach. With this second one, Carl gave ground, and Walton felt a strange current of triumph and vindictiveness throb through him.

But Red was not satisfied. Fanning him, rubbing his face with a wet towel, he kept repeating a few words.

"You got him. But keep it low. Hit him in the breadbasket. His guard's too high. You can double him up. Right in the breadbasket, but above the belt. Then he'll drop his hands, and you'll have him. Hit him in the stomach. Now go and get him."

Walton did. He rushed from his corner and landed two quick blows just below Carl's chest. Retreating, Carl lowered his guard to protect his stomach, and Walton, driving in, landed one right on his jaw. Carl tottered, somehow tripped over his own feet and fell.

Mr. Barnes, acting as referee, began to count: "One . . . two . . . three . . . four . . ." At "six," grunting and puffing, Carl was back on his feet.

But it was now his face that showed fear; his eyes were narrowed, his expression strained. He staggered out of Walton's reach as much as he could and, since his arms were longer, this was most of the time. Walton kept rushing him; Carl kept holding him off.

Between rounds, Red changed his advice.

"You're too excited. You're leaving yourself wide open for a haymaker. It's your fight; don't lose your head. Keep after him, O.K., but do it coolly, carefully. With that knockdown, you've got him on points already, kid. Just don't get careless."

And again Walton followed orders. In the final round, he didn't land any particularly hard blow, but he was hitting Carl, and Carl was missing him. There was no question about the verdict.

And there was no question about its momentousness to Walton. Throughout the meeting that followed, he sat there, outwardly as calm as he could make himself appear, inwardly seething with a wild, exultant joy. The other boys had cheered; they had come over to him as he was dressing and said, "Good fight, Walt" and "That's showing him, Herrick" and "Nice going, Walt." He was drenched in a perspiration of excitement, and even though he could see his hands resting motionless on his knees he could feel them trembling. He was so afraid that he would betray the way he felt and somehow thereby lose face that he stared out of the black window as steadily as he could. But not so consistently but that, finally turning his head, he caught Red winking at him.

The rest of the year was the happiest so far in his life. There was no single other occasion so exciting, so exhilarating, as that of the fight, but the momentum derived from it was not lost. Walton made the second basketball team; with many of the older boys and best ball players needed in the fields by their fathers for spring planting, he made the first baseball team, playing right field. The very first ball hit in his first game by the team's first opponents of the season came directly to him—an easy fly which he ingloriously muffed. He was still inclined to be shy at the plate, and didn't make his first hit until his fourth game. In the sixth game, he broke a finger and played no more thereafter until the final game, in which, finger in splints, he played a single inning to win his letter.

A mediocre record—yet to him the most glorious achievement of his life. He returned to Cleveland and his old school the following fall and while, in this vast urban high school, he had no slightest chance of making a varsity athletic team, he did square his most important accounts. In the second week, when one of his chief tormentors of the past, coming upon him in the hall, pulled his necktie out of his coat, Walton promptly hit him hard, on the jaw. The consequent commotion and especially the glory of being escorted to the principal's office for a severe reprimand, the first such distinction he had ever won, earned him, not a prominent or renowned place in the hierarchy of the school community, but at least a place. His last two years of high school were relatively peaceful; he suffered no more persecution.

To be sure, this sequence of events did not mean that Walton became popular, was recognized as "a regular guy," or even followed what could be considered a normal boy's course during these years.

Red Stewart's generosity could and did give him a chance to end the most drastic, immediate part of his misery; it could not probe and cleanse the deeper wounds.

Yet Walton did not realize this. The laying of the phantom of terror that had so long haunted his trips to and from school, stalked the corridor and playground, and sat, grinning obscenely, at the steps he climbed to attend (protesting) a party at a schoolmate's house—the laying of such a ghost inevitably meant a great shift in his orientation. It pushed out of sight for the most part that despised image of himself as a weakling; it gave far freer outward play to that expansive self, long confined to reveries and fantasy, that believed in his heroic image. He even ventured, with some success, into school dramatics and social events.

Despite these changes, however, he was still lonely—lonely, he realized much later, almost without knowing it. For it was a long time before he was able to recognize with any full emotional perception the inordinate demands he made privately and internally on other people —the appreciation, love and even homage that he secretly, with unconscious arrogance, expected *as his due.* What it amounted to, he ultimately understood, was that he took it for granted that others should see him as he was inclined to see himself. The great lover and the daring adventurer, the conqueror of She and innumerable lesser females and the victorious warrior were becoming real again. And while he was at least maturing to the extent of confining his exploits (for the most part) to activities that recognizably existed in the world of external reality, what he did was still colored luridly by his fantastic imagination. He spent far less time in daydreams, but when he took a girl to a dance he carried an invisible lance or six-shooter; when he performed on the stage, he was an intimate and peer of Rudolph Valentino. And after seeing Greta Garbo and John Gilbert on the screen it would be hours before he was content to accept the fact that he was Walton Herrick, high school student—before he could shake off his intense participation in diplomatic intrigues and his passionate identification with the dark, gay, handsome hero of gunplay and boudoir.

Moreover, the power of his secret world was still so great, its emphasis upon perfection so integral to his private thoughts, and the habit of seeking its realization only in imagination so ingrained—that whatever in outward reality seemed most consonant with his dreams he felt constrained to assign to them. So he preferred, in his last year in high school, not even to make the most casual acquaintance of the only girl since Carol to engage his full attention, approval and even adoration. He dreamed, half hiding it from himself, of Nora Hamilton of the dark hair, the creamy skin, the large black haunting eyes and the upturned nose, without even speaking when he passed her in the hall or sat two desks from her in the classroom. Without reasoning about it, he had no desire to experience again how importunate and alien, how self-dividing and frightening the dream made flesh could become. Lending his physical presence only, then, to the life around him, he reserved for his inner vision the ultimate values of perfect beauty.

And indeed easy associations of any sort with his contemporaries were blocked by his grandiose notions of himself and his role. He could not endure even warmhearted teasing or laughter at his expense; his lordly concept of self left little room for a sense of humor. He took it for granted that the other person should come three-quarters of the way if there was to be any close alliance between them.

Moreoever, he was fastidious to an extreme: blood and excrement and dirt had long revolted him disproportionately; coarseness, dirtiness and sloppiness of person, of taste and of mind disturbed him almost as much. He vacillated, therefore, between moods of austerity, almost of asceticism, and ones (however unfulfilled) of hedonistic sensualism. And as the former required no cooperation from others to become effective, and the latter not only a very active cooperation from at least one other but considerably more daring and defiance of home-imposed inhibitions than he could manage—he settled grumpily for austerity, which took on frequently a puritanical censorious quality toward others' gaiety and lightheartedness.

Underneath this tendency, of course, was an unacknowledged envy and a resentment that those others, by refusing to come more than halfway toward him, had excluded him. "I'll show them," a voice within him repeated, but he did not really hear it. He would gaze in the mirror after dressing in his best suit with the then fashionable bell-bottom trousers and his red polka-dot tie, and lacquering his hair with Stacomb till it glistened stickily—he would gaze in the mirror with eyes narrowing, completely unaware of his imitation of Marcia standing up to the world in the mirror despite the disintegration of the Nicholsons. And he would not hear the inner voice.

The voice had become too habitual for him to hear it. The phrase "I'll show them" had begun to be his way of keeping himself from utter impotent frustration when he was only five or six; when his mother would ask, "What *are* you whispering to yourself?" he would not reply—but then he would hear the words. What he meant by *them* then, and for a long time after, was that he would "show" everybody when he grew up. The promise of adulthood loomed in the remote distance like the tower crowning an impregnable fortress. Once he got *there,* he'd show them. He was clear enough on the general subject: despite his emotional heat and—over the years of childhood—his growing vindictiveness, he understood why. Adults did not demand the same kinds of achievements, were not interested in the same abilities and attitudes as children; they respected rather talents and accomplishments that he felt intuitively confident he possessed. He was not, of course, nearly so clear on the particulars—but once that drawbridge into the adult world had been lowered, and he had crossed it, then . . .

And so he went to college at sixteen, still lonely and proud and tormented; equally convinced of his superiority and of the un-likelihood of others recognizing it; excited over the fact that this departure promised the imminence of longed-for adulthood, yet close to terrified over going so far from home and—for the first time in his life—going alone.

The college was Amherst. Cornelius Herrick had been an Amherst graduate of the class of 1856. Lloyd Herrick had sojourned there briefly; it had been the scene of the first of his five attempts to secure an A.B. degree. William Herrick had, of course, stayed home and attended Western Reserve. There was, then, a family tradition, but not a very strongly established one.

The tradition was, in fact, just strong enough to give rise to cautious, vague discussions between Walton's father and mother during his last year at high school. What brought the issue into much sharper focus, made the whole possibility suddenly seem real to Walton, was the presence and the interest of a young man in his late twenties—Charles Hatfield, Amherst '17.

Tall, thin, conservatively blond and possessed of impeccably con-servative tastes and ideals, Charles Hatfield became an habitué of the William Herrick home, appearing punctually in the family pew by invitation every Sunday morning at ten-thirty, accompanying the family home on its long streetcar ride and having Sunday dinner with them.

He had, shortly after being transferred from the Pittsburgh to the Cleveland branch office of the Crosley-Alexander Paint Company, pre-sented his credentials to William Herrick. He was the impecunious scion of a regal Main Line family of Philadelphia, and his father had known Cornelius Herrick well during the latter's days as secretary to the Board of Missions. But while the acquaintance was established through William the relationship was between Charles Hatfield and Marcia.

In the first place, he was as nice a young man, in the terms of Marcia's lexicon of life, as one was likely to meet in 1923. In some mysterious way, although he had technically participated in both, college and war alike had glided past him like ships in a heavy fog— great ominous hulks visible suddenly, looming up like monstrous apparitions, transfixing him where he stood for a moment, and sliding past, gone as though they had never been, except for the melancholy hoarse blast of their whistles, echoing, hovering on the air.

Charles had not listened. He had resolutely closed his ears to all sounds that would distract him from the voices of his forefathers. Their admonitions, a godly catalogue of "Do thous" and "Thou shalt nots," were written on his soul. Venal and venial sins alike he resisted by walking grimly forward in a straight line. He did not know that he was grim; he did know that he was right. He did not drink, he did not smoke, he did not say "damn"; he was, Walton became convinced when he thought of it years later, a virgin. But far beyond these trivial mundane matters he never entertained any perceptible rebelliousness or doubt about the necessity and sufficiency of his course.

Of course he must have. In maturity Walton was astonished at his own naïveté, which had enabled him to believe that Charles had never wavered, never suffered temptation, never cried out aloud in the darkness over the void in his life. Astonished—until he realized that the reason for his earlier conviction about Charles was understandably enough grounded: for the fact was that Charles himself had no idea of the degree of his cruel repression of himself; he did not doubt or rebel consciously—save against fate and the immoral laxity of others, which meant that one who lived virtuously had no kin upon the earth. The shining princess who would look surprisingly like one of the prettiest girls he knew and acknowledge fealty to his own, Charles's, principles, never appeared; the friends who were at once jolly—for cheerfulness and wholesome fun were among his ideals—and *good* were all too few.

And so he fell, curiously, under the spell of Marcia Herrick—no, Marcia Nicholson. For it was not the prematurely gray though still striking-looking middle-aged woman, embittered, lonely, tyrannical and entertaining a growing hypochondria, who discreetly enchanted him— but the latent and now revived idealistic young woman of the Stamford days: intolerant of ugliness and compromise, versed in the ways of righteousness, yet with an added poetic flair, and allegiance to beauty as well as to goodness which, for Charles, spiced virtue just sufficiently, gave it a *decent* romantic tinge.

It was Marcia's Indian summer, and she thrived in it. During these years, her color was better; she ate more; she laughed unconscionably more. It was a romance without blood—or, perhaps rather, with only a little tingle of blood to it. William did not mind, except when he was tired. Then the perpetual presence of what he quite accurately found to be a dull young man might irritate him. But irritability was not his forte; irritation meant that he would shrug his shoulders and retire to his room or—if that was impossible without incurring Marcia's articulate anger—simply into polite silence and a state, peculiarly his, of suspended participation—a state that gave enough of his attention to the activity around him not to be actual daydreaming, and yet permitted him to detach a part of himself to wander in other pastures.

So William tolerated Charles; Marcia nourished him with a spiritual flirtation; and Elinor, now in her late teens, incited him to dreams of marriage. Actually, Walton could see much later, Charles was dreaming of marrying the mother-in-the-daughter, although Elinor had little enough of Marcia in her: physically, emotionally, in every way, she was a Herrick. Yet she was reasonably attractive, necessarily flattered by the attentions of an *older man* like Charles, and innocently willing, a good deal of the time, to be the ostensible focal point of the whole relationship.

As for Walton, at this time he revered Charles. His own mounting interest in sports, particularly in baseball, meant that when a grown-up man, coming to visit his family, always found time for a half hour of playing catch or hitting fungos, that man's place in Walton's hierarchy was secure.

There came a time, long years later, at an awkward meeting between Charles and Walton after five years of not seeing each other, when Walton understood how important a part Charles had played in his life—how he had become an admonitory symbol, a desolate reminder of the desert wastes of a life of self-denial. On this occasion, as they stood before the restaurant at which they had eaten, Walton experienced a sudden moment of illumination in which he recognized the face and the head before him, despite the unlined, bland pouchiness, the thinning blond hair, as those of a prep school boy: a middle-aged prep school boy with cloudy eyes and a defensive way of holding his head.

Yet it was this very immaturity, of course, that had made Charles so agreeable to playing ball with a fifteen-year-old boy back in 1923.

For he had not played as an older man—a father or an uncle—might, but with an enthusiasm and a tendency, even, to exhibitionism, that was more appropriate to an adolescent.

At any rate, Charles was at this time of equal importance to Walton and to Marcia, and it was the weight of his opinion that was decisive in Walton's going to Amherst. William's doubt of the wisdom of this course grew into an impotent fury. Elinor was going to Reserve; why wasn't it good enough for Walton? The costs involved were prohibitively high; Walton, only sixteen, was too young to go so far away at an impressionable and vulnerable point in his development.

In vain. And when William finally flared up into a rare towering anger and shouted, "The whole thing is ridiculous. That insipid young fool has bewitched you," Marcia set her lips and determined to use the money willed to her by Cornelius Herrick, and long cherished in a savings account, for Walton's education.

So it was that, on a prematurely cold night in September, 1924, Walton stood in the back yard of his home, frantically and surreptitiously rubbing dirt over the pebbled surface of his brand-new yellow pigskin satchel, as though by this action he might exorcise his fears and propitiate the gods who governed college affairs.

1953

JOURNAL: *6*

from the journal of Walton Herrick . . .

July 20, 1953

My confidence of two days ago was ludicrous. Yesterday I awoke deeply depressed; all day long, with the weather flawless—not a wisp of cloud to be seen—I wandered around like some tormented vagrant. Hell must be full of displaced persons. I made up my mind to go to the beach, but even while hunting for the car key thought of how crowded it was sure to be on a Sunday, and decided not to go. I began my long-postponed mowing of the lawn, and in fifteen minutes ran out of gasoline, cursed, and gave up. I thought of calling up Dud Foote; then, with my hand on the telephone, knew I didn't want to see him. I decided that a nap would refresh me, only to squirm and twist on the bed, wide awake, for three-quarters of an hour. I tried the newspaper, a book or two: they bored me. When I went to my desk to attempt a start on the report due next week, I sat there, staring blankly at the typewriter, accomplishing nothing.

And all the time I was aware of the evanescence of that fresh, serene blue day. It was passing; it would never return; and I was spending it fuming in petulant, indecisive irritability, unable to persevere at anything for more than a few minutes, incapable of giving myself wholly to any activity. I was filled with self-loathing.

That was it—though I was unable to understand it until now. I suffered from a pernicious attack of self-hatred, brought on by my previous day of illumination, by all the discoveries about myself set down in this journal the day before—*and by what I left out.* The encrusted habits of thought of half a lifetime were too much for me. There in black and white was the open admission that I was riddled with shameful faults and weaknesses: I was dishonest, cowardly, falsely proud, so raw to the touch that I could not bear to feel even a friendly hand. Worse, and paradoxically, I was wholly dependent upon others for the direction of my life; like some animated toy, I could not act unless I was wound up. Self-confessed, self-accused, self-prosecuted, then, I was condemned to wander alone, shut out from all the warmth and life.

And so, when I had an utterly unexpected, astonishing long-distance telephone call from Julie, I was cold, remote, finally angry. When she asked me what I was doing, I asked why she cared. She was not easily discouraged; apparently she had called on the strength of a really warm, generous impulse, and she was not to be dismayed by my frigid monosyllables. But finally I wore her down; a strain came into her voice; then we were silent. At last she hesitantly reminded me of the bi-weekly check, and I burst out savagely, "That's *one* thing I'm good for, isn't it? Is that why you called up?" There was a long, awful silence and then she hung up.

An hour later, I was on my way to New York and Sonia. . . .

But tonight I am back home. I stayed with Sonia after work until close to nine o'clock today and then suddenly I knew I *must* go home. She said all right, with no apparent bad feeling. I caught the nine-o'clock train.

And here I am—at eleven. I see plainly that on Saturday I had really come to grips with a good deal in myself. But the power of that very bogus self I had been writing about reasserted itself in reaction, and by the time Julie telephoned I was so deeply saturated again in self-accusations over my failure to be this and that that I attributed everything I had been thinking about myself to Julie, and struck back at these imaginary hurts *she* had inflicted on me—on the phone and in going to New York.

Is it that I cannot bear the realization that I am so cruel to myself (I think now of the black clown and the white one) and therefore must assign the cruelty to someone else? Do I also, then, by some kind of rationalizing hocus-pocus, feel free to claim that the charges are not just, and so lift from myself the heavy weight of self-contempt?

I see a new aspect of my dependence on others for the discovery of meaning and direction, a *new use for them: they* can be blamed, when the internal fires burn too hotly in me—since they are responsible, in their "failure" to appreciate me.

And this, in turn, leads me to a better understanding of my rages: my rages—and my sadism. For if the latter is largely confined to fantasies—and to thin, subtilized manifestations in my overt life, it is still there. Does one always strike out in wrath and cruelty because one's pride—one's false pride—has been hurt or ridiculed, however unintentionally, and does this hurt occur only when others refuse to acknowledge one's claims on them to see one as one would be seen? Probably not always—but surely often. And in any case, such rage must have its deep origin in this sort of pride, this pride of Lucifer that will brook no realistic appraisal. If I hate myself for shaming my pride, I may strike out; if I hate others for hurting this same pride, I surely will.

I have had many times the fantasy of striking someone on the street. Often it has taken the form of walking along, brooding half consciously to myself over some slight, and suddenly, seeing a figure just ahead of me, having an almost irresistible urge to lift my fist and bring it down savagely on his unprotected head. Occasionally, it seems to me that I have just completed the act, and I enjoy to the full the impact, the shock of which has traveled the length of my arm. Surely the span between the criminal blow and this imagined one of mine is no more than the length of a man's arm. . . .

I feel now a great deal more sympathy for old Jas. H. than I ever have before: when, as the Great Avenger, he built his "masterful" cases against those hapless offenders, who was the criminal he really pursued with such vindictiveness? When he watched at the window, and then accused and indicted the young minister, what secret claim on Emmy Burgess, what swollen dreams of his own, had been violated? To what mountainous heights had that black, stony hatred of his risen, what torments had he undergone in the defeat of his plumed pride—so that Patience Nicholson could no longer suffice to draw off his pent-up fury?

This thought about Jas. H. and Emmy leads me inevitably to the relation of pride and rage to sex. Emmy and the Elders . . . When I think back to the fantasies of puberty, I remember that they were in the main of two sorts. There were, first, those in which I was Walton the Well-Beloved. I had only to wait—and not long—before throngs of beautiful women would come to me, pleading for my favor. This particular narcissistic image seems to me now only the sexual application of my general one—and as shakily established in this respect as in others. Let them come to me as they have in my fantasies, was my thought: it is my due.

Startlingly enough, a great many have—in real life. I am inclined to think that there must be some psycho-chemical afflatus involved—that for a certain kind of woman (Sonia is one), this sort of arrogant indolence, this savage passiveness (for I am sure that the expression of my eyes must convey the nature and direction of my desires as clearly as honest overt action), has an almost hypnotic attraction. And therefore there was some basis in fact as well as in fantasy when I blurted out an angry (it was clear to me later that there was absolutely no cause for anger except hurt pride) retort during a cocktail conversation a good many years ago.

Another man present, a large, bearlike portrait painter with a black spade beard, had told, his eyes rolling in a parody of lasciviousness, how, on Fifth Avenue one day, he had bumped into a famous movie actress, the symbol of sex appeal to all America, and put his arms around her to keep her from falling. Wholly unaware of the trap into which I was leading myself, and eager to take my place in the center of this performance, I related in my turn a similar experience, with an almost equally famous actress.

"And what did you do?" he asked gaily—but with, it seemed to me, that glazed look that I associate with men who are so satisfied with their virile good looks that they attain a kind of numb satiety that most of us know only after Thanksgiving dinner.

"Nothing," I suddenly admitted in crestfallen honesty. "I was in more danger of falling than she was."

He roared with herculean laughter.

"Then you should have grabbed her to keep yourself from falling. What a lack of ingenuity—to have the chance of hugging her, and instead just fall down by yourself."

Whether it was the introduction of the word "lack" or the ridicule attendant on the picture of falling down by myself I don't know—but rage flooded me. I know now, of course, that he was simply carrying on the tone of the conversation, however unconsciously or indirectly pointing up the contrast between us, but at that moment I felt unbearably humiliated.

"I don't attack women," I said icily. "I let them come to me."

I kept hearing for more than a year the hoots of derision that followed. It was all I could do not to leave the room and go home. I am sure in fact that the only reason I stayed on, literally sweating out the evening, was that I knew all too well the stinging contempt that Lydia, to whom I was then married, would express on her return home.

Yet there were in that room two women, as well as I can remember, who *had* come to me. I had undoubtedly, in the passive way I've described, invited them, but not directly in the traditional masculine way— and perhaps even in terms of suggestive looks they had taken the initiative.

I want to pause here, before going on to the second sort of sexual fantasy I set out to describe. For the words "the traditional masculine way" have brought back to me a conviction that has continued to grow on me throughout my life—a conviction about the sexuality of American men in our time.

I have spoken in another context about that "many-headed regent": others. I was referring to specific others whom I have encountered, and who influenced me, "directed" me. But there is, of course, a collective "others" as well—the huge anonymous Society in which one lives and which makes its gigantic impact on one daily, without one's actually knowing that this is happening, except in a vague and diffused way.

Masculinity—or masculine sexuality—in America, and perhaps even more in England, has been caught in a rip tide. On the one hand, we are all subjected throughout our lives to an incessant exhortation, explicit and implicit, to rugged virility, to initiative, to leadership, to driving competitiveness. The awards are to the aggressive, and the awards are success, prestige, wealth and the adoration of fair women. So runs the legend, and I see daily on the commuters' train, in the office, in restaurants and at dinner parties sheeplike hordes of middle-aged boys trying desperately to live up to this strenuous, if addle-pated, ideal.

But the other half of the pincer movement that holds American men, kicking and squealing silently, in its jaws, is the historical conjunction of this advertising campaign for obvious masculinity and the rise and middle age of feminism. I say "middle age," for it seems clear that the pure original drive of dedicated feminists to win equal rights—at work, at home and on the adult playgrounds of the country—has won its case and subsided. What is left, I think, is a settled condition (one of some sort always follows such a drive) in which many women, having found that there was not so much satisfaction in holding down jobs traditionally those of men as they had anticipated, have turned their now muscularly developed sense of administration to the home, thereby instituting a new, if not startlingly original, sort of matriarchy.

The subsequent irony lies in the fact that there are now alive at least two or three generations of boys and men who, while under constant pressure to emulate the most robust male ideal, have been or are being raised in households in which the mother image is dominant and un-challenged. The husband-father may be a lion in Wall Street or the Loop or Madison Avenue, in downtown Cleveland and San Francisco and At-lanta; at home he is usually a tame tabby. I paused just now to count on my fingers the number of couples Julie and I know well in which the man is the stronger, the more influential family figure; of twenty-six, I found only three—and in one of these the decision would probably be a draw.

I am writing about the section of our society I know best, of course —the vast middle class. Small wonder that the incidence of homosexuality, active and latent, grows at such a pace. Torn between the semiimpossible popular masculinity that they feel they *should* attain, and the active challenge of our vigorous and largely discontented women, American men, still literally sucking one thumb and holding with the other sticky hand to Mother's skirt, do well on the whole if they earn a good living and the respect of their colleagues, and maintain a certain passive and uninfluential dignity at home. Their weaker brothers, scared and wary-eyed, play at being men together at gin rummy, poker and baseball games; aided by the dichotomy of suburban commuting life, they enjoy fleeting and often not very satisfying sexual adventures with other women, affording themselves an easy masculinity because there is not sufficient intimacy to disclose their fears; or they declare bankruptcy and retire to the tawdry dead end of homosexuality—a dead end because the impulse that leads down this narrow, littered lane is a female principle: each wants to play the traditional woman's part of giving gratification.

There are of course minority variants on this general theme. A number of the intellectuals I know are tepidly married—so tepidly that one wonders if their offspring are test tube babies—yet in some of these circles only the men gather in the evening: I have no idea what their wives do. And when the evening is devoted to heterosexuality, there is one group of men and one of women—and, if there is any choice to be made, I should say that the husbands seem to be having more of a gossip club, a hen party, than the wives.

In justice, let me add that I am not blaming the women, who certainly enjoy the situation even less than the men. We are all—and none of us—to blame. And for the purposes of this journal, I have of course oversimplified. But I believe that in the main I am right, and that whereas once—no longer ago than the time of my grandfathers—the preponderant family picture was that of the wife and mother in apron, working valiantly and crucially in the making of a home and the honorable raising of children, while acknowledging the priority of Father as a sort of tutelary deity, it has now become one of the husband and father, in his shirt sleeves, working, whether in tension and loneliness or in happy fulfillment, to provide ample material means for his family, while tacitly admitting, whether in a placating or sullen way, the precedence of Mother as a sort of general manager, even Big Boss, of the family.

This was true of my father and mother, and has deeply affected my life, my character and my marriages. I do not know why I was never driven into homosexuality, beyond the fact that I have always, with tenacity, managed to keep a precarious balance in all sorts of ways, despite the tremendous odds against me. (There—good: I have said something favorable about myself.) I do know that although I have often and deeply doubted my manhood—both the absurd prevalent popular sort and a more realistic kind—I have never felt any conscious pull toward homosexuality. I am sure that I—and all men—have known some sort of impulse of this kind, sublimated in friendships, but it has never been sufficiently strong to worry me.

(I have just reread these pages and their large generalizations. "What about the Greeks?" I can hear someone asking. "The Arabs?" Well, I can't pretend to have covered the subject, and I don't know much about the Arabs, though I do, of course, understand the context of the alleged question.

(But the Greeks? With rare exceptions, even now, *men* write history. And what of Xanthippe? What of the plays of Aristophanes? Or take the ideal of the Roman matron and juxtapose her with the general state of things from Caligula on. If I've oversimplified, at least I feel confident there is much truth in what I've written. Yet at this point I find myself smiling. Am I really still writing for myself?)

My God, man, how can you write like this when you're in the middle of what you are? I don't know, I don't know—but I can. And I'm remembering that two of my three wives and most of the women with whom I have formed passing or longer sexual attachments have been physically small. I also understand now that in marrying Joanna I ignored many signals warning of incompatibility, in the interest of choosing a wife as remote from Marcia Nicholson's domineering nature as possible. Then, on the rebound, I married in her image—though, in all fairness to Lydia, superiorly; I know now that the failure of this marriage was three parts mine to one part hers—and finally returned to my original intent with Julie, but with a deep if inadequate sense of compatibilities impossible of realization with Joanna. . . .

But to go back to my two kinds of early sexual fantasies and the ways in which they have affected my sexual life. I have described the narcissistic aspect: let them come to me. This is all pride, self-love, the fear of rejection. The other is the one that concerns hurt pride, rage and sadism. One frequent consequence of hurt pride, unrealized claims on others, has been to seek out a woman and re-establish my potency. It is as though I have been so infected by the general epidemic, as well as by personal viruses, as to feel that being a male will do more to restore my pride than being a man, in the more humane and civilized sense. And conversely, though I do not enjoy acknowledging it, I believe that I have felt humiliation and shame more intensely over the times I have experienced sexual impotence than over any manifestations of inadequacy as a distinctly *human* being. Then, again, an old friend remarked the other day that he believed there would be far less sexual activity than there is were it not for the pride involved in potency.

So I am persuaded that with me—and probably with many other men—pride and rage are deeply interlinked with sexual activity, and that this helps to explain the prevalence of sadism, and the range and diversity and multiplicity of sexual experience in our society.

Two related axioms—one of which must be true in a time and place of extensive extramarital sexual relations and divorces and re-marriages. Either we are so desperately dissatisfied with ourselves as to be determined, through sexual athletics, to prove ourselves again and again—or highly neurotic people have no true memories. That is, only the ineffectiveness of memory could account for the unimaginative repe-tition of an act that provides at best a short semi-identical delight fol-lowed by a long dissatisfaction of various sorts. I am talking, of course, of sexual intercourse without love—and by love I think I mean all those common experiences of sharing together hopes and joys and griefs and disappointments in the context of daily living. It is an unusual affair—shut off as such relationships almost always are in secrecy and short stolen bouts of time—that can long survive its exclusive emphasis upon sexuality. At least I believe this to be true for men: what begins as a reckless delight and an exhilarating pride in wanting and being wanted ends, often quickly, in a cloying sense of being shut in with the odor of stale powder and animal tallow. There follows a longing for sunlight and salt water and a brisk breeze.

Yet if maturity has dawdled on the way and now seems wholly lost from sight, the cycle may soon begin again: affronts (real or imagined or—more likely—real, but blown up out of proportion by overweening vanity) at work or at home are followed by rage and the driving but frustrated need to explode, to *leave one's mark* on something, in someone, in order to re-establish one's conviction of importance—and one is launched on another affair. The men to whom this possibility is no more than a cloud shape, the picture formed in fancy of smoke on the horizon, are sometimes the men who are driven inward, to smolder away their resentment in ulcers or colitis—or eventually to erupt still more danger-ously.

I am further persuaded that my certainly excessive denunciations of cruelty in any form and of any degree are as ambiguous in motivation as they are unrealistic in their sweeping coverage. Surely a part of my vehemence about cruelty is an unconscious recognition and fear of this element in myself, just as my rage at and contempt for men who are obvious weaklings must relate to self-contempt for my own weaknesses. To be sure, there is also in my reaction to cruelty an admixture of fear, even when the cruel act is not directed at me, a fear engendered when my feeling of a lack of autonomy gives me a particularly acute sense of helplessness, emptiness. Indeed, perhaps the combination of these two factors—the unconscious shame at my own sadistic potential and the terror over being helpless when confronted by aggressive hostility—may explain the reaction fully, may have reached for me its clearest symbolic representation in the dream of the ballet of the two clowns.

For a long time I would not admit to myself the existence in me of the slightest strain of sadism, whether manifested sexually or some other way. During the long years when I retired from life to nurse my family, between my first and second marriages, I went through a period in which my secret and glorified image of myself was exclusively—and necessarily, to retain sanity—preoccupied with selflessness, sacrificial love, passive resistance to force. I thought of myself, not quite consciously, to be sure, as a blend of Jesus Christ, Albert Schweitzer and Mahatma Gandhi, and it was at this time that I was most intolerant of "cruelty": of bull fights, of hunting, even of fishing. (It is interesting, I realize now, that these thoughts had to do with cruelty to subhuman creatures.) I was the champion of all the exploited and abused, and the lower in the order of species, the weaker and the meeker the victim, the fiercer my championship. I was the scourge of sadism.

In fact, this conviction of my own freedom from any cruelty in my makeup persisted, in somewhat diluted form, for years. I remember a taxi ride back when I was locked in the furious daily struggle with Lydia. I was on my way to a rendezvous with the most unlikely woman with whom I have ever been entangled, a half-Russian, half-Mexican dancer whose exotic masochism fascinated me briefly, then violently revolted me. The cab driver was garrulous; he noted a horror billing on the marquee of a moving picture theater and said, "I used to wonder where they found the people who liked all that blood and shit. Not no more. I took my wife to a boxing match and I was ashamed of her. She went crazy when they drew blood. There's something in everybody that likes to hurt or to see somebody get hurt."

I stopped myself short of a ponderous optimistic rebuttal. For the moment I didn't know why—but an hour or so later, with the dancer, this statement of the taxi driver's came back to my mind, and I have never again asserted that there is no sadism in me.

It was also during the course of my marriage to Lydia that I poured out my heaped-up fury over what seemed to me her domination of me upon the luckless head of a quiet, wiry little man, a guest in our house, whose sole offense was that (at least, in my unreliable opinion) he allowed his wife to be the spokesman and administrator of their family! There are few of my acts of which I have been more ashamed.

I mention this incident because I do not of course mean that sexuality is the only, or even the chief, expression of vindictive rage. What is certainly and generally true is that the refusal—whether deliberate or through unawareness—of others to endorse my claims to be accepted as my fictitious grandiose self finds its positive outlet in aggression, its negative in black sulking, a formidable withdrawal.

I am not, of course, using the word "positive" in any ethical sense. Perhaps "active" would express better what I mean. And if that aggression is finally unwarranted by the context from which it emerges—as such aggression almost always is—it seldom brings the relief that accompanies the expression of justified and valid anger. Indeed, it is often followed by a fear of retaliation or retribution that borders on panic—and this leads me to the other side of the coin: guilt and fear, shame and self-reproach. There is an interwoven structure here, of which I become increasingly aware, even though a great deal of it I still don't understand.

But I do understand how much I have been oversimplifying, in dealing so consistently with opposed archetypes, when they are really more complementary or mutually supplementary than counterpoised. I think again in this connection of my use of my two grandfathers. And incidentally—thinking of them—how much easier I have found it to write of them than of myself directly; how much less difficult to forgive them than myself. But the invocation, to which such symbolism is appropriate, is over—at least for the time being. It is perfectly clear now that I was never really writing of Jas. H. Nicholson and Cornelius Herrick, simply using them as masks. What do I really know of them?

I must push on directly into myself, however much I dread it, however painful I find it. And now—now—now.

July 21, 3:30 A.M.

First, the square shape of the alarm clock, growing bigger and bigger, but retaining the same form. Then the hands pointing to five minutes to three—a big square clock high on the wall, a stout wire netting protecting the glass. A corridor somewhere institutionalized (hospital, jail, school?), identical doors opening everywhere throughout its length. Then children, filing out . . .

And so it all came back. Every day in that first school, the lineup at five minutes to three; the orderly procession out, boys with caps held over their shoulders, at three; complete freedom (to me, complete helplessness) outside on the front pavement by five minutes after three! The rediscovery of the malice and hostility of the world. Recognition and absolution. I don't think I'll wake up again around three o'clock in the morning. . . .

Two things: this experience pokes a large hole in the fabric of my skepticism about tracing back a neurotic difficulty to a single incident in childhood—what I have been prone to call "the traumatic fallacy." I do not say "destroys it," for I do not believe that—not on the strength of a single exception—and of course what I have connected, through association, is a single persistent fear with a single original incident. Where the fallacy I deplore is practiced, it is rather a question of attributing a whole adult neurotic structure to a single early traumatic experience. . . .

The other: a platitude hoary with the frozen, aged breaths of multitudinous others. A hint only, really, of those bubbling mysterious depths in each of us, and how incredibly seldom we lower the rope ladder and climb down in gingerly terror, shuddering each time our hand scrapes the slimy inhabited wall against which the ladder swings. And yet, too, the feeling of relief, of fulfillment, when one is able to reach down, swaying precariously on the bottom rung, and actually pluck from the murky broth down there an object, an insight. The sober triumph, the little square inch of freedom retrieved . . .

I remember suddenly those several years of psychoanalysis with that kind and generous man who labored with me, for me, and, necessarily, against me for me, and never succumbed to what must be, in the face of the general human condition, an almost overpowering temptation to give up, to reject, to hurt, to destroy this patient-enemy, this being filled with hatred and negation—for himself, for those who would help him, for everyone and everything. (Perhaps this journal will prove a delayed harvest; I wish I could see him.) And I remember how, as I finally plodded across the first stony acre of the associative process, having until then resisted this exploration fiercely, and merely carried on an endless debate, with myself and the analyst, I kept seeing a recurrent image—one so ludicrous that I disliked increasingly having to admit that there it was again.

What I saw and reported was centered in the figure of a toy duck—one of the kind that, when pulled across the floor on a string, waddles and goes "Quack, quack." Only this fellow, painted a bright blue and yellow in the fashion, perhaps, of that hero of twentieth-century folklore, Donald Duck, was attached to no string—waddled and quacked on his own. He was always genial, the very soul of affability, and he always coaxed me to follow him over to the dark door that stood ajar—over to it and through it into the anonymous recesses of the huge storage room (I was sure this was its nature) beyond.

I would not go. I would follow the duck to the very door, and peer fearfully in, observing only dim shapes hulking in the shadows, but I would not enter. In vain he cajoled me, now with dulcet quacks, now with joyous, urgent ones. In vain he would glide into the dark room and there, as though suddenly luminescent, could be perceived waltzing, racing, coasting about its vast expanse, dodging in and out among the shadowy objects, for all the world like some euphoric roller skater in a huge, hurdle-strewn arena. He exuded happiness; persuasion was in his every movement. Yet, even when I felt my nerves and muscles, suddenly resolute, tighten in anticipation of the plunge, I would at the last moment draw back and refuse the invitation.

There were many variants to this recurrent pantomime, but the essential outline was what I have just described. And now, at last, I understand something of the whole antic business: the decoy and the storage room containing all the secrets of my troubles, their origins and their resolutions.

July 22

WALTON watched the red sun sink slowly into the dusty haze above the city's spires. With its disappearance, it was as though something moved in the sky. Not, Walton thought, the illusion of displacement caused by the loss of the sun—as though air (space itself?) shivered into new position to avoid the vacuum. (Had he, then, thought *that* another time?) No, there had been a *something* that moved. Or was the "sky" merely readjusting itself, as some gigantic "person" might tug at his waistcoat, brush from his coat sleeve adhering crumbs? (worlds?)

Hypnotized, he watched more intently, apprehensively. Low over the horizon, the angry red dust gave now the illusion of shaping itself into purposeful clouds and advancing upon the city. At the same moment Walton had a hallucination of the roof being lifted from the building. He was seated at his desk, high above the city, with no covering, no protection; and three feet from his chair the floor dropped off into space. It was the ultimate exposure. In an attack of vertigo, he pushed back, away from the window.

Then it was gone; he relaxed, slumped in his chair, and continued to stare dully at the darkening pink of the western horizon. He remembered the siren for the atomic raid rehearsal at eleven o'clock that morning—first the wavy wail, with its chilling accent of terror, then the hoarse three-minute honking. The Atomic Goose, wild over the city. He remembered it now with a flat feeling of desolation. He was quite clear about the prophetic fear he had felt in the morning, but now his recollection was numb; it was as though the great catastrophe had actually occurred, and he was surveying, without hope, the decimated city. "At eleven o'clock, on Wednesday, July 22, 1953, the first bomb fell," kept running through his mind: "At eleven o'clock . . . the first bomb . . . At eleven . . ."

But it hadn't. In fact, there was no proof that the Russians had mastered The Bomb as yet. But all through the summer there had been these raid drills—in hysterical expectation, it had seemed to him. And yet, today, he too—

So, perhaps, they too . . . For he realized now that he was blurring universal and personal desolation, contemplating with deadened, lack-lustre eyes both a man and a world bent on self-destruction.

Where had this flat, dead hopelessness come from? Only seven months ago he had sat before the Congressional investigating committee and in a clear, confident voice said stirring and resolute, yet realistic, things about the nature of freedom and commitment and the course of hope. In defiance of that sinister horn.

He knew that what he was thinking was true, that he was not fatu-ously deceiving himself. And he knew, of course, that the events related to his present feeling were Julie's declaration and departure, his affair with Sonia, the row over the Asiatic Studies program, and in some per-verse way the suggestion of his candidacy for the governorship.

The deadlock with P.H., he thought wearily—while Haldane post-poned his return to New York again and again (to be sure, for sufficient reason: he had been appointed to the Atomic Energy Commission)— had taken away Walton's zest for work, had sapped both his ability to concentrate and to take an interest in other projects that arose, had milked dry both initiative and imagination. He had been alternately short-tempered and apathetic, forced himself painfully to accomplish routine matters, leaned heavily on Evelyn.

Evelyn hovered over him; Dennis avoided him; Peggy, it seemed to him, gave him odd, speculative looks; and only today he had caught P.H. gazing at him with an expression he could not define, but felt to represent some sort of anxiety. Even Dud was a bit strained and removed.

Or was he reading all this into their words, manner, expressions? Not apprehensively—he felt too flattened and indifferent for real anxiety. But did he? What then of his vision of the menacing dust clouds, the lifting of the roof, and the abyss at his feet?

But dead and dull most of the time, he insisted. And a recital of all the problems, difficulties and defections of the last months did not ac-count for this deadness, which was dissipated only when he was with Sonia—and not always then. Defections? The word caught at him. *I have deserted myself,* he thought, and again, *I have betrayed myself.*

These words stung him, penetrated his numbness. To be sure, his first reaction was the sardonic rejoinder, Which self? Hadn't he admitted, even in tears, back when he first began to write in his journal, that he had lost his way—no matter how well he functioned superficially, and in some parts of his life, fully?

Lost his way? Lost, in some deep stirring sense, *himself*. How then could he betray or desert what wasn't there?

But rationalize and catechise as he would, twist and turn, grow cynical and sneering—he could not shake off this conviction. It was in his bowels.

There was the quick tap of high heels; for a moment Sonia stood at the door of his office. She said nothing, simply stood there with that look that was at once appraisal and invitation, then raised her fingers to her lips, said "Nine-thirty" softly, and left.

But now, at last, for the first time, he felt no quickening of pulse, no whisper of his blood, no stirring of excitement. Nothing—beyond the cold thought that she was well made. He did not even shift his position in his chair, or feel any change of expression on his face.

He had betrayed himself. But now they were only words. He felt no longer their deep physical meaning. Yet there was a change; the experience, though so brief, left him less deadened—rather, melancholy.

He knew that he must bestir himself, go out into the heavy evening heat for dinner, before going on to Sonia's. But he had no desire for either. He would like to sit on here indefinitely, in this dim coolness, freed for once from what sometimes seemed to him his sentence to endless activity—sit here, and as he had watched sunset turn to dusk, so observe dusk become darkness. He was tired; with surprise, he realized how often it was true, and how seldom he acknowledged it.

But now, again to his surprise, footsteps. A man: brisk and yet tentative. And then, in the same doorway, Dennis Byrnes.

There was, it seemed to Walton, in this first moment of silent examination, a sense of impending confrontation that was too pervasive to be wholly subjective. Dennis' very posture suggested his own sense of this confrontation, even of having come to bring it about.

Walton stirred, swung his chair around.

"Yes, Dennis?" To himself his voice sounded almost ominously quiet.

Dennis advanced into the room. He moved jerkily, awkwardly.

"Why do you hate me? What have I done?"

Although his words and attitude were theatrical, his voice was so short-breathed that Walton was sure he was not acting. "Hate you?" he repeated. "I don't hate you." But, even as he spoke, he was aware that to tell someone (and especially Dennis) that he was mistaken about being hated was somehow to diminish his dignity.

Dennis stared at him silently. In the gathering darkness, it was impossible to discern the quality of the look, but its intensity was unmistakable.

"You won't say it?" Now Dennis' voice was shaky with, it seemed, contempt. "I didn't think you would. Well, I will. I hate you."

Walton found, even without surprise, that these words calmed, almost soothed him.

"You do, Dennis? Why?"

"Because for the first months you treated me like a son. You seemed to me to be the father I'd never had. You helped me, you taught me, you confided in me. And then suddenly, after that morning when I urged you to give up Kiefer, you either avoided me or were cold to me when you couldn't avoid me. Because, the night we all had drinks together, you made fun of me. Because you haven't any right to pull people to you as though they were important to you and then push them away, toss them off like old sacks. That's why."

His quivering tenseness was visible. The great rush of words was stilled, but there had been no catharsis.

"Sit down, Dennis. That's a good deal to answer. Let's take the least first. How did I make fun of you that night we had drinks together?"

Dennis hesitated. When he spoke, his voice had lost its previous passion, was almost sulky.

"You and Sonia and Dudley Foote. With all your innuendoes and double meanings in that game."

Walton felt a resurgence of the tiredness he had been indulging when Dennis appeared.

"Innuendoes and double meanings I remember, but none that made even an indirect reference to you. Dennis, I think you're confused about that."

Dennis took another abrupt, jerky step toward him, and his voice rose again.

"I may be mistaken about that, but I'm not about you and your attitude toward women. And that's a part of what's hurt me. I—I idealized you so; I didn't dream of what you were really like."

Walton began packing his pipe.

"What I am like, except in terms of my relation with you, is not any of your business," he said heavily. "Nor is it mine to conform to your idea of me. I got us off on the wrong foot. Let's go back to the main charge; I think there really is some justification for that. I did, certainly, give you a lot of attention and—I hope—help. And I've given you very little since the morning you referred to. So far, so good.

But far from the being pulled toward and pushed away you speak of, I think you had a pretty active hand in the change between us."

Dennis was again glaring at him.

"What do you mean?"

"I mean," said Walton, lighting his pipe and speaking between puffs, "that you took it upon yourself—or at least made it possible for Mr. Gates to think of you as the person to do it—to persuade me to abandon Kiefer. You came to me, ostensibly on your own, to advise me. If that had been the truth, it would have been at the least impertinent, and my only share of the blame for that was my overimpulsiveness in 'taking you in.' But it was not the truth, for I asked Mr. Gates directly, and he admitted that he'd asked you to speak to me."

"Well, that's his fault," Dennis burst out. "And if you're angry because an old friend let a new one speak for him, you should blame the old friend, not me."

Walton looked at him thoughtfully, tapping the stem of his pipe on his forehead.

"Perhaps, Dennis. Perhaps. But I saw something else in the whole incident—both in your acting in this capacity, and in your manner in doing it—something I didn't like and didn't trust. You've come to me on all this, directly at last, and I respect that. I won't mince words with you.

"I suspect that you persuaded Mr. Gates to suggest to you that you speak to me. No, wait. And do sit down; you can concentrate better. I don't mean that you did this explicitly. There are all sorts of ways of being suggestive; I've observed that you're skillful at a number of them, and I know from my own experience that P.H. is suggestible, once he likes a person. Anyway, I can't prove that, but what is clear to me is that, in terms of a sense of self-respect, as well as respect for us and a proper sense of functions and capacities, even if your speaking to me was wholly his idea, you should have refused to do it. If the older man—and our president—didn't see the incongruity and bad taste involved, you are bright enough to see it, and, whenever you want to be, tactful and subtle enough to set him straight respectfully."

"You sound like a handbook for office manners."

"Perhaps. But I doubt it. Anyway, I was trying to give you the benefit of the doubt. A doubtful procedure, for it was patent, in your manner and your words, that you were thoroughly enjoying playing your part: pseudo-modest, pseudo-concerned, pseudo-reticent. And therefore you either hatched, in your ambition, the whole business, or you leapt at the chance when it was offered."

Dennis' voice was choked now.

"You ought to be a psychoanalyst! But I'll tell you this: you ought to go to one, too—for yourself."

Walton heard his own voice proportionately cooler.

"Sometimes I think so."

"Anyway," Dennis rushed on, "suppose I did do the wrong thing. Does that justify your turning me into an outcast?"

There was a long silence. At last Walton lifted his head from his contemplation of the desk.

"No," he said wearily. "No, Dennis, it doesn't—if one *can* turn another into an outcast. My mistake was in being thoughtless in the beginning, in leading you to feel that you were a very important part of the department, and then, when this incident occurred, too easily and suddenly deciding that you were untrustworthy, that you had taken me in all along, and that I should be very careful what I told you from then on."

"There!" said Dennis. "You see!" His tone was one of almost childish glee.

Walton sighed.

"We've both been at fault," he said, "and I don't know whether we can really pick up the pieces. But at least it's better to have had it out."

"But it's not fair," Dennis cried. "I think you've poisoned Mr. Gates' mind against me too. He's been different with me lately."

Walton shook his head.

"I haven't mentioned you to him since the very day we've been talking about."

Dennis sprang up from the chair into which he'd finally dropped.

"Maybe so. But everything's changed, and I'm not afraid to speak up. I don't have any chance here any more. And you're not in a very good position yourself. Peggy's told Mr. Gates about you and Sonia."

Walton felt a cloudiness in his head, but he met Dennis' glare levelly. After a moment, he switched on his desk lamp and looked at Dennis sharply.

"What are you talking about?"

"You know damned well what I'm talking about. Peggy's seen you entering and leaving Sonia's building half a dozen times. She lives down the street, and she told me first. I told her to mind her own business and not tell Mr. Gates, but she did, yesterday, and he fired her. Didn't you notice the new girl today?"

Walton shook his head.

"He fired Peggy?" he asked increduously.

"He gave her two months' pay and told her not to come back."

Walton looked up and at him again, saw the wild excitement in his eyes, and said, "Dennis, how does all this make you feel?"

There was no answer for a moment. Then Dennis, with a visible effort, quieted himself, and when he finally spoke, his voice was almost silky, his expression, for the first time that evening, bland and modest. "I feel very badly," he said. "I think we're in serious trouble."

We are indeed, Walton thought, but yours is quite different from mine. It seemed to him now that his own situation was so hopeless that he was almost calm about it.

"What did you mean, Dennis, about having no father?"

Some animation, some spontaneity, came back in Dennis' voice and manner. "He left my mother when she was carrying me," he replied. "He never came back."

"That's very hard," said Walton. "And I do see better the harm I did you by taking you in the way I did. But you still must know that I didn't plan to hurt you."

Dennis nodded eagerly.

"I want to believe that," he said, and then his voice became attenuated, almost as though he was thinking aloud, alone. "I want to believe that you are as fine as I thought you were, as fine as I would want my father to be. I think in some funny way, though, that you and I are alike, that we both have a big potential, and I thought you had filled yours, and I knew I'd barely started to fill mine. So when you did these things, and treated me badly besides, it was as though I'd done them. I felt guilty, and I've got enough guilt of my own." His voice suddenly rose again, stopping just short of a scream. "And I've got enough of my own, do you hear?"

Walton nodded.

"Yes, Dennis, I'm sure you do. A little while ago, you mentioned psychoanalysis. Have you ever tried it?"

Dennis looked at him suspiciously.

"Why should I tell you?" he demanded. Then he added abruptly, "Well, I do go, and I'm not ashamed of it."

"No. It's nothing to be ashamed of."

After another short pause, Dennis said, speaking as though he were afraid Walton would try to stop him, "I'm going now. I'm going. But I want to talk to you again."

When the sound of his footsteps had died away, Walton stood up and went to the coat closet. From the shelf he took a bottle of bourbon and poured himself a drink. But he did not touch the glass. For an hour—two hours?—he sat there, smoking and staring out at the New York night, filled with solar systems and galaxies and universes of light, and saw, with moments of terror and moments of detached calm, the imminent destruction of eight million people. Saw this in vivid, hallucinatory detail as Cranach, as Bosch, as Breughel, as Picasso might paint it, felt a lurching sadness in his heart, and turned back to the half-lit confessional of Dennis, and those words that had ripped apart his own world. Turned back to them, and with a dumb horror asked himself why he had done what he had done, why he was always walking the edge of an abyss, pulling back only just in time. And now, at last, he had not pulled back soon enough.

When the telephone finally rang, he picked up the receiver. In answer to her question, he said, "No, not tonight, after all. I can't come." And then, "No, I'm all right. I just couldn't be there if I came." And finally, "I don't know. I'm not sure—of anything," and hung up.

Inflammation of the Eye

Eye feel Eye'd like to say something more to you on Walton's behalf. Nothing partisan, though; Eye don't have it in the nature of Eyself
to be partisan, as you know.

But first, let's get something cleared up and squared away. By now,
Eye'm sure, a number of you have been saying, "What an affectation: this
pun, this tricky spelling, this sort of avant-garde playing to the gallery.
'Eye' indeed!"

If you're one who has, Eye'm speaking to you now. Are you sure?
If you really were, would you need to pounce on it so quickly, hold this
eccentric spelling aloft, dripping, so to speak: a catch! What's the matter
with you, that this kind of triumph gives you such a glow? Eye know:
you're the sort of fellow who used to wave his hand madly at the teacher
when you were in the fifth grade, pump it up and down victoriously, filled
with knowledge! "He's trying to be obscure and willfully difficult; he's
an avant-garde cultist!"

Eye spit on you. Not excitedly, quite calmly and judiciously. You
and your fifth-grade triumphs. Eye spell Eyeself this way because it is
Eyeself's name. You, maybe, if you were bright enough to recognize it,
have an Eye too. Not those orbs that the minor poets used to write about,
but an Eye.

Enough. Eye leave you with your hard-top convertible; your very
dry martini, your casserole and your frozen broccoli; your irritable
mornings on the commuters' platform. Eye really want to say just two
things; you may take them or leave them. But if you take them, you may
find them useful.

Not you (you've already caught on and needn't read any further),
but you: Eye name you Ibid.

The first of those two things is that Walton Herrick is not unusual.
Not any more. He may be unique, like everyone else, as the old cliché

runs, but not unusual. He's not even on the periphery of functioning human beings today; he's well into the crowd—sometimes ahead of it. You know that. But Ibid.—and Ibid. and Ibid.—don't want to believe it. That's neither here nor there; but if you, Ibid., can allow just a small spot somewhere in your consciousness to curdle with the idea that you might, just possibly might, be as screwy as Walton if you didn't keep that old invisible corset laced so tight, if you didn't wear your psychological bifocals all the time, if you didn't hide behind the Unitarian Church or the League of Women Voters or the University Club. And ibid. *Anyway, if you can just entertain that possibility, Eye'll entertain the proposition that something may work out for you, after all. Maybe.*

Listen, Ibid. Take a good big fistful of stuff out of your dreams (you don't have any? Tsk-tsk. Try again) and your plain old ordinary daydreams—just for one day really examine them, force yourself to stop whatever you're doing and really look and listen. Just for one day, kid, refuse to keep on seeing and hearing what you want to see and hear. Rub your eyes; clean the wax out of your ears. Ask why. *Why did you yell at your kid this morning? No, really why. Why do you have to sleep on the left side of the bed? Oh, come on—why? Why did you sneak by the puppy's leavings on the floor and pretend you didn't see them? And why did you lie to your wife about—oh, never mind. You old Ibid.*

Just get this straight, Ibid. Walton Herrick's no nuttier than you. He's just unfortunate enough to have a sharper Eye.

So much for you squares who want to keep life in two dimensions. The second thing Eye want to say is to you moralizing Ibids.—you who think you're Moralists or merely Decent People. Eye know what you've been saying about Walton and Sonia, and how indignant you are for Poor Julie, and how cynical Walton is to go right to Sonia after that phone call from Julie. And after the postcards from those Darling Children!

But do you know what Eye think, old libidinous Ibid.? Eye think you're disappointed—you with the inflammation of the imagination, that makes you need everything played out immediately before you: anatomy, bedsprings, statistics. You finger-sucking, masturbating, envious little Ibid.

Enough. You're tiresome. If this book belonged to Eye, Eye'd put it all in, just to watch you wet your dry lips, to watch that hectic flush on your little cheeks, to see your hands tremble. You goon. Ibid.

So go on and be glad that he's In Trouble. Go on and despise him, and feel superior and wake in the middle of the night from your bad dreams, quaking and terrified, and reach for your mother's hand to find she's dead. And your father, who didn't like you. Pant all alone, sticky-

eyed and sweaty in the Middle of the Night. For day will come and you can crook your little finger, holding a coffee cup, or tell a dirty story and buy a new cigar.

    Screw you. Ibid.

July 24–26

As he left the car and started up the Footes' sidewalk, Walton felt a sudden temptation to turn, bolt back and drive away. Was it Dud's voice, obviously self-conscious both times he had telephoned to postpone their engagement for dinner? Or what Dennis had told him— with his consequent concern over just how many people, through the combined ministrations of Peggy and Dennis, had heard about him and Sonia?

He didn't know, but he wished himself anywhere else as he pushed the doorbell and braced himself against the eruption of Foote children. The one time he had seen them this summer, it had seemed to him that they were so active, so perpetually on the move, that he couldn't count them. Vaguely he knew there were between four and seven of them.

But no sound followed his ringing of the bell. The silence was pervasive. Puzzled, he rang again. And this time, through the light summer air (from around the corner of the house?), a shrill exclamation, a cry—of pain? of exasperation? Then a man's voice, yes, Dud's, earnest, expostulating? remonstrating? pleading? And the thin slam of a screen door and again the wounded, angry feminine cry that lingered in the softness of the evening, shivered through the dusk's delicacy, ripped it with the perpetual lament of woman over the ways of man.

Wearily Walton rang the bell again.

It was cool in the ramshackle little summer house, and dark; the tinkle of ice in their glasses, the exuberant blinkings of the fireflies and the sawing chorus of cicadas—all these were soothing after the constraint of dinner, with Cynthia's compressed lips and falsely bright questions, and Dud's drawn face. He looked suddenly, prematurely aged, and so unfamiliar that Walton could not recognize his friend except, he had thought at one point, as a projection into the future, into old age. If the remainder of Dud's life were to be largely unhappy, then this is how he would look at sixty-five.

Walton sighed and sipped his drink. He gave sufficient attention to Dud's surprisingly long monologue (he talked compulsively, desperately) on the details of his findings on the national language training program, to be able to comment briefly now and then. But he found himself pulled back again and again to the scene at dinner. Cynthia's bright pink face, startling at this late point in the summer, had increased the effect of tightly suppressed anger; her mind, Walton had thought, must be as sunburnt as her forehead and cheeks. And every little while Dudley would blink, as though to exorcise the pain of whatever he was feeling, which otherwise burned in his eyes.

So the present darkness and quiet had been hard-won; even after dinner, the return home of the children from here, there and everywhere (they were six) had created an emergency state of irritability and parental contradictions and bickering. But all were now either tucked in bed or huddled around the television set. How in the world did Dud maintain so regularly his even disposition?

Walton was aware that he had allowed his thoughts to wander too far this time. Dudley was no longer talking, and the silence had a lifted intonation, as though it had begun with the tentativeness induced by an unanswered question. But since he was not sure, he kept silent.

"Men," said Cynthia suddenly, "men are all babies."

It was so abrupt, and spoken in what seemed to Walton so shrill a tone, that he chuckled before he could control himself.

"It's funny?" Cynthia inquired acidly.

Walton pulled himself up from his lazy, slumped position.

"What I thought funny," he said placatingly, "was how true it is, how universal a complaint, and yet how many light years away from what Dud was talking about—for that certainly wasn't babyish."

"I wasn't thinking about language training," Cynthia went on with acerbity, "though that's all I hear about every day—that and who punched who at the beach and who stole whose shovel. I was thinking about men's expectations of women. Their greedy infantile expectations of endless comfort and nursing, which can never be sufficient, so that they take all any one woman can give, and still go around asking for more wherever they can find it—and usually without the slightest discrimination." She paused for breath, but there was so fierce an urgency to her voice, so admonitory an insistence on being heard, that neither man spoke. "And then, let the man push his baby need for warmth and understanding and appreciation to the point where he

tells her about some of these other things he's done and felt and thought"
—and now her voice at last grew low, husky with passion and indignation—"tell her as though he expected her to feel pride over his accomplishments! Let him do that, and let her yelp. He's hurt, he's unbelieving,
he's deeply wounded. My God!"

Despite the difference in tone, there was the same note of inconsolable anguish in these last words as there had been in the cry Walton had
heard on his arrival. Cry? Yelp *was* the word—Cynthia had unerringly
found it: the eternal Female Yelp.

And he was dumbfounded. His own contribution to the festered
silence of this moment was as much the result of astonishment as of
good taste. For when she had begun her complaint, he thought, as he
had felt in uneasy intimations at dinner, that she was talking about him,
and that her quarrel with Dud had been over him. But slowly, with
bewilderment, he realized that he could not be either the subject
or the object of this angry lament; it was too unmistakably that of an
outraged wife.

Dud spoke one word, low—almost in a moan: "Cyn."

She turned on him, her white dress flashing in the darkness.

"Yes, Cyn! Cyn, Cyn, Cyn, *Sin*. And *Foote*. My God, what irony.
I'm the foot of the sin ladder, all right! I'm marvelously named! You
make me sick!"

It was another, a different, deeper cry—the final cry of hurt and
disillusionment, guttural with a sense of waste and shame and despair,
torn out of the very vitals of life. *"You make me sick!"* It seemed to
Walton now, as she broke into wild sobbing and he felt his deep share
of guilt for that shame and hurt and despair—not hers, not hers, but
Julie's—that this cry permeated all human experience, had echoed down
all the decades of his life, this angry, passionate lament for the broken
word, the severed trust, the wrenching discrepancy between the bright
promise, the lived dream, and the hidden, then revealed actuality. "You
make me sick!"

Dud had his arms around her now, lifted her to her feet, and,
clasping her, was stammering, "No, no, it wasn't what you think! I
didn't— You don't understand— You didn't let me finish."

Walton stood up, put his hand on Dud's shoulder for a moment,
and strode away to his car. All the way home, he held the steering
wheel as tightly as though he were afraid it would take its own initiative.

Walton sat late in the kitchen again, again staring at a glass of
bourbon, but from time to time sipping it. This sadness was different

from the familiar depressions, the recurring melancholies and self-loathings. It hurt, but it felt peculiarly clean. Its burden was an acknowledgment of waste and shame and guilt, but he felt neither self-pity nor self-distaste. He had done what he had done because he could not help himself, and he would pay for it. He had, he felt sure, this time hurt Julie and himself irreparably.

Because he could not help himself . . . And again he heard that basic animal cry of pain, "You make me sick!" and somehow what he had called the Female Yelp and the honking of the Atomic Goose became confused in his head. Could not help himself? Did not want to help himself? These questions were for the Sophists. He had been hurt and he had sought comfort, tawny, sweet-scented comfort. He had willfully held off with one hand all thoughts of Julie, of September, of the purpose of the summer, and with the other stroked, caressed the rounded cap of Sonia's golden shoulder, her indolently lifted knee. With this hand . . .

For they were, as she had said, voluptuaries. They used ritual in harmony, as though they had rehearsed, learned the ancient words and gestures of an ancient and immemorial ceremony. And all this, he thought suddenly, almost without emotion. They plunged into the senses and, when close to drowning, returned to the surface, but not satiated—only to rest and then plunge again.

He knew every indentation, every line, every gradation of her body. For him she was bathed always in a golden sheen. He knew the hollows where it paled; he was fond of the faint brown stain spreading out in the wrinkles and creases near her armpits. He knew the downy golden hairs at the base of her spine. But he did not know her heart, nor she, he thought, his.

Sometimes they played a two-handed version of strip poker, drawing out the denouement to an agonizing length. Sometimes they legislated helplessness to one or the other for a half hour in which only one of them was permitted the use of his hands. Sometimes, in the middle of the night, resting, they would talk and drink for two hours, a dialogue brittle with wit, with titillation, a *tour de force* of private myth and paradox and ambiguities, while at his request she would wear, perhaps, only a wide-brimmed straw hat with a narrow black velvet ribbon tied under her chin. Or she would clothe herself in jewelry: barbaric broad bracelets of gold or brass, long golden chains around her neck, an anklet; he mourned that he could not find a knee protector like that worn by basketball players, but made of gold mesh.

Their only concession to everyday reality was to talk occasionally of the work and people at the office. One evening she handed him, with an air of mystery, a long envelope. When he asked her what it contained, she replied that it was a letter to Huntingdon Haldane, dictated to her by P.H. Walton refused to read it. She shrugged and found him quixotic: P.H. said nothing bad about him, but his tone was ambiguous. Walton said that everything was ambiguous. She said he was an idealistic fool. He threw her roughly on the bed and they made love.

They made love, employing all their resources in theme and variation, but they did not speak of love. They did not say, "I love you." He said, "I wish I could get inside of you, really live inside you for a little while." She said, "You have." When he angrily insisted, she said, "Try. You can't, but try anyway."

As he had told her early, it was the way she moved that completed his infatuation. Twisting her lithe body, she would toss her head from side to side at the moment of ultimate penetration. And at times she would insinuate her body toward him in a sliding movement like a swimmer's. These never failed to inflame him still more. He spoke of wanting to enter her, to possess her; she possessed his blood, whispered in his arteries.

So it had been with them from that night of July 12 until the night Dennis had stopped in his office, July 22. Except for last Friday and Saturday. Ten days. Ten nights. Walton shook his head. It was nearer to ten months. No, it was a lifetime, and only ten minutes.

The way she moved . . . It was She of long ago, of the inter-planetary fantasies; it was the culmination of the long pursuit, the erotic obsession that it now seemed clear to him he had never shaken off, only submerged and blurred, kept behind bars. And Julie? The dreams of Julie, life with Julie, issued from the gate of horn, those with Sonia from the gate of ivory. So he could at once admit the essential falseness of these dreams, this vision of life, and still not give them up. Falseness? To what? To life, his life, what he had painfully made of it, what more he hoped to make, what it had meant and could mean.

But then what of this other part of it, what he thought of as the long stealthy, hooded pursuit down the corridors, the streets of night? It was facile to say this was false, to see it only as an alien element entering the him who was the husband, father, provider, citizen.

He pounded his forehead with his fist. One must not deny the dark: that was death or, at the least, inanition. One must somehow find a binder, pour the dark and the light together, pound them, together with the binder, till the whole held, no longer crumbling apart to fall into two dry segments. But how?

He did not know. He could not do it. While the sadness had lasted, it seemed not only possible, but *felt* true, realized. But now, he suddenly knew, the sadness was dissipated. His thoughts of Sonia, his invocation of her person, had inflamed him again. The fever licked at him.

Wednesday night she had telephoned, and he had said he would not come. Thursday she had stopped by his office late, as usual. She had stood as before, saying only, "Tonight?" He had shaken his head, and she had gone off without another word. Tonight he had not seen her, had left early for dinner at the Footes' and a weekend home. Tonight? It was two o'clock.

He poured another drink. The weekend stretched ahead, empty and open. If he went in to New York now and awoke Sonia— He groaned. He drank and groaned again.

Then, after a moment of shame over the easy cynicism of the thought that, since he had already destroyed hope for Julie and himself, he might as well enjoy (what a euphemism!) these last days (why last?), he went to the telephone and called the local taxi company. He was told the fare to New York was $25. He ordered the cab.

They slept most of Saturday, awaking twice, in their now established way, to engage each other and return to exhausted sleep. Walton awoke finally to a feeling of sufficient sleep for restoration shortly before midnight. He felt restored, but also hot, sweaty, hungry and irritable.

Turning his head, he looked at Sonia, sleeping. Her lips barely parted, she was breathing deeply, with an evenness of rhythm that suggested repletion—a repletion that, for some reason he did not understand, angered Walton. Roughly he reached out and drew the sheet over her exposed breasts. She did not awaken.

Standing under the shower, he felt the first assault of guilt. It invaded him like grief, in battalions. It swept away the irritability, the hunger, the pettish spite. He had broken away, that night Dennis confronted him with the news about Peggy, and he had determined to reclaim what was left of him (so he phrased it to himself) with no hope of winning anything thereby except his self-respect. And his resoluteness had lasted three days!

The water poured over him, but he was insensible to it as it gradually lost its heat. He was insensible to everything except his far vision of Julie and the grief of having lost her. And here he was, at midnight, standing naked and lost himself in the home of a stranger with whom he was intimate. He felt he could not bear it; he must find comfort.

When the water had turned wholly cold, he came to his senses.

Despite the heat of the night, he was chilled as never before, except for that one night after Julie had told him she was leaving. Even the rough towel could not warm him. Shaking, feverish, he dressed hurriedly and awkwardly, muttering to himself of comfort, which he saw oddly as a green meadow, with wind-rippled grasses, a place of secrecy and peace.

Peace, peace, he thought, and made for the door. But with his hand on the knob he turned and found Sonia, awake, regarding him. He gave a wrench at the door knob, but under her steady gaze he could not go out. He closed the door again and slowly walked over to the bed.

Those gray-green eyes were unwinking and almost expressionless. Walton slowly, as though a toy pulled by a string, lowered himself and sat down on the bed, his eyes still engaged by hers.

Finally she stirred and, with something contemptuous in the act, deliberately shrugged and then kicked the sheet to the foot of the bed.

"Walking out?" Her voice was hard, the words slurred.

Walton looked at her miserably. He could find nothing to say.

"Go ahead. I knew I'd be too much for you."

Still he sat there, staring dumbly at the floor, and again her voice went on, as though prodding, poking at him.

"I'm a fool. I knew better. It disgusts me that I gave in when all the time I knew better."

Walton thought miserably, Gave in? Gave in? and bowed his head into his hands.

For a moment he heard the stillness gathering around him like a storm. Then she broke.

"You make me tired!"

In astonishment he stared at her. She was broken by sobs. Her shoulders were heaving, her whole body shaking, and although she held her hands over her face as though she would hide it in an agony of shame the tears ran through her fingers.

He sat there, paralyzed, staring at her. Until she thrust away her hands, lifted her contorted and tear-streaked face proudly and repeated, "Tired! You make me tired! Do you really suppose I have no feelings at all? You stupid, stupid *boy!*" and returned to her wild weeping.

Then he reached out and swept her into his arms. For a long time he sat there, staring at the wall before him and rocking her bare, stricken body as though she were a wailing baby.

DEPOSITION: 7

A fragment of the talk between Dennis Byrnes and his psychoanalyst during the last part of an hour on August 3, 1953. Dennis on the couch, the analyst in a chair behind him . . .

DENNIS (vehemently): . . . and I don't see why Mr. Gates doesn't fire Sonia. She's no better than a Polish whore. Secretary to the president of a foundation!

ANALYST: What does her being Polish have to do with it?

DENNIS (slowly, cautiously, neck and shoulders stiffening): Nothing, I guess. I'm not a snob. I've never been anti-Semitic.

ANALYST: Is—Sonia Jewish?

DENNIS (hastily): No. No. I don't know why I said that. Let me see. I think there are three reasons for what I said. [Voice becomes bland] First, you spoke to me sharply, and I kind of froze. Like I always do before authority. I don't know why. Second, it seemed to me that you were accusing me of prejudice, and I have a lot of faults, but racial or religious prejudice isn't one of them. If I had been, I'd have said Polack. And so, since I thought I was being accused of prejudice, I associated with anti-Semitism. And fourth, well, I used "anti-Semitic" as a sort of general term for racial prejudice.

ANALYST (dryly): What happened to "third"?

DENNIS (distressed): I said third. What I said was third was— I can't think what it was but [urgently] I did have a third point.

ANALYST (gently): No, Dennis, you didn't. And that's one of the best things that's happened to you in here.

DENNIS (suspiciously and angrily): You're always trying to confuse me. I never get mixed up that way when I'm not here.

ANALYST: That's what's good about your being here. You can let down

491

your drawbridge or take off your mask—whichever means more to you—and there won't be any retribution. Maybe you'll learn in time that you can do it elsewhere too. There's nothing so dreadful about making a mistake. And this one meant that you've loosened up some on that rigid control of yours. You've been counting ever since you came to me: first, second, third. And this time, after fifty hours, you still counted, you still felt the need to hold things together by this kind of mechanical numbering of yours, but you made a slip. Hurray for the slip

DENNIS (sullenly): You're making fun of me.

ANALYST (earnestly): Never less so.

[A long silence, during which Dennis twists and turns on the couch, rubs his head, closes his eyes, opens them]

ANALYST: How do you feel about Sonia?

DENNIS (savagely): She's a slut!

ANALYST: Yes. Maybe. Go on. Say whatever comes to your mind.

DENNIS (sitting up abruptly): You're so goddamned condescending. [He looks stricken] I didn't mean to say that. It's not true. You're kind to me and patient. You've helped me a lot. I don't know what's the matter with me. I owe you everything. [He sinks back on the couch]

ANALYST (dryly): Sonia?

DENNIS: Oh, all right, so you don't believe me. [Defiantly] Anyway, she *is* a slut. Always trying to look mysterious and always moving her body so as to inflame men. And tough—hard as nails. I don't see what Walton can see in her when he has the wife he has. I met her once; she's lovely. A fine woman. I'll never forgive him for turning out so cheap.

ANALYST: How much do you really know about Mr. Herrick, his wife, and Sonia? How can you be sure that that girl—Peggy, is that her name?—is telling the truth. Or, even if she is, that seeing them together proves they're having an affair?

DENNIS (hotly): They couldn't fool me. I knew from that moment at the bar when they looked at each other. They were on fire; I've told you how she tries to inflame men.

ANALYST: Does she inflame you?

DENNIS: No, I'm onto her tricks. But any fool could see she'd trapped Walton. That was why I told Peggy to keep a sharp eye out—

ANALYST: You told Peggy *what?*

DENNIS (sullenly): I just told her that I knew what they were up to, and that if she looked about her on her way up and down the street she was bound to see them together sometime. She didn't have to do it; I was just telling her how I felt about it. I didn't mean that she was to spy on them. She's responsible for what she decides to do, isn't she? She's not in my employment.

[Another silence]

DENNIS: I can feel you looking reproachful. I can hear it. You're drawing a mighty long conclusion. I've done nothing to be ashamed of, and you have no right to make such arbitrary judgments!

ANALYST (sternly): We've all done things to be ashamed of. And with all this evasion, you're accusing yourself. Dennis, this is a very destructive thing you've done, and you'd better face up to it, before you bury it so deep that we can't pry it up, and it will stay there and fester.

[A silence, broken finally by a sob from Dennis]

DENNIS (brokenly): I know it is. I did it. I did do it because—because —Oh, I'm crazy. I hated seeing him look at her like that and I hated her because she'd never look at me that way and if she did I'd be scared I'm scared of sex I tell you. Who ever heard of a virgin at twenty-eight! I'm hopeless and no good I don't know how I can go on but I tell you I can't stand it and Walton will never have any use for me any more I hate women. Women— women—my mother.

ANALYST (rising and putting his hand on Dennis' shoulder): I'm sorry we have to stop, just when you've opened up. But, Dennis, this is good. It's the first time you've let go this way and you feel bad now, maybe even despairing, but you'll feel better. Stay with this destructive thing. Don't hide from it; don't hate yourself for it. It's in everyone—you, me, everyone. And we have to learn to live with it and turn it (for its energy too) into constructive uses. Just stay with it till next time, for we're getting somewhere now.

August 12

"WELL, that about does it," said Abe, as he and Walton emerged onto the hot front steps of the Stamford City Hall. "Comment needed?"

Walton grinned and shook his head. "Relatively painless, though. Each of us knew the other would never do for him, so we didn't even have to bring it up."

Abe nodded. "Yeah, all clear to me. You didn't like him, but what did you *think* of him?"

Walton hesitated. As they walked slowly to Abe's parked car, he thought back to his first vision of Armour Ward, of whom Abe had said in advance only that he was one of the most powerful party men in Fairfield County.

"When I first saw him," he said, "tall, bald, portly, cold, I knew I wouldn't get along with him. But I wasn't prepared for how downright rude he'd be."

Abe grunted.

"Don't know what got into him. Can be gracious if wants to. Even though he's got his own candidate, no need—" He stopped abruptly and looked up at Walton with a meditative, searching expression. "Amateur. That's what he thought. 's favorite words: 'old pro.' Man of principle, intellectual, is 'outsider.' Now why didn't I know he'd feel like that?"

Walton gave him a sardonic grin.

"You did, *you* old pro. That innocence of yours!" He opened the car door and climbed in, leaning way over to hold the other one open while Abe limped around the back of the car. "Now, while you drive me to the station, tell me at last why you've gone to all this trouble when you knew all along—and even I knew—that there wasn't the remotest chance of my getting the nomination? And hardly any more of my wanting it."

Abe started the car, with no comment beyond, "No station tonight. You come home with me and go in in the morning." He swung out into the street.

"But, Abe," Walton protested, "tomorrow's a big day for me. P. H. Gates and I are finally getting together with the Chairman of the Board. You remember my telling you about the row over an appointment I want to make? I'll have to be in the office early."

Abe swung left in the direction of his home.

"Get you in as early as you want," he said decisively. "And I'll answer your questions."

They sat over their coffee a long time after eating the simple supper Abe had prepared. But there were too many interruptions to settle down to the subject of the meeting with Ward. First, a friend of Abe's called excitedly to tell him that the Atomic Energy Commission had just announced that a thermonuclear explosion had taken place in the U.S.S.R. Walton remembered his premonition of the previous month, told Abe about it, then thought of tomorrow's meeting with Haldane.

"I wonder if he won't have to stay in Washington," he said.

"I don't think so," Abe replied. "Malenkov announced its manufacture four or five days ago. This a big day only for uninformed. But not belittling. It's Doomsday, boy, and there'll be more. Others—and different."

There were other telephoned interruptions, trifling ones, more cheerful ones. Each time Abe put back the phone, he cursed and limped back to resume their conversation.

Then there was Jane. Almost punctually every half hour Abe would go up to see if her migraine headache was lifting. The report was negative until he came slowly back at ten o'clock, and with a gesture of relief fetched a bottle of gin and one of bourbon to the table.

"Asleep," he said, slopping the gin into his old-fashioned glass. "Out like a baby. Help yourself."

He added ice and bitters to his drink, stirred.

"Funny thing. Jane. Comes from cold, proper family—Wisconsin. Lutherans, father president bank. Scared the life out of her. We met here—New York—twenty-five years ago. She'd made the break, came to study art, but scared to be out after dark. Met her through friend of mine. Honestly think my game leg gave her security—and me being so alien to her pseudo-Nordic background. Anyway, began to go out with me."

He paused and sipped.

"What happened to your leg?" Walton asked.

"Football. Set wrong. Anyway, played it slow with her, so wouldn't frighten her away. Meanwhile making money fast making paper tissues. Got in early after original Kleenex company with small borrowed capital. Grew fast. When I sold out seven years ago, had made enough to last us. Fortune's fortune."

Walton was absorbed.

"So that's it. I've wondered ever since you first said you'd tell me."

"Sure. Life's work—clean things up. Noses, behinds, politics. Use Fortune to get rid of your pickings and droppings. Company and trade name—changed my own to it after got going."

"I'll be damned," said Walton. "And before that? You said, that night I talked so much, that you'd tell me about your early days."

Abe shook his head.

"Nothing much to tell. Typical Lower East Side. Father and Mother migrated from Russian pogroms. Poor. Worked my way through City College. Want to talk about Jane. You know those pictures she showed you? Proper, conventional people, but little devils, gnomes, grotesques peering out of nowhere at them?"

Walton nodded.

"Well, that's what I meant—about being stuck with dreads and drolls of childhood. Even I don't know all details. But no matter how much she finally got to enjoy sex (and wasn't quick), still feels it's sinful—knows it isn't, feels it is. Sometimes—often. Wonderful woman, full of natural vitality, but they did her in. Going to be crude—" he paused and his keen eyes searched Walton's face—"but when I've got it, it's been good. I haven't got it so much. They scared her of childbirth too. Scared her sterile, I think. Tried all the hormones, that junk—psychoanalysis, too. Didn't take. Too private for it. And now—menopause. Now I can't produce enough for her. Frustration and cycles of guilt do her in—migraine. *There.*"

He refilled his glass, still looking sharply at Walton.

"First time I've told. You ever have trouble like that with your wife?"

Walton felt a spasm of shame, and was prompted to ask "Which wife?" Instead he said, "With my first wife, something not so different. Not my second. And certainly not Julie. She was brought up with more healthy ideas than I was. Not without other troubles, of course." After a pause, he added, "You've been good to Jane—and for her."

Abe nodded. "Yes. No more than she for me. Life. We're all crippled, but if we can hold on, get the peculiar human satisfaction.

Call it self-respect. What's the matter?"

It burst. It came out of Walton as though he had taken an emetic—all of it, dammed up, undigested, the engorgement of the whole summer. With a hand that shook, he refilled his own glass twice. But these moments, and those when he drank, were the only interruptions for a half hour, while he talked on and on in a strained, passionate voice, beyond the summer, back, back through his childhood and youth. Abe grunted and nodded and cocked his head to one side. At last, when Walton fell silent, looking at him as if in appeal, with eyes he felt himself to be anguished with anticipation of the verdict, Abe spoke.

"Rough," he said. "Knew something was wrong—some strain. Didn't know it was so bad; it doesn't show that much. And it is bad. *I* know results of keeping all shut up inside. Why do you care so much how things look to other people?"

Walton shook his head. "I didn't know I did. Oh, in a vague way, but clearly only when I'm writing in that journal. I remember a passage in which I wrote that, took it back to the time I couldn't walk down the street with any of my family without being stared at. . . . Anyway, Abe, now you can see the irony of suggesting I might be a governor."

"No," said Abe. "Both times. You knew it when you spoke those words to the Committee. I have them by heart: 'I believe that everything most destructive in human nature, whether in individuals or in groups, is fomented, finally to burst out in some violent form, when segregation, secrecy and deception are practiced or, in one way or another, enforced.' "

Walton stared at him, stricken.

"You see," he said hoarsely, at last. "Those words—and then . . . governor!"

The kindness in Abe's eyes was familiar. Sometime, long ago, someone else had hit him—hit him where he lived—and still showed that there was no malice, no vindictiveness, no cruelty.

"No, Walton," said Abe. "That's true of all of us. Not 'either or'; 'both and.' And I'll quote you back to yourself again: 'All *lived* life—as against mere existence—is commitment, is risk.' From all you've told me, tonight and the other night, you were almost literally born in a straitjacket, and it's harder for you than most to go out and commit yourself. But you know what the truth is, and in that session in Congress you committed yourself beyond anyone else who testified. You'll tell me that doesn't take guts?"

Walton rubbed his head fiercely.

"I don't know," he said slowly, "whether that was guts or something else—maybe just that I'm such an innocent politically that I really believed if I told the truth I couldn't get in trouble. Then again, sometimes I think it's got more to do with a—I don't know how to say it—a determination to impose my will on other people, that I'm so determined that they *shall* see it my way that I lose realistic fears."

"We can puddle in motivations too damned much," Abe declared, and pulled himself up from the table. "So it's both. But in my book it's guts. I'm going to make sure she's still sleeping."

When he came down again, he smiled and nodded, and his face, suddenly softened in relaxation, showed now a terrible fatigue.

"You're worn out," said Walton. "Forget the rest of it."

Abe made a strange gesture of dismissal: strange because, although certainly dismissal, it also conveyed to Walton some sense of—was it despair?

"I can't," said Abe heavily, and as heavily dropped into his chair. "I literally can't. Sometimes I pace that floor for hours." He paused to pour himself another drink, and Walton remembered that night in early July when, after dinner, he had sat in comfort, thinking of Jane's marvelous adequacy and wondering about those limping footsteps overhead. "Or take this stuff—the broth. I use it, I use it, I use it. It's grim, but couldn't get along without it."

Walton looked at him wonderingly. "But what—Abe, I don't get it. When you told me about Jane, something about the way you looked—I felt that you were telling me that much partly, perhaps, because you needed to talk about it, but even more to open me up, to give me a chance to spill—that you knew how much I needed to. But, Abe, you know, when I called you Abe the Phoenician, I meant that I found in you—well, a kind of richness of experience, a wisdom, an unusual strength and maturity, so that I couldn't think of you as having this kind of problem."

Abe shook his head sadly.

"So maybe I am—some of that. Then I can't also be puzzled, whipped, have my own nightmares? I'm a man, Walton. That's what I meant when I said 'not either-or' but 'both-and.' 'Both this and that.' You look to me for strength, and I have some—maybe more for you than for myself. And what do you think I see when I look at you? Stop now, let me tell you. You should always be covering your face with your hands if it's praise?

"First after I heard of you, I read the record. Leon Goodman sent it to me. And that record tells me of a man who is a man. Who stands on his own feet when it's dangerous to—is his own man, yet never forgets his responsibility to both his country and the Foundation. Never mind what complex motives his subconscious has. I speak of fact, the printed word. I can read, no? I can interpret. I have brains?

"I see other things. The same strength can be bullheadedness, egotism. But it's tenacity, it's life. You're younger than you are. You tell me your story and I see why you've been slow developing. All the better: at seventy you'll be middle-aged. And I see a combination of all those things that make America, those things you talked to me about. Ten generations of Americans; it shows in your face. This means something. And you use words; they bend and turn and dance for you. Not just sounds, but meaning coming out of life and going out to life. And you shouldn't be governor?"

Walton was regarding him with shining eyes when Abe looked directly at him in conclusion.

"You're romanticizing me, Abe. But what gets me is how *you're* using words. What's happened to the Abe Fortune kind of talk?"

Abe grinned sheepishly.

"When I get excited, I fall back into the way I learned. Walton, do I have to tell you? That clipped talk is a mask, too. I taught myself not to talk like a Jew. Shut up I can't. But make a play, be an eccentric —laconic, nouns, those lonely verbs: that I can teach myself. I have tenacity too, and I don't give the show away except when I don't care any more—like with you. In politics, to be an obvious Jewish Jew is not good in most places. So I have my little tricks and disguises. Now I'm not rich and wise and mature any more? These I am, and that I am, and desperate too. This is life. And the trouble with you is that you reject your own rich mixture and want to settle for some little perfection with angel wings that your Mama taught: 'Either do this or you are dreadful.' You cannot accept praise because you know your faults. I would like to have got my hands on your mama, poor thing."

"Poor thing?" Walton frowned.

"Yes, poor thing. That, too. Because she so badly raised you, she had no sorrows, no dreams, no hopes of her own? And who raised her? You told me."

Walton bowed his head and studied the table.

"Yes," he said softly. "Yes. Yes. And Abe, you do understand a lot about me. Then why can't you see that a man who can't govern himself doesn't have any business being a governor?"

Abe raised his hands in a parody of despair.

"Can't govern himself! Who can? Think of all the governors you've known—Connecticut, New York, Ohio, anywhere you want. These men—let's not name them—all these men are governors of themselves, like Plato tells us? How can you be the man before the Committee and talk that way?"

Walton grinned widely.

"Either-or?" he asked.

Abe laughed and thumped the table.

"So all right, you got me," he said. "And I know the brains are there. May you use them in good health. Let's go back to the governorship and Armour Ward, Irish-German boss. I am serious about you for governor of Connecticut. Not this time—I played that a little cute. You're young, but not so young it isn't time to start. And I am sure of my man, Walton Herrick. Anna Manges and Leon Goodman are not wrong. Only they leave out, Anna especially, a great deal. You supply it. I supply more for myself. What do I find? A man. A man with faults, with potential he hasn't filled, a man with a lot of miseducation to overcome. A man who cheats a little, is disloyal here and there, has a cocked eye for the women, is ambitious and doesn't believe in it, so tries to cover it up, forgetting what he said to the Committee about secrecy. So? A man. A man who has not yet learned how to put himself together, and is only all of himself now and then. But he is growing, and he can grow more. He will learn to commit himself.

"Walton, do you know what most of our candidates are like? They can't grow; they aren't alive. Fossils! Fossils at thirty-five, forty, forty-five, fifty. So let me tell you about you and Armour Ward."

He stood up and began the now familiar pacing.

"Ward I don't like. But he is made of granite. If you must be inanimate, granite is strong stuff to be. He has no imagination, and no intelligence beyond the craftiness he needs at his work. This I feel. But I'm still not sure, and one point in taking you to him is to find out. Do I underestimate him? I must know this about him, not for your sake, but for my own the next few years, and for the party. I want him out of there; he is a block, a roadblock to the growth and vitality of the party in this county.

"He doesn't see you. He sees only the amateur and the egghead. And the rudeness you spoke of, which is not the understandable rudeness of a man meeting someone he doesn't like but sees as an opponent, a competitor, but the rudeness of a man who won't bother with someone he finds irrelevant to his purposes—so, unimportant. And it's a small, narrow man who acts like that. This helped me; I know now that we can beat him eventually and get rid of him."

He paused, poured, emphasized what he said next with the glass in his hand, and the gin slopped over into the remains of the potato salad.

"But was all this simply to use you? Of course not. No either-or. From now on, Ward, having met you and dismissed you, won't be worrying about you. If you show up with me at the state convention, or at some shindig in Hartford, or even at the county meeting, he'll think, 'There's that crazy Jew's candidate,' and forget it. So you get to know the important ones, the worthwhile ones, right under his nose. And these men do know quality when they see it. I'm building for the next election, four years from next fall—that's 1958. When that time comes, I want them to know you."

Walton shook his head, chuckling.

"Machiavelli."

"No. Abe Fortune. I can think too."

Walton stood up in his turn, and began walking the rectangle of the room, hands thrust deep in hip pockets.

"Yes," he said, "you sure can. But Abe, you're leaving out a lot. My vanity has made me a little coy about it, but I really don't want a political career. I've other work to do that will be both more useful, given my nature, and more satisfying to me. And no matter how well you've planned your campaign, there are obstacles—like my three marriages (and now you know how risky even the third one is)—that will take a lot of overcoming. And suppose this affair of mine gets out— beyond the Foundation? But for the present, I'll say no more about my shortcomings—just that I don't have the time or even the inclination to go through all these steps you've figured out. I think I've really played along with you this far chiefly to get to know you better. And I don't regret it."

Abe spread his hands out in that immemorial gesture of suspended effort.

"So all right, I can try. And I will, I warn you. That way, we'll still see each other, even if you never say yes and don't go to a meeting."

As though in tacit consent (end of chapter), they fell to clearing the table and washing the dishes. Finally Walton stopped in the act of drying and polishing, and spoke hesitantly, dish towel held high in his hand.

"Abe," he said, and again, "Abe. These nightmares, you called them, and your not being able to sleep, your drinking. All this—tension. Want to tell me any more?"

Abe put the last piece of silver in the drying rack, frowned.

"That's not easy, Here's where I'm shy—about my own innards. Just say that I've got my fears, my goblins, like everybody. Sometimes, being so full of Jane's, I feel it's too much, too heavy. But even when everything's all right with Jane, I have troubles. I can't put myself all together, either. What helps me is keeping track of everything I can, and at least trying to know why I'm doing what I'm doing. Look. As I see it, life here, now, permits you to go only one of two ways. You can resign, and keep that tension you speak of at arm's length. Or you can accept tension, the confronting of everything that's out there—" he waved his paw vaguely in the direction of the front door—"and try to learn to live with it. Between you and out there, between you and in here—" again he gestured, this time indicating the interior of the house—"and between out there and in here, what they both mean to you. It's a lot to carry around, especially with the Big Shadow hanging over all of us. But I'm not going to resign (and I know you're not either). So I do the best I can. The hardest part is two things, both of which you want but they don't go together. Or two responsibilities that pull against each other."

"Yes," said Walton thoughtfully. "Just lately it's hit me in the middle. And so does this Foundation business, which I've got to meet head on tomorrow."

Abe nodded, but he was suddenly preoccupied. In the silence, a thin voice was calling, "Abe. Abe."

He hurried away, up the stairs. Walton sat alone for a full half hour, all that Abe had said swirling in his head, painfully aware that he would find it hard to maintain his grasp of it, knowing how much there was to be assimilated, yet knowing also his proclivity for not retaining such vital knowledge. Outside the waterfall thundered.

At last he looked at his watch. Abe had been gone for three-quarters of an hour, and it was getting late. He turned off the lights and went upstairs to the room he had slept in before.

After a moment there was a knock at the door. When Walton opened it, Abe shoved an alarm clock and two pieces of paper into his hands.

"I'm not sure I can make it in the morning," he whispered hoarsely. "Here's the train schedule and the number of the taxi company. We have a charge account with them; they'll take you for sure."

Then he was gone, but not before Walton had had a sufficient glimpse of his face to see its grief and pain.

August 13

THROUGHOUT lunch, with the talk urbane and general, Walton had studied Huntingdon Haldane. The more attentive he was, the more he realized, uneasily, grudgingly, that he was impressed with this man, after all. He realized that his established distrust of him had been more a subjective matter than any direct and clear appraisal. This was the sort of man who, in his quiet confidence, his manner of courteous firmness, the suggestion he gave of being comfortably at home wherever he went—this was the sort of man who discomfited Walton, by inducing in him a sense of his own lack of these very qualities. This had been a fairly regular experience ever since his school days.

Haldane had the Roman look—not an emperor, nor a consul or senator, perhaps, but a prefect of the Praetorian Guard, one of those men who made and unmade emperors in the declining days of Rome. He had crisp reddish brown hair, a face made of planes—nothing rounded or oval. His square chin, dented by a dimple, jutted out. Yet the final impression was not so much one of ruggedness or hardness as of leanness, all excesses trimmed away. And the blue eyes could, when he smiled, bring the whole face to a vivid, easy charm, apparently utterly unstudied.

Beside him, P.H., clearly nervous, seemed to shrink. Not, Walton thought, in the sense of any subservience in attitude or manner, but simply through the fact that the juxtaposition exaggerated all P.H.'s softnesses, made him seem tentative, unduly cautious.

When the waiter, having served coffee, left and closed the door to this private room at Haldane's club, there was a moment of silence. Then Haldane turned to P.H.

"Well, Phil?" he said. Nobody else called P.H. Phil, and Walton felt a further uneasiness, as though this suggested an intimacy that somehow lined the two men up together, against him. "Well, Phil, what point have things reached in the Asiatic Studies program?"

P.H. plucked at the tablecloth, then, in his characteristic gesture, spread his small brown hands flat and studied them.

"We've been at a standstill, Hunt," he said. "The letter I wrote you toward the end of June gave you the picture then, and nothing's changed since. We've been waiting for this meeting, which we've had to postpone a few weeks."

Haldane looked at him reflectively.

"Yes. I see." He turned to Walton. "Mr. Herrick, as I understand it, what's holding us up is your determination to appoint Clarence—is that name pronounced Kifer or Keefer?"

"Keefer."

"Keefer—to appoint Clarence Kiefer to the directorship of the new Institute. Whereas Phil—and from what I know I must say I'm inclined to agree with him—feels that, in view of Kiefer's open record of association with three leftist organizations, it would be unwise to do so."

P.H. sighed painfully.

"No, Hunt, that doesn't quite state my position, which is at best an ambivalent one. I felt the way you describe when I first spoke to you, though I didn't fully articulate this to you. But Walton's confidence in the man, unshaken after a number of talks with him and a careful search of the record and conversations with people who have known Kiefer a long time—all these factors have made me, despite my uneasiness, back Walton if he insists. My hope is that today one or the other of you can be persuaded of the validity of the opposite position, and that we can adjourn with an agreement." Again that heavy sigh. "It is important to me, in view of my friendship with Walton, and my faith in him, to say this and to have you confirm to him that this is where I've stood for some time now."

Haldane nodded—curtly, Walton thought.

"Certainly. Of course I'll confirm it. I oversimplified. But that is not the same, Phil, as saying that I can agree with you, either on what to do, or on your reasons for your stand. Friendship and faith—no one is going to attack them. But the situation in which we all find ourselves today is one in which individual friendships and faiths must be subordinated to the preservation of our country and the free world. That, for me, is the heart of the matter."

Walton, packing his pipe, punched at the tobacco in emphasis.

"But I don't believe that this is what is at stake. But first, let me say thanks, P.H."

Haldane looked at him thoughtfully.

"Well, that's what we're here to discuss. I should tell you both that, in the interests of dispatch, whatever we can decide today, though unofficial, will probably be as sure as though the Board were meeting. For I have written at some length to four other trustees, and they have given me their informal proxy. Hence, I will represent a majority of the Board, and although it will require formal ratification at the meeting, we will know, I hope, just where we stand when we break up today."

Walton set his jaw.

"Isn't that arrogating rather extraordinary powers to yourself, Mr. Haldane?" He felt P.H. wince, even though nothing broke the smoothness of his face.

Haldane's eyes had a hard glint.

"Perhaps," he said shortly. "But I think wholly justifiable under the circumstances. This is beginning to look like the Year of the Apocalypse. From Stalin's death in March to the Russian explosion of yesterday, we have been standing in the anteroom. Now we're *there,* in *there.* The Atomic Age. No more guesswork, no more foolish hopes.

"To be sure, there are plus marks on our side. Ike's in office, he's kept his promise in Korea, and we're finally through there. But that's only a drop, not in a bucket, but in an ocean. And we don't know how much time there is; time has replaced money as the negotiable symbol of barter. But it can't be handled with the confidence that money can. We don't know our way; we don't have the requisite experience.

"So listen to me, Mr. Herrick. The United States and Soviet Russia are not engaged in a local squabble; these are not parochial matters with which we are concerned. The God of Events also observes the fall of a sparrow; our problems are bigger birds. The proposed Institute can have an immensely valuable, perhaps crucially valuable part to play in improving the American position in the Orient. To delay getting it going, and going vigorously, would fall little short of treason. And since my other commitments had prevented me from meeting with you until now and will again claim me fully, I was doubly concerned to come today equipped to prevent any further delay." He relaxed, and his voice softened. "But I also want to assure you, Mr. Herrick, that I have not prejudged—nor caused the others to prejudge—your man Kiefer, and that I am open to any decision warranted by demonstrable evidence."

But Walton felt the inevitable warning signals within him—that tightening and rising of internal temperature that presaged anger.

"Kiefer is not 'my man,'" he said stiffly. "And if I understand the organizational structure of our Foundation, it still seems to me that you have been highhanded in proceeding as you have. The Schuyler Foundation is not in a state of war, Mr. Haldane, to warrant the use of extraordinary emergency powers."

Haldane smiled, with what seemed full and genuine humor.

"You have a gift for imagery, Mr. Herrick. But I think you're wrong. I think we are in just such a state, and what I've just said proves it. Phil?"

P.H. considered his hands. When he spoke, his voice was soft, regretful.

"Yes," he said, "in a sense. I'm afraid so."

Walton shrugged.

"Arguing this point won't get us anywhere. I'll accept the situation, if only because I must. But what I'd like to know, Mr. Haldane, is where you got whatever information you have about Kiefer to make you feel he's unsatisfactory, and just exactly what that information is." He finally lighted his pipe, and puffed on it.

Haldane looked at him in steady speculation.

"The first question I don't feel that I should answer. You both know that I raised the question of Kiefer's qualifications to Phil, not the other way around. And I raised it in the fashion I did to prevent possible embarrassment, or worse, should the recommendation come, unqualified, from you two, only to be turned down at the meeting of the Board. Since my informant did not want to be identified, I shall keep faith with him, unless—as indeed I told him—the time comes when there is a clear usefulness in revealing his name." He paused, and when he resumed spoke more slowly, as though for emphasis. "The second question I am perfectly willing to answer, although it does seem to me under the circumstances more appropriate for you, the sponsor, to state your case for Kiefer and then let me present my contradictory evidence. But this is an informal meeting, and I'll do as you request."

After another moment's pause, which lay between them like a deep, unrippled pool of silence, he began, "Clarence Kiefer is a full professor of Oriental Languages and Literature at Dunston University. He was the administrative head of his department for ten years, and has now been dean of the graduate school for six years. There is no question about his academic record; it clearly establishes him as an able administrator and a first-rate scholar." He paused, clipped and lighted a cigar, holding it off for a moment while twirling it in the flame from his lighter, as though saturating its tip in fire. "So far so good. But he also, in the mid-forties, was a sponsor of the Pacific Institute for Cultural Relations, an organization about which there has been a good deal of unfavorable comment, with a policy that had, to say the least, a soft attitude toward the Communists in Asia. He was a member of the Volunteers for Global Peace, generally accepted as a leftist pacifist organization, if not actually a Communist front. And, worst of all, he was on the Executive Committee of the Independent League of Educators, Artists and Scientists, which was cited by the Attorney General."

Walton broke in.

"There are some clarifications that I can make. It's thoroughly ascertainable that his membership, or sponsorship, of the Pacific Institute was a nominal one. There were some fifty or sixty sponsors, and the list of names includes every important name in the Oriental field. Whatever nucleus at headquarters, on the staff or among the officers, may have had leftist sympathies, I don't know. But I do know, from the man who was secretary at the time, as well as from Kiefer himself, that beyond lending his name Kiefer took no active part at all, and received only those communications and bulletins sent to all sponsors."

"Who is this secretary, Mr. Herrick?"

Walton stiffened.

"I have no desire to get *him* into trouble, Mr. Haldane. He is a man of some directness and assured me without hesitation that, while a certain number of sponsors worked quite closely with the central office, Kiefer was not one of them. I see no more reason for revealing his name than for you to tell us who aroused your suspicions about Kiefer."

"I do," Haldane replied firmly. "My informant simply told me in which of these organizations Kiefer had been a member. You are using the word of this unidentified man to evaluate the meaning of one of those memberships. You speak of his directness, but this is an intangible. How do we know that you are not mistaken in your estimate of him? How do we know that he hasn't Communist sympathies to this day, and is cleverly shielding Kiefer?"

Walton answered coldly: "I think it was clear at the Congressional hearings that I am not inexperienced in pursuing these matters. This man has none of the readily identifiable characteristics of the Communist sympathizer. And he speaks quite freely of his distrust of Soviet Russia and of Stalinist policy. He holds a responsible post at a university now, and is much respected by his colleagues."

Haldane drew on his cigar and meditatively considered its long ash.

"Very well, but I can't accept such assurances as definitive. There is still too much of the subjective involved to consider them proof. Did this man comment on the policy and position of the Pacific Institute? Did you ask him about it?"

Walton nodded.

"I did. He said candidly that he felt that there were definite Communist sympathizers among those who ran the Institute, though he doubted that there were any Party members or that those he thought sympathizers took orders from the Party. Moreover, he said that the executive director, a firm anti-Communist, more than balanced the leftist element. Had it not been so, he said, he would never have consented to stay on as secretary until 1948, when financial difficulties and the general change in political climate began to make it difficult for the Institute to continue."

P.H. broke in.

"Walton, what about the Volunteers for Global Peace?"

Walton shrugged and smiled.

"Anyone who has examined that organization very closely knows that it was run by a crackpot fringe. If any Communists or fellow travelers belonged, they had no real effect, for Dodge and Phillips, who completely ran it, have a long record as professional pacifists. There is documentary evidence on this. Volunteers lasted only from the fall of '45 to January, '47. Then, before long, Dodge and Phillips started another one. And Kiefer has shown me his file on this—his letter accepting membership on condition that this was not a political organization and had no association with the Communist Party."

Haldane asked, "Were no other letters in the file?"

"Yes," Walton replied, "one concerning a fund-raising campaign, and one stating he could not attend a given meeting."

Haldane's cigar had gone out. He laid it flat in an ashtray and looked sharply at Walton.

"You call it a crackpot outfit, and yet you want us to have confidence in a man who joined it. Whether or not the Volunteers had any Communist bias, this does not constitute a very satisfactory recommendation for Kiefer's judgment."

Walton shrugged his shoulders.

"If so, you must condemn on the same score the following men." He drew a sheet of paper from his pocket and read a list of some forty names, including those of distinguished and immediately recognizable educators, scholars and professional men.

Haldane shook his head sadly.

"What a pitiful record for the intellectuals of this country! Mr. Herrick, one thing I want to say to you is that I have no doubt at all about your integrity, your loyalty, your principles and intentions. If I seem to you to be skeptical about much you tell me, I do not intend to suggest any doubt on any of these scores. Not only Phil's strong endorsement of you, but everything I know about you reinforces this opinion. So please keep that in mind.

"What I *am* concerned about grows out of my brief experience with the Atomic Energy Commission. I am not at liberty to give particulars, but every day I see new instances of how genuine and honest liberals have been taken in by clever and ruthless Communists and Communist comforters. I fear much of this may have to be made public before long."

He picked up his cigar, dusted off the ashes and pointed it at Walton.

"I want you to know that I am not a McCarthyite, a reactionary, a peeper under the bed of the sort you mentioned to the Congressional Committee. I am gravely and deeply concerned about the laxness of the Roosevelt and Truman administrations under their liberal dispensations, but not because I am a rabblerouser or a liberal-baiter. Those attitudes I deplore as much as you do. But that doesn't mitigate for one minute the real past and present danger of Communist-oriented Americans or disloyal leftists. Security has become a scoffed-at word among liberals, but without genuine security measures the freedom you fight for will no longer exist."

Walton nodded.

"I think we agree completely on general principles. Our disagreement is about their application."

Haldane considered the statement.

"Perhaps," he said. "I will have to admit, however, that so far, while nobody has dug up evidence to refute what you've said about Kiefer's relation to the first two organizations, the favorable interpretation rests heavily on opinion, hearsay and your own weighing of his and others' testimony. But let's leave them for the moment. Membership in the third organization, the Independent League of Educators, Artists and Scientists, cited by the Attorney General, is the most damning. And not only general membership, but membership on the executive committee."

P.H.'s brown forehead was corrugated. Walton saw in his eyes an expression of alarm, engendered, he was sure, by a sudden recollection of Walton's statement of his own membership in the ILEAS, and his acquaintance there with Kiefer—and probably a regret that he had not warned Walton to silence about this. And Walton, in turn, felt a certain sardonic amusement. He was aware, too, of a perverse feeling of recklessness—and tried to press it down, by sternly reminding himself of the seriousness of the issue under debate, his own obligations both to the Foundation and to Kiefer.

"Yes," he said at last, and realized with this first monosyllable that he was not going to be able to control his strange elation over the direction in which matters were moving. "Yes, he was a member of the ILEAS' executive committee. There were, in all, fifteen members of this committee, and he was one of them. Let me reconstruct for you, Mr. Haldane, the beginnings of this organization."

Haldane, studying him with intentness now, merely nodded. But out of the corner of his eye Walton could see P.H.'s frozen attitude, for all the world like that of some hapless father awaiting in consternation the revelation of his child's misconduct.

"It was founded," Walton began, "in 1944 primarily to organize people in education and the arts and sciences in support of FDR's campaign for a fourth term. This was the reason I joined it, and I am quite sure Kiefer's reason as well. Large numbers of men—"

Haldane's voice cut across Walton's sharply.

"Will you repeat that! You joined it?"

Walton found it difficult to restrain laughter, so incredulous, so naked was Haldane's voice.

"Yes," he replied calmly. "I have never made any secret of the fact that I belonged to ILEAS in 1944 and '45."

Haldane swung sharply to P.H.

"You knew this, Phil? You knew this when you allowed Herrick to represent us in Washington?"

P.H. shook his head miserably.

"I learned only this summer. Walton has told me he was not active."

Haldane's face was set in hard, jutting lines.

"But surely you inquired, before you entrusted that responsibility to him, Phil? Think of what it would have meant to the Foundation if the Committee had investigated *Herrick's* record."

P.H. examined his hands.

"I never thought of it, Hunt. I've known Walton so long and so well that it was inconceivable to me—It still is, though I haven't the faintest doubt of Walton's innocence, as far as any slightest connection with the Communist Party. But I do see the danger you're referring to, and, friend or no friend, I was negligent. Thank God we were lucky."

Haldane swung around to Walton, eyes and voice so steely that Walton could almost see the Praetorian helmet.

"And you, Mr. Herrick? It never occurred to you that you were endangering the Foundation's reputation—indeed, in view of the circumstances, the good name of all American foundations?"

Walton resolutely summoned himself back from the dark swamp-land of guilt to which he had suddenly felt banished as Haldane spoke to P.H. Guilt? But he was not guilty.

"Yes," he said quietly. "It occurred to me. In the first place, what-ever the justification for the Attorney General's citation, I knew that I was never guilty of the slightest action that would justify the citation's referring to me. Satisfied by this fact, I felt no concern over my member-ship when the Attorney General's list appeared, and when I thought of it at all during my preparation of our report, I thought of its discovery and mention as a first-rate, immediate opportunity to make my points about the difference between facts and allegations."

Haldane shook his head in a way that suggested awe, but his voice was as hard as before, his tone sarcastic.

"'Because my heart is pure!' Herrick, it's incredible. No, not in-credible—I don't want to say that—but extraordinary and very alarm-ing." He paused and shook his head again. Then he said grimly, "Suppose you tell us about your association with this organization before we go on to Kiefer's. First of all, you were already with the Foundation when you joined. And I remember, Herrick, your noble words before the Committee about the evils of secrecy, to say nothing of your assertion a few minutes ago that you never made a secret of the fact. How does it happen, then, that Phil never knew about it till a month or two ago?"

Walton set his jaw again.

"*Mr.* Haldane," he began, for he had observed Haldane's new way of addressing him. "What I have told you is true. It is rapidly becoming a matter of indifference to me whether or not you do believe me, but I care a good deal for P.H.'s feeling of responsibility in the situation. I said that I made no secret of my membership. But neither did I boast of it. In fact, my membership was so nominal that I never did anything active for ILEAS until early '45, when I was appointed to its education committee. This led in turn to my resignation. But let me make clear that it was both simple and natural for P.H. and me never to have my membership come up in any of our conversations. Aside from exchang-ing the facts that he was going to vote for Dewey and I for Roosevelt, we seldom talked politics."

Haldane said sharply, "For whom did you vote in 1948?"

"Mr. Haldane," said Walton, "I am not on the witness stand. And it is my understanding that we have a secret ballot in the United States. But I don't object to telling you that I did not vote for Henry Wallace, which I am sure you thought, but, as a protest against all their houses, for Norman Thomas. There were times during that long election night, however, when I wished I had voted for Harry Truman."

This time Haldane waited silently.

"So to go back to ILEAS. I joined as an effective way—so I thought—of backing FDR. But I was still fairly new to New York and the Foundation, and did not have the time or, frankly, the inclination to work actively for the organization. Then, early in 1945, I went to several meetings of the education committee. I did not like the way they were run—the secretary seemed to me more bureaucratic than most obvious bureaucrats—and I saw very little usefulness in the committee's work, so I resigned. From it and from the ILEAS altogether. With FDR elected and then dead, there was no further appeal for me in it."

"That's a rather vague description of the education committee's activities," Haldane remarked dryly.

Walton looked at him levelly.

"What further would you like to know?" he asked.

"More specifically, what reason such an organization had for an education committee. More specifically, what its members did. Exactly what sort of 'bureaucracy' led to your resigning?"

Walton looked at P.H., at the misery in his brown eyes, and back to Haldane.

"I take it that I have joined Kiefer for a hearing before your investigating committee?"

Haldane stood up impatiently, and tapped out a beat on the table with his cigar clipper.

"Mr. Herrick," he said, "I've been shaken by what you've told us. First, by your irresponsibility in not recognizing the peril you put us in when you accepted the post of presenting our case before the Congressional Committee. Second, by your stubbornness, in the face of these facts, in backing Kiefer. Third, by your apparent callousness over the position in which you have put Phil, your friend, your superior in the Foundation, and the man to whom you owe your present—eminence. Under these circumstances, it does not seem strange to me that I want to find out more about your association with the Independent League."

"No," said Walton, "I suppose it is not strange. And what you say of P.H. would persuade me, if nothing else would. But let me remind you, Mr. Haldane, about the political and intellectual climate of the mid-forties. The Roosevelt era was, of course, a great one for all liberals —the many different kinds of liberals, pseudo-liberals and semi-liberals, to say nothing of the different regional sorts of liberals. As was true in the government, so in organizations of this sort, genuine anti-Communist liberals, Communists, fellow travelers and liberals who were more interested in achieving certain legitimate goals than in who their associates in working for those goals were—in organizations like ILEAS, these people, and even some totally nonpolitical ones, were all mixed together.

"Bear in mind, too, that in the years '44 and '45 both the official position of the United States and the popular attitudes of Americans were much more tolerant of the Soviet Union than before or since. Suspicions were being re-established, but in New York and among these organizations, it took a politically sophisticated person to be fully on guard against Communist infiltration. Such a person I was not, nor, I am sure, was Clarence Kiefer. He had been in New York for seven or eight years, but never active politically; I was fresh from Ohio, and, for a complex of reasons, never active politically."

"I am quite prepared to accept the notion of your political naïveté." Haldane's voice was by now icy.

Walton stared at him in silence for a full half minute.

"Mr. Haldane," he then said, "I am not apologizing. I am saying that, viewing the matter historically, in the context of those years, no thinking person can condemn someone for mere membership in one of those organizations. Only in the hysterical present, induced by McCarthy and others like him, could there be so general a panic. I want to be accurate. Some of us were probably duped, some others certainly so. But most of us not for long, and not for much beyond the use of our names.

"At any rate, to get back to the matter of the education committee. You ask why such a committee; and that is the first question I asked, on the very first day it met. I was not yet acquainted with who was who, but observed a little touchily the smile, half-unbelieving, half-contemptuous—or so it seemed to me—on the face of a woman present, over the question I'd asked. It was a face that would have been markedly pretty had it not been so toughened, and the eyes so blank, like the proverbial marbles, and without expression, that I remember thinking that the rest of her face was a mask."

He paused to relight his pipe and noted with satisfaction that both his listeners were raptly intent, in their very different ways.

"I learned later that she was Janet Neale, the executive secretary of the entire ILEAS, sitting in *ex officio*. At this point, she did not reply, but the chairman of the committee, a fussy, self-important man from one of the New York colleges and clearly, as time was to show, of little more political sophistication than I, tried to answer me. He said that in the 'time of troubles' (he spoke the words as though he had minted them) we were in, it was unfortunate that our colleges and universities gave so little attention to the local and national political scenes, and to the various political faiths of the world. This lack was even greater in secondary education, and the committee had been formed for the purpose of finding ways and means of ameliorating the situation.

" 'In a nonpartisan way?' I asked, and he said, 'Yes, of course,' stiffly, while Janet Neale smiled again.

"Let me cut this short, which I can do and still give you the full gist. We met several times, and I came to realize that, of the seven committee members, the chairman, one other and I were clearly innocents—at least in the sense of taking literally the avowed purpose of the committee and stressing throughout its nonpartisan educative mission. Two others backed Janet Neale solidly on every issue, and the remaining two, both scientists, were impatient with us for being so 'finicky,' as one of them put it, and holding things up. But there was a difference between them and the Neale axis, for they were quite independent in their judgments."

Walton's pipe had gone out again, and he went about relighting it in a leisurely fashion, peering at them over the bowl, while words and smoke spurted from his mouth at once.

"Some of the ways and means discussed were the raising of funds for the establishment of chairs in the leading universities for courses in contemporary politics (I realized right away that my presence on the committee was in the hope of interesting our Foundation and perhaps others); the organization of student discussion groups where none existed (I kept asking through what agency, but never got a very satisfactory answer); through recommendations to public education systems; through proposing legislation on the state and federal levels. There was much discussion, pro and con, about federal aid for the over-all program, but at the end of two meetings it still seemed to me that we had barely broken ground.

"Then—" he paused significantly—"came the third meeting. Present were several men I'd never seen before. Janet Neale introduced one of them as a Dr. Burnside or Bernstein or Burnholt (I can't remember which), 'a student of these problems'—I still remember that these were her words—who had proposals to make to us. Proposals! He had the whole bill of goods drawn up: a platform of ten planks, half of which we'd never discussed, and including the establishment of a lobby in Washington, to be run by this very man!

"I protested immediately that this was highhanded—" Walton

paused to enjoy Haldane's grin—"and that it ignored the whole process of the committee, that the conclusion one must draw from it was that the committee had only been set up as a 'front,' a façade, and presumably the whole course of action had been planned long ago. The other committee member with whom I had felt some sympathy joined me, but Janet Neale denied this, and said that this Dr. B—— had been working on his own and, unaware of the committee's activities, had brought this plan to her. Since the committee had had so much difficulty in coming to grips with the problem, she had invited Dr. B—— to bring in his excellent summary, as a clear starting point. She regretted that there should be such suspiciousness among a group of friends!

"The vote came in ten minutes, after a motion from one of her stooges on the committee that we adopt the plan immediately and go to work on the details. Five for, two against, the chairman of course abstaining except in case of a tie. It was only then that I learned that Janet Neale had a vote, and that one scientist, absent, had given her his proxy as well.

"I was furious. On the way out I caught up with Kiefer—"

"Kiefer?"

Haldane was leaning forward incredulously.

Walton smiled and nodded.

"The other man who voted with me was Kiefer. That's how I came to know him. We went off to a restaurant for coffee, and decided to resign from ILEAS. I asked him about the doings of the executive committee and he told me he was troubled about that, too. The meetings were short and routine, passing on matters that had never been discussed, but which were presented by staff members. We deliberated on whether or not we should present any charges, or make public our reasons for our resignations, but decided it was best simply and flatly to resign. There was nothing we could prove, and there was nothing illegal in what ILEAS was doing. That was the end of it, but Kiefer and I have occasionally met since, and the respect I have for him grew out of this situation."

Haldane stirred, rapped his knuckles meditatively on the table beside him.

"That's quite a dramatic story, Mr. Herrick. It does render things somewhat different that you had this ace up your sleeve. But didn't you or Kiefer ever feel that you should report all this to the government, especially after the Attorney General's citation?"

"We talked about it. We didn't see what good we could do. Janet

Neale, I read in the paper two years ago, went to Europe to stay. None of the others are more than nameless figures to us, except the scientists, who, we agreed, were not Communist-oriented, just impatient scientific utopianists. Oh—and the chairman, we learned later, resigned after we did."

"And you didn't tell Phil about this, even then?" Haldane's eyes bored into Walton's.

"No. Though I had no particular reason not to. But that year was quite a hectic one for me. I had been divorced, and in '44 was remarried. I had two invalids on my hands—my mother and sister. And this was the period when, as P.H. can tell you, our work, though roughly in the same department, was quite separate. I was reporting in regularly to Mr. Ingersoll and I did tell him about it. I'd be glad to have you ask him to confirm it, and I'll admit I'm even more glad that at eighty-eight his memory is still quite clear."

It was to P.H. he turned then, and found the relief and gladness he expected to find.

"Walton, I feel much better to know that."

Haldane cleared his throat.

"Yes, Phil," he said quietly, "I can see why you do. As a matter of fact, I feel better too. But there are still some matters for us to clear up, and a good deal more to consider. Mr. Herrick, why didn't you tell Phil about your own membership in ILEAS and acquaintance with Kiefer on this committee—why didn't you tell him this back last spring, when Kiefer's candidacy first became an issue? Even granting that by reporting to Ernest Ingersoll back in 1945 you cleared your skirts there, and that last December, at the hearings, you had your own peculiar justification (one with which I have little sympathy, and which I frankly find irresponsible) for not speaking to Phil about your own former membership—granted all that, why your silence last spring?"

P.H. was listening and watching intently.

Walton hesitated. "I have no sure answer," he said finally. "Much of the time, it didn't cross my mind, except to remind me of my good firsthand reasons for knowing of Kiefer's integrity. The few times I did think of telling P.H. about that direct experience, I think I failed to for two reasons. These come hard, P.H. But I half thought of this knowledge as an ace in the hole, to be used only when and if necessary. And second, the harder, I didn't feel sure just how you would interpret these facts. Yet you must know, from the casual way I finally told you at lunch this summer, that neither of these two reasons was a deeply worked-through line of action with me."

P.H. was flushed. He did not meet Walton's eyes.

Haldane broke the silence.

"Whatever the reason," he said, and his voice was almost gentle, "you withheld important evidence. Weren't you both somewhat secretive and quite highhanded?"

Walton grinned, though he felt suddenly shaky.

"Touché," he said, and was relieved at the relative ease, the freedom with which he conceded.

Haldane stood up, went over to the tall window and stood there for several minutes, gazing up at the sky. P.H. and Walton sat quietly, smiling at each other.

Haldane swung around.

"There are a few things more I want to say now," he said, "but I don't see how we can settle matters today. The situation has changed, and I feel I must at least think it through overnight. I'll be staying here. And incidentally, neither of you lives in New York, do you? You'll be wanting to go home and batten down."

"Yes," said P.H. "I've been thinking about that. Sometime in the middle of the night, isn't it?"

Walton looked from one to the other in perplexity.

"What are you talking about?"

"The hurricane," said P.H. "Due to pass offshore tonight. I wondered what you've heard from the Vineyard. I don't think it'll get the center of the storm, but probably some of the edges."

Haldane was looking curiously at Walton.

"You didn't see the morning paper?"

Walton shook his head.

"I stayed overnight with a friend in Stamford, and had to run for the train this morning. I must call Julie, and I'll have to go home and clear the yard."

Haldane nodded.

"Right. So just a few things, Mr.—may I call you Walton? I think I've begun to understand you better. You're what I call a poet. No derogation. Poetry may be out of my line, but I respect it. But poets should stay out of politics. Your epic before the Congressional Committee was an exception—and for more people than not you put it over. But not for everybody—I've heard some unfavorable reverberations in Washington. Nonetheless, a really fine poem, and ever since I read it I've been divided as to whether you were a great man or a fool. If you'll forgive my impertinence, I've concluded that you're a little of both. Don't be angry, Walton: I mean a great poet and a foolish politician.

"A word more. In a letter to me about you—one I requested of him—Phil said something about you that struck me particularly. You have, he wrote, 'a kind of authority vested in no other power than that of himself.' I sensed that in your testimony, and again today, but Phil's words sum it up beautifully. And it is at once your strength and your weakness. You impress people; they trust and admire you; they even take strength, I believe, from your stature, the fearless quality of your mind and character."

Walton extended a hand in involuntary protest, but Haldane rode on.

"Don't protest. I'm coming to the other side of the matter. Both your record and your personality suggest that you don't work particularly well with other people: that's the style of the poet, not the politician. You're too forceful, too full of your own ideas and principles, to be patient of the logistics of politics, or even of committee work, to accept and negotiate compromise. You're too proud a man for discretion, and you're contemptuous of convention and public opinion. I state all this as opinion, of course, my opinion, yet I've given it a good deal of thought."

Walton looked at him ruefully.

"I don't know whether I want more to protest the praise or the blame," he said, "so I won't do either. Certainly much of it seems to me partially true, but I don't find that I'm as consistently any of these things as you suggest."

"Consistency and inconsistency are private matters," said Haldane, "though often publicly invoked. They are dependent upon the complex of relationships and aspects of one's life that only a few people, if any, can ever know. I know you only in the context of the Foundation, and it is in that context that I speak."

Walton looked up and directly at him.

"So?" he asked.

"So. So I have these things to say. I believe you—all you've said today, and specifically, about Kiefer. I believe that Kiefer is a valuable man. But the interests of the Foundation, and my own interests, especially in terms of the Atomic Energy Commission, force me to consider other angles than my estimate of the characters of the men involved. It is now over three years since Alger Hiss was sentenced. Ever since, less notable men have been examined, some discredited, some exonerated, some left standing in the desolate outer court of suspended judgment. Perjury, loyalty, security, sedition: these are the words that keep ringing the changes of our time.

"The Rosenbergs have been executed. The Communist Party

leaders have been sentenced. The Attorney General's list has been posted. The foundations have been investigated. Senator McCarthy has been riding high. People all over the country have come to a pitch of fear and suspicion and hate that has brought us to a trigger-finger atmosphere."

He paused, looked full at Walton and went on, speaking very slowly now.

"In such a situation—and even though I deplore it—the best interests of the Foundation make me believe that it would be unwise to appoint Kiefer. I also think, Walton, that it may be unwise for you to work with the new Institute any further. No matter how clean your hands, in this climate, your membership in that damned League might be enough to discredit the whole project in many eyes."

"But the whole thing was my idea," Walton protested. "This is my baby."

"I know. It's another poem. And may you dedicate many more to the Schuyler Foundation. But the architect seldom lives in the house he planned. And to put it bluntly, Walton, I'm not going to find myself in the position that John Foster Dulles found himself vis-à-vis Hiss as the President of the Carnegie Corporation. Not while I'm serving on the A.E.C."

"But that's hardly an analogy," said P.H.

"Right—and I shan't try to press it. To this day, I'm not even sure whether Alger Hiss was guilty of disloyalty. I'm talking of our reputation and our need to *seem* to be without blemish. You have said in a number of different ways, Walton, that you don't care about appearances. Well, I do, because I must—and are you sure that there's no aspect of your life, no corner of your mind, in which you don't care, at least a little, about them?"

"No," said Walton in a low voice, and he was remembering Abe's "Why do you care so much . . ."

Haldane's look changed; Walton saw in his eyes both respect and kindness.

"Then," Haldane said quietly, "I'm going to leave it there for now. Nor am I going to use those vetoes. With your permission, Phil, I'm going to call an extraordinary meeting of the Board in the next week and ask you, Walton, to be ready to come in and tell your story to the trustees. I'm not completely sure yet that my position on Kiefer —and you—will be what I've just said. But it may be. What I am sure of is that I shall tell them at the beginning of the meeting of my admiration and complete confidence in your character and work."

Walton smiled.

"Thank you," he said. "But just one question. If it worries you to have me associated with the Institute, doesn't it worry you equally to have me heading a department at the Foundation? Are you sure you wouldn't like my resignation?"

Haldane rose and came over to him, holding out his hand.

"I am very sure," he said. "Most of the work of your department has no political overtones at all, and the Foundation could ill afford to lose you. Even were your association with the League to come up, my mind would not change. It is only in the sensitive area of the Asiatic Institute that I'm worried—about appearances, not about you. And I congratulate you, Phil," he said, swinging around to P.H., "on having brought Walton to the Foundation in the first place."

Outside, the sky was gray and listless. Gusts rattled grimy newspapers and cartons down the gutters. Heading for Grand Central, Walton kept muttering, "Julie, Julie."

MANUSCRIPT: 4

STUDY OF NO FRIEND

Chilmark, Martha's Vineyard
Sunday evening, August 16

The storm is over, Tim's all right, and Walton's gone back to New York. Thanks to the kindness of P. H. Gates, Cyn and I will stay on till late Tuesday—and I guess we need two extra days, to catch our breath after a weekend of storms, natural and human.

Up to late Friday afternoon, the island was a bubbling pot of rumors about the hurricane, which was moving north along the coast at about twelve miles an hour. The U.S. Weather Bureau and the Coast Guard said it would turn east at Nantucket, and the worst we would get would be a northeast gale. But some of the old-timers here, who persuaded many people that they knew more than any weather bureau, went around muttering that it looked to them as though the eye of the storm would go right through the fairgrounds at West Tisbury. Plenty of excitement.

Walton called Thursday night; he'd just heard about it (Lord knows where he'd been; it's been in the papers and on the air since it was first sighted four hundred miles southeast of Florida) and said the winds in New York and Connecticut were high but not dangerous. To judge from Julie's end of their conversation, he wanted to come up here. She pointed out to him that we're on high ground, that her father is an old and experienced islander, and that the Weather Bureau was confident we'd have only a nor'easter.

He must have been very insistent, and very concerned, for they talked more than ten minutes and finally Julie's voice softened. I couldn't hear what she said except at the very end: "But I am glad you called and wanted to come, darling."

Friday morning was strange, very foggy; the whole island was bathed in a hot haze. We drove past the fairgrounds (the fair will open Thursday), and it was spooky. Something about the way the mist swirled around the tops of the few tents already up, and the strings of bare electric bulbs had a funny kind of naked look—desolate. Reminded me of that title (Connolly's?): *The Condemned Playground.*

During that afternoon Tim developed what seemed to be a bad case of summer complaint, so when, about four o'clock, the winds began to blow, Julie stayed with him while the rest of us went up to still higher ground on the ocean side to see what was happening.

The Colonel (Julie's father) was a good man to have along. He's lived outdoors most of his life and has a real eye for nature. He pointed out how, although there were heavy fog banks at the water's edge, the sky was completely visible. Heavy clouds, but a creamy color, not dark, and in between them, here and there, a very pale blue sky. He said he'd seen similar skies in the Mediterranean before a squall.

Then he showed me how the edges peeled off the clouds, and these fragments whirled swiftly "to leeward," as he said, thus showing where the wind was about to strike. "Rain soon," he said. "We'd better start the children back." He was right. We felt the first drops on the way back to the house, and showers developed quickly.

On our return, we found Julie worried about Timmy. Not even paregoric could stop his diarrhea and she had sent for the doctor. Timmy was pale and listless; he actually looked thinner than he had in the morning; his eyes were big and apathetic, and the only signs of real life in him were his tears when he had to make another trip to the bathroom.

Until the doctor came, we all sat around in a kind of fearful, awkward quiet, making an attempt at some false animation whenever Julie passed through the room. Even the children, until Cyn persuaded Jenny to go out on the porch and play with her for a while. Peter would not budge. He sat, staring with blank intensity at his own tightly closed fists, looking up only when his mother came close to him.

"I wish Daddy was here," he muttered.

Julie stopped short, looking startled. Then she turned to the Colonel, who stood nearby in his own version of the general stricken attitude.

Her eyes wide in fear, her whole body unnaturally stiff (I'd been amazed at how really terrified Julie seemed; I'd expected her to be cool and efficient), she said, "I do too. Father, I think I'll call him."

The Colonel's seamed face remained expressionless, but his voice was gentle.

"You've forgotten the storm," he said. "It's begun to pour, and it'll get worse all night long."

Julie pressed her hand against her mouth; the fear in her eyes turned to something close to terror. We all watched her in pain. I know I wanted to put my arms around her; I guess everyone else there did too, but only Peter was free to fling himself at her, and join her sobbing.

"I know what I'll do," she said, her voice muffled against Peter's head. "I'll call him now, so that he can come up as soon as it's over. Later the lines may be down." She turned and spoke to her father and me as though she must defend her action. "He's so strong and comforting. He always knows what to do and Tim loves him so."

Peter said brokenly, "Yes, Mom, yes. Call him. Call him."

A wail from overhead. The Colonel swung up the stairs.

"I'll take care of Tim," he said. "You go ahead and call him."

Suppose, I thought, as Julie gave the operator the number, suppose he isn't there. Suppose he's with Sonia at this very minute. Six-thirty on Friday: he'll never be home. And I felt a curious irritation over her words "strong and comforting. He always knows what to do . . . Tim loves him so."

Well, it just upset everything for me—everything about Walton and Julie, I mean. Of course it was good that she felt that way—or would have been if he was really there for her. That was how I was feeling when I heard her say, "Oh, Walton. I'm so glad you're home!"

At this moment the Doctor arrived, his bag wet and glistening, and hurried upstairs, saying, "No time to waste tonight." So the next words of Julie's I heard were "Peter and Jenny are fine. Maria's over in Edgartown for a few days with some friends, the Lincolns. They have a girl her age. Walton, she is a darling—and we'll see she's all right." A pause, with his voice crackling more urgently. Then: "Fly? But you hate to fly" and then a short silence and "Oh, Walton. I love you."

I went out on the porch. It was coming down in torrents, and night had set in already. I want to be honest about this: I felt something like hate for Walton. Here he was a hero, and presented with Julie's heart on a platter, when all the time— And all because he was coming for his sick boy—and what father wouldn't? And on a plane! Well, I've flown a hundred times and nobody ever gave me a medal for it.

Sour. Bile in the mouth. I don't like it.

The doctor was sober, crisp. He said there was no danger, or almost none, if Timmy went to the hospital now, where he could be watched constantly, and fed intravenously to bring back his strength. He really was as weak as a dishrag. Yes, Julie could stay with him. The new maternity wing was to be dedicated on Sunday, and not yet occupied; there were plenty of beds.

Cyn insisted on going with Julie, once the doctor said there were plenty of beds. Jennifer was given her choice and said it was "too wet"; she'd stay with "Damps," who caught her up in a fierce grandfather's grip, until she complained about his prickly mustache. So those two and Peter and I stayed and the doctor carried Timmy out to the car with Cyn helping him and Julie rushing around giving last-minute instructions. Walton would fly up as soon as the storm was over. I must tell him what the doctor had said when he called back in an hour. I must call the people in Edgartown with whom Maria was staying, to be sure she was all right. The Colonel would tell me what else to lock up and batten down for the storm. Peter was to sleep in Jenny's room, to keep her company. Good-bye, good-bye, good-bye.

She was feverish, but from elation. Timmy would be saved, Walton was coming, ta-ra-ta-ra, the U.S. Cavalry.

I'm just setting it down the way I felt; I guess it's obvious how it was with me, and I don't like it, but there it is. And as I peered out into the wet blackness, I saw Cyn reach out and kiss Julie, then help her into the car. They were gone.

Women. Cyn, the night Walton came to dinner, when I told her about coming up to the Vineyard and spending that weekend of June 20 here with Julie. She didn't even wait to find out what the basis of the weekend was, or that Julie's father was here, or that Julie wasn't the sort of woman to have an affair—or anything. Julie was a bitch, a vixen, a faithless no-good wench—all this after Walton left that night. And then Julie invites us both up for a week, and P.H. says, "Take it and stay a week longer in September," and we come. And then the kiss and the vigil together in the hospital.

Yet—it's funny—I was glad Cyn went with Julie. I didn't want to be with her Friday night. I'm not clear why.

Damps and Jenny were already upstairs when I came back into the house. Peter (he never had before) shook hands good night with me and told me, "Don't worry"!

Walton called in a half hour.

"Dud!" he said. "What in hell? Never mind. What about Timmy?"

I told him—all the details. It was hard to satisfy him. He wanted that triple-plated reassurance everyone wants from life and never gets, but he finally did seem a little reconciled and approved of our plans. I told him that he'd been out of the Foundation so much and I'd seen so little of him that I'd had no chance to tell him that Cyn and I were coming up. I told him I'd meet the first plane from New York whenever it reached the Vineyard.

None of this interested him; he wanted only to hear more about Tim and Julie. On a sudden impulse, I asked him to call our house in Northport and check to make sure our kids were all right. My excuse was that we didn't know the sitter very well. As a matter of fact, one look at Mrs. Briggs and you'd know she was a better protector and defender of the home than a machine gun.

Anyway, that seemed to please him and he offered to call me back. I said no, not to, unless there was something wrong. No news, good news. We hung up.

The Colonel came downstairs and we fastened everything tight. He had decided to make a cot in the room with the children, and when we had everything shipshape he laid out the decanters and ice for me, told me to use the refrigerator if I wanted to, and went back up for the night. He was very calm and thorough about everything; nothing except another person's emotion ever troubles him.

Peter came down in pajamas to take a final peek at the storm. He seemed much relieved, knowing that Tim was in good hands and that his father was coming. "You know, Dud," he said, after a little hemming and hawing, "my father's very busy because he's important. And sometimes he's—well, cross. And you might not know this, but anyway he's, well, he's just right when there's trouble. He doesn't get scared or angry; he just makes you feel—well, that you're safe. Do you know what I mean? He's a safety-like feeling man."

Coals to Newcastle. I assured him I knew what he meant and we said good night. But just then the phone rang again, and it was Cyn. Everybody tucked in properly and Tim in good hands.

"You know, Dud," she said in her contrite voice. That's what I call it, but it doesn't sound like anybody else's contrition: it's soft and happy, as though she's discovered a miracle. "I'm so ashamed of how I felt back there when you told me about—Julie. She's a darling."

I grunted, said good night. Peter carried the good news upstairs, and I settled down to a bourbon.

To a number of bourbons, in fact. It seems to me that I've drunk more since I came to the Foundation—I was going to say since I've seen much of Walton again—than ever before. But Friday night they didn't even make me mellow. I just stayed sour as I went back over the summer.

The starting point? Not the spring, nor even the weekend I spent in Northport with Walton. No, it was that evening, a Wednesday I think, when I stood in the hotel doorway and watched Walton and Sonia drive off in a cab. I remembered the curious feeling I'd had then—it wasn't just anger at Walton for what he was doing, or what I guessed he was doing, but that mixed up with the knowledge that on Friday I was flying up here to the Vineyard, and that I hadn't told him. I hadn't told him, and at that moment I was sure I wouldn't.

Up until then I hadn't been sure. That previous weekend, when he told me about his and Julie's trouble, and then danced the wild fandango with Gail the next night, only to seem to take it all perfectly calmly on Sunday—all that was what started me off. That was how I came to phone Julie and ask her if I could come up the next weekend. And then, when by the middle of the week he had had this bout with Sonia—well, that was the last straw.

Julie had hesitated when I asked her; then, in a kind of rush of words, said, "Yes, yes, do come. And don't go to any hotel. Stay with us. There's plenty of room."

We spent all day Saturday and Sunday together, talking, talking, talking. We'd go to the beach with the kids, and talk for hours. And both evenings, on the old screened porch. The Colonel eyed us unobtrusively, but withdrew. I found myself wondering what he thought of this, but almost decided that he would know, that Julie would tell him, quite simply and truthfully, that we talked endlessly of Walton.

For we did. I started it all by telling her about Walton's and my talk in the kitchen in Northport just one week before—especially that he had told me about their separation. She listened quietly, almost silently, for a long time as I described that weekend—all except Gail. Then she said, "I thought that was why you wanted to come. At first, when you called, I was surprised, but then I thought how kind you'd been back in April, and that there was no one else I would feel so free to talk with about Walton."

She has a grace in putting things that would embarrass other people. For she meant, of course, that she wondered about my motive in asking to come when I'd known her only for that one week. That's not strange. How could she know how close I felt to her and how much I wanted to comfort her?

Along about midnight last Friday, I finished my third bourbon, put on my trench coat and went out on the porch. The rain was torrential, like the only tropical storm I was ever in, years ago in Haiti, and there was wind—but nothing like a nor'easter, let alone a hurricane. The trees were bending and swaying, but nothing was breaking, only creaking, and what most impressed me was that I could hear the booming of the surf on Stonewall Beach, two or three miles away, like heavy cannonading.

After a while I came back and poured another drink, and fell to thinking about this manuscript. "Notes on a Friend"! It's not even that, certainly not notes for a novel. It's that last April something new happened to me. My life has changed, and I don't mean just the obvious matter of work at the Foundation. I'm not content with what I've been, but I don't know what I want to be.

Certainly not a writer. I haven't read this entry back, but it's clear to me that I haven't a real writer's feel. The first entry or two, I tried to make some effects; I strove for style. Last time I wrote, about Lydia, I was consciously trying to ape the Lardner-Anderson school. But reading it back, I know it didn't come off. And I'm impatient with words. They're not a real interest for me; I don't really care how many clichés there are here, in this private—what? journal?

So what am I doing? Assessing my life? The change in me? Perhaps it's the best way for anyone to come to grips with himself. Certainly a man like Walton, with real analytic powers, could do himself a world of good this way. But he never will. When it comes to himself, he analyzes only to justify himself or work off his guilt by beating his breast.

I suppose the reason I ever thought of this manuscript as working toward a novel, the only reason I ever thought of writing a novel at all, is my need to get more out of my life than the daily round. A novel—any serious novel—is an attempt to find one's vision. One's vision of what it means to be human—or some aspect of it, anyway.

My life has lacked poetry. Something from Goethe about the green tree and the—what? not dry *tree*. *Well?* I don't remember. And though I've never even tried to kiss Julie, except on the cheek, I feel guilty to Cyn because Julie has come to be the poetry in my life. So it's only negatively Walton who's upset me.

There. I've written it. And all through that weekend, the last before Cyn and the kids arrived in New York, I was with that poetry. I don't intend to try to describe it. That's for me, not even for my manuscript. And I'm not a writer. But I said we talked endlessly about Walton. That's not quite so. We did, but this or that about Walton would lead to ourselves and to others. Anyway, I didn't mind that it was so much about Walton; I know she's obsessed with him. What I'm not sure about is whether she really loves him, or just can't get him out of her spiritual hair.

These were some of the things I was thinking on Friday night, and I dozed off. From the predictions, everybody on the island had been saying, "Four o'clock. It'll be worst at four o'clock," and sure enough, when I woke up it was almost four, and I had dreamt that I was in the eye of the hurricane. And suddenly, waking to a great roar, I felt that maybe I really was, and sprang out of the chair.

There was now a difference in the vast surging sounds outside. All through the night there had been the groaning of branches and so uninterrupted and massive a movement of leaves that the usual words, "rustling" and "tossing," convey no sense at all of the almost deafening roar. But now there was a new element, the *separate* sound of the wind—not that of the instruments on which it had been playing, but its own voice: high-pitched to the point of hysteria, a kind of supersonic whining, a complaint so sonorous that I was both chilled and sweaty.

I've always felt, sometimes with pride and sometimes with—maybe not shame, but shamefacedness, that I'm a plain man, incapable of the heights and the depths people sometimes talk about, and more often than not skeptical of their existence except as misinterpreted subjective states, hallucinatory or at least abnormal. But at that moment, alone (as I felt) in the eye of the hurricane, I realized, if only briefly, my own mortality.

What do I mean? It's all remote already. But something like this: how fragile our lives are, how delicate the balance of every day, how minute and yet precious our selves, how complex and ambiguous our relationships, how timid and yet pretentious our strivings—and still how empty our lives without them. And, as for myself, I had been one of the sleepwalkers, fatuously proud of my "plainness": mistaking blandness for evenness of temperament, laziness for a philosophic quietness, the lack of inspiration for common sense, and envy for reasoned disapproval.

All this—in a flash—and then, like any fundamentalist Presbyterian or Baptist, a terrifying sense of fear and guilt, and the ridiculous conviction that the eye of the hurricane was the very Eye of God, Who was summoning me now, not me in particular, a puny little chip tossing on mountainous waves, but me amongst the multitudinous waste of Creation, to be swept into discard by the Hand.

All right, I thought, all right then, and put on my raincoat. It took all my strength to tug the door open, and when I finally succeeded I staggered into the Colonel, holding on to the railing of the porch and dressed in old-fashioned mackintosh, round rain hat and fisherman's boots. A grizzled New England Noah. (Ahab?) I tried to speak, but the wind carried my words away.

He bent toward me, cupping his mouth for a moment with his hands. "This is the worst of it," he shouted, "Nor'easter gale on the edge of the hurricane. I'd say the eye was out past Nantucket."

For a little longer we stood there, braced, staring into the uproar, for there was nothing to *see*. Then together we forced open the door and shed our sopping coats in the warm living room.

"Quite a night," said the Colonel. "Tim and a gale force wind. But we're all all right. Now I can sleep with a clear conscience. Good night, Dudley."

That was more than I could do. I poured a valedictory bourbon. I was a fool, either way you looked at it. As a "plain man," my credentials shriveled fast beside the Colonel's. And my moment of confrontation had not been with the Almighty, or even one of the archangels, but with a gale force wind!

Yet, sipping the bourbon, I felt better than I had in a long time. I knew where I was. "Midway along the path of life . . ." I was married to Cyn and in love with Julie. I owed Walton more than anyone else except Cyn, and I resented to the point of hatred his hold on Julie, moribund though it might be. I felt that I had wasted much of my life and was not sure what I could do with the rest of it. But everything looked clearer than it had in some time, and though nothing had really been resolved, and most of what I'd discovered was unpleasant, the roaring of the wind became soothing, and I fell asleep with an elusive but warm sense of peace. I was huddled in the middle of somewhere.

Monday evening, August 17

I've read back with a feeling of ambivalence. I think it really is well written. But it also is as unfamiliar as though someone else had written it. I wrote that? It reads to me like the kind of fantasy psychoanalytic people are always talking about. How they love that word! But the difference is that they believe the fantasy to reveal the deepest reality, and I can't help believing it to be an account of the unreal, due to overwrought nerves.

Yet I can't deny it its own kind of truth, I suppose. The sense of those thoughts being unreal is like the feeling I had Saturday morning about the storm. Saturday was cloudless, with a washed, perfectly blue sky and small, feathery whitecaps. But did this make Friday night unreal? And I suppose the fact that on Sunday night I could recapture my feelings of Friday must show that I really had them.

Walton arrived on the first plane, at eleven Saturday morning. He showed up immediately, over the heads of the passengers before him, his face tense, his head turning eagerly. He saw me, waved, and almost pushed the man ahead of him down the gangway.

"Timmy?" he asked immediately.

I had been rehearsing.

"In pretty good shape, I think. They've stopped the diarrhea and fed him intravenously. Only trouble now is that he's still listless, apathetic. Julie thinks seeing you will bring him out of it. We'll go right over to the hospital; everyone's there."

He sat rigid beside me as I drove, his eyes fixed straight ahead. He hadn't shaved since the day before, and his eyes were a little bloodshot. But he had on a clean summer suit, and, as I studied him covertly with what felt like a new eye, I got a sense of power in him unlike any I'd seen before. Not the drive that had led to his successes, but some deeper, darker energy closer to the source of life. Well! I haven't recovered yet.

"How was the trip?" I asked.

He looked at me directly, and there was a kind of nakedness in his eyes that was also new to me. That is, I would not have known that I had never seen his eyes bare before if I hadn't looked into them then. They were *peeled.*

He spoke slowly, simply. I remember thinking later, as I recalled the moment, that every pound of him counted.

"Pure hell," he said.

We were silent even when we reached the hospital. The Colonel met us at the entrance, and as he shook Walton's hand his impassive old face changed, came to a different order of feeling that again brought me that painful tension I was beginning to recognize as envy.

There was a moment of greeting in the waiting room, with Peter and Jennifer, Maria, whom I'd picked up in Edgartown earlier, and Cyn; then Walton strode down the hall to where Julie was waiting in the doorway to Tim's room. I forced myself to watch.

They came together as though they were two parts of a single being that had been ripped apart. There they (it? he? she?) stood for what seemed to me an immeasurable stretch of time, and I couldn't look away.

The Colonel tugged at my sleeve. "Bring Julie up here," he said. "Timmy needs him most—alone."

It seemed strange to me then, and afterward, that he selected

me, but he did, and in a voice that had long been accustomed to obedience. So I went down the hall like some shamefaced schoolboy. But
just as I reached them they separated.

"The Colonel says—" I blurted, and stopped, because Julie had
already broken in.

"I know," she said. "Go on in, Walton."

And again that radiant face, shining through the tears that ran
unchecked down her cheeks.

I didn't want to escort her back, like some faithful Cassio, and
I did want to see Tim. So I watched in the doorway for a moment.

Tim turned his sunken-eyed look on his father, and then recognized
him. I can't describe what happened, but it was an immediate transformation. I know—or I think I know—that Tim was not in danger, yet
it seemed to me that death stirred and disappeared, and that a kind of
joy appeared in Tim's eyes, and in his reaching arms, as he said,
"Daddy!" It was like the morning after the wild night.

Tim could not reach far, for he was partially strapped down, to
avoid disturbing the needle at the end of the tube that ran from the bottle
of glucose. And Walton didn't dare touch him, for fear of hurting him.
So he stood, a foot away, his hands spread out, and I could see that the
tears were running down his face, too.

"Daddy, Daddy, Daddy." And now Walton was stroking Tim's
head and bending over to kiss his face. I found that I couldn't see any
more, and turned away, with the chant of "Daddy, Daddy, Daddy,
Daddy" following me down the hall. Only then did I realize that Julie had
returned, and been watching over my shoulder. . . .

They sent me back after an hour. There must be something about
my appearance or personality that makes me play the messenger, as
Shakespeare used clowns, servants and gravediggers. There they were,
Walton holding Timmy's hand with one of his, and Julie's with the
other. He was talking in a low voice, and the two of them were looking
at him in the same way: it was as though they were feasting on him.
I waited. Walton looked up.

"Thanks for all you've done, Dud," he said, and his voice was
so earnest it made me uncomfortable. "Does everyone want to go along
now? I'll stay here with Timmy."

So we left him with Tim, but not until Peter, insistent, had come
down, shaken his father's hand and said awkwardly, "I took care of things
the best I could, Dad. Me and Grandpa—" and to Tim—"You'll be all
right now, Tim, with Dad here."

The rest I don't know. But Tim was literally well by evening and came home Sunday morning. Walton spent the night in the chair by his bed. That's the kind of thing that burns me, too. To come and to help is fine, but staying all night when Tim was practically well—that's heroics.

Walton and Julie had several hours off together Sunday afternoon, after he had chosen to stay and take the evening plane. Nor, of course, did I see them say good-bye before the Colonel drove Walton to the airport. Maria went with them, chattering her head off, and Peter, listening intently and nodding.

But I saw enough to know that he had restored her, and that he left with some sense of vindication or atonement or fulfillment. He looked pretty haggard, but all his tenseness was gone. If he was afraid of the return trip by plane, he showed no sign of it.

Cyn and I took a long walk that night, past Beetlebung Corners and along the Middle Road. We didn't talk much, but as we approached the house on our return she said, "Dud, you're all mixed up about something, aren't you?"

I cleared my throat. "Aren't we all?" I asked.

"No," she replied with some spirit. "Right now, I'm not at all. I understand that things happen that you don't mean to have happen, and then you have to live with them, and find out what you do about them. And I've learned that strengths lead to excesses, and the excesses should not be isolated and condemned without any knowledge of where they came from. And that the knowledge of your own weaknesses can keep you from hating and condemning those of other people. And that you can't make something different from what it is by fiercely wanting it to be. And that something can hurt you, and you can still love the people that cause it."

I stopped short and stared at her, all lit up in the darkness. I put my arms around her and hugged her. I wanted to, and I felt everything was going to be all right.

August 20–21

THE captains and the kings depart. . . . When the last well-tailored
back left the Board room and the well-modulated hinges of the heavy
oaken door brought it back to rest, shut, with only a quiet sigh, Walton
turned to P.H. But P.H., hands thrust deep in trouser pockets, head
bowed, was standing staring down at the busy street. He was framed
in the tall rectangle of glass that rose from the floor to the ceiling.
Framed like some captain of industry or banking, to grace one of the
pennons of the Western World, whether proclaiming the distinctive
and elegant merits of a whiskey, a cigarette or a renowned tailor.
Framed? Walton smiled wryly.

There is something in me, he thought, that wants to feel framed—
that is hurt past all reason, all proportion. Haldane had kept his word
meticulously. Clarence Kiefer's name had been presented, his credentials
established, Walton's testimony about their experience together in ILEAS
summarized clearly and accurately, with no slightest suggestion of doubt-
ing its veracity, either on Haldane's part as he spoke or on the others'
as they listened.

Haldane had expressed his conviction that, for reasons of vulnerability alone (should these past associations become known), it would
not be wise to appoint Kiefer to the Institute post. It was a sad world,
he seemed to be saying, in which an excellently qualified man must be
passed by for fear of busy and malicious tongues, but this was the world
in which they lived. Mr. Herrick's world was a better world, but unfortunately it had little material reality. Mr. Kiefer's candidacy was
shortly rejected by a unanimous vote.

And then, as he had said he would, Haldane spoke of Walton.
He listed his achievements, paid him full credit for conceiving of the
Institute and for other projects he had initiated. He hoped that Walton
would head his department for years to come. And with a conviction

that Walton was grudgingly forced to accept as genuine, Haldane paid a short personal tribute. It was Brutus, this time, Walton thought, who came to bury . . .

"I have had only one meeting, though that a long one, with Mr. Herrick," Haldane said. "But in that one meeting I have come to respect and admire him. I have met the impact of his force, I have laughed at his humor, and I have admired the dexterity of his mind. I like him and I trust him. But—"

But. What was it about their cushioned ways, Walton wondered, their parliamentary procedures, the sensible and courteous formality, their rational, measured and impersonal urbanity, that so enraged him? Their? They? Trustees, trusties? Men of the world, businessmen, bankers, magnates, attorneys, trustees. He did not know.

But he did know that Haldane, in effect as surely removing him from any further association with the Asiatic Institute as though invested with dictatorial powers (properly endorsed five minutes later by a vote)—that Haldane had some further quality of imagination, of insight, beyond the capacities of the rest of them. He did not want to know this, but he did, and could admit it, despite the hurt and the feeling of being framed—both in the colloquial and in the literal sense: hung on the wall with the decorations of dismissal.

P.H. turned around and addressed him sadly.

"Let's go into my room," he said.

Walton followed him silently, with some impinging sense of climax, of a confrontation. He welcomed it, was so absorbed in it, by it, that he passed Sonia in the outer office with no more than a nod and a brief impression of the cool green she was wearing.

Closing the door behind him, P.H. regarded Walton mournfully.

"I feel bad about this," he said. "We knew it was coming, but I'm sorry, Walt."

Walton lowered his head and looked at P.H. over the horn rims of his eyeglasses with what he hoped was a quizzical expression.

"Thank you," he said dryly.

P.H. stared at him sharply, questioningly for a moment, hesitated, then walked over to his large mahogany desk and took a cigarette from a silver box. He rarely smoked, but now he drew on the cigarette so deeply as to suggest that he was drawing some life-giving substance down to the very center of himself.

"I did what I could, Walt."

Walton shrugged and nodded.

"The shoe's on the other foot, P.H. So did I, back there in the past.

Each time, we did what we could. But could's an ambiguous word. Given what you are, I think you did. Given what I was, back when your project was at stake, I think I did. Yet I feel sure you've never been satisfied with my abstaining, and I guess I'm not wholly satisfied with your part this time. It was pretty much the same thing. You never said a word against me, you said you were for me, but you too abstained."

He began to pack tobacco into his pipe with sharp, savage thrusts.

P.H. spread out his hands.

"I didn't abstain. Unless you mean that I should have fought for Kiefer and you."

Walton again shrugged his shoulders.

P.H. moved closer to him.

"When you and Hunt and I had our talk, I said—and he confirmed my having said it before—that if you insisted, I would back you. But even then I expressed my hope that one or the other of you could be won over, that there would be no deadlock. And all this, Walt, was before you'd told me your story about how you came to know Kiefer. The reason I couldn't fight today was that under the circumstances I honestly couldn't help agreeing with Hunt that it was running a risk for either Kiefer or you to be connected with the Institute."

"But you knew before then that I had belonged to ILEAS."

P.H. reached out and touched his sleeve almost pleadingly.

"Yes, but I didn't see the connection, the *point*, until Hunt made it clear. I guess I didn't want to see it, but he forced me to. And he's really keen on you, too, Walt."

Walton could feel a burning in his eyes.

"Yes. Yes, very keen on me. I wonder what he'd have done if he hadn't liked me."

P.H. drew back.

"You're angry. Very angry and—hurt. But later I'm sure you'll realize that he meant all the good things he said about you. When he and I were alone before the Board meeting, he repeated them to me. And Hunt's not a man to flatter."

Walton did not reply. He puffed on his pipe and stared coldly at P.H.

"And as for me," P.H. went on, pacing the floor, "I've had a dreadful time. Walt, don't let this come between us. I was torn between my feeling for you and both my conviction that Hunt was right and that I owed it to the Foundation to act on that conviction. I had to choose and risk your hurt. Now at last I think I can understand how you came to act as you did in terms of *my* project—even though they're not really analogous. And you're right; sometimes it has rankled. Only now can I see the struggle you must have had."

Walton's voice held open derision.

"You see *nothing*. You and your Hunt Club. You've always been scared to death of looking inside and finding out what you really feel. And you always have to reduce complex things to some simple civilized formula. Don't try to tell me that you understand my motivations of five years ago, when I don't understand them fully myself. Quit being so goddamned bland, P.H. Among other things, you've always regretted having let me make the report to the investigating committee, and you're not half as sorry as you're saying about my getting mine today. In fact, I guess we've just about come to the end of the road." Breathing heavily, he dropped into a chair and morosely studied the carpet.

There was a long silence. P.H. had ceased his pacing and stood so still that finally Walton looked up at him. His expression was difficult to parse. Pain, yes. Indecision, yes. But beyond that? For there was another element, a peculiar sense of fear—almost of terror.

"No," he said softly. "No, Walt. Whatever jealousy or envy I've felt, I've tried, God knows, to push down. I've felt my own meanness, and I've struggled with it. But under all that there is no man I've admired, respected and loved more—even as much. You're wrong, Walt. If I did today what I felt right—against your hopes—that only frees me the more to work with you and stand by you. You're unjust about this."

Walton felt a swift thrust of shame at the hurt he had done this good man, this friend, through his own wild laying about him in pain and anger. He bowed his head in acknowledgment.

"But," he said then, "that's the way it's got to be, anyway. Dennis told me why you fired Peggy, how you covered for me. But the truth, P.H.—"

P.H. held up his hand, palm thrust out.

"I don't want to hear about it," he said with an unwonted firmness. "I did what I thought right, and I would do it again."

"Perhaps," said Walton sadly. "Perhaps. But Peggy told the truth. However maliciously, she told the truth."

One look at P.H.'s stricken face, and Walton sprang up, came over, and placed his hands on his shoulders.

"Forgive me," he said. "P.H., forgive me. I load too much on you. And I have been unfair to you. I believe you and I trust you. I've been foolish as hell, and proud and destructive. But since this matter with Sonia is true, I think it's best if I resign altogether."

P.H.'s face was ashen.

"You mean that you—you're going to divorce Julie for Sonia?" Walton shook his head.

"No, no. You know I'm just back from the Vineyard and something of what happened there. I love Julie more than ever. If she'll have me, I'll never leave her. And it's all over with Sonia. But especially with Peggy and, I suspect, Dennis, embittered about this, it will get out too, and make another mess for you. It's better I quit."

P.H. held out an eager hand.

"I can find Sonia a job somewhere else," he said. "She—"

Walton broke in.

"You can't go on forever firing or transferring people because of me. Especially when I'm so much at fault. No, P.H., that won't do."

P.H. crushed out his cigarette, grinding it into the ashtray with force.

"At least," he said slowly, "at least promise me you'll think it over till you get back from your vacation. You said—" he hesitated— "you said that you'd never leave Julie *if she'd have you*. I don't want you to tell me any more about *that*, but perhaps, after the trouble with Tim and all these other things, when you go up there you'll find a new—closeness together. And I don't mean I'd fire Sonia—she's a good secretary—but transfer her to one of the department heads on the floor below, with a raise, so that she's not right here before you all the time. Promise me that, Walt—it means so much to me."

Walton was astonished to find that his eyes were wet.

"I promise," he said. "And I wish I—"

P.H. stopped him, took hold of both his arms with those small, strong hands.

"Don't," he said. "Walt, I'm grateful. This is good for me. For me, Walt."

On the way out, Sonia stopped Walton. For a moment she stood there in his path, her eyes searching him, neither coldly nor warmly, but inquiringly. Then she handed him a note.

"Here," she said. "Please take it and read it. Not now."

Walton looked down on the rush-hour crowds scurrying, jostling, dodging, strolling far below. It seemed incredible that it was only twenty-four hours since he had watched P.H. standing in similar scrutiny, and only a month since that other night he had stayed in his office and stared at the ominous sky with intimations of catastrophe.

He sighed and moved away from the window, remembering last night's long sleepless vigil—unwanted, miserable, almost unbearable.

There he had sat on the edge of the bed pounding his fist on the mattress, time after time, knowing there was something he did not understand.

Something? Something! Everything. But he meant that out of the strange snowstorm of letters that he had found on his desk when he returned from his talk with P.H. a reluctant realization was hovering on the brink of consciousness. But he could not let it over the threshold. And then this morning a further, a sixth letter—the note from P.H. There was a resolution, imminent understanding, there in the six letters stacked under the paperweight, but as yet he could not identify it.

Last night, in the middle reaches of his long wakefulness, his thoughts had gone back to the visit to the Vineyard—to Timmy's overwhelming trust, the instant security that he (he, Walton Herrick!) had brought him. To Peter's manly exchanges, to little Jenny's early-morning dewiness, to Maria's challenging, "My goodness, I love you as much as anybody. But doesn't it scare you a little, Daddy, that you just arrive and everybody feels everything's all right?"

To the Colonel's extra unspoken warmth—a silent expression of confidence and respect that brought the taste of bile to Walton's mouth. "How would you look," he wanted to blurt out, "if you knew the things I've done this summer?"

And to Julie. In those brief hours alone together, the slow blossoming within him again—slow through the caution with which he had approached, must approach it—of a sense of union, of her there and him here, yet joined, meeting as two—two what? for God's sake! he could not say it with what else hung in his mind—two parts of music, nature, whatever might come together, separate, complementary, and yet joined. And in her words, her face, her gestures, her very movements, a promise that when he returned they could take up their life together again . . .

If. If. If he could. If she could forgive. If he could forgive himself. If he could stand the strain.

What strain? He did not know. And suddenly, impelled by the thought of strain, by a recurring sense of disaster, by the intrusion of the memory of that night when he had had his vision of the fantastic horde of invaders climbing the stairs, he had risen and gone to the head of the stairs, gazing down into the darkness and thinking, "Somebody down there hates me."

Down there? This time there was no hallucination; he knew that "down there" was interior, internal to himself. Down there where his pajama cord became too tight across his belly—the something he could not bring up, the something he did not understand. And the fear he knew was not that of the earlier fantasy, fear of the actualizing of fantasy, but fear of what was in himself that he could not apprehend.

And now, now, Friday, August 21, 1953, at six o'clock, with the offices, the building emptied for the weekend, he sat down wearily before his desk and put his head in his hands. Time and understanding slipped through your fingers; the bowed head rested, heavily inert, upon them, as the slumped body in the chair.

A touch. Timid, yet warm, compassionate. A hand on his arm. He looked up. Evelyn.

"But—" he said, bewildered, and stopped.

"I came back. You didn't look well. Please, please go home and rest all weekend."

Walton, still dazed with the whirling thoughts in his head, looked at her and thought he saw the eyes of love. She had never touched him before. For a moment now he thought, She loves me. And a slow ripple of peace came over him, as the wind rippled those tall grasses in the meadow he had never seen. Not for her, he thought, not for love, but for the blessed touch of a hand that cared, that noticed and remembered and returned, to touch.

Her eyes were pleading.

"Why, Evelyn," he said, "I'm all right. You shouldn't have done this," and instantly regretted his words, for she withdrew her hand and shrank away a little into her secretaryship. "Ah," he said, "you're very sweet and kind. Why do we always say, 'I'm all right'?"

She smiled.

"Because it's so hard to accept a gift. To respond. We've all been trained to suspicion and caution and to self-reliance. I—I was afraid to come back," she added shyly, "afraid I might offend you. But you've been so tired today, and you're worrying, and you were alone. So I came."

Something broke inside him, with a lurch. He stood up and put his arms around her, burying his face against the light wool covering her shoulder, and leaned against her for a few moments, dry-eyed but shaking, supporting himself with her.

Then he drew away, but kept his hands on her shoulders and looked into her eyes, reticent but clear, feeling in his own a freshness, a candor that seemed strange to him.

He didn't say thank you aloud, but knew she had received his thanks when she moved to the door.

"And you will go home," she said with satisfaction. "Soon. Good night, Walton."

He stood there, listening to the sound of her heels in the hallway, and thought with tender amusement that tomorrow she would be as formal as ever, and would never call him "Walton" again.

But "amusement"? A streak of irritability abruptly crossed his feeling of comfort. "Gratitude," he growled to himself, and began to open again the letters under the paperweight. First, the note from Sonia.

DEAR WALTON,
    I can't hang here in a hammock fastened to nothing forever. I'll wait at home for you from nine till one Friday night. If you come, you're not committed to anything except talking honestly. I think you owe me that, but if you don't, and don't come, at least that's decisive and I know where I stand.
                                            SONIA

He looked at his watch. Six-thirty. Then he shook his head, hunched his shoulders, and turned to the note from P.H. that he found on his desk this morning.

DEAR WALT:
    Stay. I need you. Julie needs you. We *can* work everything out.
    Perhaps Hunt is wrong about one thing. Perhaps friendship and family—the human ties among individuals—are even more important than the national commitment, for there can be no commitment without them.
                                            P.H.

There was some link there, but feeling feverish and confused he couldn't find it. All that came through to him in this reading was need—and a dumb astonishment that P.H. seemed to need him so much.

Then there was Dennis', which also had not been sent through the mails. It was typed, and in the lower left-hand corner the words, *cc: Philip Henderson Gates.*

DEAR WALTON—
    Since our talk that evening a month ago, nothing has changed. You've said "hello" a couple of times. That's all. I haven't exchanged five words with Mr. Gates. I'm doing what amounts to a clerk's work. The only reason I haven't quit is that I can't bring myself to the decision. And that's because I can't feel myself *as a self.* How can you commit what you don't have?
    But I've just heard the outcome of the Board meeting. I

don't suppose you'll believe me, but I never dreamed, when I told Mr. Haldane about the organizations that Clarence Kiefer belonged to, that it would come to this. I'm in despair about the whole thing. I can't understand why I did it. And I can't expect you to forgive me.

But having written this and sent a copy to Mr. Gates, I can do one thing—get out of your way. If you want to call it that, this is my resignation from the Foundation. I won't be back. And you won't any of you hear from me again.

DENNIS

P.S. [handwritten] I'm not saying this to Mr. Gates, but I've been seeing Peggy Thomas, and I'm afraid she's going to write your wife about you and Sonia. I'll try to stop her, but I don't know if I can.

Walton passed his hand wearily over his forehead. The next letter was in Abe Fortune's tight, jagged hand.

WALTON—

I got your note about the trip to Martha's Vineyard and your boy. I'm glad he's all right.

I haven't answered before because I've had a bad time with Jane. I finally had to commit her to a private institution in Massachusetts. It's tops; there's no clinical institutional feel to it, more like a comfortable club—but with a difference. *That difference.* [The line under these words had torn the paper, which had been mended with Scotch tape.]

I'm up there weekends, here in Stamford through the week. As soon as I feel like seeing anybody, I'll call you.

ABE

P.S. I can't go upstairs, so I live downstairs with the Devil. I've gotten to know him well; he's a schlemiel.

Walton sat staring at the torn and mended place in the paper. For a moment he was again torn by a quick, rending pain for little Jane—that was how he thought of her—and then a strange sense of comfort came over him, as he thought of her slipping away to rest, free of— Free of what? All the intolerable daily anguish, confusion and conflict. And he envied Dennis for a moment, too, simply for having *resigned.* A wonderful, peaceful word—resigned. But then he saw Dennis rushing down dark, wind-swept streets as he had often seen himself. There was nothing for envy there.

Yet it was Abe for whom he felt most now, to whom he felt closest: living downstairs with the devil, who had turned out to be a jerk. He picked up the fifth letter.

MY DEAR WALTON:

It's been much too long—six months, I think. I hear of you; every so often I check with Abe Fortune.

So, recently, just before his big trouble, which you must know about, I heard from him that he had given up on your candidacy, about which, he tells me, you were never very serious anyway.

This leads me to ask you whether your lack of interest stems only from your having no political ambitions. I wouldn't even consider the possibility that your present post doesn't wholly satisfy you, if it were not for a chance meeting of several weeks back. At a dinner party I met a Dudley Foote and his wife. It turned out that he is not only at the Schuyler with you, but an old friend as well. Nice chap. But when I asked him—really only casually—if you were still the pillar of the Foundation, he hesitated and his "yes" didn't quite come through. So I wondered.

All this, if the implication is correct, leads me to suggest a meeting to discuss a fine opening in another but related field —a job for which I have been asked to make a recommendation. And I have thought of you as the best possible choice. So here I come, at the tag end of larger matters, with something entirely new—like a brand-new character near the end of a badly constructed play or novel!

So do drop me a line. If you feel firmly committed to the Foundation, say so, of course. But even if you are, let's lunch together. A lunch with your lawyer can do you no harm. How about September 1, 2, 3—Tuesday, Wednesday, Thursday? With warm regards, as always.

(LEON)

LEON S. GOODMAN

Walton tossed the letter aside, took off his glasses, rubbed his eyes. A new field! He couldn't cover this one. Yet there it was: at this moment he could hardly afford simply to say, "Not interested."

He stood up. "If you feel firmly committed . . ." Remembering Leon's short, chubby person, his shrewd, twinkling eyes, he felt a rush of affection for him, part of which to be sure centered in his somehow unerring gift of lighting on exactly the opposite of the reality. Yet was this so? Would he even have written the letter if he had believed Walton "firmly committed"?

Whirling words, thoughts, feelings . . . Having reread the five letters, he could no more find a theme, a connecting thread, than before. Only that three of them spoke of the pain of living; two offered to relieve some of it, sounded the note of loyalty, friendship, the indispensable other out there—indispensable if one were not to die of loneliness. Oh, even that wasn't true: things weren't that simple. In Abe's despair, there was his loyalty to Jane; in P.H.'s loyalty, his own need. Enough, enough. He sat down again—to Julie's note.

DEAREST WALTON,

By the time you get this, only about three weeks until you come. The children can't wait.

Darling, I can't wait, either. But I will.

JULIE

He sat there, holding it against his cheek, waiting for the dark to come, to cover him and wrap him in quiet.

It was at ten o'clock that Walton abruptly woke from a doze, to see spread out before him, through his window, the blazing sea of lights. It was breathtaking, dazzling, seen with newly awakened eyes. Magic, he thought—and at once the lights wavered, blurred and paled. Somewhere, sometime, he thought vaguely, he had been out at night in a great wind, filled with exultation, under a sky blazing with cold white stars. Not lights, stars. But it had been long ago; the memory faded. . . .

Drawing a long breath, Walton rose and stood by the window. Magic, he thought again, and dismissed impatiently the self-charge of banality. No, the banality, the sentimentality had been in his emotion over those letters. Turning back to his desk, he swept the letters aside with his hand.

A cold loneliness was in him, and he admonished himself: remember the last day before Julie went to the Vineyard; remember her final look; do not forget the stress she was under a week ago, with Tim. At such a time words are not to be trusted. She would wait! Yes, until the first time he said or did something that didn't measure up to her picture of him.

There was a last sound of sadness dying in him, something about those letters, about their meaning. . . . Absurd. He muffled the sound. What had he been about for a month? Trusting P.H.—and look at the outcome. Believing Julie, when all sensible evidence, their lived lives, showed that she couldn't mean what she said. Playing at dreams with Abe, who now knew the cold hand of reality, and that the devil was a jerk, was themselves, was the endless animal hunger in every man—his loneliness and need of warmth. And avoiding Sonia, to the very ultimate edge of their relation—tawny Sonia, dispenser of magic.

Yes, magic: he looked with burning eyes at the city of lights. And why not? From the long ago Biblical past of his childhood came the words, "all is vanity and a striving after wind. That which is crooked cannot be made straight. . . ."

Again that poignant sadness smote him. What had he dreamed just now? He did not want to know. Yet a thin echo trailed across his mind, saying that the words from *Ecclesiastes* were answered in that very book, that he was perversely snatching them from their context, isolating one individual from its family chorus. And family suddenly meant Timmy, and Julie, waiting there. And the six letters, with their common voice—

What was he going to say next? The family of man? Sneering, railing silently at the image of himself racing down the labyrinthine corridors of mine own—what?—away from the following voice, turning only to shout, "It's not so! There is no such thing! Let me alone!" then pounding on. He wrenched himself from this vision and from his office. In the elevator, though, he heard the voice again, "For there is neither love nor joy . . ." and something in him shriveled and whimpered.

On the street he thought, "Go to Leon Goodman and get the new job . . . Go to Sonia," and he muttered aloud, "Go to the devil!"

There had been that late July night on which, his hand on the doorknob, he turned to find her watching him. That night he had cradled her in his arms as a father might have until they had both returned to sleep—to wake on Sunday morning sad, constrained, silent, closed to each other, so that when Walton left, shortly before noon, it was as though with her tacit consent to their permanent separation.

There had been that night, a week later, when he had come, unannounced, because he could not stay away. That night, an hour later, he had roughly pulled her dress down from her shoulders, baring her breasts, and held her there in his fierce grip, looking at her with glittering eyes before thrusting her away and, muttering incoherently, leaving her.

And now there was tonight, and he had come in desire and in

rage, not knowing which engendered which, not knowing whether he wanted to possess her or strike her, love her or wound her.

"Well?" she said at last. There was a gravity, a dignity, about her that was not familiar. She had made no effort either to incite or to excite him; she had shown none of her challenging toughness, none of that once-disclosed vulnerability. "Well?" she repeated quietly.

Walton met her eyes with difficulty, and controlled a rising exasperation.

"I—don't know what to say. I thought I made it clear that I was staying away because I must. I guess you know I went to the Vineyard —and about Tim. And I'm going back, for a month, in three weeks. I just can't—do both. And it doesn't mean I don't want you. You know that. That one time three weeks ago—"

"That one time three weeks ago—" and a slight steeliness came into her voice— "you came with no warning, aroused me, and went away. And that other time, the last time before, you made me feel that you really did care, that I really was a person to you, but in the morning you couldn't wait to get away. I don't want to hear any more about how you want me, but won't take me. Put up or shut up."

Her voice had risen, and Walton found it hard to reply calmly. "That Sunday morning," he said, "that Sunday morning, you were just as anxious to get rid of me."

"You *wouldn't* know," she said contemptuously. "You just *wouldn't* know. You never take enough time off from thinking about yourself to know how anyone else feels. That's the only excuse I can think of for the way you've used me. When your dear little conscience is working, it's just too bad about how I feel—I'm not even there for you. But when it isn't, then of course I must be waiting, all wet and open for you, you great lord. Great lord from Winnetka, that's you. You make me tired."

As his heart sank into a bog of despair, of shame and humiliation— that was exactly how it felt, *his heart did sink*—he made his voice icy.

"You've said that before. I heard you both times. And you've forgotten all you said the first night we were ever together. So there really isn't much point in our even going on talking, is there?"

She stood up, her eyes suddenly blazing.

"Injured pride! Now his little feelings are hurt! Jesus God, will you ever come out from behind those closed blinds? Stiff and wounded and cold."

With shaking hands she poured herself a full two inches of whiskey and drained it, choking and coughing and stamping her foot in a paroxysm of anger and pain.

Walton watched dully. It was as though he were drawing a shawl—that was what he thought, a shawl—tightly around his feelings.

At last she caught her breath. "So why don't you do something—" She was choking again and, to recover, thrust her arms up high over her head. Standing thus, she looked to Walton as though she were cursing him, about to utter imprecations and exorcisms, and in spite of his attempt not to he shrank back in his chair.

Her bitter laughter filled the room.

"That's right! That's right! Look out, I'm going to hit you. Poor timid little man. Ah, you—"

Something broke in him, and he sprang up to seize her savagely by the arms.

"Shut up!" he said. "I've heard all I'm going to listen to. You shut up or—" He broke off as something within him floundered, lost pace, stopped.

"Or *what!*" She thrust her face close to his. "Or, what, big man?" She kissed him then, kissed him fiercely, bit his lip, until he cried out and pulled away. For a moment longer, she stood there, staring at him staunching the flow of blood with his handkerchief, staring at him with a kind of wild uncertainty.

"I'll tell you what," she suddenly screamed. "I'll tell you *or what.* Here—" and she ripped her dress off, over her head—"and here and here and here and—here I am. Now where are you? What do you dare to do about it?"

Walton stared back at her from over the bloody handkerchief, knowing only that what he felt was fear, and humiliation again, and that he could do nothing.

Then, even as he stood there, as though paralyzed, she walked slowly across the room to him, naked, swaying slightly, to stop, two feet from him, hands on hips.

"I'm not going to see you any more," she said more quietly. "You don't have to worry about that. This is the last time. Now do you want it or are you afraid?"

It was as though her insolence had turned to blood in his head. His throat was dry, his voice harsh.

"I'll show you," he said, as he caught hold of her. "I'll show you just how afraid I am."

They did not speak another word, even while he slowly and awkwardly dressed. When he put his hand on her shoulder, where she lay, head averted, she jerked away from him. And, after a moment of staring down at her, he left. Emerging onto the street, with twenty minutes to catch the last train home, he felt so purged, so relieved, so calm, so final that he was barely surprised to find Dennis Byrnes waiting for him.

"I—I just wanted to say good-bye." Dennis' voice was subdued. "That was a silly, melodramatic letter. I'm taking Mother back to Toledo tomorrow and try to find a job there."

"Toledo? I didn't know you came from Toledo."

Dennis nodded mournfully.

"I'm just giving up. New York, the Foundation, psychoanalysis. I'm surrendering. So I might as well do what she wants."

Walton felt chilled—sufficiently to forget to ask Dennis what he was doing here.

"Look. I've got to catch a train. But don't. Don't do this. I know what I'm talking about. Take her back, if you will, and get her settled. But come back. Or go somewhere else. Don't give up. Don't commit yourself to Toledo, but to yourself. You can start again."

Dennis shook his head mournfully.

"I can't. I'm done."

Walton seized him by the shoulders.

"Don't do it. Get down on your knees—to life, to yourself, I don't give a damn to what, but get down there and then stand up again, learn to walk again. That's what it means, Dennis, goddamn it, that's what it means. Don't ever give up, even if you have to hang on with your teeth."

He thought he saw color rise in the pale face, a gleam, a response in the eyes. He clapped him on the shoulder and hurried off, waving to a cab.

All the way to the station, until he heard himself and stopped in bewilderment, he kept repeating, "Get down on your knees and then stand up again. . . . That's what it means. Get down on your knees. . . ."

Part Four

THE

DRY

RUN

AMERICAN colleges—or at least the Eastern ones—were, in 1924, very much what Scott Fitzgerald and other, less talented depictors of the Jazz Age made them out to be. They were a good deal more than *that,* and a good deal different, to a majority of those who attended them. Yet somehow the combination of glossy self-assurance and desperate conviviality, of precocious world-weariness and frenetic social activity, that characterized the articulate and dominant minority of Amherst students during Walton's four years there gave the place its tone for him. And whenever he visited the other Eastern colleges during these years—say, Dartmouth, Yale, Williams, Brown—he was aware of a similar condition. If there was any difference, it was that in these places the impression was even stronger—the sophisticated if superficial paradox of self-assurance and desperation more pronounced.

What it amounted to, Walton remarked one summer evening in 1947 to a classmate whom he had not seen in a long time, was that for their generation this paradox *was* the temper of the times. Save for a few, fortunate in their grounding, those of this generation who had not actually participated in this perpetual mardi gras—those who had never, or at best seldom, climbed on the gaudy carousel of the twenties—had felt inferior, wistfully regretful, lacking in courage and the spirit of adventure: most of all, in some perverse way, lacking in stature. To be sober and conscientious in the company of the beautiful and the damned was to feel like some black crow of a Malvolio, croaking away moralistically at the outskirts of the revels. (*And dost thou think . . .*)

"Let me qualify that," Walton had added, and ordered another drink. (After dinner they had moved from their table in the midtown restaurant to the bar.) "In the first place, you and I both knew some fellows who really had their feet on the ground, walked through the middle of this thing, won recognition, popularity and even leadership, and weren't scathed by it. That's one thing." He paused to take a sip. "The other is that, while I was one of those on the outskirts in one sense —that is, no drinking and no whoring, not even any easy give-and-take with the really gay ones—I did participate superficially. I went to the parties and liked them—was even enchanted by them in my own peculiar way. And I didn't feel inferior or wistful then at all; I was sure—or believed I was sure—that I was both having a good time and, well, being a good boy. I straddled the fence and most of the time didn't even know it. It was later—eight to ten years later—that I decided it had all passed me by, and felt cheated."

Yet Walton had felt anything but passed by at the beginning. Only six nights after the one on which he had scrubbed the bright yellow sheen off his satchel, he had stood, looking out the window of his dormitory room, watching the dusk settle slowly over this quiet New England village with its expanses of green and its great brooding elms, all ringed round with a sweeping stretch of hills—had stood there, looking out to those hills, and through the sharp conflict he was experiencing let an elation wholly new to him bubble up and spill riotously through him.

He had known, even before leaving Cleveland, that the fraternity rushing season took place on the three days before college opened. He had been visited at home by three undergraduates of varying degrees of suaveness, representing various fraternities whose Greek-letter names he could not remember. He had been duly astonished when told by a Cleveland sophomore that the fraternities financed trips by car for the rushing chairmen during the summer, so that they could make the acquaintance of promising freshmen-to-be before these even set foot in Amherst. Astonished—and secretly downcast. For, despite the improvement of his lot in the last two years of high school, Walton had not been asked to join any of the half-dozen high school fraternities; he had instead, with five or six friends, formed their own modest one. Despite the summer callers, he felt unhappily confident that he would not be any the more sought after in college—and there, he knew, he could not found one of his own. But he had been wrong.

The rushing program was conducted with ritualistic stateliness and the precision of a railroad schedule; you began Monday morning with an 8:30 appointment at one fraternity house; at 9 you were escorted to the next by a member of the first house, at 9:30 to the third by a member of the second. At each house, you were ceremoniously introduced, clapped on the back by your departing guide with a "See you later, old man," welcomed with almost frightening heartiness by your new one. There were thirteen fraternities, and every freshman made the rounds once. If you were being sought by, and were yourself interested in the possibility of joining, a particular fraternity, you took along with you, when you left, a small card that constituted an invitation and a promise to return.

How you spent the half hour at a given house depended on how the members of that house regarded you. If they wanted you to join, they said, "Come on upstairs and see the rest of the place." Then, behind a closed door on the second floor, the most articulate or attractive brother recounted the glories of membership in Chi Psi or Delta Kappa Epsilon or Psi Upsilon.

The difference in methods of attack would have fascinated Walton if he had not been so stunned at finding that he was wanted by so many fraternities. It took him the better part of his second round of visits to discern that where the pressure was heaviest, the insistence most urgent (in one or two cases, the spokesman even tried to put the pledge button in his lapel without waiting for an answer), there was a group less sure of itself and probably less desirable.

Only two of the thirteen fraternities failed to offer membership to Walton. Later, he was grateful to those two. Without these experiences, he would not have understood the cruelty of the system. For, invariably, the freshmen who were not going to be bid sat in the living room downstairs, and were entertained by those members of the fraternity who were not conducting the actual rushing.

The pattern was consistent. Since only five or six freshmen arrived at a house at one time, and only one or two, if any, were asked upstairs, there were plenty of fraternity members to talk to them. Cigarettes and matches would be offered in loving cups and, the introductions over, two or three brothers in, say, Theta Delta Chi or Phi Kappa Psi, would engage each undesired freshman in conversation. He was from Scranton, Pennsylvania, wasn't he? Did he know Joe Johnson? How did he like Amherst? Was he interested in athletics?

In spurts and desultory starts and stops, the talk would go on and then, usually, languish. Only the most conscientious of brothers would persist for the full half hour. The rest would drift away, to form an intimate circle of their own, laughing, talking, and playing the phonograph. Sometimes the freshmen would be left for the last ten minutes of their visit entirely to themselves, sitting stiffly together, their feet shifting, their hands perspiring—too miserable to talk to one another. Walton shuddered as he thought what it must be like to have this experience thirteen consecutive times. And, even at the end of the first day, he could pass another freshman on the street and know whether or not he was destined to be a nonfraternity man. If he was awkward, gawky, wore unfashionable clothes or had a bad complexion, he was probably one of the unwanted; his only chance of a better fate lay in the possibility of his being a "legacy." This meant that his father or uncle or older brother had been a member of a particular house, and that this house, however reluctantly, would recognize its consequent obligation and overlook his lack of the graces. But even this reprieve was not always extended; the chances of its being were in direct ratio to the extent to which his forerunner was an influential alumnus.

The unwanted included all Jews, all Negroes (there were very few of them at Amherst, but most of these impressively outstanding boys) and (with an exception Walton was to learn about) all boys of Oriental extraction—regardless of how attractive or athletic they might be, or how right their clothes. Brains were not wholly irrelevant, and not discriminated against at all if they were handsomely cased. . . .

By Wednesday morning, Walton, who had somehow—whether intuitively or because he was afraid to make up his mind—shown a better than average poise in refusing to be high-pressured, had narrowed down his choice to two fraternities, Alpha Delta Phi and Beta Theta Pi. Even his fourth appointments with those two houses had failed to make him feel certain which he wanted to join, and by common consent they had called off further appointments, with the understanding that he would go to the house of his choice that evening.

And so, as he stood, still undecided, at his window, watching the darkening campus, although he felt the pull of inner division, he was warm, almost jubilant with the knowledge of being wanted, even of being prized. Not only had most of the houses wanted him, and these two finally fought for him, but he had also been chosen, at a noisy and incoherent meeting of the freshmen, as one of the three leaders of the class in the forthcoming flag rush with the sophomores. It was intoxicating, and bewildering.

Yet, under his bewilderment, he thought he understood the choice he had to make between the two fraternities. The Betas looked much more like college men as he had envisioned college men to himself. With his recently awakened interest in clothes, he knew that they, and not the Alpha Delts, dressed the way college men should dress—just as he learned on arrival that in his sartorial zeal he had had the trousers on his new suit made at least two inches too wide, and so had rushed down to the tailor to have them altered.

He knew finally then that the Betas were college men, whereas the

Alpha Delts were much more like ordinary boys and men of the sort he was already acquainted with. Instead of shaking hands with the arm cocked to form a right angle, with the elbow bent and raised, they shook hands in various simple, unsystematic ways; instead of clothes made by a New Haven tailor, they bought them at home or in the local Amherst stores. Instead of talking and acting like sophisticated clubmen, they behaved in a very commonplace, natural fashion.

In short, it was the old choice between the familiar and the exotic, the prosaic everyday and the glamorous. Yet that was not all; if it had been, borne as he was just now on the crest of a wholly new wave of self-confidence, Walton must have chosen the Betas without hesitation. Difficult though it was—had always been, since his prolonged sojourn in bed—for him to venture into the strange and new without fear, he had just made the most decisive transition of his life successfully.

Curiously enough, what made this further choice so difficult was the very thing, he thought later, that superficially would seem to have clinched his immediate preference for the Betas. Each evening, after rushing hours, there was much unruly and often incoherent talk about the fraternities among the freshmen in the dormitories. What Walton heard about the two houses in which he was most interested was surprisingly consistent, although attitudes toward these conclusions varied widely.

The Betas, it was agreed, were the *smoothest* house on the campus— except, perhaps, Psi U. This confirmed, in the local idiom, Walton's satisfaction with them as college men of the sort to be found in the popular magazine *College Humor*. There was unanimity, too, on the fact that the Alpha Delts tended to be *Christers*—that is, puritanical. Drinking was effectively forbidden (legally, of course, in 1924, it was forbidden everywhere) in their house; the fraternity literary exercises were taken seriously; the freshmen were treated more humanely during the pledge season from September to November than in the other houses.

Here, fear and rebellion pitched their tents and prepared to battle in Walton. The Walton who had overtly accepted the basic principles of his parents (not too dissimilar on questions of social morality, except in the differing spirit of their motivation) struggled with the Walton of exotic fantasies. The Puritan crossed swords with the Hedonist.

Hence the superficially greater pull toward the Betas. But it was not so simple as that, for he was still very much within the orbit of his mother's power, still inclined to endorse her sympathies and prejudices, still disposed to accept, at least formally, her evaluations of the dignity of defeat and sacrifice—despite the pleasure and recognition he had just been experiencing as something very like victory and fulfillment. And from this point of view the Alpha Delts represented conscience and right, the Betas self-indulgence and wrong.

He was, of course, not being just to either group. His highly subjective picture of both was not even a vague approximation of the actuality, and he was, in time, to qualify it considerably. But now, on this first Wednesday evening of college, he had only the vivid and conflicting pictures of the past few days on which to base his decision.

He felt a new silence. The chapel bells, ringing seven o'clock, ceased. Like a sleepwalker, he went down the hall and washed his hands and face. He was aware of feeling both lonely (homesick? He did not know) and determined. Back in his room he brushed his hair, straightened his tie. Then he went out and down the stairs into the night.

As he neared the Commons which divided the Beta and Alpha Delt houses, as well as others, he felt hot and empty in the stomach, as though he were going to be nauseated. He was queer, he suddenly thought— really and hopelessly strange, the sort of person who sometimes went insane. And despair filled him; he felt a secret conviction that he would never escape. From what? Into what? He did not know; he knew only that he must go on acting as though he did not believe this—as though, he found himself thinking, he were really there to move from one thing to another. Then it was not escape at all, he thought with a sudden flash of illumination; there was something that was not himself inside him misleading him, tricking him with the casuistry of poetic symbols, feeding him the opium of exotic dreams, and making him confuse the finding of himself with the escaping from himself.

He reached the corner of the Commons, where a narrow path cut diagonally across the green under the elms. Resolutely he set out on it, toward the Alpha Delt house, and he had taken only a few steps when he remembered, with a comforting warmth, what had happened there yesterday. It was as though he had purposely concealed it from himself tonight. Concealed it? Why?

On the day before, only a minute after he had entered the house, a loud shout had come from its rear and suddenly all the Alpha Delts had converged on the back door, howling, waving and pushing, leaving the freshmen to stand alone in the front hall, looking in bewilderment at each other. Then, after a moment, the brothers began to straggle back, in their midst a short black-haired Chinese boy, whose teeth were flashing in a smile that was intensified in his large dark eyes. Laughing, protesting, he was trying to break away from the blows of welcome descending on his shoulders and back.

When Jim Haywood, the tall, easy senior whom Walton had liked the best of those who had talked to him, finally returned, Walton asked him what was going on.

"It's Georgie Lee," Jim explained, grinning. "He's a member of the house, and he thought we wouldn't want him around during rushing season, the damn fool, because he's Chinese. So we went after him—he lives in Holyoke—and got him. Brought him here by force," he added, chuckling, then suddenly turned sharp eyes on Walton. . . .

Halfway across the Commons now, Walton saw the lights of Alpha Delt. There it was. He broke into a run.

[*Part Four*]　　　2

THE decisive and sometimes conflicting influences of Walton's college life were Ezra Barker, John Collins Howe, the Alpha Delta Phi fraternity, Irene Wertz, Carlton Crocker and his own tenacious ambition, fully uncovered—you might almost say, Walton thought, *discovered*—for the first time.

The combination of Ez Barker and Walton's ambition would have satisfied any astrologer as the conjunction of planets in their favorable aspects. Ez was the first of fifteen Alpha Delt fellow pledges (identified, in the undergraduate lexicon of the time, as a *delegation*) with whom Walton got below the surface of things. On the third or fourth night of their acquaintance, they left the fraternity house together after evening chores there, and Ez proposed that they go down to the town diner for a cup of coffee— the first of several thousand they were to drink together.

Perhaps they got together so soon, Walton often thought in later years, because of the traditional pull of opposites. Ez was two years older than he, and six inches shorter (by this time Walton had passed six feet). His blond hair (almost white) was already thinning, but he had so rosy a complexion that his likeness to the famous advertisement of the Fisk Tire Company: "Time to re-tire," showing a small blond boy in his nightshirt holding a candle aloft, was, to Ez's weary disgust, a commonplace. Ez was friendly and outgoing, Walton reserved. Ez had knocked around and was shrewd in the ways of the world, Walton had been unusually sheltered. Ez was, if not indifferent to clothes, unable to afford any in the mode; Walton was already preoccupied with ways and means to achieve a wardrobe comparable to those he saw around him.

On this first evening of their friendship, as soon as they had ordered their coffee, Ez swung around on his stool and asked, "What're you going out for?"

Walton regarded him in silence for several minutes; during the less than two weeks he had now spent in Amherst he had been asked so many questions he didn't understand that he now fell back on this protective measure as a matter of course.

Ez did not seem to expect a reply.

"With your record, you ought to try for the *Student*," he went on. "You've done some writing, haven't you? And I'd guess you'd have the best chance in the delegation, along with Chuck Wells, maybe, for a major sports managerial competition."

Ez had a way of squinting when he smiled that was in some peculiar way endearing; to Walton, it somehow seemed as though it were the result of looking into the sun too long. Walton's reserve broke down.

"I haven't thought about it," he said.

Ez turned very serious; the characteristic tapping of his cigarette on the ashtray took on a faster tempo.

"We've got to think about it, Herrick," Ez told him. "Christ Jesus, the Alpha Delts hold damned few worthwhile jobs in activities. They're too damn content to sit on their asses. This house has had a fine record and it's still one of the three best on the campus. But it isn't going to be very long, if we don't do something about it. We've got one Scarab now in Jim Haywood, but he only got it because he's so damned well-liked—"

Walton interrupted him.

"What's Scarab?" he asked.

Ezra Barker stared at him as though he had committed an unforgiveable blunder.

"Jesus H. Christ, Herrick!" He shook his head sadly. "Don't let anybody else hear you ask a question like that. Scarab—why, haven't you seen those little round white hats with the yellow and green bands around them? Christ almighty—" The hand that lighted a fresh cigarette from the stub of the previous, the nicotine-stained fingers, trembled a little—"haven't you seen the hat Jim Haywood wears? Scarab is the senior honorary society—what every man in his right mind would give his eyeteeth for. You get tapped for Scarab only if you're one of the really big men in the junior class. Anywhere from six to twelve, maybe, get it—no more."

He paused for breath, shook his head again. Walton, properly abashed, waited in silence.

"Well, the point is—" Ez looked him hard in the eyes—"there isn't a guy in our junior delegation who stands a prayer. As for the sophomores, Dunn and Hobart have the stuff, but Dunn will have to take his football competition to make it, and Hobart's not popular—he's too, well, reserved. It's no sure thing for either of them, and it's none too soon for us to get going. I'm going out for the *Student,* but I'm not the type ever to be editor-in-chief, and—"

Walton could hold in no longer.

"How do you know all this, anyway?" he demanded.

Ez twinkled.

"I've been casing the place," he said. "Look here, I'll be frank with you. It means a lot for me to be an Alpha Delt." He flushed a little. "My folks are poor, see—poor as the mouse that didn't get into the church, not even its basement—and there are six of us kids. To come to college at all I had to bell-hop at a hotel at Lake Placid for a year. And I've got to wait table here and get some other jobs too. Christ, a guy like you doesn't know what I'm talking about. But, anyway, I'm just feeling sorry for myself. The thing is, I'm grateful to the house for taking me; I want to do something for it in return. And I'll do everything in campus activities I can, to bring back the house's supremacy. But I'm not the answer that way, so my job's going to be to beat the tail off guys like you and Wells to make you do your share. For you're the guys who can really do it."

Walton eyed him suspiciously.

"Why me?" he demanded.

Ez grinned.

"Come on, wise up. You're not that dumb. Because you look the part; you act it. You've got an air of authority—or do I mean authenticity? I'm a farmer—no good on long words. But look here— why do you think you were chosen one of the three leaders for the flag rush? Why do you think all the houses bid you?"

"Two didn't," Walton stated cautiously.

"Two didn't! You know how many beside Alpha Delt bid me? Two. Two out of the other twelve. And the only reason I made A.D. was because I got up here early, and struck an acquaintance with Dunn, not wholly by accident, at the boardinghouse. They'd hardly checked on me during the summer. O.K., Herrick, now stop playing dumb. You've got the brains; you're tall (you're not an athlete, are you?); you've got the looks. Maybe you could be Junior Prom chairman, too; you're a pretty smooth guy. But we'll get all that worked out later. For now, I'd like to get a line on what you think of the other guys in our delegation."

They talked until one in the morning, with Ez in command. Only when they parted, Walton to go to his dormitory and Ez to his rooming house, did Walton's new friend turn suddenly shy.

"It's been grand talking to you," he said, almost muttering, and gave a funny awkward wave of his hand. "G'night, fellow."

Before going to bed, Walton spent ten minutes in the third-floor washroom, looking intently at himself—big ears, slightly bumpy nose, and the cowlick that so pained him. He couldn't really see that he looked any different from before, but somehow he felt more contented than usual as he finally turned away. . . .

From that time on, Walton and Ez were close to inseparable. There were other boys in their delegation who interested Walton, and with whom he spent a fair share of time, but none with whom he felt the comfortable easiness he did with Ez. There was, for instance, Claude Moore, who read or, at least, quoted Schopenhauer, drank heavily and talked about women with a sophisticated familiarity that had Walton gaping. Claude soon found his classes boring and after a decent interval was persuaded by the administration to browse in other pastures than those of Amherst. There was good-natured, black-eyed Chuck Wells, stout and gregarious, the son of a Kansas City meat packer, who was too popular and easygoing, and eventually flunked out in his sophomore year. There was Sidney Highgate, whose semi-feminine propensities were not sufficiently obvious for the Alpha Delts to recognize them at first, but over whose initiation into the brotherhood in November there was considerable controversy. And there was Doug Henry, tall, bony, one to keep his own counsel, who did his best to disguise by rough talk and mannerisms the lyric poet he nurtured within him.

Of these four, only Doug went through the four years and was graduated with Ez and Walton. In fact, only five of the original fifteen in the delegation completed their course—and this, too, was probably a contributory factor to Walton's and Ez's continuing closeness.

At any rate, the friendship prospered, and Walton followed Ez in the adoption of a fanatical patriotism. Alpha Delta Phi was the fatherland, and no Machiavelli himself ever endowed the state with a greater autonomous importance or served it with a more dedicated reverence than Ez did.

In this respect, it was fascinating to Walton, years later, to look back and see, with some clarity, the varying attitudes toward the fraternity of—for instance—Ez, Doug Henry and himself. The analogy with Machiavelli was not far-fetched in describing Ezra's position—if one meant, as Walton did, the historical Machiavelli and *not* the popular distortion of Old Nick, the ultimate double-dealing cynic. For Alpha Delta Phi gave to Ez an official status, a public stature, that secretly seemed to him just and appropriate. Yet, without it—or some comparable recognition—it was questionable, Walton came to think, that

Ez would ever have grown to anything like his full potential. For, however much he had possessed, up to now, a core of tough and decent self-respect that had assured him of his own dignity and worth and had helped him to keep his head up through lonely hardships, his eyes addressing on terms of equality those who had (in Ez's opinion) more obvious advantages—he had fought alone too long, and he needed, by this time, an external acknowledgment of his caliber.

So Ez, like Machiavelli, gained a needed sanction from his public recognition, and gladly paid for it by his celebration of the fraternity and his service to it. To him, the fraternity was almost an organic entity in itself, capable of health and illness, growth and decay. *It* he served, not those who comprised it—and woe to the brother who, whether through indolence, selfish indifference or perversity, failed to contribute to its well-being. Ezra Barker, physician to the state, would without hesitation have amputated an arm or leg—that is, a recalcitrant or delinquent brother—to the greater health of the body public. And since, as a freshman, he could hardly diagnose, heal or treat the defections of upper classmen, his own delegation mates suffered the closer attention.

To Doug Henry, this was unmitigated nonsense—which he would have described in stronger and terser language. Doug was a gentleman poet who wore lumberjack shirts when they were out of fashion and refused to comb his hair; he possessed a fine tenor voice and a strong left arm that eventually made him light heavyweight champion of the college and a formidable if wild southpaw pitcher. He would have fought the man who applied the word to him, but he was, Walton realized in later years, a romantic of the first order. Although not a genuine Southerner technically—he came from one of the border states—he governed his life by a code of honor as strict as that of a Renaissance gentleman—but emotionally conceived and fiercely private. On occasion, especially with the assistance of alcohol, his temper would flash like that of Harry Hotspur. Yet, in their sophomore year, after their first extensive exposure to Shakespeare, it occurred to Walton that Doug kept his passionate nature under a dangerous control—a control suggesting the quality of Othello, when he says, for instance, "Keep up your bright swords, for the dew will rust them."

At any rate, to Doug a fraternity was—or should be—a club, an association of gentlemen and fine fellows who sang and drank and gambled together, all in reasonable moderation, and occasionally even studied together. Its members should expect from one another a decent courtesy, a willingness to consider and respect the tasks and needs of others—no more. Neither in the exalted name of a childishly misplaced devotion to the fraternity, nor through reformer zeal, should they make any further demands upon any individual member. Where Ez Barker was a serious citizen of a body politic, Doug Henry was one of a loosely associated band of knights with a common fealty but independent codes and idioms.

Walton found his own relation to the fraternity harder to analyze. It was decidedly different from that of either of the other two. It held some of Ez's intense concern, Doug's romanticism, yet was really like neither. To him as well as to Ez, his membership seemed a belated recognition of his own evaluation of himself, but not in nearly so realistic a set of terms as those of Ez. Throughout Walton's freshman year, Alpha Delta Phi was to him perhaps most nearly a religious brotherhood—one the more beloved because it combined high principles and aesthetic beauty. The principles, as they were stated (however irregularly observed in practice), contained such familiar elements as friendship, loyalty, decency, self-improvement—all of which he recognized quickly, whatever the discrepancies of terminology, as consonant with the ideals honored at home. The beauty he found for himself, at the weekly Sunday-night sings, with the entire membership gathered on couches and in easy chairs around the huge, well-seasoned logs in the big fireplace.

As the light flickered over the dark, handsome face (like that of an Arab chieftain, it seemed to Walton's baroque imagination) of Dick Huntington, house choragus, and he lifted his hand and gave the note for the opening song, "Another Busy Week Has Passed," Walton would experience something approximating religious fervor. This, at last, was his cathedral and, as the evening progressed and the fire dwindled, with the mood of the songs shifting from the brisker and gayer sort to the quieter cadences of the "Kenyon Song" and "Paige's Horse," the smoky light cast a nimbus, a wreath of shadowy radiance, over the head of each of the seniors, investing them with something of the legendary grandeur of, say, the Knights of the Table Round. The voices, hushed, lingering on the dusky air, with here and there a sweet, abandoned tenor piercing the more somber tones of the others; the ecclesiastical light; the unaccustomed gravity of the faces—all this transported Walton to a realm of noble sentiments and aspirations.

And when they had all risen for the solemn finale of "Kaire Alpha Delta Phi," when the few guests had departed, and the freshmen rose, one by one, from their seats on the freshman bench to recite from memory the words of the songs and the data of the fraternity's history before the stern faces of their betters, Walton would perform with the rapt, expressionless intensity of the soul-intoxicated neophyte.

What was of most value to him, unquestionably, he came to understand, was that for the duration of his college years he believed for the first time that virtue was not necessarily incompatible with pleasure, noble ideals and principles of conduct with beauty. This was new in his actual experience; for the first time, the world around him approximated the values of his secret, private visions of heroism, beauty and delight— visions to which he had clung, while believing them actually somehow *wrong.* . . .

As September dwindled into a golden, hazy October and it passed in turn into the bleaker, steeper climate of November, Walton became surer and surer that no other fraternity would have suited his taste and needs so well. However much individual brothers might gallivant about, Alpha Delta Phi had a more genuine loftiness of purpose and sobriety and earnestness of practice than all save one or two other houses on the campus—and these, in turn, lacked the prestige that Walton found equally gratifying. The gayer, livelier and more sophisticated freshmen whom he came to know in the dormitory tended to rate Psi Upsilon and Delta Kappa Epsilon higher, but even they at least acknowledged that Alpha Delt was one of the Big Three, and what fault they found with it (they charged overvirtuousness and overseriousness) merely enhanced its value to Walton.

Then, too, it was the only Amherst fraternity that had abandoned corporal punishment for pledges. When his dormitory mates returned from chores at the houses to which they were pledged with their well-paddled tails so sore that they could not sit down with comfort, Walton would shiver with secret relief. Perhaps mostly because of the formidable power of James H.'s punitive right arm, Marcia had forbidden the spanking or striking of her children. Walton well remembered the one time his father, pushed to the very limits of his considerable capacity for patience by his little boy's insolence, administered two solid whacks to the seat of Walton's pants. Marcia had rushed to the scene, cradled the sobbing boy in her arms and, rocking him back and forth, hissed at the unhappy William, "You sadistic brute! Sating your evil temper on a little child!"

In retrospect, it became evident to Walton that this code which excluded physical punishment had had a great deal to do with his later fear of physical violence of all sorts. To be dumped unceremoniously into a public school playground after such sheltering had been almost catastrophic.

Red Stewart had done his work well, and Walton settled, early in his college career, what lingering doubts he had about his ability to stand up to rough treatment. Physical violence in itself no longer frightened him. In both the traditional Chapel Rush and the Flag Rush, between the two lower classes, he conducted himself as well as the next fellow, emerging from both half-naked, his clothes hanging in tatters and his body covered with dirt, sweat, scratches and bruises—so happy a distinction to him that he was reluctant to clean up.

But it was quite another matter when he thought what it would be like, every day, to be told, "Bend over, frosh," and "Touch your toes, freshman." What he *was* still afraid of, he discovered, was being singled out, having—as he thought of it—The Finger leveled at him and the fearful punishment administered to him alone. When imagining what it would be like, waves of wild protest, fear, guilt and humiliation broke over the inadequate barriers of pride and dignity that he had erected, and he was face to face with stiff-necked terror. In their different ways, both Ez and Doug tended to feel a little cheated by the leniency of their treatment, but from Walton the Alpha Delt program drew the results at which it aimed: he worked unprotestingly, even feverishly, at all tasks assigned to him, in gratitude for not being roughly handled.

Hence, when initiation time came, early in November, he was all the more startled and outraged by what happened on the night before the formal and solemn ceremony by which he was inducted into the brotherhood.

All that the freshmen knew in advance was that they were to appear at the fraternity house, wearing their oldest clothing, at eight o'clock in the evening. Ez said quietly, "We're going to get it." Doug grinned ferociously and half growled, "It'll be a rough evening, men, to make up for all this pretty time we've been having."

A bleak emptiness settled within Walton. He tried to grin in deference to the spirit of the conversation, but the attempt was less than halfhearted. That dreadful feeling of the early days at grammar school returned to him: a deep nightmare sense of hopelessness. Once again, he reverted to his only tactics of defense against it—a grim, teeth-clenched determination to endure, to last through whatever horrors awaited him, with a fervent clutching in both hands of a sort of baton of blind faith —faith that the ordeal would somehow, sometime, come to an end.

At this moment he learned one new thing about the nature of his fear—learned it and then, after the initiation, promptly forgot it again. Looking in startled realization at Ez and Doug, he saw that they were not really so lighthearted about what was coming as their words suggested, but that whatever the degree of their fear it did not freeze them or overpower them as it did him. There was a gleam in their eyes, a tense, anticipatory tightness in their muscles, that suggested to Walton, however vaguely, that they were mustering some mysterious resources well down in the depths of themselves with which to meet the situation.

And so, in a somnambulistic way, he peered within himself, seeking a similar source of strength. He did not find it. Instead, for an eerie moment, he had a feeling—it was more a sensation than a thought— that his whole person was of an insubstantial and weightless character. It seemed to him that the envelope of his body must be thin to the point of fragility, and transparent, revealing the absence of anything within. He was, he suddenly thought fantastically, a wisp, an almost hallucinatory shred of a person, to be blown into oblivion by the most trivial of winds. And this, he saw in a transient insight, was why he was so afraid; a vision of a multitude of vicious, sadistic figures trampling his puny self under their feet, exterminating, obliterating him, rushed into his mind. He felt giddy and forlorn. . . .

That night, when he entered the front door of the fraternity house, Walton was rudely seized and blindfolded, and his hands were tied behind his back. The image of his wispiness returned to him now, and in some strange way helped him to undergo what followed. It seemed to him that the more he entertained this hitherto terrifying sense of his own inconsequentiality, the less fear he felt, and the more his awareness of and vulnerability to what was actually transpiring were dulled. He almost enjoyed his helplessness, the peculiar fatalistic irresponsibility engendered in him by the crude fact of being blindfolded and having his hands tied.

This feeling lasted through the first hour or so (as nearly as he could calculate time) of the program. The pledges were paddled once or twice, hustled roughly into what seemed to be the straw-filled back of a horse-drawn wagon, and jolted over many roads. Then they were finally dumped out (it later was established, right back in the fraternity yard from which they had started their journey), and a scene began which Walton somehow saw and experienced the more vividly from being blindfolded. When he read Dante in his senior year, this evening came back to him in its full dimensions.

The night was filled with unseen demons, brandishing pitchforks and wailing like lost spirits tormented by flames. The flames were present too; every so often Walton's private demon (apparently each freshman had been assigned to one sophomore), with threats of destruction by fire, would push or drag him so close to a bonfire that the warmth scorched him and a ruddy light flared through his blindfold and even his eyelids.

Everywhere he was pulled, he approached a new stage of this

multiringed Pandemonium. Between his own pitiful performances of grotesque dances, speeches, songs and ordeals like that of crawling up a hill that seemed endless, to drop three feet into a pit—all these punctuated with paddlings—he could hear Doug intoning a filthy song, Ez protesting that he couldn't dance, Chuck Wells in the grip of uncontrollable laughter from which no paddle could dissuade him, and Sidney Highgate protesting and screaming in unconvincing hysteria. And through it all, the grunting and cursing and wailing of the demons, some of whom, it was clear, were releasing a hidden capacity for moderate brutality through drinking. This somehow terrified him most, most threatened the structure of his faith in the fraternity.

And then his guide barked at him hoarsely to lower his head and run: "Run like hell, freshman, for that abyss in front of you."

Walton ran, but he did not drop into an abyss. His lowered head hit a brick wall with full force, and to the circus brilliance of Roman candles and pinwheels exploding in his brain he lost consciousness.

He awoke to a comforting sense of having run the race, not without injury, but without impairment of honor. This was partly because he could conceive of nothing worse to come, and partly because of the almost maternal solicitude in the hoarse voice of his frightened demon.

"You O.K., Walt? You O.K.? Christ, man, you turned yourself around and ran right into the wall. Jee-sus, but you scared me; I thought you'd killed yourself. Look, fella," and the voice turned to rough camaraderie, "I'm afraid we got to leave the blindfold on, but that's all the rough stuff for you. You're a sport, kid, and you'll get it easy the rest of the way." And when Walton, dazed, did not answer, the voice rose again, anxious: "You sure you're O.K., kid? Don't need a doc?"

Walton nodded his head feebly, to indicate that he was all right, then shook it to show that he didn't need a doctor.

The sophomore was not satisfied. "Whadda you mean? Are you O.K.?"

Walton said weakly, "O.K." and sank back again against the ground. He lay there a long time in a happy state of suspended animation, thinking over and over again, "It's all done. It's finished. It's all done." Voices advanced, hovered and receded, with his faithful demon explaining to each what had happened. Several times someone whose voice he could not recognize in this only hazily conscious condition would whisper a few words of encouragement or congratulations. Boots crunched back and forth over the hard ground, making friendly music through the ache in his head, and every so often Walton would hear a gurgle as his demon drank from a flask, always asking, as he screwed the cap back on, "You O.K., Walt? Sure you don't want a drink?"

Then, at last, some portentous announcement was shouted, and Walton's sophomore stirred himself, wavered and stood up. "We're going in the house now, Walt," he said thickly, "and I'll make you comfortable in there. Come on."

In their stumbling progress, they jostled against other sheep and shepherds, and a sense of companionship, warm and comforting, stirred in Walton from these encounters and from recognizing this or that freshman voice.

Once in the house, his guide lowered him gently, so that he was propped up against a corner wall, in the midst of the other freshmen. He could tell that they were all together partly from the muffled sound of breathing and squirming bodies, partly from the sheer animal warmth exuded.

An explosive sigh finally broke through the uneasy silence, and Doug Henry's voice was recognizable. He whispered loudly, "You all in one piece, fellows?"

It was Ez's familiar chuckle that Walton heard next.

"Nope. Two pieces. My tail and the rest of me. But somebody really got it—hit his head on a wall or something. They were scared; I heard 'em talking about it. Wonder who?"

"Me," said Walton, his voice harsh and eager in his own ears.

"Walt? What'd you do, fellow? Did you—"

Ez was cut short. An alien voice, stern and sharp, broke in.

"These freshmen are talking. We've been too easy on them. Let's give them the shock treatment. These two first."

Walton listened to the noise of two stumbling freshmen being led off; he listened with mingled feelings. On the strength of the companionship of the last few minutes, he felt warmly and fervently for the victims; he felt gratitude anew for being exempt; he felt a faint stirring of disquiet lest somehow the brothers change their minds about that exemption or forget what had happened to him. The last of these feelings increased in strength each time two more freshmen were led away, and when he heard Ez being yanked to his feet beside him he was not even surprised to be hauled up roughly himself. In subdued misery, his head suddenly hurting more again, he let himself be hustled without protest down a hallway. But within him was a sense of terrible outrage; he had been promised and lulled to a relaxing of the state he had induced in himself to carry him through the ordeal: now he was totally naked to his enemies.

He stopped to hear one door close behind Ez and his guard; then he was led on to another, thrust into a lighted room filled with jabbering, frenzied voices and hands that reached out to seize him and propel him forward—dozens of clutching hands, it seemed to him. Where was his demon, who had promised him, lulled him to rest with his promises? He was betrayed and lost.

Roughly his shirt was stripped from him and he was thrust upon his back on a table.

"Freshman," said a voice so fiendishly cold that Walton could not believe that it belonged to a college student, still less to one of those illustrious upperclassmen who sat there in such dignity and grace at the Sunday-night sings, "freshman, we are about to apply to you the truth test. We have here a powerful electrical machine which is now connected to your body." Walton jerked away as he felt something cold touch his chest. "I shall ask you questions, freshman, and if you answer truthfully, nothing will happen to you. But if you lie, two hundred volts will shoot through you. Do you understand?"

Walton did not trust himself to speak. He nodded.

"Freshman," and the voice seemed still more awful, "did you ever kiss a girl?"

Looking back on the scene long afterward, it seemed to Walton incredible that he could not, even after what had already happened that night, have seen anything humorous in the discrepancy between the voice and the words. But he did not. Gripping the sides of the table, he said weakly, "Yes."

"Ha!" said the voice. "Vile and sinning creature. At least you speak the truth. Remember the consequences if you do not speak the truth. How many girls have you kissed?"

Walton swung his body from side to side in a new agony, and felt more hands grip him. "One," he confessed miserably.

"Liar!" The word swelled, monstrous, over him from, it seemed, a multitude of voices, and even as he felt that in a moment the room would burst from the noise, a violent shock struck him, his muscles contracting and jerking. It was too sudden, too tremendous, for him to be able to cry out, but when it was over he lay there, feeling that he could endure no more, that he was in the hands of insane, sadistic monsters, and that he must, in the next moment, burst out weeping or screaming.

"You lied," the voice said. "The machine has punished you. Do not lie again or we shall increase the voltage. Evidently you have on your conscience particularly one virgin whom you ravished. This particular girl—did you screw her?"

"I did not lie. I didn't lie," Walton said frantically. "I—"

"Careful, freshman. Answer the question. Did you screw this girl?"

Walton gripped the table harder.

"No," he said.

And again the thunder of the single word and the lightning streak. His body jerked convulsively; then he lay still, numb, aware that he had not cried out, but finding no satisfaction in the fact.

"And now," said the voice, "you miserable liar, although you are unworthy, we shall apply to your bare stomach the brand of Alpha Delta Phi. This will hurt, freshman. What you have endured thus far is a delight to the senses in comparison."

At this moment, a door banged violently.

"Hey, you guys, is that Walt Herrick? He's not supposed to get the treatment; he damned near killed himself—ran into the wall and cracked his head. Lay off."

"Aw, nuts."

"There's nothing wrong with him."

The voice of his questioner commanded the rest to be silent, while Walton lay there, hanging, it seemed to him, over the brim of the world.

"Freshman," said the voice, "are you able to undergo the branding?"

The next few seconds expanded into a universe of time, through which Walton hurtled in a violent and tortured course. He felt that he was being torn in two by conflicting urges—not thoughts: he could not think. Then he drew a deep breath.

"Yes," he said. "I'm O.K."

He was aware of two things: the voices lowered, murmuring now, and, despite the cold sweat all over him, a sudden sense of relief, even of peace.

"Now," said the voice, and somehow even it seemed softened.

Then Walton felt the agonizing fire on his belly, heard the sizzling, smelled his own scorching flesh. After the agony of that moment, it seemed almost indecent to have the bandage ripped off his eyes, hear the voices babbling that it had only been a piece of ice, that he'd been a good sport, that he was a game guy, that he was O.K. When at last he grew accustomed to the light and was able to see clearly again, he stared in stupefaction at his unmarked belly. And throughout the remaining hour of cider and doughnuts, while the weary, beaten freshmen were feted and the events of the evening were gone over again and again, he remained dazed—and, despite his aching head and rebelling stomach, conscious only of that same wild elation within him that he had known the night Red Stewart had been his second in the boxing ring. . . .

Twenty-four hours later, this initiation night had no more reality for Walton than a vivid and terrifying nightmare will retain after the passage of the following day. For, twenty-four hours later, he had undergone the solemn and formal initiation rites into the fraternity; he had seen and listened to the explanation of the symbolism of the star and crescent; he had heard the holy words of the arcana; surrounded by august, black-robed figures in the sacerdotal light of the fraternity meeting room, hitherto always locked against him, he had knelt and pledged devotion and honor to the brotherhood. And afterward, again in a brilliantly lighted room, with a startlingly white cover laid for all the brothers—undergraduates and visiting alumni alike—he had rubbed shoulders with great men.

A week later, on a Tuesday evening, traditionally fraternity meeting night throughout the college, he found the whole occasion, business and all, as enchanting as a foray into some legendary court. And when it was over, and they all descended the stairs in a long line, each with his hands on the shoulders of the one before him, to stand on the porch and sing, "Kaire Alpha Delta Phi," he raised his head like some young fox to bay at the frosty night, exultant in the knowledge that he stood here in equal brotherhood with the great men whom until now he had only served.

JOURNAL: 7

from the journal of Walton Herrick . . .

Sept. 5, 1953

I am haunted by a figure I call the Truant Officer. When I close my eyes to see him, he looks like the movie version (which is, for all I know, the real thing) of a gangster—long black double-breasted overcoat with collar turned up, half shadowing the lower part of the face, gray hat with snap brim. With his hands thrust deep in his coat pockets, he stands motionless, watching, under a store-front awning.

I'm not sure just when I first began to personalize in this way the countless fears that rise like mist from the swamps and low-lying meadows of guilt and self-reproach. But just as, for a long time, I have had fantasies of striking others, so I have had ones of being struck—blasted, stabbed, clubbed, garroted. And for a long time I have asked myself, What am I really afraid of? How can I invent such outlandish perils? What is the origin of these fears that seem suddenly to appear from nowhere? And I have found myself empty-handed for answers, except the weak generalization that, since my mother always conceived of the world outside our immediate environment as a place of violence and sin, it was almost inevitable that I should make a dark, crime-infested alley out of every dimly lit street, a den of desperadoes, pimps and prostitutes out of each second-rate café.

But such surroundings have played only a small part in my elaborations of fear. These, at least, are distorted and wildly extended versions of an actuality; many of my fears have no counterpart in reality at all. They seem to rise, wingless, even formless, from their unknown breeding ground and swirl about me without a moment's warning—even when I am in the most secure, pleasant and cheerful situation. And the fear of some retributive blow that will come crashing down on my head

572

from behind has more often than not been of a vague nature and origin—so vague that there have been long periods during which I accepted this trick of fantasy in much the way other people have resigned themselves to hay fever, chronic indigestion or sinusitis.

It is only since I have commenced my more or less regular entries in this journal that I have begun to understand the sources of this fear of the fist raised behind my back, the need to glance over my shoulder to see if the Truant Officer is really there. I believe that the sources all stem from guilt and shame. Not the honest guilt felt for some wrong unmistakably committed, to be recognized immediately as such by a majority of people. Not the deeply human shame that one may feel over having done something sly or mean or dishonest. No, I mean that guilt and that shame experienced from one's failure to live up to what I call one's Heroic Image. If one is in servitude to such an image, one is in an almost daily state of fear, guilt and shame—a state so constant that unless one concealed it from oneself it would be insupportable. Hence the perpetual minor malaise to which such people are susceptible. Such people? Including myself.

I have tried to make a distinction between this sort of guilt and shame induced by one's failure to achieve something, be something, that one cannot do or be—between this phenomenon, on the one hand, and what I have called honest guilt and shame, on the other. I think that I now see clearly that I have distorted my distinction. There may be, I think, in either of the two situations I have just described, a reason for entertaining an obscure and uneasy fear; there are at least two separate sources for the vague fear of the Truant Officer.

One is that, since one's action or failure to act under certain circumstances has been judged by impossibly absolute standards, one finds it hard to experience real guilt or shame, and so translates these emotions into an undefined fear—fear of the punitive element in oneself enforcing these impossible dictates. There may also be, then, an unnatural insistence that one should not feel such "debasing" emotions as shame or guilt. But fear is more difficult to exorcise.

The second source is that one may willfully, even though unconsciously, refuse to recognize one's guilt, to feel one's shame, and therefore diffuse their impact into this generalized sort of apprehensiveness. Thus, ultimately, my original distinction between honest and dishonest shame and guilt diminishes into this: if one recognizes, feels and honestly evaluates one's guilt, then shame follows and the process is complete: one may be purged and takes steps to atone. If one does not, or will not, recognize and feel that guilt, or wrongly evaluates its just degree, one fights against acknowledging it, consequently does not experience shame, but allows both emotions to fester within, thereby creating an interior sore or ulcer that manifests itself in an unexplained feeling of fear. Guilt and shame have gone underground.

Enough. I like those paragraphs, for I have a feeling of having sustained logical thought, and expressed it clearly. But this is too abstract to do me much good: let me try to embody all this, give it a more immediate meaning for myself.

A simple, because exceptionally direct, example relates to an incident last spring involving Tim. I was setting out in the car on a Sunday afternoon. He begged to go along. My plan was to drive to the nearby beach, sit on a rock and meditate. That is how I described it to myself, though the chances are that I really wanted simply to vegetate. Julie and I had had a violent quarrel the night before; I felt that I wanted the chance to go back over the ground and see if I could establish more clearly for myself the degree of my own fault—but in actuality on such occasions I have been prone rather to swim in resentment, to swamp analytical thought in the need to find justification for my vindictiveness. Nevertheless, I stuck to my version of the effectiveness of such a retreat, and I refused to take Tim with me.

He wept. I drove away furiously, feeling mean and selfish. He went back into the house, pushing his fist into his eyes. On my way to the beach I had so horrible a fantasy—of his running, weeping, after the car, falling flat on the muddy road and sobbing heartbrokenly—that I could not bear it. I was filled with the premonition that some accident had occurred—that he had followed the course of my daydream and then been run over by another car. I turned around and went back—to find him happily engaged at his workbench!

This I call the simplest and clearest form of Truant Officer fear. One can trace its derivation instantly; the protagonist of the fantasy is the person involved in the actual incident: cause and effect are openly established.

Usually, however, the chain of consequence is much more subtle, even wholly concealed. The dramatic images and actions by which my fear is symbolized frequently involve the children. This is, I think, natural enough—if I feel threatened, and am unwilling or unable to experience it in direct terms of myself, who else has the necessary *immediate* value to me? Yet I suspect that the radical threat usually involved must also indicate an involuntary reversion on my part to my mother's oversolicitude. The altar deities before whom she bowed were staring-eyed Fear and grim, skeletal Duty. But peering between their shoulders was the grinning epicene mask of Guilt.

Often in these dreams and daydreams of mine one of the children plays the alternate for myself. In panic, I may be feeling disguised guilt for an action in no way concerning the children, yet the vision of one or more of them in danger embodies my failure to live up to my standards, whether sound realistic ones or—more frequently—those of the Heroic Image.

I must remind myself, when I refer to the Heroic Image, that it is not only amorphous, since it requires me to have so many contradictory qualities; it is actually plural—or, perhaps, collective. My failure to live up to it sometimes refers to an ideal of adventurousness, sometimes one of duty, sometimes one of courage or rakishness. There is usually a palpable relation between the particular aspect of the Image invoked and the identities of the participants in the fantasy. It is most often when Duty is invoked that the children become symbols—obviously, never when it is a question of playing the Great Lover.

Another example. After a day at the beach last summer, sprawled on the bed for a nap, I imagined that the recession of the tide had left a huge hole in the local beach. Our children and their companions fashioned a long rope ladder, attached it at the top to some heavy driftwood, lowered it into the hole, and swarmed happily up and down it. Suddenly I looked up and saw that in some impossible way the tide had reversed itself and was coming back in now—worse, that what seemed to be a tidal wave was approaching. I had time only to yell a frantic warning before the huge wall of water was upon them. In the fantasy I tried desperately to rescue the children. But I could not—and I could not erase from my mind the picture of them scattered here and there in deep water, screaming and waving their arms and drowning. With a violent effort, I willed away the picture, only to have it replaced by that of one or two of the little corpses lying far below the surface, wedged at the bottom of the deep hole. All my mental tugging could not release them; the image was stuck fast.

Only now does this dream have more than its immediate ghastly effect on me. Only now (I wonder more than ever at the processes of memory: if we were not afraid or ashamed to, could we really remember everything, back to the beginning of our lives? Bergson?)—only now do I recall clearly that on the day previous to this fantasy I had, at a staff policy meeting, voted with the majority for a decision I did not believe in. I did not have a documented case for my own position, and was extremely reluctant to assume the unpopular role of dissenter without greater knowledge. Yet, as I voted with the rest against my half-formed convictions, I felt wretchedly dishonest. I went home, vaguely miserable, but determined not to recognize the condition and hence unable to examine the cause. I exhorted myself to cheer up!

Moreover, as I began to work the connection out just now, there came into my mind the Shakespeare quotation "There is a tide in the affairs of men." But the unconscious is very tricky—or perhaps I am tone-deaf and can't hear it aright. For a moment the associated quotation meant for me that I had failed to grasp an opportunity, but when I remembered that the tide in my fantasy was an unnatural one, I began to believe that I had been trying to make so decisive a moment out of one that did not hold such a potential for me at all. Since I was not sufficiently informed on the question at the meeting, I would have been rashly foolish to speak up, simply on the basis of an emotional conviction. So—when Brutus' words come back in this connection, actually misapplied, it can only mean to me that I am trying to dress out in grandeur a rather mundane situation: hence another incident illustrating my need for the grand stage, whatever the expense to truth. Rather the tragic fault, the heroic failure, than a plain human confusion and the inability to resolve it . . . Perhaps—wheels within wheels—I even wanted to avoid recognizing a real cause for guilt and transferred it to the situation at the Foundation so that, should I be "found out," the ultimate cause would still be hidden. . . .

Most often, the chain of causation—failure to live up to the Heroic Ideal: concealed or disguised guilt and shame: unidentified fear—does not work so elaborately or symmetrically as in the examples I have given. I feel, so to speak, the Truant Officer's inimical stare behind me: this is the signal, I realize now, for an investigation of why I am secretly ashamed, of what I feel privately guilty. But in the past this sort of fear has often gripped me so intensely that I have telephoned home on any pretext—to find out indirectly if the children were all right.

Apropos of all this, I suddenly remember how many times I have met people who have talked about experiencing this sudden overwhelming apprehensiveness—always to prove that they possess some sixth sense, some secret sight. For in their stories, some actual catastrophe has always occurred when they have had the feeling. If they are not deliberately exaggerating for dramatic effect, I suspect that they forget rather facilely the many times they've had the experience without any actual counterpart having occurred.

No, I am sure that this phenomenon has no occult or extrasensory significance. It is not only a lighthouse beacon blinking out the existence of internal reefs, of fear induced by guilt and shame, but as well a sure sign of self-hatred, self-abuse.

For what causes one to be *afraid* over failing to do something one is not equipped to do—except a virulent dissatisfaction with one's honest human limitations? Why should it be *fear* that is provoked, unless there is a threat? And what can cause that threat except so vicious a disapproval as to amount to self-punishment? And since the punishment is unjust, is it not more rightly named abuse—and specifically self-abuse? For no one else even knows of the whole process. Fear of the Truant Officer is devaluation of self, often severe enough to amount to self-hatred, bearing the threat of sadistic self-inflicted punishment. The clowns again. And suddenly now I catch myself thinking of the black clown *as* the Truant Officer. And just why does the Truant Officer, the representative of authority and law, dress and look like the prototype of the American criminal? Why have I invested a gangster with this legal power? A door is opening somewhere. . . .

It closed again. A strange thing: I wrote the last sentence in the paragraph above almost as though I were doing automatic writing. Then I stopped short—abruptly—and it was as if a material, actual curtain were pulled together before my mental eyes; it seemed to me I could not think, and I felt nervous, confused and afraid. Yet off in the corner somewhere (what corner?) something—someone—is watching, sly, malevolent, amused. . . .

Another long pause. Evening. Saturday evening home alone. I've now gone back and reread the passage before the black clown broke up the sequence of thought. There's nothing for it now but to complete that passage. I can go back there, but I can't recover the understanding I had just before the curtain closed. At any rate, there is ample reason for the person caught in the sequence of guilt and judgment and self-punishment or abuse to feel fear. For, trapped in such a bondage, he is capable of extraordinary cruelty to himself. It is the Faust legend celebrated in a hundred cultures under a hundred names: seek the glory of the Heroic Image and you must surrender your natural human soul and prepare for the eventual inevitable punishment. All inner: all the more terrible for it.

Indeed, I realize now that I have come to anticipate so fearfully the psychological punishment I will assign myself for my failure to achieve some special grace or power utterly alien to my nature, that when I begin to feel fastened on me the implacable eyes of the Truant Officer, I unconsciously take up a cajoling, placating attitude, hoping against hope to escape. Sometimes, I see, I will address someone else—often, in the past, Lydia—in a ridiculously incongruous way, as though I were placating *her* for some offense I had committed against her. And when Lydia would ask me, "What are you cringing about?" I would swing into a rage.

Cycles of rage and self-depreciation. As I have noted before, I am quite prone, after a bout of hurt pride and rage, to be chilled suddenly by an acute fear of retribution. These extremes are closely interlinked. Fear of self-hatred may lead to rage; realization of my failure to control myself may lead me back into self-hatred. And, as I wrote earlier, if I hate myself for shaming my pride, I may strike out at others. On the other hand, I may strike at myself, rage inwardly, sulk.

Again, with the emphasis I have placed on the role of sexuality in my Heroic Ideal, no shame has been more painful to me than that over sexual impotence. I have experienced such impotence perhaps a dozen times in my life, all concentrated in the period of a single year. *Yet* I have feared its occurrence intensely at other times— whenever, I see now, I was most deeply immersed in self-depreciation, in the failure to be heroic. Perhaps the combination of my mother's outspoken abhorrence of sex and my secret immature overvaluing of it have led me to exalt ridiculously the potent male member as the one great symbol of health, rightness, vigor and satisfaction with self. Yet this tendency is everywhere in our society—in most societies, perhaps in nature, and Freud (or is it pseudo-Freud?) has put his seal upon it.

One thing I know: my mother castrated me; in taking away so enormously large a share of my initiative, in denying me my selfhood. A torrent of the sentences I have written in these journal entries pours back as I make this one statement. I feel suddenly quite incompetent to continue. The steady flow of thought and association I have been enjoying is over; just as it took me a week of apathy and false starts to get into today's entry, I know now that I am through for the day. I am far from satisfied with these last pages, but I have learned that it is no use to try to push thoughts that won't come freely. Muscular will is irrelevant to this kind of understanding.

GREAT men—always great men . . . It was with the same dedicated sense of associating with the exalted that Walton sat, throughout freshman year, in the classes of John Collins Howe. From the very first of these classes, he was sure that he was in the presence of a commanding personality—and one of a kind he had never known before.

In a way, the fascination John Howe exercised for Walton was supplementary to that exerted by his fraternity. For the force of the impact again lay in the realization that true goodness was not incompatible with a joy in life, that the devotion to beauty did not necessarily preclude that to duty and responsibility. As in his experience with Sunday-night sings, it seemed to Walton that these extraordinary classes, in which for sometimes as long as forty minutes that mellifluous voice intoned the verses of, say, Edwin Arlington Robinson, those sad wise eyes were impregnated with the suffering and the ecstasy of high romance —it seemed to Walton that he recaptured all the longing and the dreams of that early world of fantasy which he had so loved. When the voice celebrated the cold sea washing the rocks of Lyonesse, when the voice sang of Iseult—whether she of the white hands or the maid of Brittany—Walton was transported again to shores that had for a long time (it now seemed) stayed unvisited, remote and unreal. More, he came to believe that the enchantment of the sensual and the passionate that earlier had been the more beguiling since (he had been sure) forbidden, wrong—was not only nothing to be ashamed of; it might even be a matter for proud, open allegiance.

It was not until much later that he perceived that the substance of the erotic fantasies of adolescence and that of John Collins Howe's lectures and readings were not identical. What deceived him was that they were both, as he might then have put it, drenched in beauty. They were both products of a religion of beauty—not unlike, for all the

difference of idiom and perspective, that which flourished in fifteenth-
and sixteenth-century Italy under the guise of Neoplatonism. Even the
carnality of Walton's version was not really a dissonant note, for it
was a tempered and conditioned carnality, a sexuality wholly dependent
on the prior existence of glamorous physical and, as he then thought
of it, spiritual beauty—in no way akin to that grosser and healthier
variety that, free from any evasion or finickiness, is prompted directly
to action by the undeliberating senses.

As for John Collins Howe, he was a Southern gentleman who
found nothing contradictory in being a poet as well. Possessed of a
quiet but authoritative charm of manner, a beautiful resonant voice, a
distinguished face grooved with deep lines that seemed to bespeak a life
of passion and renunciation, a tall and muscular body, and a temperament that proclaimed the gospel of beauty without self-consciousness
—he was a figure to command the admiring attention of almost all
freshmen. If this one or that one had been brought up to regard poetry
as sissy, there was the irrefutable evidence that John Howe coached
freshman football and—at forty-odd—could still outbox everyone else
on the faculty and most of the students. If to chant in that grave organ
voice that "Poetry is an old man, dreaming in the sunlight of his years
of passion, or a child scrabbling with infant dignity in the sand, or a
young girl facing the sorrow of her first love with luminous eyes" was
the sort of thing that induced a titter—why, still, how to giggle in the
face of this man's having knocked a policeman down in the street for
speaking coarsely to a town girl of ambiguous reputation? If such a
man did such things, bringing to startling, even embarrassing life half-
formed and shamefaced daydreams, how could any young man fail to
nourish at least a secret respect for him? How could he, even, fail to
lend at least an occasional ear to his championing of poetry?

Walton, readier than most through nature and experience to listen
and to worship, was a devout disciple within a week. He took advantage of every opportunity to linger after class, to secure extra conferences, to have Howe inscribe copies of his books to Marcia, who
promptly surpassed Walton in the extent, if not the discrimination, of
her enthusiasm. She did not prefer the same poems that Walton did, but
she recognized in many of those she liked best a longing akin to her
own for a beauty that had never shaken its light across land or sea.

Walton also took to the writing of plays in blank verse, the nearest
he felt competent to come to poetry. Influenced by Howe, by Maeter-
linck's poetic dramas and by E. A. Robinson's long narrative poems,
and streaked with his own callow romantic idealism, these were replete

with unrequited love, generalized selflessness and the heroic endurance of grief. Their shepherds and shepherdesses, knights and ladies, pierrots and pierrettes, were bloodless and attitudinizing: he did not dare to articulate any longer in outright erotic terms the thicker substance of these dreams; he no longer even felt the uneasy presence of such terms in his consciousness. These implications were as truly played out off stage within him as in the scripts.

Yet, pallid and tiresome though the plays were (this was apparent to him, rereading them only five or six years later), Howe encouraged him and even endorsed the staging of one not much better (written later, in senior year) by the college dramatic club.

Why? Walton was to wonder in later years. Howe's own work, although often condemned by critics as possessing only one key, one tone, even one note—and that a minor one—was lacking neither in decent intellectual substance nor in technical adeptness. Walton never knew. Wrapped in the cocoon of his slow adolescence at the time he had the best opportunity to observe and analyze, he was never in the emotional position to take inventory.

Great men . . . John Collins Howe was a great man, one in the catalogue of heroes Walton scanned. He was a bard, a troubadour, a cavalier poet—one of those singers and celebrators of the poetry of life who stood in direct defiance of the cheerless and unlovely line of Walton's inheritance as he then knew it.

Walton secretly dreamed of becoming such a one. Yet he was depressingly aware of encumbrances; he doubted his own capacities: as a poet, as a lover (Howe, a bachelor, was believed by the students to be irresistible to women, but to forgo them because of an early, tragic love affair), as an intrepid adventurer. Walton felt his own brain to be drier, somehow better adapted to prose. He was only too aware that he lacked the dash, the verve, the courage to initiate exciting relations of whatever sort, whether with girls or among the fellows around him. He had painfully learned how to cope with some of these relations; it was another matter to take the lead. Besides, something in him shrank from—he knew no other way to put it—the impact of most other personalities. He was so accustomed to being a loner that, when the idea of his desirability as a companion was—it seemed to him—thrown at him so suddenly during pledge week, he developed a new anxiety. *They* must not learn what he was really like, must not come close enough to discover the boy who had been so severely left to himself during high school. The only solution he could find was to let *them* take the lead and to assume a nature that shared their tastes, their opinions, their habits, while holding them off far enough to keep them from violating what was truly his, what he would then have called, if he could have articulated the idea at all, his inner life. It was the process he had developed before when confronted with his mother. And such visions as those John Collins Howe engendered in him were at the very heart of what was most private to him.

Yet this was only one aspect of his obsession with great men and the secret overriding passion for eminence and prestige, a life instinct with power and beauty. If, on the one hand, he found himself too prosaic, too gray, too cautious to be a Howe or a Lancelot (he had never liked Galahad) or even a Pelléas, he still coveted a Scarab hat. Ever since Ez Barker had been scandalized at his ignorance of the senior honorary society, causing him to remember how one of the most aggressive bidders for him during rushing season had said flatly, "We want you. You're Scarab material," he had dreamed of the day when he might walk around the campus wearing this testimonial to greatness.

And this honor could be *won.* Some members of each senior class became Scarab because of their popularity, which enabled them to hold elective offices like that of class president or president of the Student Council. But others—and as many—won the editorship of the paper or a sports managership, hence usually Scarab, through ability and hard work. If what came through personality was beyond his reach, what came through brains and application was not. And Ez was there to push him.

Walton was not—was never to be wholly, perhaps—what Ez called "a self-starter." But he had proved long before, to himself and to others, that he had a terrible tenacity, once he was started. And Ez was there—not only to push him, to start him, but to provide a solid counterweight to John Collins Howe. Ez, alone, kept Walton from drifting into Thule or Cockaigne, from lingering for four years under the transforming enchantment of the Circe-hold of his romantic imagination.

Ez took him aside, one cold gray November afternoon in freshman year, and said, "Let's have a cup of coffee." Down at the diner in which they had held their first conversation, Ez squinted at him over his steaming cup and said, with a quite unsuccessful attempt at casualness, "Where've you been?"

Walton did not ask him what he meant. He stared abstractedly at Ez's already thinning blond hair combed so neatly back from that rather prominent bumpy forehead, looked straight into those candid eyes, then turned in discomfiture to an apparent perusal of the specialties of the diner, described in flamboyant white script on the mirror behind the counter: Beef stew 30 cents; ham 'n' eggs 25 cents. Discomfiture—for Ez's directness, however much masked in an attempt at nonchalance, prohibited evasion. But discomfiture, still more, because of the feeling that this unadorned question was of great importance to him and—at the same time—that he was once again in the grip of something stronger than himself. Stronger—but not malign: this tempered his malaise.

And so he turned back to look directly at Ez again and at last replied, with only a slight lining of defiance to his voice, "Mostly I've been reading and writing."

Ez nodded. It was extraordinary, Walton sensed even then, how much sympathy Ez managed to convey through even the simplest and most commonplace of expressions or gestures. There was no bullying here, no hint, even, of tyranny—yet Walton's not wholly unpleasant sense of relinquishing the controls was undiminished.

"I know," Ez said slowly. "Howe—he's a wonderful guy. But, Walt, you're not just a literary bird. You're not like Doug Henry. I wouldn't even be sure that you're ready yet to do the writing you will be ready for someday. You're more—balanced. And that balance is the thing that'll help you someday to have the more to write about—for it'll give you a more rounded experience."

They sat in silence, sipping coffee. Then Ez cleared his throat.

"Basketball starts in a week," he said as though he had just stumbled upon this information himself. "You told me once that you played basketball. Going out for the freshman team?"

What was so curious, Walton thought, was that he didn't know himself whether he wanted to or not. Despite an exceptionally good eye for the basket, he was slow and—he knew with unmistakable certainty—not good enough in passing or defensive skill to make the team. Still—

Ez finished his coffee and lighted a cigarette. He inhaled deeply and blew out a cone of smoke that seemed to Walton, who did not smoke at all, a thing of great beauty.

"I don't know how you'd feel about it," Ez began and then hesitated, stopped outright, gazing off down the diner. "You may have made other plans . . . or maybe you don't want to decide so far ahead of time, but— well—" Walton, dumbfounded, suddenly realized that Ez was acutely embarrassed, that his face was a deep pink and that he was faltering and fumbling for words—"Well, how would you feel about our rooming together next year?"

It was an unaccustomed warmth that kept Walton from replying immediately—a warmth that suffused him, flooded him so abruptly and so fully that for a moment he was incapable of saying anything.

And since he didn't speak, Ez went on more rapidly, his voice pitched a little higher.

"I snore bad and I'm sloppy as hell and you don't smoke and I smoke like a chimney and I'd advise you against it if I had any interest in what's good for you," he said all in a single rush of words—but then, turning back to Walton and suddenly regaining his usual slower cadence, concluded, "but how about it, fellow?"

Walton felt at once shy and proud.

"Gosh, I'd like to," he said.

On the way back to the fraternity house, they walked side by side in silence, sauntering, each with his hands in his pockets. At the foot of the steps to the porch, they paused.

"Have a try at the basketball," Ez said suddenly. "Even if you can't make first string center, you'll probably be the only really tall guy out except Bum Tyler—he played for Andover—and Dusty Reed (he's the coach) will have to keep two centers. I've looked the situation over pretty carefully. Then, in the spring, let's both get into that competition for the editorial board of the paper. We can help each other, and that'll be good training for you as a writer."

Walton didn't hesitate for a moment.

"O.K.," he said. "I will—and let's."

That was how it began: with the decision to room together—and with basketball. Walton worked. Through the long winter evenings, hopelessly outclassed, he chased doggedly from one end of the gymnasium floor to the other, in futile pursuit of the accomplished Bum Tyler, the first team center. While he failed to win his numerals in basketball, he didn't quit, and Ez repeated to him at the end of the season the comment of the coach: "I never had one like him. He can't move off a dime, he's slow, but he's got more heart than the rest of the bunch put together. It would've been a joke, and a mean one, to put him into the Williams game, even for a minute, but I had to sit on my hands to keep from waving him in."

Walton failed to win his numerals, yet he went on to achieve an outstanding success in interfraternity basketball: in his senior year, not a single team was able to bottle him up, to keep him from scoring at least fifteen points. . . .

Ez and Walton roomed together throughout the rest of their college course; their close friendship lasted halfway through senior year.

Looking back, that was the way Walton thought about it—and then suddenly asked himself what it was that had lasted until midway through senior year. His close friendship with Ez, of course—but something else, something *more* that accompanied that friendship, dominated it. Discussing it with other fellows, he could say lightly, "Sure, Boss Barker runs me the way he does the rest of you"—but that didn't say it. Ez was his anchor, his balance wheel, his counselor, his bellwether, his emotional barometer: everything that signified security, comfort, leadership, the insurance of consistent meaning. Without Ez, he would have been very lonely; lacking Ez, he would have made many more mistakes than the considerable number he did as it was.

Why? What was the nature of the peculiar bond between these utterly dissimilar boys from wholly dissimilar environments?

Walton did not know at the time; he never fully knew. What he did understand was that Ez was full of ambition for him, Walton; that he believed in Walton's capacities; that he was only the second or third person Walton had ever known who could and would criticize him without leaving the sting of ridicule or stirring the acrid deposit of shame, humiliation and self-contempt that bubbled faintly always at the bottom of the caldron that was Walton Herrick. The ensuing mutual loyalty was deprecated by both of them; it was—or seemed—unshakable.

It lasted through the grueling pace of the competition that next spring for places on the editorial board of the college newspaper— places that they both did win in a final scramble to collect enough news items to enable them to finish ahead of the other candidates. For one stretch of seventy-two hours in May they went without sleep, pounding away at their typewriters, slumping down the street side by side in the middle of the night, under the stirring budding maples and vast old elms, to pour black coffee into themselves, then—back in Walton's dormitory room, where he would reach over from time to time to punch or shake Ez back into a waking state.

"We're goddamn fools," Ez would groan. "We're godforsaken idiots, Herrick. We should have our heads examined." But it was Ez, nevertheless, who would set the pace, Ez who would retain his essential good humor, Ez who could cajole, plead, threaten when Walton, feeling as though he were preserved in some solution that insured functional perfection but the loss of feeling, would stand at the window, staring out blindly, for ten minutes.

In the spring of sophomore year, they both began writing editorials on the first leg of that further competition for the position of editor-in-chief. In the reportorial work, Ez had always led Walton by a few steps;

now Walton forged to the front. When all but two final candidates were dropped from the contest that June, Ez, with several others, lost out.

"It's nothing but your capacity for gas, Herrick," he said in summarizing the situation—said it in the scolding, half-barking manner that was one of his comic poses. "It takes a goddamn windbag to write editorials." He was really disappointed: a dream had been snapped in two. But he remained fiercely loyal, and when the board chose a new editor-in-chief in March of their junior year, and Walton was elected by a margin of one vote, Ez was almost equally as pleased and proud as Walton.

"For the house, you fool," he scolded. "Don't thank me and think I give a damn about you. I'd have liked to see you fall on your fat ass if it weren't for what it means to the house."

Only one thing marred for Walton his satisfaction over the election; his opponent, a boy named Charley Meigs, howled to high heaven that there had been a "fix," a "deal," and that Ez had engineered it. It was customary for the outgoing editor-in-chief to nominate one candidate to succeed him, and the board usually elected that nominee. But this time the editor found Walton and his opponent too nearly even to be willing to nominate either; he contented himself with expressing a slight preference for Meigs, but declaring his satisfaction if either was elected.

Meigs pointed to this expressed preference in leveling his charge of chicanery against Ez and, incidentally, Walton. "It was dirty politics," he said to Walton, "and I'd think you'd feel pretty cheap."

Walton didn't feel cheap, but he was troubled, uneasy. His sense of achievement was tarnished, and he raised the question again and again with Ez. Had there been any "deal"?

Ez gave him no satisfaction.

"What you don't know won't hurt you," he'd drawl. "What are you, a goddamn idealist? You got the post—now do a job."

Or sometimes he'd spin out an elaborate account of the trickery he'd worked out—a piece of burlesque that tantalized, occasionally even infuriated Walton.

"Then I went over to Higgins at Chi Phi and promised to let him marry my sister (that's my younger sister) if he'd sell his vote. Aldridge was tougher; I had to shanghai him and dump him in the crick a couple of times before he gave in." He would pause, make a thoughtful slow business of relighting his pipe. "It's all a question of infinite adaptability, boy, that's all. I had to find out what was each man's weakness. Could you intimidate him, swap with him, flatter him—"

The exasperated Walton would stomp out of the room. And it was only a few days before their graduation that Ez finally gave in (they were not such close friends the last term) and said tersely, "No. There was no deal. Naturally the other guys on the Board and I talked some before the election, argued. *But there was no deal.*" He looked Walton sharply in the eye. "I'd have told you long ago if you hadn't made so much of it. There was something fishy about the way you nagged at that thing. It was like you were saying, 'It has to be perfect, without a blot, or it's no good to me.' Who do you think you are, God? Nobody else gets it with spangles all over it."

With spangles all over it . . . Something about this expression rankled in Walton for a long time. Wasn't it natural to want the honor you had won to be fairly won? How was any false idealism, any greediness for spangled glory involved in this business? It was a straight question of integrity. Yet he kept getting the same gnawing little pain somewhere in his rib cage whenever he thought of it. It was, he told himself finally, because Ez had said it, because his relation to Ez had lost its intimacy and its strength and had become strained.

How? Why? Like most processes of disintegration, there had been nothing abrupt, overt, decisive. A small stain here, an unevenness there; a jarring note of irritation, a disagreement that grew into a quarrel, a jeering remark no longer, as once, cast off lightly.

Walton attributed much of the difference to Ez's tendency to drink more during the last term of senior year. In the course of his schooling in the academy of hard knocks, Ez had early come to sample liquor. But he never drank much until the last half of his last year at Amherst. Then he let the reins slacken. It was as though he felt that he had done his share for the greater glory of Alpha Delta Phi, and deserved a rest. Moreover, he had worked hard, mentally and physically, throughout the four years—to keep his scholarship and to earn his keep. Now he was resting.

"Goddamn son of a bitch," he remarked one evening that last January, "all I'm going to do this spring term is lay on the grass and drink beer. I can get me a fuckin' 60 in every course I'm taking and still get a diploma. I've worked my ass off to get a chance to get an education, then to get the education, and now I'm going to lay back and take a look at what I've got. And I'm a pissing she-goat if I think it's very much." His vocabulary had flowered in those four years; it now contained some rare and exotic growths.

But he did more than lie on the grass and drink beer. He played gin rummy and poker; he lay on his bed and slept late; he drank whiskey and gin. Then, once a week, on Saturday night, he'd get roaringly, melodiously drunk, and, coming in at two or three in the morning, wake Walton to harangue him on the sins of puritanism.

This was to Walton the ultimate betrayal. With furious and un-gainly perseverance, he had finally taught himself to smoke in junior year. But drink he did not, would not. The time that others spent in the spring of 1928, in the tag end of the Scott Fitzgerald pre-crash and pre-depression era, drinking and generally carousing, he spent trying to keep from seeming a Christer while not yielding on his standards—as he thought, for example, of his determination not to touch alcohol. And this determination seemed to drive Ez to ridicule, to these taunting early-morning persecutions.

"Christ, Herrick," he'd shout after awaking Walton with a friendly whack on the head, "you stuffed shirt, you miss all the fun in life. You're a little tin god. You've got your Scarab cap, you've got Phi Beta Kappa; you're a big shot and a big-man-on-campus. And what does it all amount to? Nothing. You're full of starched shit, boy. You've never relaxed in your life."

Walton would glare at him in infuriated frustration. It never oc-curred to him that Ez was partially motivated by that uneasy intolerance the man drinking feels for the nondrinker, partially by a really honest and rosily amiable desire to see Walton ease the tension under which he moved, acted, lived, and perhaps partially because he envied Walton the very achievements at which he scoffed. All that he could think of was that it was Ez who had prompted, prodded, teased and goaded him into all the activity that had made him a "big-man-on-campus"; that it was Ez who taught him reverence for the very honors that he had now won. And so it was a betrayal: the word occurred again and again in Walton's mind; it summarized all his darkest unhappiness over what had hap-pened to Ez and himself. It was a betrayal—and for some reason this made it impossible for him to answer, to strike back. All he could do was to sit there in miserable sleepiness, rubbing his head in frustrated resentment and glowering at the drunk who had been his best friend.

His pride was hurt, was even raw. Perhaps what contributed most to this condition was that he had himself found so little satisfaction in winning a position of prestige on the campus. He was a great man— but also a lonely and unhappy boy.

He was the editor-in-chief of the college paper; the manager of one of its athletic teams; a member of his class's social committee (Sophomore Hop, Junior Prom, Senior Hop) each of the past three years, and he'd missed being chairman of the Junior Prom by only three votes; the president of one of the two upperclass social clubs; a member of Scarab and Phi Beta Kappa (one of only two boys in the class to win both the highest extracurricular and academic honors). When an undergraduate committee was chosen to meet regularly with a faculty committee to determine whether the honor system was to be continued or given up, the president of the college appointed him to the chairmanship of the student committee. Even in athletics, once the arena of fear and ridicule, he had experienced modest success.

Yet he had not digested these triumphs; they were not *his*. On a Sunday morning in April of his senior year, after one of Ez's midnight-to-dawn harangues, Walton wandered out after breakfast, to a spot behind the college church, and sank down on the faintly damp, sweet-smelling grass. Staring moodily at the hazy, sun-softened pubescent hills that spread in a semicircle out beyond the rolling valleys surrounding Amherst, he nursed a troubled reverie. Some of Ez's charges, his very words, drifted through his mind; it felt sore, bruised, the way one's body does after a severe pommeling. The resentment—fierce and raw—that he felt toward Ez was mixed with bewilderment, a perplexity in no way allayed by the regular recurrence of Ez's drunken lectures.

Walton remembered, for the hundredth time, that evening long before, when Ez had told him, incredulous, that he had all the makings of an outstanding undergraduate. He could still see Ez, sitting with his feet up, one evening a week later, admonishing him—nicotine-stained fingers with the brown smoke curling over them raised to punctuate a thought, the mock-scolding voice, the funny gleeful smile. Thereafter, Walton had grown pensive whenever he passed, on a worn campus path, one of those austere, majestic figures in sneakers, slacks and dirty sweaters worn backward with elaborate carelessness, so that the large A showed only when you turned and stared after the retreating sauntering great man—with the Scarab hat topping the rest. Topping? Transforming—for all the refulgence was light refracted from that ultimate symbol.

And now? He was one of those figures. But he felt like a clothing store dummy. He felt as though the costume would fall off at any moment. He felt that the hat, although he had jammed it on at a jaunty angle, was perched precariously on the top of his head. He suddenly felt now, morosely chewing grass, that he was a little boy masquerading in man's clothing.

Directly behind and above him, the chimes of the church began their playing of the hymns that warned the sleepy and the dilatory of the imminence of the Sunday service. The very antiquity of the bells somehow enhanced their tone; a slightly cracked note seemed now to Walton to hold an especially poignant sweetness. Their sound hovered over him and then slowly moved out and away, to merge, in a translation of sound into sight and smell, with the shimmering hazy fragility of spring out there in the burgeoning hills that withheld, it seemed, the secret lure and promise of fulfillment. Withheld it—for as the last echoes of the first hymn whispered themselves to silence, Walton felt tears forming in his eyes: the first tears he had known with full awareness since he was a little boy of eight or nine.

A little boy—and as the chimes began another hymn, he was transported back to those years, and to the family pew in Grandfather's church, watching those stately and magisterial figures, the elders, rise one by one from their pews, and advance gravely, singing, to the altar in the front of the church, where the bread and wine of the communion awaited them:

> Just as I am, without one plea,
> Save that Thy blood was shed for me.

Walton *was,* for an inexorably heightened moment, again the small boy sitting beside his father, feeling an undefined exaltation—a sense that all the nobility and beauty of human life were somehow epitomized in those handsome dignified figures advancing to the altar, where waited the minister, benign in robes. He felt again this exalted sense of the purposeful pilgrimage to the shrine of life—and felt again that uncrystallized dream of the little boy: he, too, would rise and advance—this was the word that held the key—*advance* to where meaning and fulfillment waited for those who kept unsullied the banner they carried through life.

But most of all—and in some strange way, most moving of all—he felt his own physical presence as the little boy, stiff Eton collar cutting into his neck, the kneebands of his knickers pressing tightly against his calves just below the knee, the sensation of being scrubbed and shining clean, hair combed precisely.

O Lamb of God, I come. I come! What was he doing here? Where had it fled, the purpose and the dream, the promise and the beauty?

[*Part Four*]   *4*

THE formal social life at Amherst College was as precisely regulated as a minuet. It was also as susceptible to nuances of personal interpretation and subtleties that were part of a code perfectly familiar to the initiated, yet not only unknown to others—perhaps invisible as well.

The regulations were set, oddly enough, not by requirements having their origin at Amherst, but instead at Smith College, a few miles away in Northampton. The reason was that Smith girls were allowed only a few nights away from their campus each semester. No girl who was popular wanted to spend even a single one of these nights at Amherst: it was too close to home and their own regulations; it would be almost like spending a holiday with a member of your family. With the beckoning splendors of Hanover, Princeton, New Haven and Cambridge to consider, who would waste one of those delicious nocturnal reprieves, when she was entirely on her own, in the neighboring village of Amherst?

No girl who was popular . . . And since Amherst boys were sufficiently like other college boys to want popular girls—for this meant smart, attractive, even seductive girls—at their dances, almost the whole schedule of Amherst social activities was set up in sensible recognition of the situation at Smith.

True, the class dances—one a year for each of the three upper classes—were more elaborate, with formal dress, later hours, girls from farther away than Smith, and (in the case of Junior Prom) even the consumption of a whole weekend, crowded with minor festivities in addition to the one big dance. But the rest of the social program was the round of fraternity dances—tea dances, running from 3 to 9 P.M., in deference to the Smith girls who must be back in their campus houses by ten o'clock unless they had "signed out" for one of their precious overnight stays.

There was an invasion each Saturday. Promptly at three o'clock, a large chartered bus would stop before the designated fraternity house, and out would spill some twenty-five or thirty astonishingly pretty girls, gay, laughing, chattering. It was as though crocuses of all colors—bright yellow, purple, pink, white and red—suddenly turned a drab lawn into a garden.

On those few occasions after his college days when Walton thought back to these parties, he remembered chiefly his uncritical delight in them, beginning with his pleasure in being so often invited to be one of the stags. They were heady stuff for a boy of sixteen whose social life had been so carefully supervised and circumscribed at home.

First of all, he danced well, and he enjoyed dancing itself tremendously. Almost feverishly alert as he was to the new fashion, the new mode, he made the transition from being a good dancer to being a good dancer in the prevalent Amherst manner in very short order. Few of the favorable things said to him during the following four years pleased him so much as the judgment conferred by a saucy Smith sophomore named Lucy Latham, who assured him at one party in the spring of his freshman year that he danced "just like a boat." An outsider, especially one of more mature years, might have pondered the degree of praise in such a statement, but to Walton, cheek to cheek with the author of these words, feeling as well as hearing the fervent husky whisper in his ear, this was an accolade of the highest order.

Moreover, these dances provided the one chance for a boy of his immaturity and timidity to attain some physical intimacy with girls. Except for the one unfulfilled relationship with Carol, and a thin sprinkling of incidents involving hand holding and a few painfully chaste kisses, his sexual experience had been limited to the encounters of his fantasies, the violence and vividness of which had made his inhibitions the more difficult to endure.

And dancing in those days did constitute at least a secondary sexual experience. To all the pretty little prom trotters and even to many of their less sophisticated sisters, it would have seemed insulting or inept if you did not clasp them as tightly as you were able, with the flat of your right hand on the thinly covered space between their shoulder blades or on the softer, more pliable flesh just above the curve of the hips, and if you did not place your cheek against their fragrant cheeks or—if your height was much greater than theirs—have your lips against their shining and equally fragrant hair. And now and then thighs met; eyes locked in the mute discourse of the sexes.

All this was a minor ecstasy to Walton. The feel of this young flesh, the perfume, the melting eyes (however false and patented the expression; he did not, at any rate, recognize it as such), the sleek, pampered beauty of these exquisite young things. Impervious to the fresher, more natural girls present, he sought out the ones he fondly thought of as sophisticated. The whole experience intoxicated him so wildly that he was never able to understand why the other boys needed alcohol, or at least claimed that it heightened their pleasure. To heighten this, he felt, was to explode.

Not that he ever exploded. Those girls who mistook his ardor at the dance for the sign of a more direct courtship than he was capable of and themselves suggested walking outside between dances must, he realized later, have returned in pique, self-doubt, easy contempt or— perhaps more likely—wondering whose property he was. For he never ventured beyond walking arm in arm, hand in hand. He was still, emotionally and sexually, in early adolescence. So he had only his favorite dancing partners, many of whom, no doubt, were quite content with this arrangement. Yet a few of the older ones even asked direct questions which greatly embarrassed him. . . .

What could one think of all this, looking back twenty-five years later? Chiefly, Walton thought, that there was definitely a hothouse atmosphere to this whole round. What was most harmful in it, he thought, was its intimations of opulence, glamour and style as being in the natural order of things—a tendency prevalent, to be sure, in many aspects of American life in the late twenties. It was as though what crowded the billboards and the advertising sections of the magazines was true, after all: the world was full of beautiful girls, smiling, looking dreamily at you, pursing their lips at you, being kissed by you. And you were dressed as magnificently as though you were a millionaire—while all this took place in resplendent roadsters, in richly appointed living rooms or on the soft green lawns of pillared mansions.

The girls were undeniably there, at least on Saturdays; the mansions were there seven days a week, for the fraternity houses were often mistaken by ordinary mortals for the country homes of wealthy businessmen and financiers: some of them cost $200,000 to build—a tidy amount in the twenties. And so, inevitably, any undergraduate who bought this ornate and opulent dream must also buy clothing for himself appropriate to it.

Walton had absorbed not a little of Marcia's haughty and unrealistic attitude toward money. Since she provided the fund for Walton's college course, he was fairly comfortably situated. In addition to the money for his tuition, his meals and his room, he received twenty-five dollars a week—to be spent as he found necessary, or saw fit. He spent most of this on clothes.

As the family's fortunes underwent one of the periodic downward cycles to which they were habituated—the graph reached what they thought of as either extreme peaks or depths—letters from home in the fall of sophomore year stressed the need for Walton to supplement the money that could be sent. He had won a partial scholarship before entering Amherst, and he managed to retain it throughout the four years. Now, however, he began to look around for jobs, and before long was making a fair amount each week selling tickets at athletic events. The college paper was run on a participating basis that paid something to everyone who worked in either its editorial or business department, and as one advanced a notch in its hierarchy the amount received was proportionately greater. Still craving more clothes than these extra sources of income could provide, in his junior year Walton persuaded the representative of one of the expensive New Haven tailors who visited the campus regularly to let him work for him on an unusual commission basis: for every ten customers whom Walton induced to buy a suit or overcoat, he himself should receive a $100 suit free.

Characteristically, he made this pay off with a minimum of effort, by the simple device of persuading several very rich boys to buy all their clothes through him. Having taken the precaution to insist that part of the bargain should be that, once he had brought in a customer, everything purchased by that customer counted on his tally, he made a most profitable business out of the deal, acquiring six suits without charge in two years.

In the face of all this, it seemed incredible to Walton as, in later years, he looked back to the situation, that he had still managed to get into debt senior year—to the amount of several hundred dollars.

Knowing that this was more than Marcia, however indulgent about money, could supply him—knowing too that he would find it difficult to face his father if he either asked him for the money or, later, were to confess the debt—and looking ahead to the pleasures he wanted and intended to enjoy in his last undergraduate spring, Walton wrote in February to his Aunt Emily, who had long since moved East, promising to pay her back from his next summer's job. She responded promptly with a check for five hundred dollars, which she had intended to send later as a Commencement gift, but saw no objection to donating several months earlier. Walton paid his debts and celebrated by buying a thirty-five-dollar Fair Isles sweater. He was a little color-drunk throughout college; while adhering strictly to the style and cut endorsed for the

New England college man, something in him made it impossible for him to accept also the conservative colors that fashion dictated.

This exchange with Aunt Emily was an episode that Walton came later to feel was important to any diagnosis of his method of operation. If he wanted something, he must have it. If he did not have the immediate means with which to buy it, he was willing to take on any amount of extra work to pay for it, often overloading himself. But if he could not work it out this way, he was still unwilling to give up, to admit that for once there was something he could not have. Then, just as he would recklessly take on more work than he could handle, so he would take on an obligation which he had no clear and visible means of paying back.

In the letter to Aunt Emily, he stressed two things: the difficulty the family was having, and the sureness that he would pay back a loan from next summer's job. He disliked strongly asking for anything; he at once felt humiliated by the necessity and feared inordinately being rebuffed. Telling his aunt at length about his family's inability to help him (he did not mention that he was in debt) relieved his embarrassment a little; it made him feel as though he were therefore not asking *for himself*. And assuring her about paying her back the next summer made him feel almost as though he had already paid her back. Yet he had no summer job lined up; indeed, this being his senior year, a *summer* job was no longer the real question before him. But he had also as yet no real idea of what he wanted to do upon leaving college.

How, Walton eventually reflected grimly, could one be much more irresponsible than *that?* To be sure, in this case, the proposed loan magically turned into a *gift*. Yet this fortunate outcome was not the part of the transaction that illustrated his regular way of functioning at the time: what *was* was the manner in which and the basis on which he asked for the money. Promissory notes, financial and emotional: in middle age he realized that he had left a long trail of them behind him. Eventually he always found a way to pay off the former.

As the college semesters passed, Walton acquired, little by little, some
dash and sophistication in his style and attitude toward girls. In his
freshman year he was wholly inept, except for the courtship of the dance.
During his second year, he managed a few shy, awkward kisses, which
reinstituted in full vigor those fantasies he had largely put aside with
the advent of college, with its distractions and imputed manhood. Were
a particular girl to hint, with softly brilliant eyes and quickened breath,
that he need not desist—even, with surprisingly urgent hands, cling to
him—he would back away, at least figuratively. It was evident that he
was suffering, even before he stammered out the painful acknowledgment of his loyalty to a girl "back home": so pure and dedicated a
loyalty, it became clear, that, although he was tortured by his present
desire, he just barely had the strength to stop, if they stopped now. The
wonder of it, he was often to think before he understood anything of
the feminine complexion of these matters, was how often his playlet
not only persuaded, but won an admiration, an affection that persisted.
Word got around in Smith and Mount Holyoke that Walton Herrick was
"different," that he respected girls and himself—that, being uniquely
faithful to one of them, he deserved special consideration from the
rest—of a semi-"Platonic" sort.

This development suited Walton exactly. On the one hand, it permitted him the confident assumption of mild liberties (a kiss at arrival
and departure and, as time wore on, even a little discreet petting) with
three or four of the prettiest girls (he was discriminating in whom he
chose as a confidante about his sorely tempted but impregnable loyalty
to *that girl*); these publicly bestowed favors and his complacence over
them soon brought him an enviable resentment from the boys who
regularly escorted these girls—and hence a slightly rakish reputation;
and yet he was in no danger of having to run the full race and prove

himself in the common and immemorial fashion.

This suited him precisely because he was terrified of the consummation. The truth was that even at seventeen and eighteen (during sophomore year) he did not fully understand the ultimate sexual act. He was not stupid, but ignorant. Hence, while he was familiar—thanks to Carol—with the physical configurations and could deduce the nature of the act from its concomitants, he was uneasily convinced that there must be some further element of which he was not aware and which would finally reveal him, at the very moment traditionally given to triumph and gratification, to be incompetent and ridiculous.

His father's evasions, his mother's expressions of revulsion and contempt, and her sufficient squashing of his curiosity and initiative in this matter, as in so many others—these influences combined to overcome, without any drastic conflict, his stirring and stiffening desire. He did not yet understand how much of his vitality he had given to the world of fantasy he had devised, where there was never any possibility of humiliation and ridicule. But he did know that it was only *there* that he was safe from the scorn (comparable to that he had known as a little boy when he had first gone to school) that he felt sure would attend any daring and complete foray into actual sexual experience. And so, with an ingenuity worthy of a better purpose, he invented the girl back home and won his own special place in the adolescent society in which he lived.

All through his life, Walton reflected sometime during that summer in which he began keeping a journal, he stayed sufficiently close to empirical actuality so that its reality and that of his fantasies came to touch, even to overlap—with whatever detriment to proportion and accuracy. Perhaps—though he was not sure—by withdrawing early from his mother's ultimate reach, he had kept intact in his inner life sufficient vitality and curiosity, after all, to enable him to touch and establish real contact with the very palpable life of others, so long as this act did not require sustained continuity and a sufficiently prolonged intimacy to force the revelation of the many aspects of his incapacity for—as he thought of it—plain, everyday life.

At any rate, the summer after his sophomore year supplied a fuller opportunity than he had known before to explore the reality *out there*. By this time, his sister had suffered the immediate worst of her illness, and Marcia had managed to contrive a summer on the Cape for Elinor and herself (the new magic formula was salt air), leaving William and Walton to manage housekeeping at home as best they could.

William, perhaps partly because of the discrepancy between his son's stalwart frame and his own worn and crippled one, assumed Walton's normality and competence to take care of himself. Suddenly, therefore, when the summer's job in the stockroom of a pharmacy was over for any given day, Walton found himself free to go out on dates, as other boys his age did. Until now, Marcia's permission for such activity had been so qualified with buts and ifs, so documented with curfews and the specification of approved companions and destinations, that any spontaneous joy in the occasion was suffocated. Hence, when Walton abruptly realized that almost overnight he was free, having earned his own pocket money, to pursue the chosen course of his own evenings like, and with, his contemporaries, he was almost too dazed to take advantage of the opportunity. His fears momentarily forgotten, his head swam with the possibilities of pursuing the adventures he had known exclusively in imagination.

But this was only the immediate and short-lived way in which there was a conjunction of the fantastic and the real. Occasionally, during the college year just over, while he was enacting the passionate but forsworn lover, a girl had been sufficiently caught up in his story to want to know the name of that fortunate girl back home who had earned such devotion. The first time it happened, Walton, caught off guard and hard pressed, blurted out "Nora Hamilton," only then re-calling to himself that secret devotion of his final year in high school.

So now, in the freedom of William's benevolent administration— and after his first dizzying intoxication with the concept of liberty— Walton set out, however timidly and haltingly, to make fantasy into reality. He sought a date with Nora Hamilton.

It was an awesome experience. Asking a girl for a date—and with confidence—had long since become a matter of course. There was some other, some new and alien element in this situation, however, that set it apart. Was it a reluctance to risk disillusionment by making direct contact with the ideal? Was it the half-realized intuition that, having invoked Nora to protect himself from intimacy with the girls at college, he would be ashamed to invoke someone else to keep her, in turn, near, but not too near? Or was it more simply, that, never having approached her during the years of high school, he was afraid of being rebuffed?

He did not know. But for two days, whenever he could do so unobserved, he sat by the telephone, staring into the black mouthpiece as though it were a replica of the living Buddha. He studied the little perforations in its surface as if they were the lineaments of the beloved; his hand came to know the contours of the earpiece as the caressing hand of the lover dwells on particular curves and indentations of the cherished flesh. The Hamiltons' telephone number became an ancient inscription, a piece of Delphic wisdom subject to initiates' interpretation, ultimate dispenser of illumination.

On the third evening he called. She was out; he left his name and mumbled something about "classmate." The following evening—a Wednesday—he spoke to her. Yes, she remembered him. Yes, she had just finished her sophomore year at Swarthmore. He was at Williams? Oh, Amherst. Yes, she was free Friday evening and would love to see him. Did he remember Grace Wilson? She would ask her and a Dartmouth senior who was visiting Grace to come over too. The lilt in her voice suggested that she was genuinely pleased.

Walton came. Walton saw. Walton was enchanted. But he did not like the Dartmouth senior; he thought Grace lumpy and graceless. The need was for a car, and the Herricks had none. Walton recalled an old friend, Sam Kendrick, who owned a Marmon touring car. Sam was prematurely monogamous, good-natured and unobtrusive; his little Charlotte (it took Walton, bemused as he was, most of the summer to learn that her last name was Larsen) shared these virtues with him.

So this became the Summer of the Touring Car. Sam and Charlotte, like Siamese twins, glued together behind the steering wheel—Sam as adept at one-armed driving as though that single arm were the only one with which he had been endowed by nature; Charlotte shifting gears silently, efficiently, without lifting her head from Sam's shoulder. They even grew during that summer, it seemed to Walton, to look alike: both blond, pale, silent and endlessly good-natured. And always touching each other.

That was the only flaw—for it provided too emphatic a contrast to the pair in the Back Seat. Three evenings every week throughout July and August these two couples—for they were not a quartet, never a unit; when they stopped at outdoor dance halls, the boys would trade partners for a single dance only, and after the first two weeks gave up even this pretense of coherence—roamed the countryside around Cleveland in the touring car. Yet it was the first of August before Walton held Nora's hand; it was only in the last week of the summer vacation that he kept his arm around her shoulder, and only on their final night together before returning to college that he kissed her good night and good-bye and they clung together with sudden desperate ardor.

But it was as early as the third week in July that Walton asked her to marry him. Solemnly, formally, he said, under cover of the starry night above their private world of the Back Seat, "I love you, Nora, the way knights loved Guinevere and Iseult of the White Hands.

And I want you to marry me when we are through college and I have a job."

Nora's laughing protest was a compound of pride and genuine amusement. But she was not insensitive, and when she saw the deep, if hopelessly romantic and exalted feeling in Walton's expression, she melted into tenderness and her own white hands fluttered gently and soothingly about him.

Who was Nora? What was she? To Doug Henry, who stopped off in Cleveland for two nights in August on his way back to an early start at Amherst, suddenly probing in his explosive way after having shared the back seat of the touring car for an evening—to Doug Henry, relaxing over beers while Walton sipped Coca-Cola meditatively, Walton's intense devotion to Nora was puzzling.

"Sure," he said. "Sure, sure, sure. She's pretty as a picture with those big dark Irish eyes and a skin like coffee cream. And she's fun—she's a merry broth of a girl. But where do you get off, you old melancholy Hamlet, you brooder over ultimates, with a girl that giggles like that, and plays helpless so that you'll carry her over a mud puddle, and hasn't a thought beyond clothes and dates. Or have I got her all wrong?"

Walton felt dark red. He controlled himself with difficulty, waited until he could reply with a semblance of calm, "You've got her all wrong," and set his jaw in silence again.

Doug ordered another beer, chomped on a pretzel, studied Walton shrewdly for a minute or two.

"Check," he said at last. "Put it down to my being left-handed."

But Walton could not leave it at that. Years later, he could see the truth of this analysis, even understand that he had equated Nora's "helplessness" with perfect femininity—had indeed found in this quality, in some obscure fashion of his own, a complement to his own sexual timidity; had sensed that here was a girl so endearingly passive as to incite his latent masculine aggressiveness and thus to make him believe, beyond the power of others to date, in its authenticity. Years later, all this was clear, but that night he continued to extol Nora's "depth" until Doug's admirable forbearance must have been severely tested.

What was really troubling Walton most was that he had a rival—one Bert Austin, a dashing junior from Williams who, he well knew, confiscated the remaining evenings of Nora's week. Walton's uneasiness, he reflected much later, must have been some unacknowledged realization that, while he pursued the noble and formal courtship of this summer, Bert in his forthright and earthy fashion may well have been winning more tangible favors than Nora's protesting receptiveness to Walton's suit. Indeed, eventually Walton knew this to be true, as junior year passed with Bert appropriating more and more of Nora's time and attention, and Walton's long, romantic letters receiving fewer and briefer replies.

It ended—this strange courtship—late that year when Walton, learning of Nora's presence at a dance in Williamstown, unexpectedly appeared with two friends at Bert's fraternity house—to find Nora quite cold to him and obviously, gigglingly, Bert's property. But, by this time, significant changes in Walton's relation to girls had taken place, and he fooled himself about his despair over losing his black-eyed Nora for only a day or two, before becoming bored with the transparency of his pose. When, two years after his graduation from college, Walton learned of Nora's approaching marriage to Bert, he felt only a passing twinge of reminiscent interest.

Yet, on that early September evening before he returned to his junior year at Amherst, they clung together in the dark of the Hamiltons' porch as though they were immortal lovers suffering the universal mortal lot of anguished separation, and Walton's agony was sufficient to brave the anger of the returned Marcia, who had commanded his presence at home two hours before this prolonged and renewed embrace.

His agony—but also something else. Hot little flames beyond the urgency of anything he had before experienced licked at him, made themselves felt through the pain of parting, asserted a new kind of insistence that was to become too demanding that fall to be ignored—or denied—any longer. . . .

On the third day after his return to Amherst, Walton reported to the office of the director of student activities, to confirm his resumption of his job selling tickets at athletic events. He was so full of the pleasure of being an old hand, of knowing his way around, of renewing acquaintances and relationships, that he began to speak to his good friend, Miss Helena Crider, even before he passed through the open door to the office.

"I hope you've missed me, Miss Crider. I'm ready—"

He stopped short. For it was not Miss Crider behind the desk, but a short, slender, dark-haired girl he had never seen before. She regarded him through black horn-rimmed glasses with a look of cryptic bemusement, but said nothing. For a long moment they stared at each other in silence; then Walton, having assured himself with a furtive side glance that he was in the right office, asked, "Where's Miss Crider?"

The girl indicated the closed door behind her with an incongruous jerk of her head and shoulder—incongruous, Walton realized even then, because her owlish expression and the defensive hunching of her slight shoulders had suggested primness, even severity, to him, and in contrast this movement seemed raffish, almost rowdy.

"Sure," she said, slurring the word so that he couldn't tell whether this enunciation was an affectation or some unfamiliar regional peculiarity. "Sure. Miss Crider. Do you want to talk to her?"

At that moment the door opened and Miss Crider's homely face appeared in all its customary round benignity.

"Walton Herrick!" she declared. "And it's about time. A couple of the fellows were in today and I told them—it was Swarthout and the little baldheaded Deke, what's his name, Loomis—I told them if you didn't show up before the day was over one of them could have your job. Why should I save it for you, big apple-polishing no-good that you are?"

Walton grinned.

"You always did make light of my passion for you, Miss Crider," he said. "But we both know you'd bring me back the day after you fired me. Anyway, what's happened here? How come you're in Doc Evans' office? What's happened to him?"

Miss Crider shook her head in mock sorrow.

"He's the freshest boy in college, Irene," she announced. "You'd better watch him from the word go. Though, to be sure, I suspect he only makes love to safe old maids. Doc-tor Evans, Mr. Herrick, has a new office in the Administrative Building, and I've been made Assistant Director—" she pointed to the lettering on the glass of her door—"and you'd better mind your p's and q's from now on. Oh. I forgot. This is Irene Wertz, my new assistant. And this is Walton Herrick, Irene. You be careful with him. He's crazy."

"Sure," said the girl, enunciating the word with the soft slur again. "Sure. I'll be careful."

She continued to regard Walton with somehow mocking, owlish intensity as he followed Miss Crider into her office. . . .

During the next several weeks, it was Walton's job to work over grandstand plans, sorting out and banding tickets, and assigning ticket booths to other student workers. The previous spring he had helped Miss Crider in this work; now she entrusted him with the instruction of Irene Wertz.

Walton found that he enjoyed this task. He did not quite understand the nature of his anticipation of these occasional late-afternoon

hours he spent bending over the desk in the empty office with Irene;
certainly, he reasoned, it was not similar to the eagerness with which
he awaited a particular dance and the arrival of his favorite Smith
girls—or to the feeling he had for Nora. Irene was not attractive to
him in that way. She was not pretty or smart, as they were—though,
to be sure, he thought cautiously, she was not unattractive.

She lacked style: that was one thing that placed her in a totally different category from the other girls he knew. She mostly wore skirts with
plaids or stripes that he found loud—unaware of the irony of this
opinion in the face of his own colorful taste in clothes. And her one
black skirt was always shrouded in lint.

With these skirts she wore blouses or sweaters that she tucked
in tightly (again unlike college girls) under her narrow waistband.
The resultant revelation of the lines of her surprisingly—for so slight
a girl—full bosom Walton found wickedly delightful and happily out
of fashion, in almost willful disregard of 1927's straight lines and almost shapeless bodices. And her skirts were tight too; by their third
work session, he began to devise short errands for her ("While I'm
finishing these, Irene, will you go in to Miss Crider's and get the
red ink on her desk?") so that he could surreptitiously watch the
supple movement of her trim hips under the plaid skirt.

Irene's lack of style was also apparent in what he thought of as
her deficiencies. His sharply critical, more than half snobbish eye
quickly noted her bad carriage, the slight slumping or even hunching
of her shoulders as she worked. At their second session together, he
suddenly observed that she kept nervously picking at one of several
small sores on her cheek and on an impulse exclaimed, "Irene, you
should be ashamed of yourself! Picking at your face that way."

In a quick childish gesture, she thrust her hand into her lap.
She glared at him in so fierce an anger, almost hatred, that her yellowish-
green eyes, so like those of some wild cat, intimidated him.

"I'm—I'm sorry," he stammered. "I was just kidding."

She set her rather thin lips in a severe straight line.

"I'll have you to know," she said, in what seemed to Walton a
strange, unlikely caricature of a Western heroine confronting a villainous
rustler, "that my personal appearance is none of your business, you
fresh kid."

When they met again the next afternoon, she was distant, cool,
drawling her words in an unnatural voice that Walton found ridiculous,
but also discomfiting. But he was aware, too, for the first time, of her
perfume. He was not sure that he liked it; it was very different from

the elusive fragrances used by the girls he knew. It was heavy, and almost bitter. Like it or not, however, he felt pleased that she was wearing it, and it evoked exotic intimations in him.

"You smell like an Egyptian princess," he blurted out, to his own surprise. How did he dare to be so bold with her? He wasn't with any other girl.

"Egyptian princess!" She snorted delicately, and unexpectedly abandoned her affected drawl, reverting to her habitual slurring of words. "Sure. Sure. Fat chance."

Suddenly feeling daring swell in him, Walton reached out and captured her hand. Deliberately then he reached out and touched with his finger a spot on her cheek. He said softly, "I'm sorry I said that. It was rude. I think I like you to have some imperfection."

And he did. Surprisingly, perversely, he felt affection because of these little sores on her face—an affection increased by his observation, now that he turned her hand over, that the palm was slightly grimy, perhaps from carbon paper. Affection—but something else, too: a stirring in him over the plumpness of the pad below the thumb and the satiny smoothness of the skin on the back of this small hand. It intoxicated him to stroke it: there was some richer softness to it than he had ever felt in the well-cared-for hands of college girls. Startled by the intensity of the sensation and her passiveness—she had made no move to withdraw her hand, had not moved at all—he looked up, directly into her eyes.

For a long moment, they looked at each other in silence, and he saw in her eyes something bare that he did not understand. Pain? greed? He wondered at his choice of words; they were not right.

Then the moment was gone. She pulled her hand away and laughed—an artificial, almost rasping sound.

"Release me, suh," she said as though she were declaiming poetry, and emphasizing grotesquely her caricature of Southern speech. "I'm old enough to be your mother."

Walton found that his voice was husky.

"You are not," he asserted in unfeigned indignation. "I'm nineteen"—he would be in a month—"and you're—you're about twenty-one."

Unexpectedly, she removed, for the first time, her eyeglasses. Her eyes seemed to him to loom before him, suddenly enormous and pathetically yet beautifully near-sighted. It made her younger, he thought, more defenseless.

"I'm twenty-three," she said softly and naturally. And then, as though scandalized at herself—as though he had caught her naked at her bath—she snatched up the glasses, replaced them, and said with unwonted briskness, "What nonsense! Let's get to work."

When he left the office an hour later, she had promised, after his third invitation, to go to the movies with him Friday night. "Well, all right," she had finally said ungraciously. "It's the only way I can get rid of you."

Walton spent the next several days in violent reversals of feeling. During that time, he went to Irene's office (so he had come to think of it) only once—and that once only because he had no choice: Miss Crider had summoned him, to go over plans for Saturday's football game. He felt so shy in Irene's presence—for the first time —that he barely managed to say "hello." And he prolonged his appointment with Miss Crider, through much amiable joking, sufficiently to outstay Irene. But as he went out it seemed to him that she was there in the empty chair, smiling and mordant behind the tortoise shells, pointing scornfully with a jerk of shoulder and head, saying softly, "Sure. Sure." He felt ashamed, and worried lest she call off the date.

But she did not, and he continued to teeter back and forth between almost feverish anticipation of Friday night and terror— terror over the fact that this was not like having a date with a college girl, terror over the very nature of his anticipation.

There was another element in his feelings too: one that he attempted, disliking it, to deny, to push out of sight. Most fellows who dated "townies" did so for only one reason; if an undergraduate dated a town girl regularly, and treated her with the same respect and attention as a college girl, he lost caste. It was a snobbish society, and only those who didn't care about campus prestige flouted its code. Intellectually, Walton sided with the rebels, but, unlike most of them, he was a fraternity man and ambitious of recognition and college honors: these two sides of his nature were in constant conflict.

Of course, technically, Irene was a college employee and, having come from Brooklyn and reached Amherst only through an appointment with Miss Crider at a New York employment agency, was not a "townie" at all. But there was no place in the undergraduate categories for such an "unclassifiable." Since she was not a college student, she was a townie. And hence Walton must prepare himself for embarrassment on Friday night. It would either be clear to his fellows that he was not out "bagging," as the expression went, and hence he would lose face for his "serious" date with a townie, or his intent would not be clear and then Irene would be subject to the usual crude talk and whistles.

Why, he wondered desolately, had he ever gotten himself into such a mess? But he knew why, and twist and turn as he might he also knew that the excitement and the urge outweighed his misgivings. How he wished, though, that he had the courage and poise of Jim Haywood, who, as a senior two years before, had quietly forced the other boys' respect for Sally Jones, a beautiful town girl who went everywhere with Jim.

But Jim had been unique: for the rest of them there were only the college girls, the "college widow," Cathy Baker (who enjoyed a special and tolerated position), the town girls of ambiguous virtue, and the "bags" in Holyoke. By the time Walton called for Irene (that name: Irene Wertz!) on Friday evening he was so nervous that he was planning to persuade her to take a walk instead of going to the movies.

But she was transformed. She wore a simple and semi-stylish gray dress and the approved high heels; her black hair was done up (Walton had wondered at her constant preoccupation with it; she changed her way of wearing it almost daily), lending her a new dignity; she did not wear her glasses until they were, without any undue attention, seated in the dark of the theatre.

Even afterward they attracted very little attention. They passed Doug Henry, who grinned cheerfully and said, "Hi!" One or two other boys waved casually. Walton escorted her to the Candy Kitchen, where they had a sandwich and a cup of coffee. To his astonishment, Irene lost her reticence about herself, and discoursed at length about her love of Marvell and Donne and Herrick (whose acquaintances he was just beginning to make) and the Imagists and Aiken and Eliot (whom he had barely heard of). She quoted poetry in a softened husky voice; she told him of her family, her father who could speak no English at all and whose name had been changed from Wertzheimer, and how she had been forced to give up her education at one of the New York city colleges because of lack of funds; she recited something in Yiddish; she told of her adventures and mishaps in her first secretarial jobs in New York City—and of her ambition to be a writer.

Walton was enchanted. He knew now for certain that it was her exoticism that so delighted him: her background, her idiom, her age—all so alien and heady; for his part he responded with the unselfconscious native courtliness that he undervalued—insofar as he knew of it at all—and rarely permitted to show.

"You're a wonderful person," he said shyly as they rose from the table and he helped her on with her coat. "I've never met anyone like you."

Only then did she suddenly seem to change back to the office manner, with that abrupt, metallic laugh.

"Oh, sure," she said. "Oh, sure. I'm wonderful. You come to Brooklyn and I'll only show you a few thousand wonderful people like me."

At the door to the rooming house, however, she smiled shyly in her turn.

"I hate being crowded into a room in a place that doesn't belong to me," she said in what was almost a whisper. "Miss Crider's trying to get me a little house of my own. It's the gardener's cottage— fancy that, gardener's cottage—of a summer place about a mile from here. It has one big room and a kerosene heater, and I think I'm going to get it. And it would be all my own. I'd be all alone."

And she lowered her eyes so mysteriously that on the way back to the fraternity house Walton felt stirring again, even pounding in him, all the excitement that had dissolved into gentler emotions as she had talked of herself and her life at the restaurant.

Yet the next noon, when he stopped in at the activities office for the afternoon football tickets, he found her as distant as though they had never exchanged a word beyond those required by their working relation in this room. It seemed to him an especial affront that she wore no makeup at all and had pulled her hair back in a tight, severe knot; there was a spot on her sweater and her black skirt was covered with even more lint than usual. And to Walton's first eager greeting and happy account of how good a time he had had the night before she replied listlessly and yet primly, "Yes. Thank you very much." Then, ignoring him, she fell to picking languidly at a hangnail.

He left the office in an abrupt and uncomprehending disillusionment, to return only when his duties necessitated it on the following Monday. Then, and thereafter for two or three weeks, they were entirely businesslike when together, working in perfunctory politeness. She forced the tone, and the rejected Walton, in his immaturity, could find no alternative to accepting it. But he was unhappy and bewildered, sure only—and that in a vague way—that he had failed her. . . .

It was on a Saturday morning in late October that Walton, entering the office in the mood of dull resentment that had replaced his former anticipatory eagerness, found everything changed. Everything? Irene. For the first time in weeks, she had taken some pains over her appearance. She was wearing a new dress with a wide white collar, incongruously suggesting, through its superficial demureness, the very opposite effect. Her hair shone as though brushed tirelessly into a new lustre; her eyes were bright with excitement behind the horn-rimmed glasses. She rose and laid a softly restraining hand on his arm.

"Miss Crider's gone," she said. "Come in to her room; I want to talk to you."

He followed her, not daring to entertain the wild hopes that flickered swiftly across his mind. But he shut the door behind them.

Instantly, she turned to him and placed both her hands flat against the heavy sweater covering his chest. He had never realized before how small she was, had never so acutely and pleasantly felt his own size. And now she looked up at him with so intimate a smile that his head swam.

"I have it," she said softly. "I have my own house. And because your birthday comes next week and this is Saturday, I want to give you a little party tonight. Can you come—about eight o'clock?"

And then, in obedience to some mysterious compulsion that was wholly new to him, he put his arms around her, drew this small, sweet, heady creature close up to him, and learned what a kiss meant. . . .

At two minutes to eight, Walton knocked softly at the door of what looked like a garage. All the way down the long graveled drive-way, past the big white empty house that shone so palely in the moonlight and the hoar frost, his romantic heart had kept time with the crunching of the pebbles under his feet. Here at last, they chanted in unison. And yet, remembering all the self-doubt that assailed him when he thought of the heroes and maidens that populated the poetic world of John Collins Howe and his own confused and confusing dreams, a dry corner of his mind commented wryly, "You've misunderstood. It was her house she was kissing, not really you. She is so happy that she had to share it with someone. She didn't mean what you want her to mean."

The giant shadows of childhood marched with him, looming vast on the side of the white house. And then he was clear of the house and knocking at the door of the plain little cottage. And the door opened and she stood there, still smiling.

"Sure," she said. "It's you."

She was so small, and the shadows he had been walking with so large, that he blurted out, "Aren't you afraid to live here all alone?"

She closed the door and leaned against it. Then she spread out her hands, grimy again, and said, with the soft, slurring sound, "Afraid? Of what? I have one door, and I lock it—" she did "and then I have nothing to be afraid of but me."

This was exciting talk, this sort of talk where words, while answering questions, also meant something more than what they said. Walton felt as though he were learning a new language, but not well enough as yet to speak it. So he stood there, silent.

Her eyes glowing, she came over to him and kissed him. It was not the same sort of kiss; it was gentle and friendly.

"Happy birthday," she said. "And how do you like my house?"

She must have been living in it for several weeks, he realized— perhaps fixing it up. For it was complete: curtains, chairs, a dresser, some small rugs and a sort of couch-bed in one corner. A vase, lamps, a cigarette box, books, a victrola. With the kerosene stove, snug and warm. Cozy with the shades drawn against the night. Complete.

A kind of rapture filled him; he sat down on the nearest chair.

"It's wonderful," he said reverently. "Gosh, I certainly see why you like it."

She moved swiftly and silently, with a kind of grace wholly incompatible with her office self, to the victrola and put on a record that Walton recognized, from the collection he shared with his father, as a Mozart sonata.

"Would you like a drink?" she asked.

He had never had a drink—except once, at the home of a friend's parents, when he had misunderstood the invitation and expected ginger ale, then been too shy and self-conscious to do anything but drink it. But now, here, he didn't hesitate.

"Yes," he stated, "I'd like a drink. Let me help you."

"No," she said, "it's your birthday. You sit still. Ginger ale or water?"

He did not answer immediately. Straining to reach the top shelf in the corner cupboard, arm and hand extended toward the bottle, she stood poised on tiptoe, her short skirt pulled by the effort well above her knees. He sat and stared in silence. And when, after a moment, she turned, twisting her head and shoulder to peer down at him inquiringly, she did not cease her grave smile and the fluid upward line of her body was not broken.

"Ginger ale," Walton blurted out. He could not take his eyes from her. With her hair massed on top of her head and secured in some miraculous fashion by a narrow ribbon, she looked like Marie Antoinette or Madame de Pompadour, he thought. Slender, graceful—with satisfaction: aristocratic. She—reaching . . .

He looked with suspicion at the glass she extended, took it, tried a wary sip. The taste was all ginger ale, but it burned—and then, after a moment, spread pleasantly reaching fingers of warmth through him.

"Wait," she commanded and raised her glass. It was only half filled, and the liquid was darker; he surmised that it was simply whiskey and ice, but did not want to betray his ignorance by asking. "To your twentieth birthday," she said, "and to your very good health, suh!" She took a big swallow, made a face, and shuddered delicately.

Never mind that he would be only nineteen. Right there, Walton thought, just above the corner of her mouth, he would like to put a beauty mark. He raised his glass.

"To you," he said. "You're beautiful." He gulped, to cover his embarrassment.

She presented him with three tissue-wrapped packages. He opened them clumsily, attempting futilely to untie the ribbon on the first, then in anxiety tearing the paper off. A necktie he would never wear in Amherst, a copy of John Donne's poems, and a change purse that would fit on his belt and make his work at the ticket window easier.

He felt pleased, grateful, warmed. There was a sudden loosening within him, a realization—to his astonishment and horror—that he was close to tears; the thought flickered through him that he had never before really liked to have people give him presents. He stood up.

"You—you—" he said, and then he was reaching down for her, had his arms around her, felt again the spiring flame of the morning— only this time it was not simply the single flame, but a suffusing warmth that spread all through him, invested his every vein with a new vitality. He kissed her, wanted to quote, "Her lips suck forth my soule," didn't dare, and sought her mouth again.

After a while, she pushed him away, but the very act of repelling was itself a caress. She looked long and darkly into his eyes, speaking without words that new language he was learning. Then, "Drink your drink," she said softly.

They drank in silence, smoked cigarettes and listened to the music. The second time she changed the record, she poured new drinks. As she leaned over to hand his to Walton, he noticed that only one of the hitherto several spots on her cheek was left—and it almost gone. He reached out, as he had that day in the office, and touched it.

She smiled and pulled his fingers away.

"Yes," she said. "I have—ever since that night."

"Then why," he asked, again surprised at his boldness, "did you act the way you did? Why have you been so—so mean to me?"

It was now, it seemed to him, her turn to be embarrassed. She hesitated, flushed and turned away. When she finally looked back at him, her face seemed wholly changed. Her eyes were clouded, her mouth sullen, and she spoke like a little girl caught in a misdemeanor.

"I don't know," she said. "I can't tell you."

Even in this shift of mood there was something that entranced Walton. He felt an unfamiliar power stirring in him. In some way he only half comprehended, it was this quality of sullenness that he would enjoy—breaking.

"That's childish," he said firmly, and drained his second glass as though it were water.

She pouted.

"I know it," she muttered.

He walked over to her and, putting his fingers under her chin, raised her face.

"Come over here," he said, indicating the couch, "and sit down with me." Despite his new sense of his own potential, it was all he could do to get the words out.

She wrenched her head away; then, eluding him, ran to the victrola to turn the record over. From behind this defense, she said coldly, "Don't try to be masterful. It's silly. I like you better the way you were when you opened your presents."

What most pleased and impressed Walton now was that he was not intimidated, even by the charge of being silly. With Carol, he suddenly thought, he had always been passive; with Nora, he had been controlled by something in him that marked out definite lines within which he must stay. But now—now he was really free to act on his own; now, with this feeling of exhilarating freedom, he knew at last the pleasure of being male with a female.

"How was I then?" he asked nonchalantly, and moved slowly over to the couch, then sprawled out on it. His head was a little dizzy, he noticed.

She shut off the phonograph abruptly; it squawked protestingly and shrilly, and wheezed to a stop. The sudden silence was overwhelming. When at last she broke it, it was very quietly.

"I don't know," she said. "So intense. I thought you were going to cry. I like your feeling so much—and honestly showing it. Most men," she added, with an edge of contempt, "are ashamed to show their feelings, even to feel them."

Her mood had changed again. She put on a dance record and began to swirl about the room. Walton wanted to rise and dance with her, but the effort seemed too great, and even watching her made his head circle and swoop in time with her. He dropped back on the pillow and closed his eyes. It felt blessedly cool, but now it was the room that seemed to go around, tilt and sway. Like Canute, he could command it to stop, but could not control it.

Then suddenly there was a cool hand on his forehead, and he heard her whisper, "Do you feel sick, darling? I guess you don't drink very much."

It was the word "darling" that brought him up to a sitting position. But there seemed to be two—or at least one and a half—of her, and after a moment he lurched to his feet.

"No," he said. "Got to go out."

Outside, the autumn wind was roaring in the trees and thin clouds were racing across the young white moon. Each gust brought a shower of leaves, and those underfoot crunched and crackled as he stepped forward. The air was icy and bracing.

Two years ago, almost, he thought, I was being initiated into the fraternity. Two years ago and now, here— He was filled with an unbearable impatience to be sober, to regain himself. He paced up and down until he was sure that he would not be sick after all; then, exultingly, he marched with the wind, to its cadence, reminiscent of the resonant low thunder of the advancing surf and its sibilant retreating hiss.

He found himself standing in an open field, and he lifted his head to the brilliant sky. Though wisps of Halloween clouds spurted between him and the moon and the thousands of stars, these clouds were so thin and insubstantial that they were almost transparent—white spray on the vast aerial ocean, splashing now and then over the lighted barks and skiffs that thronged in celestial traffic. Walton knew suddenly that he was standing at a corner in his life, and that he was ready and eager to turn it. He plunged back through the field, running until he saw again the small white cottage.

The door opened to his hand, and he saw her standing there, by the turned-down bed, expectant, slight in her plain white slip. A single lamp burned near her, and her eyes were bright.

He closed the door and locked it.

"Come here, Walton," she said in a whisper, and it seemed to him that his name had changed.

Then he was across the room, and upon her, locked with her, and she was whispering in an exultant voice, "You're cold, cold." He was straining, searching, and a heat came upon him that he could not restrain. He could not resist it; he could not control it. With a cry and a whimper, he was gone, and he burrowed his head futilely against her in overwhelming shame.

"Don't," she whispered. "Don't. Don't feel bad. Don't, darling."

How long he had slept, he didn't know, but he was suddenly aware of the unaccustomed softness and coolness of her, and was almost instantly fully awake. His mouth tasted sour and his throat was sore, but his head had cleared and his awareness of her swept his discomfort aside. Pulling her into his arms and awake, he strained her against him and felt, with triumph and sureness, the rising strength in himself. She turned and clung to him and her mouth, soft and urgent, sought his. He moved with clumsiness now, but with a deliberate certitude that he had never known before. . . .

Afterward, she stirred, and it seemed to him that he could see her smile through the darkness. "Sure," she said. "Sure. I knew you would."

They fell asleep, still clasped in each other's arms.

JOURNAL: 8

from the journal of Walton Herrick . . .

Sept. 7, 1953
Labor Day

As the time approaches for the visit to the Vineyard, what I mostly feel is fear. I try to summon up images of joy and love (reunion, reunion, something within me keeps saying)—the moment when we knew that Timmy would be all right, the moment of saying good-bye to Julie, individual mental snapshots of all the children at their most characteristic and lovable, one by one. But it is no use: I dread going: I want reunion—permanent reunion—of that I am sure; but I have an uneasy sense that I can't achieve it, that I am not ready for it in the only sense that can give it reality: a willingness and an ability to sustain, and to build on, *what is really there.*

That is the need. That, I can *understand,* is unconditionally necessary. Without *that,* there can be no reunion, no rebuilding, no future. I know that those are Julie's terms—for the simple reason that they are the terms—the only ones—of human life. And suddenly I see that I have been hiding behind a false dilemma, false in the sense that it is not the real cause of my fear. For I have been telling myself sadly that it is my infidelity that causes my fear. Guilt over Sonia, guilt over the proximity of the visit to the Vineyard to that last time at Sonia's apartment—the old familiar combination suddenly dramatized with painful, almost unbearable reality. Guilt and fear: the Truant Officer.

I realize, too, that the last entry before this one was an evasion: a bleak academic record, in the face of recent events. Events: I am suddenly reminded how little interest I *really* take in the world around me, small or large; it requires my own participation, as in the investigation of tax-exempt foundations, for this world *in which we live*

—whether we would or not, however much we drag our feet or nurse our sulkiness on the sidelines—to engage my active and full attention.

A disgression—but important, chewy. As I started to say, I thought that, in leaving out any reference to my recent trip I was evading the facing of my faithlessness—and hence the guilt and fear I must feel when I go to Julie, ostensibly in hope of being reunited.

Well, I was evading, have endlessly been evading—but, experienced full-time confidence man that I am, was also evading *the real and ultimate evasion* through occupying my conscious mind with evading the Julie-Sonia conflict. Here is the consummate double-cross. The key to the final evasion is in those words I wrote above: "ostensibly in hope of being reunited."

Ostensibly. Which brings me back to the opening paragraphs of this entry. What I am afraid of is the hopelessness of our situation— Julie's and mine, ours and our family's—so long as I will not give up my secret determination to have everything the way I want it— or live exclusively in my imagination, where it is safe. The Face at the Window—*timor vitae*. That is my fear. When I wrote of it before, I said that it was my *fear,* but then I did not know that is was *my* fear. I want, hopelessly of course, but tenaciously, to impose my will on life —external reality. Otherwise, I won't play.

On the face of it, how absurd. Yet this, it is suddenly dazzlingly clear to me, explains the way I have clung to my fantasy life, change its costume as I may, through more than half a lifetime. From little Irene Wertz, through my marriages and all my erotic adventures, to this last encounter with Sonia, I have stubbornly and desperately tried to impose my pattern on reality, to actualize my early and febrile celebration of Eros. My dilemma has always been that if the girl— girl-woman—was mostly passive, receptive and compliant, I tired of her; if independent and challenging, I was afraid to stay close to her, too long with her.

And this applies equally to other aspects of my life. In the Foundation fracas, I honestly believe that I was neither all right nor all wrong. But an important element in the struggle was my will to dominate, to win the decision, to gain general acceptance of my point of view. Point of view, yes—but because it is *mine,* not because of *its* substance. I wanted to impose my will on the Foundation, stamp it with my imprimatur.

Faces from the past arise now: my mother's, and those under whose authority and jurisdiction I have suffered. Yes, suffered. I have not needed to be king, but the king must lean on me, must rely on me for every ultimate decision. And so, in this recent Foundation struggle, despite all the obvious indications that I could not win my point (even P.H. has *his* saturation level), I was immovable.

So, in another way, with the governorship. There has been no question in my mind at any sane, realistic moment but that I am totally unqualified. Yet for a while I allowed myself the luxury of envisioning myself emerging from the state capitol—strong, lined face and leonine head lifted above the throng of supernumeraries, reporters and cameramen gathered around me! And when I finally accepted the facts of the matter, I was—all unconsciously, of course; I am very considerate of my conscious mind—careful to do so in time to step out gracefully, no matter if all of us involved had an uneasy feeling that the real nature of things was quite different. Did Haldane understand all this about me?

And it is because I *will* not give up this insistent pretense that I wrote "ostensibly in hope . . ." without realizing what I was revealing. By thus insisting on what it is literally impossible to realize, I am destroying what *might* be—and in the immediate situation, any chance of that reunion I profess to want. Julie has eaten the apple; she will no longer pretend that there is any alternative to the necessity of our basing our life on *reality*.

And how do I feel about *that*—about the knowledge that I have planted myself, an obstacle, foursquare in the path of reunion and life? Over the knowledge, over at last facing this fantastic truth (truth is more "fantastic" than fantasy), I am glad and hopeful. It is too new a concept for me to grasp fully, but I do know it now; I will not forget it; it is there to study and explore.

But how *have* I felt? Split, I am sure. I now understand, as I have not before, sly little secret gleefulnesses, the smile quirking the corners of my mouth against my wishes, the hidden malice of which I have been no more than uneasily and vaguely aware. One me, removed, spiteful, cruelly amused. I have, to the very edge of my destruction, preferred the world, the order of things, that I invented and hence could dominate arbitrarily, to the world that is *out there* to be explored, that *is,* that may not be ordered around. Yet underneath, I have achingly, longingly, desired admission to the real world. Unable to yield up the one and enter, fully commit myself to the other, I have tried an impossible compromise, against all clear evidence: to live in the one, but belong to the other, and to try, wherever possible, to infiltrate the real with the fantastic, to carve out a little segment of the real for a dictatorship of my own. I am reminded of the fallen Lucifer plotting to regain, in eternal war, some part of God's world.

Early and long I have felt it really hopeless, convinced as I have been of my ineligibility (But why? Why am I ineligible?) to find more than a nominal place in that real world. Hence the alternation of moods and feelings, the split to which I referred. At times, in despair, I have silently begged for admission at that closed and sealed window. (But is it? Couldn't I raise the pane, open it if I had the will? Is this simply the attic door in another form?) At other times, knowing the ultimate exclusion, I have raged in hatred and bitterness against those in the lighted room, the sunlit group picnicking on the grass, any joyful manifestation of the celebration of vitality and the give-and-take of healthy human life. Then, moving away and drawing on my dark glasses, I have enjoyed what was left: the asking of alms while mocking the giver, the frustration of others, the unadmitted knowledge that I held the power to withdraw or reject them, and therefore to hurt them in proportion to the degree I have hurt myself—or been hurt.

What, in the face of the overwhelming evidence, has led me to persist in my perverse way of life?

My belief in magic. Even as I write it, I am astonished. Yet the answer came as simply and directly as though I had known it all the time. I believe, without acknowledging it consciously, that I have the power to make over the real situation, to bring it to the conclusion I want, to impose upon life the authority of my secret kingdom! And so passionate is my conviction that I often convince others.

No wonder I felt so tired, so written out, at the end of the last previous entry—with all this submerged, but almost to the surface. What strenuous control it must have required! I note the phrasing— as though I were speculating about someone else. Well, I didn't have the experience. I was relying on magic.

A little while ago I wrote "dictatorship." I begin to see with appalling clarity that my practices and my rationale, on my small scale, are not so very different from those of the dictators of history, on the grand scale—and perhaps even the rulers of the underworld. With whatever other factors, certainly a central one—in all their cases— has been the desire, the need, and the fanatic determination to impose their wills, their private fantasies of plumed ambition, upon the world around them. With how much singleness of purpose and, probably, justification through the indignities of their childhoods, must they have shaken their small fists and promised that inimical and humiliating world out there that they would show them! When there are almost no mitigating factors, such as occasional demonstrations of love and kindness, the obsession with the fantasy world after the abuse one has received, and with mastery, mounts to gigantic proportions of will and effort, of paranoia and megalomania. This is probably why no power politician has ever been able to cope with such figures. The former, however ruthless, studies and practices how to extract the utmost gain from the real situation, while the latter introduces motivations and elements from his private world of fantasy—and is often able to impose them for a time on others, since these elements are, by definition, otherworldly—though often the opposite of the usual meaning of that word—and hence unpredictable. Perhaps it was within these very terms that Machiavelli misgauged Caesar Borgia in selecting him as the savior of Italy.

"Able to impose for a time . . ." I begin to see, too, the soundness of Greek morality—in such concepts as that of *hybris*. For the fate of the man who exceeds in his ambition man's proper limits comes directly from that desire, that need, to attain to a state that is not human. It is the wish to be divine, especially in the sense of omnipotent, that leads to his downfall. And whence comes this need, this wish, unless from the original rebuffs and humiliations, hopelessness and lovelessness, that drove him inward to a world he could control, while nursing dreams of vengeance—only to seek eventually to go outward again and impose the will of his secret order upon the original enemy? So Lucifer, lame and blackened but forever undefeated, brooding and plotting revenge in deepest Hell.

History, mythology, religion . . . Nietzsche, Byron, Hitler, Napoleon, Greek tragedy, the very essence of the Romantic temper . . . All kinds and sorts of applications throng in my mind.

But what about me?

What about the cynicism, the dishonesty, the faithlessness necessarily attendant upon such an obsession? For they exist; they must exist under these conditions. It is easier to explain and feel them in their contradictory disguises of weakness, of fear, of humiliation, of self-scorn. Yet again, how to account for the genuine acts and thoughts of generosity, of sympathy and love and kindness and understanding that I *have* been capable of and actually experienced?

All to be winnowed, I hope, in good time. (So time may be *good*, after all; that must be because it is a factor in human change and growth. These operate within the limits of actual human experience; no magic may effect them.) Those last, the mitigating elements, stem

of course from all those sources of positive experience in my life: my
father, one or two teachers, Carol, Red Stewart, a few later friends,
books, perhaps a stray gene or two. . . .

Sept. 9, 11 P.M.

The vision of myself as weak and contemptible? How could anyone nurturing such dreams of godlike mastery think of any ordinary
human being as other than contemptible? To say nothing of the fact
that, viewed in plain soberness, I am hardly the most admirable of
ordinary human beings. So the gap widens into a crevice, the crevice
into a canyon—between the ruthless, amorally godlike, self-justifying
superman and the pitiable, scared mortal milquetoast.

The cynicism? the dishonesty? Covering, explaining in terms
evoking admiration or sympathy, the aberrations of a warped nature.
The faithlessness? All true, and all *necessary,* to preserve inviolate the
great myth, *its* integrity, *its* law and order, *its* propositions. Everything
grist to this mill—that grinds so fine as to bring about nothingness. A
handful of dust.

Much has been written, and more said, in our time about rela-
tivistic ethics—some of it thoughtful, a great deal simply hot air. But
the paragraph I have written above suggests an actual relativism in
the motivation and conduct of life that must cut across a great portion
of our relations with ourselves and each other. Whether the dominating
principle of mastery originating in the life of fantasy is that of power,
of beauty, of heroism, of sacrifice, of knowledge, or whatever—the
significant factor is the way in which the attempt to actualize this
hidden and distorted ideal permeates the everyday world of confused
and confusing, mixed, contradictory, conflicting everyday actual life.
Indeed, one is tempted to say that perhaps there is no such thing as
everyday actual life—that *it* is the postulated abstract—and that the
reality is the nonhuman ideal, warping and twisting and dictating to
human beings courses that are not within the conditions of their natures.
But this is a dead alley—as much as to say that to be truly human is to
insist on not being human.

No, I believe that there is such a thing, embodied in many people,
as *good* (because rooted in ascertainable actuality) though faulty and
erratic, honest, ragged human nature and human life, affected only
marginally and spasmodically by such grandiose and destructive con-
ceptions. The test lies in the soil within which the roots grow. If it
is that compound of loam and clay that is within the confines of what

is characteristically or even possibly human, then it is healthy and will blossom. If its soil is that synthetic blend of chemicals developed from nonhuman dreams, then, however towering the wild, rank growth develops, it will wither and its poison will affect everything around it.

If there is any certain meaning to sin for me, it lies here. To sin is to act against nature, one's own nature—hence human nature. This is an old concept. Variously developed by Greek philosophers, by the Stoics and the Epicureans among others; Christianized, baptized in the Middle Ages; reinterpreted by Montaigne and others. But it has new force and meaning for me now.

And just as I understand and believe it in my own new terms, so for the first time I understand and believe the Christian proposition that to be truly free is to be free to do right—even if I cannot accept the specific theological orientation.

The cardinal sin is that of pride—pride in maintaining what does not exist, the image of self conceived and perpetuated outside of reality. And correspondingly, the life-giving virtue is humility (I said it to Dennis!), not in the dictionary sense of self-depreciation, but in the sense of proportion, of reality that enables one to live justly within the authentic human limits, to accept and grow wise within those limits, to live what it *is* possible to live. And with sufficient grace of strength and purpose, I want to get down on my old scarred, gnarled, unlovely knees and make my progress there, the best I can, moving as my long-ago four-footed ancestors moved. Until I can learn to walk upright, but without false pride.

[*Part Four*] *6*

In the morning, the long late morning in Irene Wertz's little house, Walton felt so full a measure of well-being, of satisfaction with himself, that it seemed to him as though he had shed his old skin. In their repetitions of the act, she taught him, coolly, surely, several variations on the theme of pleasure that astonished him. How to reconcile the blunt, bald talk of his classmates and fraternity brothers with this joyous and subtle experience? He would never tire of it, he thought, even as, in the early afternoon, utterly exhausted, he lay spread-eagled on the bed beside her, one arm flung possessively across her belly.

"I'll make us some breakfast," she whispered, and he nodded heavily, unable to exert the effort for even a monosyllable.

Then he slept or dozed or daydreamed. To wake abruptly at the sound of her voice, suddenly miserable at the realization of his impending marriage to her, and at the knowledge that he didn't want to marry her—or anybody else: that he wanted to be free. For the first minute of full consciousness, he glared at her in unforgiving hatred, contemptuous of her face, shiny without makeup, of her hair piled loosely on top of her head, of her faded blue robe.

"Walton!" she said. "What's the matter?"

He shook his head, tried to disperse the dreadful feeling of being trapped, the sense of hopelessness, by this vigorous motion. Hunger saved him; the fragrance of coffee and bacon helped him to mumble, "Had a dream," and plunge into his clothes.

But throughout breakfast the feeling lingered, reduced to uneasiness, to a need to get out and walk for miles. Soon after the meal, which Irene, despite an occasional curious glance at him, managed to keep moderately conversational, he declared, not without some shamefacedness, that he must go back to the fraternity house to study.

"We have a Renaissance test tomorrow," he explained. And, after an awkward pause, "Besides the review, there are two hundred pages I haven't even read."

She scrutinized him thoughtfully, nodded, and said quietly, "Next time—next weekend—you must bring your books with you." Then she reached up and kissed him, long, searchingly. But the darting lizard tongue that had so enraptured him the night before embarrassed him now, even annoyed him. It was he who finally broke the embrace, said huskily, "Good-bye, and thanks, Irene," and hurried out the door.

He did not go to the fraternity house, where he feared jocular comments about his unslept-in bed, but set out along a lonely dirt road into the country—thoughts, fears, admonitions, suspicions and occasional gusts of jubilation jostling each other in his head. But gradually, scuffling the dry and resonant leaves underfoot, as he strode through the brightly painted, crisp autumn day, the premonitions and fears subsided, and he began to glow with a sense of fulfillment.

He was a man. Only now did he realize how much he had doubted his capacity; only now did he feel that at last he really fitted his skin. It occurred to him that something more than the end of his virginity, in any literal sense, had taken place. He was suddenly confident that he could face, easily and naturally, those very boys and professors who had, until now, awed him and filled him with a hostile sense of his own insufficiency. He turned around and made his way back to town.

And it was the way he had thought it would be. Only Ez, his roommate, and the boys across the hall had noticed his absence; only they made ribald comments—and he observed that his new silent grin in response seemed to please them as much as himself. By suppertime, he and Ez had finished the greater part of their preparation for the test, and there was no further reference to his disappearance, although occasionally he would look up and find Ez's shrewd gaze directed at him speculatively.

Walton's mind felt unusually clear and orderly; it seemed to him that both it and his body had acquired a new muscular tone. After the Sunday-night sing, he finished his work in an hour and, leaving Ez to struggle on, descended the stairs. Making sure no one else was about, he went into the phone booth.

"Irene. This is Walton. How—how are you?"

"Sleepy." The voice was remote, but warm and reminiscently husky.

"I—I just wanted to say I had a—wonderful time."

"Sure. Me too. You're quite a lover, boy."

"Well, you—you . . . Irene, I love you."

He hung up and raced back upstairs. He brushed his teeth vigorously for five minutes, leaped into bed and immediately fell asleep.

To wake, start up suddenly in the middle of the night, feeling lost and terrified. Guilty. Haunted.

What had he done?

All the precepts, the warnings, the stained and soiled allusions, the veiled references to dreadful retribution—all the scareheads of home and childhood thronged the icy corridors of his mind. He found that he was shivering. With a wary eye on the snoring Ez, he fumbled his way into his bathrobe and slippers, tiptoed into the study, and closed the door softly behind him.

What had he done?

He sat in his armchair, head bent forward and resting on his sweating palms. For a long time he sat there, motionless in despair. Old words drifted through his numb mind: disgraced . . . sin . . . shame . . . bad . . . nasty. Scenes from movies: young men in despair; girls, clutching their shawls against the driving snow, cast out from home, pausing on bridges to look down at a dark river. From life: Uncle Herbert, stoop-shouldered, sullen, afraid (that was it); his mother's dark hints about Aunt Ludie running away; the wicked aura around Uncle Lloyd, the giggles over Cousin Gertrude; his mother's sudden anguished outcry that her husband had left her bed.

Confusion—chaos—and despair. And through the black night air the ominous tolling of the chapel bell, three times. There was no one, Walton thought in sudden coherence, to whom he could turn, to whom, openly and in full faith, he could tell the desperateness of his situation, the hopelessness in which he was drowning. Hang on, he muttered to himself. Hang on.

And after a while, he began to plan. He would go to Irene tomorrow. Manfully, he would tell her, candidly and directly, of his shame and his regret, of his wish somehow to atone for what he had done, of—of his respect for her and his determination to do her no more harm. He could see the tears in her eyes and in his, hear the sad farewells. His heart lifted; he knew suddenly that there was hope after all: he had a confused vision of himself standing sternly before a howling crowd, with upraised hand enjoining them, "Let him who is without sin . . ."

Quite carried away, he stuffed the heavy wool of his robe's sleeve into his mouth, so that his sobs would not be audible. . . .

But late the next afternoon, when, in accordance with a hurried telephone conversation with Irene, he trudged down the path to her little house, the nobility and the elation had blurred, and the dread had formed again, like a clot, around his heart. Only now did he admit to himself the real burden of his fear: that she would be angry, insist, and if need be tell the whole story to Miss Crider. Denounced, expelled, publicly disgraced and exposed to ultimate shame and humiliation, he stood fixed on the driveway in the dismal November rain. Ahead, through the Gothic dusk, the lights of the cottage bloomed softly. Out here, everything cold, bleak and gray; in there—

Was he wrong? Had he turned everything around, backward, inside out? Slowly, reluctantly and yet wonderingly, he walked on toward the lights. . . .

Whether the look in her eyes was simply one of inquiry or whether it was really fear, he did not know. But she was vulnerable, in either case, and this very vulnerability, only half-consciously understood by Walton, somehow changed the balance of the situation. He had been prepared for proprietorship, possessiveness, demandingness—all to change radically into hostility and, eventually, disclosure, when he should tell her that they could not go on with their relationship. What he had not expected, had never thought for a moment, was that she would be tentative, uncertain, questioning.

And so he found that he could not go on with his rehearsed story. Those large waiting eyes made him feel, not guilty, but responsible; confronted by them, he could not say, "I don't believe in this kind of thing; I'm too afraid of being found out; it would kill my parents"— or pronounce other similar misgivings. The old familiar and effective story about the girl back home stuck in his throat.

And so, the door still ajar behind him, they stood, silent, regarding each other, searching, questioning mutely.

Then at last he stirred, looked down at the puddle of water around his shoes, cleared his throat, closed the door and blurted out awkwardly, "I'm so mixed up. I don't know what to say. Or what I think. I thought I was going to tell you— Oh, Irene—"

She was holding out her arms. He went to her and wrapped his arms around her, pulled her close to him, felt again all his strength, protectiveness, assertiveness—her softness, fragility, sweetness.

The winter of Walton's junior year passed with a swiftness, a winged unreality, that in retrospect he found astonishing. It was a time set apart, this winter of the gardener's cottage, with all its vitality and color and meaning confined within this single room. The rest of Walton's life—the routine of classroom and fraternity meeting and the rounds of the newspaper and the swimming team—he lent his perfunctory presence to, functioning with precision and efficiency, but as though by extension.

Through November and December, his schedule was meticulous. Every Saturday afternoon, once the football season was over, he went to the cottage directly from his noon class. He would make a Sunday-morning foray to the college church, when he could not afford a cut, then return to her. And he would go back to the fraternity house for the Sunday-night sing. During the rest of the week, if he saw her, it was by accident or through the necessities of his work for Miss Crider. He drove himself hard, but with less sense of effort and strain than ever before, every evening from Monday through Friday, writing course papers and editorials, and studying. Then, each weekend, for twenty hours, he replenished himself with Irene. They never discussed this schedule; both accepted it without comment.

But after the two weeks of separation during the Christmas holidays (a vacation that puzzled and pleased his family; they were all aware in their different ways that Walton had changed, matured in some way, but accepted the change with a minimum of questions since it had rendered him so content to stay home, so totally, it seemed, uninterested in the round of holiday parties and dances)—after this separation, when he and Irene rushed to meet each other as though after a year's absence, they added Wednesday nights to their private calendar.

Was he in love with her? Sometimes he asked himself this question as he feigned sleep in his own bedroom, to avoid Ez's tendency to prolong late conversations. He did not know. At first he would tell himself yes, of course; this was the only remaining sanction to justify—in the face of all contrary training and official convictions—the affair. Affair! At eighteen! He shivered at his own boldness.

But as time went on he grew bolder. He became honest enough to admit that, however romantically he would have clothed the whole matter in describing it to someone else (not that he ever could have), what he thought of, when at the very doorway to sleep he conjured up Irene, was the satiny smoothness of her skin, the mole by her shoulder blade, something ultimately sensual about the way she shrugged those shoulders, even more, the way she shuddered and trembled. . . .

And, to be sure, the course of their winter together was not entirely even and smooth. There were days on which, when the time to leave for Irene's house approached, he felt a curious reluctance, a sense of coercion against which he rebelled. The very regularity of their schedule, initiated by him, seemed to him then to have been imposed upon him by someone else. It acquired for him, at these moments, the constraining force of the regimes of various sorts that Marcia enforced at home.

On such occasions, although he always went to Irene, he would sulk in silence or answer her irritably or be cold and withdrawn—for the first hour or so. But inevitably, as they had become more intimate, she had learned how to handle him. Sometimes he thought of the way she drew him out of a bad mood as a kind of trickery and in retrospect resented it; at other times he felt that her patience was motivated by a real sympathy—that she understood, better than he did—the origin and nature of these moods. Then he would realize that he owed her a great deal simply because she did not hold them against him—simply because she seemed to accept them as not inconsistent with the nature of someone she could love; because she did not expect him always to be cheerful and pleasant and well behaved. And finally, with this new freedom to say what was on his mind and no need to simulate a well-being that he did not feel, he began to accept these aberrations in himself. Shortly thereafter he noticed that they were of shorter duration than before, and that even when he did feel either bleak or black he was less prone to scrutinize what he considered her weak spots: her posture, her occasional sloppiness or bad taste in clothes, the pimples or sores on her face that she would still, absent-mindedly, pick at and inflame.

There was no recurrence of the sullenness Walton had noticed in Irene during the period just before she secured her house—until one Saturday in January when he arrived a little late to find her seated on her straight-backed chair, chin propped on hands, staring dismally into space.

"What's the matter?" he demanded.

She did not answer. She gave him one wintry, contemptuous glare, and then resumed her fixed gaze at a corner of the room. In excellent humor from having had two of his editorials accepted by the editor-in-chief that morning over two of his competitor's, Walton attempted cajolery. Stroking her head, he said soothingly, "Did you have a hard day, honey?" He placed a finger under her chin and tried to lift her head.

She shook him off savagely.

"Don't," she said in a dead, sullen voice.

He whistled, still unwilling to accept patent evidence that cheerfulness would be of no avail.

"Come over here," he said, dropping comfortably into the arm-chair, "and snuggle up to your old Uncle Walton."

She swung around and glared directly at him.

"I don't want an uncle," she blazed. "I want a man who isn't ashamed of me."

He felt his heart plummet down, as though released by a trigger. When he spoke, he could hear the weakness of his voice.

"Ashamed! What are you talking about?"

Her voice was now low and lethal.

"I'm talking about the Alpha Delts' winter dance next week and some girl named Lucy Latham, whom you're taking to it. And you haven't even told me that you won't come here that day!"

Walton had the feeling that he was drawing a shell tight over him.

"Now look here, Irene," he said. "I am coming. The dance is over at nine, like all house dances. And Lucy doesn't mean a thing to me; I'm just taking her as a favor to Doug Henry, who's nuts about her sister, that's all."

"That's all!" The sullenness had completely dropped away; her eyes were blazing. "But that doesn't explain, Mr. Herrick, why you never thought of asking me. Except that it's too plain to need any explanation. Sure, I'm good enough to lay, but always in secret, hidden away. What I'm not good enough for is to go to your fraternity dance, or even to take out to dinner sometime, or a movie, or anything. Anything at all!"

Her shoulders, her whole body shook with dry, racking tears that she could not shed. She was inconsolable.

And Walton, aghast—at the violence of her feeling, at the rude turn things had taken away from his anticipation, at the sudden rush of guilt he felt: at a confused complex of many things—did try, with no success, to console her. Until, after a half hour, and in desperation, he blurted out the truth. It was, even then, an ornamented truth—but still truth, he thought.

They would be so conspicuous in this college society that their secret would be guessed at once. It was hateful, disgusting to him too that a student could not take out a worker on the college's staff without fixed and definite conclusions being drawn—but it was true. He was as much concerned over sparing her trouble and even insults as he was over any misunderstanding of his own conduct. The college was even stricter about people in her position than it was about students. His family was very strait-laced, and any hint of their affair would almost literally mean the end of the world to his father and mother. The very fact that he was partly working his way through college under Miss Crider's administration made him doubly vulnerable for being involved with a member of Miss Crider's staff. The other girls at these parties were all Smith girls—anyway, shallow college girls—who knew each other and stuck together; she would have a miserable time. He was only nineteen years old, and society (the law, too, he believed) frowned upon such attachments for someone his age.

On and on. But it was not the truth. It was true, mostly true, but it was not the truth. The truth was a presence he could not identify himself—but an admonitory presence that had shadowed him long, that had years before led him to lock his door before he sat down to paste into his early masterpiece the movie magazine photographs of She. He lived in mortal terror of the Presence, but he could not tell Irene that.

Yet the Presence reconciled them. For his very terror of it put such passion in his voice as he urged upon her his rationalizations that her wish to believe won out; the tears finally came; she finally allowed him to comfort her.

And then slowly, falteringly, with trust in those eyes that had never before lost their ultimate wariness, she told him of her early life— of how she had, back there so far that she couldn't remember just when, become convinced of her own unworthiness through the otherwise inexplicable distaste both her mother and father had shown to her, even while they cherished her three sisters (two older, one younger than she). No, she didn't understand it; she didn't know how it had begun—for surely it was that which had driven her to a lonely withdrawal, rather than being withdrawn's having alienated them. She didn't understand it, but it was true, and she had never been able to shake off this conviction, never been able to leave its shadow for the sunlight of self-confidence and acceptance. And she had never again been able fully to accept and trust anyone, and at times her despair and self-hatred had been so great that she had just given herself away to anyone who wanted her, partly to punish herself for being unlovable and partly in order to feel, however speciously, that she belonged to someone. Oh, yes, throughout high school, she had been promiscuous with boys and she had hated it and them and herself.

All in one great shuddering outburst. And Walton had at last really found himself stirred and been very tender with her the rest of the day. He renounced Lucy Latham (let Ez carry that load, shy as he was with girls) and the dance altogether. He made Irene a cup of tea; he undressed her gently and put her to bed; he read to her from her favorite poets; and while she took a nap, he prepared dinner.

He did everything except say that he would take her out some-where. She was happy, she was cherished, she was cared for, and her eyes shone. But as he undressed early in the evening and looked at her glowing face, there where she waited for him in the shadows cast by the one small lamp, he could not forget that he had not said the one thing that could really finally matter to her. And when he came over to her, and she drew the covers aside for him, he suddenly reached down and, picking up her spectacles from the bedside table, thrust them at her, saying sternly, "Put them on. Put them on anyway. I want you to see me tonight."

For weeks after that, things were better between them, but in a strange way they were never alone together again. Walton felt always two presences with them. Not his Presence, but the knowledge that he still had not really answered her, still had not made the ultimate move of openness—and the sporadic but powerful feeling that she was an invalid, a victim like his sister, and that he *must* take special care of her. . . .

Was he then in love with her? He did not know, but in love or not, he had found when all was right between Irene and him—pre-cociously, he suspected—the fulfillment of those fantasies and dreams of his early adolescence.

And this fulfillment isolated him as surely from the everyday reality around him, although it impinged on it in a different way, as had the earlier phase. Since it was no exaggeration to say that the focus of his life that winter was the time spent with Irene, and that the puritanical residue in him told him that he must earn this rapture with the full payment of his academic and extracurricular dues, he had no time for friendships—for the comradeship, the bull sessions, the poker games, the parties and shared dates in which the boys around him par-ticipated regularly.

To be sure, in college as in high school, he had never fully com-mitted himself to the communal life around him. In college, as in high school, he had a few good friends, a few good enemies, and had the respect but not the liking of most of the rest of the students. He did not understand the reasons clearly, though he knew some of the ele-ments: how his touchiness on occasion estranged others; how he felt that they regarded him as a little odd, not regular, in many ways an innocent or a "Christer"; how he himself held back, participated but not with all of himself, and with a wariness that always had an eye and ear cocked for a possible shove from behind.

He did not worry a great deal about this: he was too busy. And the slight distance between most of the rest of them and himself did not prevent their recognizing his good qualities—or, at least, his abilities—and their electing him to responsible offices.

And then, of course, he did have a few close friends. Oddly enough, he thought once, he was more popular—because more at ease—with the older boys in the classes ahead of his, and the younger ones, in the classes after his, than with his own classmates. More than this, he had several friendships with "outsiders," nonfraternity men: Nick Tsatsos, a Greek, several boys from the Jewish community, and one quiet, lonely, but intelligent and sensitive Negro boy.

These were his more or less intellectual friendships; Ez and Doug Henry and a couple of other fraternity brothers were "family," so to speak; and through serving together on several dance committees he and two boys from other fraternities formed a comfortable, casual relationship.

With the advent of Irene and the new order, he seldom saw this last group, for he gave up parties. "Family" dwindled almost exclusively to Ez. And he had little time for the long, ragged discussions of life and philosophy that had been the bond with his non-fraternity friends.

But Nick Tsatsos was stubborn. Self-deprecating, apt to clown over his big cleaverlike nose, his oddly oblong head and his general awkwardness, he made up for what he lacked in self-respect by knowing what he wanted—and had any chance of having—and hung on to Walton like a tenacious, yet oddly ingratiating bulldog. Where he really cared, he refused to be hurt, although he was adept at feeling injured and railing at improbable, or even imaginary, insults from people who meant nothing to him. So if Walton said, "I'm working too hard, Nick, to take an evening off" or "I've got an editorial to write" or "I'm too tired," Nick would grin, bob his head in his peculiarly facetious fashion, and say, "O.K. But I'll try again. You can't get away from me, Herrick. You're my hero." This reiterated assertion, half-joking, half-serious, produced an ambivalent reaction in Walton, one of annoyance blended with secret satisfaction.

And so, at least once a month during the winter, Walton yielded and spent an evening philosophizing with Nick, always rediscovering how much he enjoyed Nick's strange combination of naïveté, half-baked erudition, warmth and melancholy. And though he laughed off Nick's repeated probings into Walton's regular weekend absence (another of Nick's strong characteristics was his utterly open inquisitiveness), he felt an increasing—and to him, paradoxical—inclination to tell Nick about Irene.

Two of Walton's most persistent fears with relation to Irene had been that of discovery and that of subsequent disapproval. Whose? He was vague about this, for he had recovered from the formal specific fear of official cognizance and expulsion. His parents could hardly learn about it any other way; his fraternity brothers knew something was up, but were sufficiently engrossed in their own lives not to venture beyond, in all probability, a little desultory speculation. Ez had accepted the whole thing with his customary matter-of-fact respect of privacy (that of others, in accordance with his wish for it himself); on Friday night he might say, "You're away this weekend?" and nod at Walton's answer. That was all.

That was all, and since—after that one movie—Walton and Irene did not venture out together, and furthermore her little house was so isolated from the town proper, they were not observed. Once, when he remarked on how strange it was that they had not been found out, and that, if his fraternity brothers suspected what was going on, at least had no idea of who the girl was, Irene replied, "That's nothing. When people are found out, it's because they want to be. They feel guilty, and let it out themselves."

So it was only Nick who pried and even suggested outright that Walton was having an affair. He had often told Walton—out of admiration or malice? Walton could not be sure—that he had the makings of a Casanova; with more confidence, he would be irresistible to women. But, titillated as he was, Walton bantered back and evaded Nick's questionings.

Until his election as editor-in-chief of the paper. No one else— not Walton himself, not Irene, whom he phoned, not even Marcia, to whom he promptly sent a telegram—was so proud and elated as Nick. His friend, the head of the college paper and sure now to become a Scarab!

The election was held on a Sunday noon in March, after church. Since he could not return to Irene on a day when he would be in so much demand—for congratulations and celebration (the winning of such a post was considered as much of an honor for the fraternity to which the editor-elect belonged as to himself individually)—Walton was at the fraternity house that afternoon when Nick, who had just heard the news, telephoned. And, on the wave of elation he felt, Walton agreed to meet Nick for a late coffee at the diner after the Sing.

Flushed by the further recognition of his election at the Sing, Walton greeted Nick with even more than his usual warmth.

"Feels wonderful, huh?" Nick's sad black eyes regarded him with a look half-inquisitive, half-worshipful. "What are we doing, drinking coffee? We ought to get drunk together."

Walton shook his head.

"I'm drunk enough right now."

Nick leaned forward, his dark face aglow. Walton noticed that his ears were dirty. He had often observed a small boy aspect to Nick. Sometimes, when it seemed that his nose would never stop running, or when, introduced to someone, Nick shuffled and made awkward noises and furtive motions, Walton found himself equally annoyed and annoyed at his annoyance. Tonight, in his elation, he found the quality endearing.

"No kidding, Walt." Nick was one of the very few of his friends who shortened Walton's name. "Why don't we do it? I've got some booze. Let's loosen those puritanical cords of yours. We can go to my room and drink and talk. And you can have my bed and I'll sleep on the couch. Come on."

Since that first night at Irene's, Walton had had only a very occasional cautious drink with her, none elsewhere. What appealed to him now about Nick's proposal was not the thought of liquor, but Nick's enthusiasm and the chance to talk and talk and talk. He dimly realized that all day he had been holding in his joy over his election, playing the sophisticate, the man, at the fraternity house—until the achievement had actually lost its reality for him. Even with Ez, once he had expressed his gratitude for Ez's part in the decision, and they had enjoyed a few minutes of wild triumph, there had been no opportunity to let go fully. Ez was too sensible—and perhaps in various ways (why not?) too involved in the whole situation—to want to saturate himself in this glow, as Nick would.

"O.K.," said Walton. "But I'm not going to stay up too late. I've a nine o'clock tomorrow."

"To hell with the nine o'clock," said Nick, his somber eyes shining. "I've always told you I'd find some way to get you to break loose and enjoy yourself. We'll drink the cup of victory."

Two cups (they really were cups) of victory, gin and lemon juice later, Walton had not disappointed Nick, who, mixing his libations liberally, had himself drunk four. Again and again, they had relived the long minutes of waiting for the decision and the moment of fulfillment. Walton was discovering, with an odd satisfaction, that he was insatiable, that no amount of praise was really sufficient for this loosened unknown self.

With dignity, he accepted a third drink and chuckled.

"You know, Nick," he said. "You're a damned good friend. I don't think I could be this glad over your winning something like this."

Nick handed him the glass.

"You'll never have a chance to know," he said. "I'll never win anything. I'm a clown, a comedy figure. I'm your court jester."

Walton shook his head indignantly.

"Why do you talk like that?" he demanded. "You're always running yourself down. What's the *matter* with you? If you ever really tried to do anything, you've got everything you need: brains and personality and—"

"And nothing." Nick sighed. "Every time I begin to take myself seriously, I still have to shave or brush my teeth, and I get a good look at myself. *Then* how can I take myself seriously?"

"What the hell is all this about looks?" Walton felt a sudden falseness intrude, against his will cloy his tone—for did Nick value looks any more than he did himself?—and hurried on. "You talk as though good looks were the only thing that mattered. Hell, maybe you're not handsome in any conventional way, but you've got a strong, interesting face."

"Interesting for a clown," Nick replied mournfully, and then immediately became brisker, cheerful. "But we're not mourning me; we're celebrating you. And maybe that's why I get such a kick out of your triumphs: they're the nearest I come to any. Now if I could only get you interested in women—" he interrupted himself with another heavy sigh. "Why, man, you've got everything it takes, including sex appeal. Especially sex appeal. If you weren't so goddamn stiff and puritanical you could be a regular Casanova."

"I'm not so stiff and puritanical." Walton heard his own voice as smug, but in this curious new way felt quite tolerant of his own smugness. "How do you know?"

Nick pointed an accusing finger at him.

"How do I know? It's written all over you. Here you are nineteen —or is it eighteen—and I'll bet you're still a virgin, the only other virgin besides me in our class. When you could be a regular Casanova! How do you handle it anyway? I get pictures in my mind when I go to bed."

Walton took a slow sip of his drink. By now its somewhat raw sour taste was no longer unpleasant. He paused impressively and then looked Nick directly in the eye.

"No," he said, "I'm not a virgin."

Nick's eyes popped.

"You're not! I asked you only last fall and you admitted you were! What's—is that what you do when you go away on those weekends?" Walton nodded solemnly.

"I spend every weekend with her."

Nick grasped his arm.

"You do. You're—you're having an affair!" He jumped up and began pacing the room excitedly. "I knew there was something different about you. I've seen it. It's just like I said about Casanova. You're a man, Walt, having an affair. These others, with their cheap lays, they're college boys. But an affair with one woman! My god, what's it like? I dream about this all the time. I come in and close the door behind me, stand there, looking significantly into her eyes, you know. Like this—" he illustrated, almost dropping his glass in his drunken excitement— "and then I turn the key in the door behind me, slowly, like this. And then I walk toward her slowly and she is quivering. And then I undress her. Sometimes I tear her clothes off, like this—but sometimes I am a connoisseur and I relish slowly taking off her clothes, one at a time. I unhook her dress, let it slip and fall slowly to her feet. A garter. A stocking." He flourished his glass wildly, a splash landing on his desk. "Is it like that?"

Walton pondered the matter, nodded.

"A little," he said sententiously.

"Her breasts!" Nick exclaimed ecstatically. "I dream of breasts! Are hers pear-shaped or round or little ones pointing up? Are her nipples pink or brown? Think of it! Think of it! Is she a brunette or a blonde? Walt, I reverence you."

Walton was lost in a dreamy reverie, to which Nick's frenzied words were only a distant orchestration. In a drowsy, uninsistent way, he was considering going now to Irene; it would suit Nick's romanticism so well that surely he would not mind a sudden departure. Yet he was sleepy; it seemed a matter of such great effort to do anything but walk the two steps to the bed and—

Nick was shaking him by the shoulders; Walton's glass fell from his hand, spilling the dregs it had held, and rolled away to a corner of the room. Nick's eyes were gleaming feverishly.

"Let me meet her," he demanded. "Walt, let's go over there now. Is she in Hamp or South Hadley or where? Is she a college girl? It's not too late. If you're so intimate, she'll like it. Let's go see her now."

Would she? Walton found himself suddenly and surprisingly piqued by the idea. Yet it was after midnight; he had never before broken the regularity of their schedule; and although she had expressed her hurt at not being a part of his daily life, never meeting any of his friends, being kept so secret and isolated—this was hardly the time and the way to break the pattern. And yet again, as Nick pressed on him another full glass, it seemed right, an act of the sort he had always felt incapable of: spontaneous and reckless and daring. And open—especially *open*.

"O.K.," he said decisively, and reached for the telephone. He gave the operator the number, cast one quick look at Nick's glittering eyes and tense body, and waited for the answer.

After three rings, a sleepy voice, the "hello" hardly more than a startled breath, a whisper of alarm.

"Listen," said Walton eagerly, "I want to come over and bring a friend. I've told you about Nick Tsatsos, remember? We're celebrating and we want you to too. O.K.?"

There was a long pause, and while he waited Walton realized how he dreaded a rejection, how ignominious he would feel before Nick. Why had he given in so quickly and called her?

But there was no rejection. At last the soft voice said, "Why, sure. Come over. But give me a half hour first. I look dreadful."

Walton did not trust himself to speak further. He hung up and nodded to Nick as casually as he could. Then, "In a half hour," he said, clearing his husky voice, and crossed the room to splash cold water on his face. Nick began ripping off his dirty shirt.

"Just like Faust and Mephistopheles," he chattered. "Going to see her together in the middle of the night!"

It was then and there, Walton decided later, that the whole situation began to deteriorate. Just what he had expected of Irene and of himself that night he was never specifically sure. But in a general way, at least, to dazzle Nick—in some fashion to live up to the feverish expectations of Nick's highly sensitized erotic imagination.

This much he did know: they completely failed Nick in this respect. Walton had hoped that Irene would wear the Japanese kimono he had given her for Christmas, with her hair gathered in a loose pile on the top of her head—the "Marie Antoinette" way he liked it best. Instead, she had dressed in a sweater and skirt, and drawn her hair back plain and knotted it. If she had on any cosmetics, they were not discernible. She looked clean and plain, wholly unexotic.

Nick brought along his bottle; she refused a drink and made coffee. She was obviously self-conscious and uneasy with Nick at first; then, if puzzled, also amused.

As for Nick, he was by now so befuddled that he alternately sat, gaping, in silence, and blurted out some rhapsodic and gauche comment to his hostess. "Your legs are beautiful," he said abruptly once. Another time: "Do you wear a brassière?" And, most disturbing of all to Walton: "Is Walt a good lover?"

By the time Nick got around to this last question, Irene was fully composed. "Sure," she said slyly. "For a college boy, that is."

That was the final blow for Walton. Throughout the previous hour and a half, he had alternately maintained a somber silence and tried to interest the others in a discussion of good and evil in *Paradise Lost,* not so much because he was now studying it as because he felt it a vaguely appropriate topic. But he could not recover from his first disappointment at Irene's appearance and determined sobriety; he found, to his surprise, that he was infuriated by what he felt to be Nick's lascivious looks at Irene and his boorish comments; he was drunk, a little nauseated and sleepy, and, finally, more than a little hurt that Irene treated him (so he felt) quite formally before Nick. He missed sorely the presence of her hands, resting briefly on his cheek, his shoulder, his knee; he did not like the appraising quality in the glances she leveled on him.

So, when Irene parried Nick's question, "Is Walt a good lover?" with what seemed to him in effect a rejection, and an insult as well, he could take no more. He sprang to his feet, for a full moment stood there, glaring at Irene, and then said stiffly to Nick, "It's time for us to go."

Nick objected, but Irene did not, and her "good night" was as cold as Walton's.

Outside, stumbling in the dark, Nick protested.

"What you wanta get mad at her for? Beautiful girl like that. I thought you'd spend the night. I don't blame you. Why don't you go back, Walt? Christ, when you can go to bed with a girl like that! Jesus, think of it!"

They plodded on: Walton grimly silent, only occasionally answering in stiff monosyllables; Nick, voluble, uninhibited, often incoherent. When they reached the corner on which the paths to Nick's rooming house and Alpha Delta Phi separated, Walton turned off with a cold "Good night, Nick."

"Hey, what ya doin'? You're goin' to spend the night with me since you haven't got sense enough to stay with her. Imagine, with her bareass beside you! Come back, Walt!"

Walton turned around, hissed furiously, "You go to hell, you son of a bitch," and went on his lonely way. . . .

Then and there, Walton thought often later, the whole situation began to change. To be sure, he went to her house as usual on Wednesday night, and after an hour or so of quarreling they made love. But where once such a reconciliation would have made their feeling for each other warmer and closer than ever, now it did not. Now the combination of anger and sex was rather simply titillating. Despite the response of her body, she remained sullen and hostile, deep in the mood he neither understood nor liked. And he knew that what he really wanted to do was to hurt her. Once again, the next morning, they exchanged cold good-byes.

On Friday he received a formal little note from her, telling him not to come on Saturday; she was going to Springfield to shop. He thought he was glad; he filled the day with work on the newspaper and the preparation of a paper on Stendhal. But at eleven o'clock that night he had become so restless that he pulled on his raincoat and set out into the wet dark streets. She did not even make any pretense of not waiting for him. The door opened immediately to his knock; she stood there in the Japanese kimono and, without a word, held out her arms.

But again the next morning they were bitter and angry.

"I can't stand it, that's all!" she said. "I can't stand being cooped up here all the time, just waiting for you—like some criminal! Or a whore!

What he felt was half shame and half distaste. She looked wild and red-eyed and—and slovenly, he thought. His own voice was cold and logical: he had explained to her often enough why it had to be this way. She had agreed to it, knew the necessities of it. And when he *had* finally brought a friend, she had been deliberately unfriendly, cold—and even belittled him before the friend.

She *belittled* him? *She* belittled *him!* There was scorn and even a little frenzy in her voice. It rose till she screamed at him. Face contorted, hair disheveled, kimono half opened and a splotch of grease on it. She thrust her angry face close to his and he saw suddenly another pimple, another sore beginning on her chin. He picked up his coat and left, slamming the door behind him. . . .

It was on the following Thursday evening, accompanying Ez downtown for a late coffee, that Walton saw Irene and Nick come out of the movie. For a moment he thought only that this was a fantasy, spun from the hundreds of conflicting thoughts and feelings he had entertained in the past four days. Then he saw her turn to Nick, make that immemorial gesture of hers, that raffish jerk of head and shoulder, indicating—what? some final contempt? or an ultimate indifference, a dismissal of consequences, a giving of herself, her little-valued self, to whatever might come?

Walton felt a rush of blood to his head, clenched his fists, as he watched Nick's idiot laugh, heard his foolish cackle. He had wondered at Nick's uncharacteristic failure to telephone him, to try to make amends for their quarrel—but he had not even guessed at the reason. And now he and Ez were approaching them, were bound, in a moment, to meet them face to face. It was too late to veer off, and he advanced as stiffly as though he were on his way to the executioner's block.

Nick saw him at this moment, and gaped. A look of foolish indecision was patent on his face. He actually stopped dead in his tracks for an instant, long enough that Irene looked up for an explanation—and found it. But the recognition was in her eyes only; her face remained impassive.

Another ten paces and they passed. Nick and Irene intoned together a hollow "Hello"; Walton said nothing. A quick, curious glance from Ez, and the incident was over.

But not its effects. Hardly its effects. Walton licked his wounds for a long time. His sometimes melancholy, sometimes furious nursing of his hurt pride completely cleansed him of the lingering remnants of guilt over the way he had kept Irene as remote in her little house from the rest of his life as if he had locked her up in his fantasies. His sympathy for the affliction of her self-loathing and for the scars of those early causative wounds melted and flowed away under the heat of his anger. She was a vulgar, cheap, morbid girl with a bad complexion.

But what was hardest to conjure away was, perhaps not physical longing itself, but the expectations of his biweekly visits, the reminder, when the going in the daily round was rough, of the coming weekend or Wednesday night. He missed, with a dull agony, the ceremony and ritual of their life together: the long, eager, expectant walk, the delicious hour or so after arrival, warm, cozy, shut-off, with the certain knowledge of fulfillment coming—so that more and more he had felt free to be natural, to complain, be as grumpy or cantankerous as he had felt for the previous several days, and slowly, comfortably, let her soothe or coax or excite him out of his mood. What was physical that haunted him now was a moment or two here or there that had highlighted, symbolized his infatuation for her body: lamplight gleaming on her flanks, the mole beside her shoulder blade, a moment one night when in rare total abandonment she had lain, sprawled out on her back, her hair spilling from the end of the couch, arms flung out, somehow then, *then* wholly ravished.

Such memories ravished him now, but could not slake his anger. Longing evaporated in rage; he renewed his vows not to give in, not to approach her, never to see her again.

This last was futile: he had to see her when he went to Miss Crider's office—and finally, in late April, he begged off from this work for the rest of the baseball season, pleading his added responsibilities with the college paper and promising double duty in the fall. For, while he could endure Irene's set, cold face and her perfunctory "hello," he could *not* bear the days when in another mood, all confectionary sweetness, she would ply him with arch questions about the work, punctuated by sly, knowing smiles that made him want to strike her.

And so, in the last six weeks of junior year, he caught no more than an occasional glimpse of her downtown, twice with Nick. Nick avoided Walton altogether. It had always taken someone's effort— usually Nick's—to bring them together, when their regular courses through college were so dissimilar. Therefore, there was no strain attached to their not meeting.

No strain—except, for Walton, that of envisioning Nick with Irene. Would she—really? Imagining her in the arms of that awkward ape, Walton's rage, slowly worn to a simmer, would boil up again. And he would wonder, in the midst of angry speculation, just how far she would endure Nick, simply to pay him, Walton, off? Or was she, in a masochistic ecstasy, punishing herself through Nick, humiliating herself in endorsement of her low estimate of herself? It did not occur to him that she might find the same endearing qualities in Nick that he had discovered himself—for he had forgotten that he had ever had these feelings for Nick.

Walton's way out of all this turmoil and conflict was to work harder than ever. His course grades soared, insuring him of Phi Beta Kappa in senior year. He worked equally hard as editor, and in the other activities in which he was engaged.

Except for social ones. A member of the Junior Prom Committee, he attended the big dance of the year as a stag, and busied himself with attending to the comfort of the famous dance band they had hired. He danced himself, during the long hours from ten to six, only twice— each time to please a fellow committeeman. He felt no pull toward other girls; it was as though, once his anger was mostly spent, he was numbed, incapable of physical desire, or even attraction. And he left for home— or rather, for the western New York State summer spot at which his family had already encamped, without having had a single date.

He continued his new routine throughout the summer, working on the local newspaper and assiduously attending his family. Marcia remarked more than once that summer, "Walton's disposition has improved so much. His restlessness is all over." But when she questioned him, he would only laugh briefly and say, "Growing up at last, I guess, Mother."

When he returned in the fall for his last year at Amherst, he learned almost immediately from Miss Crider that Irene would not be back; she had taken a job in New York. A week later he discovered that Nick had transferred to New York University. What did that mean? Or did it mean anything beyond a coincidence? Walton did not try to find out. He set his course, a little grimly, toward the responsibilities of senior year.

ENTRY

from the autobiography of Cornelius Butler Herrick (unpublished) . . .

It came to pass that I entered Amherst College in the autumn of 1853. This was my first leave-taking from home— my first sight of the outside world. I went from Fabius [New York] to Albany by slow stages, then by night boat to New York, and again from New York to Hartford, this time by rail. A very green boy was I, tho' in my twenty-second year, as I strolled up Broadway to get a glimpse of the first World's Fair on this side of the sea.

From close work on the farm to close work at books, trying to take a sophomore rank, a stranger to everybody in College, was a trying experience. I passed the homesick stage, found three or four fellows of like mind in Class, most of them as poor as I was. We were all members of the Anti-Secret Society from principle; the Anti-Masonic crusade had influenced us all against the principle of secrecy. And the fact that we were all students for the ministry was another bond.

But I am not proceeding in an orderly fashion. I must first go back three years. The winter of 1850 was an epoch in my life. A very powerful revival of religion was prayed into being in the old first Church of Fabius, and the announced conversion of a friend of mine was a summons to me to seek my "soul's salvation." I gave myself up to the divine influence about me. The teaching of the period was Calvinistic and the guidance given was chary of encouraging human effort. The attitude was rather the waiting for the movements of the Divine Spirit and the revelations of the Divine Will in experience. It is enough to say that after long tribulation I arrived at the beginnings of a religious experience. It was a great change, for whatever else I had been, I was far enough from a religious life. I had, however, already for years lived in fear of death—the Millerite teaching had affrighted me and the Calvinistic discussions had impressed me that I could not do anything if I would, and that all an unregenerate man could do was sin; I was uneasy, half-fearful and half-defiant, over my state. So now my eagerness to face the issue in a revival was sincere. In my nineteenth year, for the first time in my life, it dawned upon me that God might have something for me beyond the (to me) ill-suited life of a farm—and this mostly as a result of the revival. Hence my determination toward the ministry in my College days, although the doctrine of total depravity rankled in me for some time. Nay, it rankled . . . [At this point in the journal, there are lines crossed out heavily and completely indecipherable.]

At any rate, our Chapel service was, to most of us, stimulating, if at times perplexing. I say this because among the visiting pastors—better, Preachers—were such men as Beecher, then in his prime; a gifted Scotchman named MacDonald, whose weakness was drink and who later went to Africa as a missionary and died; and Dr. Cheever, the Anti-slavery thunderer. These, brilliant and talented, were richer fare than our own Professors and the local clergy, and raised knottier problems than at times my stomach was sufficiently strong to digest. Theological ones: for these three, among other visitors, did not hold in any precise way with the Calvinism to which we were accustomed. But also other, not strictly religious confusions, such as the whole question of the pride in intellect.

MacDonald, in some curious way, also implied an ironic attitude toward the doctrine of original sin that gave me an uneasy feeling that he shrugged off moral responsibility for the sins of the flesh. This he definitely did *not* ever say; it was more a matter of my feeling that those of us who were more subtilized and mature in our perceptions and understanding were being *allowed* to perceive this if we chose: it was as though (I plead guilty here to using a gross expression for the sake of its graphic precision) he winked at those few of us he considered able to follow his meaning. I remember with a good deal more comfort old Dr. Horatio Perkins, who often, when praying in Chapel, seemed face to face with God.

But again I find that I must pause. There are some things of which, clearly, I cannot write, others about which, I cannot decide whether or not I should. Some of my trouble, surely, is caused by my not being certain for whom I am writing. My wife suggested this journal for the children, later. Yet I find myself about to say, now and again, things which will not be edifying for them.

In this case, relevant to the effect Dr. MacDonald had on me, I shall say simply that it seems to me, even in retrospect, that in Paul's sense, I was more prone to burn than my young male friends; during my College days, I came perilously near on several occasions to an engagement with one of several young women—nearer than was desirable for their and my peace of mind, since it went no further. I am glad that no really broken engagement lies against me, but I wish I had been more self-restrained. If I did none of them literal harm, I did them—and myself—no good. And I was freer with one or two of them than I should approve, even now, in others. In some curious way, it had to do with their woman's approval of me; I was not unsusceptible to the lure of vanity.

Finally, then, as to my record in College, it was on the whole surprisingly good. My work in those days was very crude, I am sure. Hence, how it was that I came to the rank of a Phi Beta Kappa, to be on the Editorial staff of the College Magazine, a Class Poet, and a prize Essayist ($24.00), I scarcely know. In this essay I took the ground that the advance of Civilization and Knowledge was not detrimental to Poetry. Wm. A. Wilkinson, my contestant, took the opposite view.

Graduating in 1856, my purpose was to study theology at Union Seminary, and accordingly after two months on the farm assisting my father for the last time, I set out for New York. . . .

[*Part Four*] **7**

WALTON'S freshman year had been dominated by two romantic attachments: the one for the fraternity and the other for John Collins Howe and the poetic vistas he opened. In sophomore year, urged on by Ez, he worked fanatically at extracurricular activities, especially the competitions for the college paper and the managership of the baseball team; meanwhile, largely under the influence of Carlton Crocker, whose course in the Romantic Movement he was taking, Walton's intellectual faculties toughened somewhat and his vision of what life might be (even if not his own) expanded.

However much the editorship of the paper meant to him, junior year was Irene's. And now, with the advent of senior year, with the actual entrance into what, only three years before, had seemed the ultimately austere arcana, Walton's values began to change.

He would still not be twenty until November; by now he knew, if only dimly, that the not inconsiderable record he had made in college was a record revealing little, if anything, of the forced, uneven and erratic growth of the boy whose name was on the record. His academic grades were good; he had achieved recognition in campus life outside the classroom; he had lived for a while, however fantastically, on the green oasis of his sojourn with Irene. Though still grudgingly, he could now admit its value to him. But of what is sometimes grandly known as the life of the mind he had experienced very little. It was relatively easy to perform adequately, or even well, in a given semester's course, without often feeling the electric shock of a challenging mind's contact with one's own, without often knowing the exhilarating realization of one's capacity for exploring, questioning, learning—the smacking impact of new concepts, the excitement of new insights.

To be sure, he had been subjected to the force of certain strong personalities. In addition to Howe in freshman year, there was the

644

compulsory course, Social, Political, Economic and Cultural Institutions of American Society, known affectionately or derisively to the class at large as SPECIES, SPECIAL, SPEC ASS or SPECKLED ASS, and SPECIOUS. The professor, Edgar Allan Smith, a ranging sociologist with a reputation for brilliance marred by an excessive love of the spectacular, was a skinny, towering, stoop-shouldered man with bland blue eyes that remained as mild as ever while he gave forth with some outrageous or shocking opinion.

Professor Smith's favorite whipping boys were organized Christianity, the Bible and genteel society. There could be no question, Walton realized much later, but that the cadaverous professor's really basic satisfaction did come from shocking this freshmen audience, many of whom wrote home in alarm over the pronouncements of this sarcastic atheist. Some of the parents protested to the administration, but were apparently soothed, for only one boy withdrew. Walton, already canny, referred to the course only once in his letters home—and that time cautiously, with a question to his father about the effect of the findings of geologists and Charles Darwin upon the Creation story in *Genesis*.

The liberal theology in his father's reply comforted him, but Marcia's sharp queries resolved him to ask no more. She, who at home professed no dogmatic faith, was, it seemed, worried about Walton's disillusionment; he, having believed himself a rebel against the family faith, was surprised to find himself troubled by Smith's irreverences.

Perhaps that was it: he was troubled by the irreverences, the blasphemies (as also by the off-color jokes Smith sometimes told in class) not so much because of their being irreverent, blasphemous, as because of the professor's tone—that consistently bland, slightly nasal, carefully matter-of-fact tone, maintained in a manner that seemed to be saying, "But who could possibly think otherwise? My dear young citizens of the world, I realize, of course, that you already share these views with me?" Or was there, Walton sometimes wondered, a deeper ambiguity in this manner, its real point being to poke fun at his largely naïve audience?

He didn't know, but aside from a hodge-podge of questions and doubts that he carried away from this course—not challenging new queries to work out, but depressed doubts and fears about anything validly positive in human life—aside from his confusion, Walton was left at the end of the year largely with disquieting thoughts about the instructor.

This six-foot-six man seemed almost of another species. Occasionally Walton played with the fancy that Edgar Allan Smith really had come from another planet, on which knowledge had progressed to such a point that all the inhabitants of Earth, in comparison, were abecedary idiots. Perhaps, he thought in less fantastic moments, Smith, whose brilliance, after all, was incontestable, simply had a mentality so far in advance of his colleagues on the faculty—to say nothing of William Herrick and early teachers Walton had respected—that only he really understood anything about life and human nature. Beside his erudition, John Collins Howe's was that of a boy.

Yet this conclusion was even more distressing—for Howe endorsed Walton's own romantic dreams and hopes. For all that one learned from SPECIES, life seemed drearier, drabber, even dirtier, after one had completed the course.

Yet Smith performed one clearly useful and specific service for Walton; he prepared him to take, in his junior year, the seminar in Rousseau and Voltaire with the celebrated Roger Vercel, without suffering from shock.

M. Vercel reminded Walton vaguely of his Uncle Edgar Briffault. Like Uncle Edgar, he had a black goatee, though it was not so well tailored; his voice, though lacking Uncle Edgar's aspirate hiss, was equally clipped and metallic.

Professor Vercel's irony was of a more subtle order than Professor Smith's sarcasm; his equally gentle delivery knew modulations and refinements of which Smith was wholly innocent: what remained identical was the matter-of-fact dismissal of romantic attitudes, idealistic theories, the exaltation of virtue, honor and even, it sometimes seemed to Walton, ordinary decency. Moreover, the amusement M. Vercel found in sexual matters was so considerable, the jokes and stories he told so far advanced in scatology beyond Mr. Smith's efforts—that girls and women were frankly forbidden to visit the course. Each party weekend, visitors from Smith or Vassar or Wellesley, informed about this class, strove to secure exemption from this rule, but were turned away with Gallic politeness but authoritarian firmness.

If Walton was mildly interested in the administration's apparently neutral attitude toward these matters, by senior year he was much more concerned with the meaning—for him—of these men's professorial attitudes. He began to see that Vercel, reveling in Voltaire and always, however indirectly, ridiculing Rousseau, had probably, years before, begun this course as a lesson in the self-deceptions, pretentiousness, and eventual downright comic dishonesty lurking inherent in the romantic attitude toward life (Rousseau, first semester), and in the caustic healing properties of astringency, skepticism, realism and honesty (Voltaire, second semester). But somewhere over the years, he had perhaps fallen in love with his own wit and the constant applause; the point of the lesson had become blunted—for all the honest aspirations, the ideals of liberty, individuality and brotherhood, also inherent in romanticism, were lost sight of, and the rapier sting of François Marie Arouet was sometimes vulgarized into a bludgeon's clout.

Partisanship, one-sidedness, was the lesson for Walton as, choosing his senior courses, he remembered the bitter lines in Carlton Crocker's New England face, not unlike that of Emerson; the surprising and contradictorily florid designs his waving arms wove in emphasis; the hoarseness of his voice as he communicated his enthusiasms—but above all, his angry incisiveness as he said scornfully, "And why, sir, should one not like Pope simply because one is ardent about Wordsworth?"

So, majoring in English and minoring (as the expression then went) in French, Walton built his senior program around Crocker's Shakespeare course. He took writing with Howe, with not too satis-factory results; he happily digressed into biology—but the heart of senior year, its tone, its aura: these were found with Carlton Crocker.

The teacher's personality was not the salient matter here. That personality was clear enough, if complex: a strange combination of mordancy, mysticism, tenderness and tough-mindedness. But the course belonged to Shakespeare; a whole new world was spread before those who could see—no, better, the old, old world was suddenly bathed in a new amber light, a sharp, clear and yet mellow light that shone im-partially, though differently, through neutral, dark or sunny skies, upon whatever lay below: sunburnt rustic revelries, dark machinations, pageants and battles, comic tangles, courtships, murders or dreams. Laughter, death and love; the anguished meditation and the rash deed; terror, idyll and ribaldry: all the various and multiple combinations of human beings—man's comic seriousness, his antic nobility, his savage tenderness, his pathetic evil—all swirling or plodding before the reader.

One vast celebration of the human state, with those master fingers playing a dozen variations on a single theme, say, of art encountering nature—or of the uses and abuses of honor. Mind was there—at once nimble and profound—tossing ideas and phrases into the air as though they were colored baubles that clutched at the sunlight as they rose and fell, shimmering, shifting, flashing through the air—surely to be caught and tossed aloft again.

But it was not this magic of the mind, and its interplay with the alchemy of language, wringing new life from old dead words, as though God had touched a street organ with His finger—it was not this play of intellect or the gift of words that most enthralled Walton. Rather it was the great stageful of players, and this man's incredible love for faulty human life, this vast impartial compassion that broke through, like sun through dissipating storm clouds, to touch with rusty splendor a Macbeth in his final despair; to redeem in dying breath the hatefully and fatuously misspent life of the great, gross, lovable Falstaff and display his innocence as God's child; with one hand to point the willful and extravagant infatuation of an Antony and the wanton faithlessness of his queen, designated by everyone as gypsy, whore and bitch—only to turn and, with the other hand, signal to Enobarbus to deliver his unforgettable tribute to this woman who "makes hungry where most she satisfies," who hops "forty paces through the public street" to "make defect perfection," and then have these most faulty of lovers demonstrate, themselves, their essential broad humanity: Antony his open-handed magnanimity, and she her rich dignity and self-respect.

Here was the very opposite world from the fiercely partisan, black-and-white worlds of Smith and Vercel. No—here was the vast and complex world of reality, that drew a circle and took them in, as it took in everything: all opposites, complements, opponents, resolved in the encompassing paradox. Here intolerance was withered with a laugh: "Dost thou think, because thou art virtuous, there shall be no more cakes and ale?" Yet tolerance was itself irrelevant; in so inclusive a world, who could have the arrogance to assume it, save one or another of his multitudinous players, performing his part, marking out his little limits, in the spectacle?

The opposites were there, the endless opponents, exponents and proponents; but the great emperor of this arena refused to point up or down. The meanest clown has dignity, the mightiest hero warts or neuroses or dyspepsia; when the observer spies and seeks to establish in the discerned tenderness—at last!—exclusive evidence of Shakespeare's preference, he has only to read on and there—there!—is equal love for the first one's opponent. Love. Not sentimentality nor lust nor romantic befuddlement nor unbearable loneliness deceiving itself—but love, the imaginative sympathy with all that is human.

And so, in his hoarse and supplicating voice, Carlton Crocker croaked on, arms uplifted, hands waving accompaniment to his version of this vision, this great chorusing celebration of human life—and Walton, tingling, enthralled, intoxicated, drank deeper and deeper from the peerless keg.

He wrote papers beyond the stipulated number—wrote on "Shake-speare's Women," "The Light in the Dark Comedies," "The Concept of Patience in Shakespeare's Plays," "Shakespeare as a Romanticist" . . . and they came back, scribbled on furiously in Crocker's ragged hand: "This is pap" . . . "Fatuous" . . . "Stop moralizing like your Aunt Emma" . . . "Now here is something to chew on—why don't you chew?" . . . "Stuff and nonsense; get down to the issue" . . . "Words and words and words/Creep in this petty pace from paragraph to paragraph"—together with a grade of A− or B+ or B and, often, the comment, "Good paper." Something in Walton's scheme of values was outraged by this seeming contradiction. At last he said so to Professor Crocker.

Crocker pushed his glasses up high on his forehead, tilted back his swivel shair, pawed at the air with a weary hand, and in what Walton thought of as his neighing tone, usually invoked in exasperation, cried out as though in pain, "Contradiction? Contradiction? Have you ever seen the *other* papers? That's what's most wrong with you anyway. Forget *contradiction!* Consider *paradox!*"

Senior year was William Shakespeare's year—and this, Walton was often to think later, was his salvation. For there were knotty problems in this year, more than he could really cope with—especially with Life, that world beyond the campus, looming larger and larger, and the portentous accompanying thought that life would end when he entered Life. How? Why? He did not know, though it had even more to do with his family than with the finding of a job. And so, though he secretly despaired of Shakespeare's generous vision of life ever having anything direct to do with his own, it restored a balance, exuded an however remote promise of broader horizons to which he might at least from time to time lift his eyes. That his own life to come, however constricted, narrow and hopeless, would be by its very existence a part of that of Shakespeare's vision never occurred to him. Jaques, Malvolio, the Duke in *Measure for Measure* (who feels older than young men?), and—yes, paradoxically, Laertes? He was Walton Herrick.

Yet, however much he associated himself with Shakespeare's secondary characters (if only to repudiate any such comparison), he was a leader on his campus in many ways—ways that he eventually came to see were the appropriate ones for the person he then was. With the comparative disaffection between Ez Barker and himself in senior year he took hard, for example, the fact that Ez was chosen president of the fraternity for the first term, and he himself only for the second. Characteristically, he concealed this feeling, reproached himself, and sturdily lauded Ez. But it was only years later that he saw that the choice and order *were* right and wise: that Ez had given much more of himself to Alpha Delta Phi than had Walton, that Ez had far more of the common touch, of give-and-take humanity, of sound administrative judgment: whether in terms of qualifications for the job or simply warranted popularity, Ez was his superior.

Walton was suffering from a confusion that arose from the impact of other personalities upon him. In any group, he could not be relaxed, simple, direct. In love with his newly discovered vision of humanity, he found concrete humanity hard to take. He was more at home with issues: he flourished as editor of the paper, and he worked hard, lucidly and efficiently at a new post conferred on him in February of his final year: the chairmanship of the student committee on the honor system.

His editorials that year were essentially conservative yet idealistic. He was no typically radical undergraduate editor. As often as not, he defended the administration attitude on special issues that arose—or at least explained it sympathetically—and drew fire from young alumni who had lived through Amherst's stormy days in the Meiklejohn era and felt that Walton was selling out to the "reactionary" element that had won and held power after Meiklejohn left.

Walton could not himself have explained very satisfactorily why he was so often a conservative spokesman. Without any deep probing into the matter, he honestly believed that he considered and studied each new problem independently as it arose, rather than from any set angle of policy. Long after, looking back and musing on this matter, he came to the conclusion that, however unconsciously, his motivation had been one part the respect for and fear of authority imbibed early, one part a certain innate cautiousness (was it really inherent?), and a third part an early intellectual maturity, an early sympathy for the adult point of view, caused, perhaps, largely through his lack of common ground with those his own age.

There was, however, one controversial matter on which he took sharp issue with both the administration and the faculty. This was the proposal to annul the Honor System in examinations—then in effect for more than a decade. This system of unproctored examinations permitted a student to leave the examination room at any time he desired and return when he wished. No one watched him work, to be sure that notes and answers were not concealed on his person or among the papers on his desk, but at the end of the examination book he must sign a pledge that stated that he had received no help of any sort during the examination and that the work in this book was his and his alone, written during the specified hours.

It was common knowledge that there was a good deal of cheating. There had been more dismissals and suspensions from college for this reason in the last two years than in the previous seven or eight— and every undergraduate knew of some cases in which the culprits were not caught. And now the president appointed a faculty committee and a student committee to report to each other and decide whether or not the system should be abandoned.

News had spread before the official announcement, however, and Walton had promptly written a stinging editorial on the regression implied in the probable abolition of the system. "The Return to Paternalism," he called it and cited, in support of his conviction that proctored examinations would lead to more cheating, the discrepancy between the ideal of national Prohibition and the resultant bootlegging actuality, as well as other dire results from various forms of coercing virtue.

He was surprised and pleased when, after this stand, the president appointed him chairman of the student committee. As it turned out, the four other boys on the committee were glad enough to have Walton determine their position and, so to speak, prepare the brief. In addition to the arguments already expounded in his editorial, he stressed in his report the effect of the proposed change as a demotion of undergraduates substantially to the status of prep school boys—too immature for self-government and ethical responsibility. He urged, as a last resort, the postponement for a year of any final decision, and the granting of an opportunity to the student government to attempt to raise undergraduate morale to such a level (which supposedly had existed when the system had been initiated) as to make the falsifying of the pledge a matter of social disgrace.

The report completed, the student committee met with the faculty committee, which had been preparing its report. First, the two reports were exchanged; then, three days later, the five men and the five boys met together.

From the moment Walton had opened and begun to read the faculty report, he had lost all but the faintest hope for the success of his cause. On the very first page, he came upon this paragraph:

> In actuality, it seems to your committee that no further reasons for the abolition of the Honor System need be adduced, once the statistics at the conclusion of this report are studied. Such a system needs an established morale, a continuing and

potent esprit de corps, an ingrained sense of noblesse oblige—
if it is to be successful. Somewhere along the way, Amherst
students have lost sight of, and touch with, this essential. We
of the faculty, as well as the administration, have been patient
with the growing number of infractions; we of the committee
do not feel that we are acting hastily or prematurely. Perhaps
another day will come, with a wholly new generation of students, when, through popular and sincere demand, a new trial
of the system may be made. But it is our conclusion that a
sufficiently large minority of the present student body has no
sense of the essential code described above, and will flout the
understanding, the "gentleman's agreement" so necessary to
the success of any Honor System, whenever the opportunity
presents itself. They have had their chance; now they must
reap the consequences of their attitude, lest the name of the
college suffer.

The logic of this position, the precision and restraint of the
language of the report were not lost on Walton. Yet these gave it a
finality that angered, even infuriated him. In the cold, definitive tone, he
saw a judgment rendered before the trial was held. And he thought that
he detected the idiom, the style and manner, of the chairman of the
faculty committee, Professor Wolfgang Herter of the department of
Physics—a man Walton felt to be a thoroughgoing Prussian.

So, when the meeting was opened and Professer Herter rose, Walton automatically stiffened.

"We have read the student report," Professor Herter stated in his
peculiarly jerky style, which accented several beats in every sentence, yet
managed, perhaps through the coldness of his manner, never to seem
excited or volatile or hurried. "And we presume that you have read that
of the faculty. These do not concur. I have canvassed the members of
the faculty committee, and none of them finds his position changed because of your arguments. Nor do I. Is it possible, however, that our
report has induced you to reverse yourselves? This seems to me a hopeful possibility. Mr. Chairman?"

His chilling china-blue eyes were fastened directly on Walton,
who rose, slowly, in his turn.

"No, Professor Herter," he replied. He was tense, rigid—angry
over what seemed to him the professor's overbearing manner. "We have
not changed our minds, either."

Mr. Herter scowled, turned to his colleagues and spread out his hands in a gesture that could have meant disdain, amusement or cynic-ism. It was probably, Walton reasoned later, not exactly any of these, but rather mild exasperation over the stubbornness of the young. But it sufficed for the moment to trigger him.

"It seems pretty clear, Professor Herter," he said hotly, "that you don't take seriously anything that students do. The whole tone of the faculty report is like that: it seems to be saying we'll abolish the Honor System, and *that's that*. I thought we were supposed to cooperate with each other, to discuss the whole thing with open minds, and really listen and try to understand. But I guess you've already made up your mind."

It was not the words, Walton realized later, that caused the uneasy or even shocked expressions on the faces of his classmates and one or two of the faculty; it was the furious, hurt and passionate tone of his voice. He had lost control of himself, and stood there, bared and wholly vulnerable. Although it was doubtful if any of the others understood the motivating force of his fierce emotionalism, all were embarrassed by it— for him and for themselves.

Mr. Herter cleared his throat. No, *he* was not embarrassed; there was a curious glint in his eyes, which were, if possible, more steely than before.

"Indeed, Mr. Herrick, we have used our minds and come to a con-clusion—which you term 'making them up.' Would you have them rust?" He made an ironic bow: Walton, in his detestation of this man, felt that he could almost hear his heels click. "As to open minds, it is an open question as to whether the phrase means more than an inability to formu-late, define and decide. But listen? Certainly we are ready to listen, if you have more to say than what is already expressed in your report."

Several professors nodded, and Bill Clements, the president of Stu-dent Council, said pleasantly, "We're sure you are, sir."

But Walton was past recall now; he *could not,* he found, retreat or retract. Something of his mother's ardor for lost causes had possessed him from the beginning; more than a little of her unyielding pride forced him on. To his dismay, he felt that he was near tears of defeat and morti-fication and anger; he felt that he was making a fool of himself, yet he must plunge on.

"I don't think you've given any real thought to our proposal for a delay and a chance to rebuild student morale," he blurted out. "To throw the system out now, on such short notice, will take the heart out of the students."

Professor Herter again bowed ironically.

"I am glad, Mr. Herrick, that you avoided the banality into which

I thought you might fall when you began. Your opening remark led me to fear that you were going to speak of throwing out the baby with the bath water. As for the suggested postponement . . ."

Walton did not really hear the rest of what he said. Nor could he sufficiently clear his head of the blood that hummed in it to concentrate on the following ten minutes of discussion. One or two of the other professors spoke in mollifying elaborations about the probable effects of abolishing the system. The students need feel no disgrace: a system had failed, not a majority of the undergraduates. It was clear that, in softer terms, they really did agree with Herter. It was obvious, moreover, that the other students were discouraged and uncertain: they said little in support of Walton's request for postponement, and accepted passively Professor Herter's eventual proposal that, wanting further discussion, they put the matter to a vote. The five faculty members and three of the boys voted for the termination of the Honor System; one boy abstained; only Walton voted a low, bitter "no."

Then he rose to his feet again.

"I should like," he said, in a voice that had gained strength and control, "to move that the student committee be empowered to submit its report separately, as a minority report, to the president."

Mr. Herter shrugged eloquently; two of the boys muttered, "Cut it out, Herrick; don't be a bad sport" and "For Christ's sake, Walt! What're you trying to do?"

"Although there has been no second to this motion," Professor Herter said, with the gleam in his eyes apparent again, "I shall put it to a vote—lest it be said later that the faculty did not give the students an adequate hearing. Will those in favor of the motion please say aye."

Walton's voice was the only one. . . .

When he received, a week later, the summons from the president, Walton's first reaction was one of alarm, even of fright. He had already experienced that first undertow of fear that always tugged him back after the full force of any violent expression of emotion. At such times, ghouls and dreads poked their unlovely heads around every corner; a footfall behind him on the night street pounded out re-tri-bu-tion; from time to time, feeling—rather than seeing—a shadow, he ducked. Yet somehow, though the experience recurred, he managed, in desperate need of at least the semblance of peace of mind, to blur his vision sufficiently to be conscious only of malaise—indigestion, perhaps, or a headache.

The summons from the president was another matter—factual, real, not to be blurred. Could it be that Professor Herter—Walton saw himself

expelled, a few months before graduation, wiring home, packing his bags
—before he sternly admonished himself for such foolish fantasies. Expelled—for, at the most, rudeness under the stress of the issue of the
Honor System! It was ridiculous: at worst he would be given a reprimand.

And then there was the personality of President Luce. Jared Luce
was a thin, spare man, a classicist who interspersed quotations from
Pliny and Lucretius in his otherwise dry, laconic New England style—
whether in presidential pronouncements or in ordinary conversation. A
shy man of utter rectitude, of gentle courtesies and conservative mien, he
was not popular with the alumni, who wanted a more spectacular leader;
with the students, most of whom found him dull; or with the faculty,
from which he had been graduated into the presidency, perhaps chiefly
because so many of them felt they would themselves have made better
administrators than this silent professor of Latin and Greek, who lacked
color, drive, stature.

But the trustees, after a stormy period in Amherst's history, had
wanted an impeccable man, a calm, sane, quiet man—and they found
him in Jared Luce. Walton was one of the few who heartily concurred
in their judgment. He had taken an advanced Latin course with Mr. Luce
in his sophomore year and found him witty, wise and just. Although he
had seen little of him in these two last years, he still counted him a
friend.

So why, he reasoned now, should he fear this appointment? For no
reason at all, he decided, but could not wholly quell his disquiet. He still
felt a need to shift uneasily in his chair during the few minutes he waited
in the outer office.

But from the moment he was admitted, to be greeted by President
Luce's handclasp and friendly smile, he was sure that all was well.

"I haven't seen as much of you these last two years, Herrick, as I
had hoped I would. But we've both been busy—at new tasks. Please sit
down. I hope you've found your job stimulating, and less difficult than
I've found mine."

Walton experienced that familiar feeling he sometimes called having
his ribs fall into place. This was a good man—that rare thing, a completely trustworthy man.

"It's been difficult enough," he said. "Though I don't think any
part of the work on the paper has been as trying as this recent task you
appointed me to—the chairmanship of the Committee on the Honor
System."

He had literally not known that he was going to mention this—and only now did he realize that it had been inevitable: that this thought, these words had been so constantly repressed, so close to the surface, ever since the meeting with the faculty committee, that they had been sure to come out, sooner or later.

President Luce looked quizzical and attentive. He always sat primly, Walton realized again now; it was as though there were no position in which he really could be comfortable. In the silence they shared now, the thought that, if his conjecture were even approximately true, then life must be a torment to this man flitted across Walton's mind. Torment? How incongruous a thought about the placid, even president!

Mr. Luce cleared his throat; it was a dry little sound.

"You found it so difficult?" he inquired.

"Yes. I got awfully intense about it, Mr. Luce," Walton replied, "and I think I made a fool of myself."

There: a weight lifted from him. There were few people to whom he could speak so directly.

The president smiled.

"I have had no report to that effect," he said quietly. "Professor Herter informed me that the student committee was not happy about the decision, but he singled out no one, mentioned no particular individual reaction."

Walton looked at him incredulously.

"He didn't? Why—I thought—he seemed to me—I don't know, both hostile from the beginning and triumphant. I felt that he not only had decisively made up his mind that the Honor System must go, but that he took an immense satisfaction in seeing it go."

President Luce tapped his fingers briskly on the desk. Then he looked up and directly at Walton; those usually mild and benign eyes were fixed intently upon him, with an unusual sharpness.

"Then you have misjudged Mr. Herter," he said firmly. " 'Nemo repente fit turpissimus': 'no man ever became extremely wicked all at once.' I have known Wolfgang Herter as a colleague for twelve years, and I have always found him an earnest and just man. Some parochial demon drives him occasionally to a harsher utterance, I suspect, than his mind and heart endorse. But we all have those imperfections. No, Herter is a good man."

He lapsed into silence again, gazed out the window at the budding trees, and his expression softened. "That was Juvenal, *Second Satire*," he remarked almost dreamily.

"You miss your classes, don't you, sir?" Walton said suddenly.

The president turned in his chair, regarded him with a look of surprise and amusement.

"You're a very perceptive young man, Mr. Herrick," he said dryly. "Yes. I miss my classes—and I miss the reading and thought that go into scholarship." He paused again, then straightened up briskly. "But I haven't asked you to come to discuss my problems. You know, I'm sure, about our Pearson Fellowship, awarded each year to that outstanding member of the senior class who seems, in the opinion of the president and the faculty committee that awards the fellowship, 'most likely to benefit from two years of study at Oxford University, and, through his residence and work there, to do honor and bring respect to Amherst College.' I have asked you here to find out whether you would be able and inclined to accept this fellowship, were it granted to you. I have already informed the committee that you are my personal choice for this year."

It was a long and ringing silence. For its duration Walton realized that he had never questioned the necessity and inevitability of his returning to Cleveland after Commencement. As he thought of it long after, he had been on lend-lease for four years, that was all, granted a reprieve for that length of time because, after all, one did go to college. He would of course return home to take care of his family; they needed him. Yet it had been as though, by giving no heed to the question as to how he was going to earn his living—his father had written him twice, gently but urgently, on the subject, yet he had made no practical move— he believed he could hold off the eventuality indefinitely. But because it had been so surely a matter of returning to Cleveland he had never thought of himself as a candidate for the Pearson Fellowship; had indeed, perhaps, not thought of it at all.

At last, slowly, he began to reply.

"I don't know what to say, Mr. Luce. Of course I'm proud, and honored, that you have chosen me. And the idea of going seems wonderful. But I don't think I can; I—I've always taken it for granted that I'd go back to Cleveland."

The president frowned in perplexity.

"Why?" he asked simply.

Walton told him—at first haltingly, with some embarrassment, but as he went on, more easily. He told him William Herrick's story, told him of Elinor's illness and as yet still undefined collapse, echoed, with an awareness of its nature that made him uncomfortable, his mother's own account of her precarious health, the heavy burden of Elinor and of having a husband unable to shoulder the usual man's load, told of their certain counting on him to make the way easier, to support and comfort them. As he talked, he realized that he himself could not distinguish, could not disentangle, the elements in his story that really moved him, and those possessed of an obligatory, almost automatic quality: the memorized account he felt compelled to give from time to time, partly to defend the family, but also partly to—to what? To paralyze his own feelings, he had been going to think.

When at last he was done, he again confronted President Luce; it was as though, while talking, he had been alone, telling his beads—but not before an altar, rather to a massive stone wall.

The president shifted in his chair, regarded Walton gravely.

"Have you thought," he asked softly, "of giving your family the opportunity to have a voice in this decision? Isn't it possible that, if you say no now, without consulting them, you'll be doing them an injustice —that it may actually make them unhappy to learn at a later date that you refused such an opportunity, invoking them, without giving them a chance to decide for themselves and act, too? However unusual your family situation, Herrick, parents find an unparalleled satisfaction in contributing to the building of their children's lives."

Walton shook his head; he could only hope that the action did not look as final as he felt the situation to be.

"I won't say no now, Mr. Luce," he replied, "if I may have a couple of days to think it over. And perhaps I'll call them, but I don't think so. Under the circumstances, it doesn't seem fair to me to put it up to them."

Mr. Luce nodded and folded his hands in his lap.

"Very well. You may have a week before I must ask for your decision. One more thing, Herrick. If you do return to Cleveland, what will you be doing? Have you already committed yourself to a job?"

Walton hesitated, felt a flush seeping into his cheeks.

"No, sir," he said, almost reluctantly. "I've been remiss about that. I think I want to teach, though. I was going to begin my inquiries right away. Now I'll wait just long enough to make my decision about the fellowship."

Mr. Luce nodded, stood up. It suddenly seemed to Walton that the president was a taller man than he had ever realized and that there was a—he didn't know—an aura of authority about him that Walton had not noticed before.

"There is a passage in Epictetus," Mr. Luce said softly, "that, translated colloquially, might read, 'Difficulties are things that show what men are.' This is a difficult time for you, Herrick, and you have a difficult choice to make. I shall be thinking of you during this week, and wishing you a steady judgment. And—" he paused and Walton, about to leave, looked at him intently again, arrested by the sudden deepening of the tone of the president's voice—"and, whatever your decision, I want you to remember that I am your friend."

Walton had his conversation with the president on a Thursday; the following Tuesday he wrote him a note and delivered it to his secretary:

DEAR PRESIDENT LUCE—

I know that you will think my decision foolish, but I have decided that I must say no to the Pearson Fellowship. I have thought of little else since I saw you; often I was on the verge of calling my parents, but I did not. I am doing what my conscience tells me is right, though I feel sad about it. One thing I hope very much is that you will not think I am unappreciative of the honor you were ready to bestow on me.

Sincerely,
WALTON HERRICK

On Thursday he had a reply from President Luce:

DEAR HERRICK:

Indeed I am under no misapprehension regarding any failure on your part to be grateful for a chance at the Pearson. You made your position perfectly clear. And you know your situation and your obligations best. It would be impertinent of me to judge the merits of your decision. I am disappointed for Amherst's sake; I wish you all success and fulfillment in whatever you undertake.

Faithfully yours,
JARED LUCE

P.S. As Marcus Aurelius says in his *Meditations,* "A man makes no noise over a good deed, but passes on to another as a vine to bear grapes again in season."

Walton wrote to friends in Cleveland, to inquire about a teaching job; to his father; to various superintendents and principals of schools. Early replies were discouraging, but only ten days after his exchange with President Luce he received another communication from the president's office:

DEAR HERRICK:

If you have not already found your post in Cleveland for next year, please come to my office on Friday at 3:30. I know of something that may interest you.

Faithfully yours,

JARED LUCE

It was evident that President Luce was excited beyond his wont. In some peculiar fashion, it heightened his shyness: for several minutes after Walton entered his office, he simply stood there in silence, his eyes bright with pleasure.

"A curious thing," he finally began. "A most curious thing has occurred, Herrick. Sit down. Sit down. I have high hopes for this."

Again Walton observed the rigidity of Mr. Luce's posture; now it seemed to him that the president's hands were trembling. But he could not be sure; he was himself too excited to trust the accuracy of any observation he made.

"One of our most generous alumni," the president resumed, "is Henry D. L. Cotterill of the class of 1888, a man now in his middle sixties, something of a recluse, a man of means who has spent a great deal of his life in a scholarly fashion, working on some opus magnum the nature of which, so far as I know, he has revealed to no one. Mr. Cotterill has long made his home in Cleveland—Cleveland Heights, I believe—and perhaps you have heard of him."

The unusual name had hit its mark instantly: Walton visualized clearly the forbidding gray stone fortress set back from the long boulevard, known locally always at Cotterill's Castle.

"Yes, I've heard his name," he said.

President Luce crossed one leg over the other, only to shift back almost immediately to his usual prim position, both feet firmly on the floor, knees bent and touching, torso stiff and straight.

"You may well have heard it here, too," he remarked. "Cotterill's gifts to the college have been munificent, although always sharply limited to his specifications—and these in turn so related to his special interests as to make the gifts or awards less useful or appropriate than I could wish them to be. For instance, the Cotterill Prize for Medieval Studies, to be awarded annually in the amount of $1,000, a large sum for an undergraduate, has gone begging more often than not because the specifications require that the work done must be on some secular aspect of the Middle Ages, and entice few students."

"Or the Cotterill Fellowship for study in the Harvard Graduate School, a sufficient reimbursement for three years of advanced work, but stipulating that the recipient must direct his central effort to the Abbé de Brantôme, that not always edifying figure of the sixteenth century, known chiefly for what is sometimes called in the English version *Tales of Fair and Gallant Ladies,* and withal—ethical strictures to one side— a rather insignificant figure in the great annals of European literature. So generous a sponsor and so lighthearted a subject do not, to be sure, go begging. Three Amherst graduates have been Cotterill Fellows at Harvard since this grant was initiated a decade ago. The trouble here is of a different nature from that of the forbidding Prize for Medieval Studies: how many dissertations of value can be gleaned from the good Abbé's interest in erotic matters? In both cases, the range prescribed is insufficiently broad and representative."

He rose and began walking slowly back and forth, hands clasped behind his back.

"And so it goes. So it goes. He offered us not long ago $250,000 for a new humanities building, sorely needed, but so prescribed it architecturally that the trustees are still undecided as to whether or not to accept the gift. He insists that it should be a single story in height and octagonal in shape. It would sit on our campus, amongst buildings already sufficiently diverse, like some squat monster from another world."

He paused again, regarded Walton significantly.

"I tell you all this, Herrick, that you may have some measure of what I can only call the man's willfulness. His outlines remain shadowy; he does not attend his class reunions or, indeed, visit Amherst at all; I have never met him. Yet he is disposed to do you a great deal of good."

Once more President Luce paused, moved toward his chair as though to be seated but, apparently thinking better of it, swung around and continued, still standing.

"He has written to me and signified his desire to employ, beginning in September, some graduate of this year's class who wishes to continue his studies and attain further degrees—to employ this student as a secretary to assist him in his own research. In return, he will pay the student's tuition to enable him to attend graduate classes in Cleveland at Western Reserve University, looking toward the degree of Master of Arts, and also pay him a handsome salary of $2,500 per annum, for a minimum of three hours' work a day—the only stipulation being that the student shall continue his academic work within the field of the humanities."

The president ceased his pacing directly in front of Walton.

"Having assumed that your declination of the Pearson Fellowship did not indicate, *eo ipso,* a desire to abandon further studies if this could be avoided, the prospects seem to me particularly salutary for you. You could achieve your master's degree in a year or two, earn a good salary, and still be with, or near, your family, contributing materially to their welfare. Do you agree?"

It was now that Walton saw a subtle but unmistakable change in the president's manner. A new quality was unmistakably there, not easy to define, but, in its very ambiguity, challenging to explore. It was not a pleading quality (why should Mr. Luce plead with him?), yet there almost seemed to be something of supplication in it, some vague fear of Walton's refusing the offer, as though such a refusal would be a personal rejection. But how could this be the meaning of the president's expression?

Then Walton said simply, "It sounds like the perfect solution for me, President Luce. I can't tell you how grateful I am for your thoughtfulness and help," and with these conventional and appropriate words, offered with the open sincerity and deference that Walton was learning unconsciously to employ with skill and conviction in such situations—it was not a false manner, a contrived appearance of candor, but it lacked spontaneity, was somehow disingenuous—with this reply the president's evident uneasiness vanished.

"Excellent," he said. "Excellent. I'm much relieved." Then he seemed to hear his own words and find them inappropriate, for he hurried on. "You must be prepared to find Mr. Cotterill eccentric, perhaps even cranky and intractable. But you will soon learn how to deal with that. And while the prospects do not have the grandeur of those at Oxford, remember: 'Omne ignotum pro magnifico'—'Everything that is unknown is taken to be grand.' Tacitus, *Agricola,* 30. There may be as much valuable and nourishing in the humbler setting in Ohio—and you will also have satisfied your conscience with regard to your family responsibilities. Splendid. Splendid."

On his slow walk back to his room, Walton's first thoughts were that what the president had never understood was that he had not sacrificed anything: that since he had never really for one moment felt that he *could* go to Oxford, *he had not had to give it up.* And then his mind drifted back to the moment before he had said yes to the Cotterill proposition—back to the president's strange manner at that moment. In a sudden clarity, he felt that he understood. The proposal had gone from Mr. Luce to Cotterill, been agreed upon and then presented to Walton. The chance the president had taken was that, if Walton did not accept, he would be forced to go back in a rather uncomfortable guise to Mr. Cotterill and explain that it was all a mistake.

Walton stopped, stood still for a long minute, rooted where he was in gratitude and affection for the kindness of this strange, enigmatic man who was the president of his college. For some intimation came to him now of a passionate and tormented inner life behind the dry, cool exterior. What had Mr. Luce said of Professor Herter? "Some parochial demon drives him occasionally. . . . But we all have these imperfections."

And we must all appease them, Walton thought abruptly—appease them or ourselves. He did not know, could not know the real nature of President Luce's inner stress, but he felt sure now that what he had thought of as a supplicating manner was not related, after all, to a concern over telling Mr. Cotterill that the student in question did not want such a job after all; rather, it was a need to have this offering accepted. And understanding even this much, he experienced for a moment a humbler appreciation of his good fortune than he had known before.

Why me? he thought suddenly for the first time. Why me? He did not know, but now he could look ahead to Life, not with excitement or any sense of adventure, but with the security of knowing that he had a place in it.

And then, the very next weekend, he met Joanna Gaylord.

[*Part Four*]   *8*

ON that exquisite May afternoon, Walton first saw her leaning slightly, it seemed to him, on a vertical shaft, a rectangle almost, of sunlit air. It was cut as cleanly as a picture frame, the illusion curiously fashioned by an opening in the budding boughs of the large maple tree beside her. Her head was lifted inquiringly toward some point above her, where the first large branches met the trunk of the great tree. Her delicate, graceful body was tilted in inquiry, and her profile, in contemplative repose, suggested to Walton a gentleness, a young peacefulness, that touched him painfully. In an unprecedented rush of feeling that made his eyes smart with tears, he thought longingly how quiet it would be with this girl before him, how there would be time for silence and thought and long, slow walks that need not lead anywhere. For waking and meditating, with no necessity to hurry, for a sequence of slow and rhythmic days that he had never known.

And then, in reaction, he felt an overwhelming fatigue wash over him. The endless turmoil and strain and activity in which he lived (lived? was caught up and swept along, kicking and tossing and cursing) seemed to him now finally unbearable.

Then, at last, she turned her head and regarded him gravely. Her pale, oval, slightly elongated face beneath the straight, dully shining wheat-colored hair, parted precisely and evenly in the middle, awoke a dancing recognition in him. It was a Renaissance face, not quite the Botticelli Venus, but of a like quality—with a serenity that might be coerced into meekness, a sweetness and depth of sensitivity that, frightened, might disintegrate into submissiveness and ineffectuality—

Why was he thinking so strangely, as though he were charting her unhappy future? And from where did these cryptic insights come? He stood there, staring at her, with an incoherent hot flood of surmises swirling in his mind, until she spoke.

"I've been looking up there. I wonder if it's a new nest. Do robins build nests so early? Or some other bird?"

Her voice was fragile; it had no resonance, but sounded as though it came from high in her throat. Yet it was not soprano—rather a forced, short-breathed contralto—and despite its lack of strength, had its own delicate beauty. Bells, Walton thought.

"I don't know," he replied, very seriously—it seemed to him wholly unimaginatively. "I don't know anything about birds." And then, surprisingly, he remembered that this was not quite true: "That is, about their nests. I was interested in birds when I was very young, and I still know a lot of them by sight."

She smiled—an enchanting smile, he thought: a gift, an expression of trust, but not without humor.

"And now you aren't very young any more?"

He smiled in return and shook his head. "Young, perhaps, but not very. Let's take a walk."

That was how it began—because the president had enabled him to solve his postgraduation problems and, temporarily relieved of conflicts and worries, he had finally attended a fraternity dance. But no such matter-of-fact description of cause and effect, motivation and consequence, coincidence of time and place and person, adequately described coming to know Joanna Gaylord.

At last, he thought, without any awareness of repetitiveness, here in bald, irrefutable, empirical actuality, he had encountered the elusive substance of his early and enduring romantic dreams. She moves like poetry, he thought again and again, as the weeks passed and he saw more of her. He found seductive the strange, shy, halting but never awkward rhythms and nuances of her speech. She had no capacity for the trivialities of small talk; in the midst of a group's discussion of a forthcoming party, summer plans, a baseball game or where to have dinner, she would turn to Walton and point out a wild flower growing nearby; tell him—without preamble—of an experience she had had in the Arizona desert when a child; or quote a saying of Gautama Buddha's, not in comment on the present context, but rather in reply to something he had said two weeks before.

What saved all this from being precious or fey or "arty" in Walton's increasingly critical code book (in which some beginning skeptical sturdiness was developing) was her complete lack of facility or pretentiousness of any sort. Before uttering one of her unexpected remarks, dropping her exotic observation into the buzz of conventional chatter and, since directing it exclusively to Walton, never interrupting the main stream of conversation, she would swallow, as though there were an obstruction in her throat that must be pushed aside to permit the passage of words. Pondering on this, Walton decided, with rash inclusiveness, that he would never again trust the genuineness of anyone who could speak facilely—that the command of an easy flow of speech was equivalent to insincerity.

There was another element in Joanna's hesitancy, however, that occasionally disturbed, even alarmed Walton. It was the suggestion of fear—of a timidity, engendered by what real or imagined rebuffs he did not know, that anticipated a contemptuous if not hostile reception, that intimated a preknowledge that what she had to say, or the very fact that *she* said it, would make it alien, unacceptable to others.

Or was he wrong, he wondered, and did the hesitancy, the timidity, mean rather a lack of faith in the audience—in the sensitiveness of his own receptivity, for example? No. It could not be *that,* for the alarm he felt was induced by his realization of her complete and almost immediate acceptance of him as one—*the* one, he sometimes thought—who did understand her; more, whose understanding exceeded her own, so that she would bring him what she had discovered as one might lay an offering on an altar.

While this aroused all his not inconsiderable capacity for protectiveness, for championing those who came to him in trust and confidence, his family had already drained sufficient of this reservoir for him to feel an uneasiness now, confronted by another with such a need. Yet what actually went on in his mind was the realization of an ambivalent burden, one which threatened to weigh too much and therefore, and simultaneously, challenged him to assume the mantle of protector: so much needed, he felt, in an unfriendly world—and so hard to find.

Still another doubt assailed him during this swift and golden month, in which he contrived to see her as often as he could. She was the princess, from every bit as remote a planet as those inhabited by the shadowy girls of his adolescent dreams. She had their grace, their adoration—no, remembering the blue eloquence of her large eyes, the word was not an exaggeration—of him, their delicacy and charm. What she did not have was their submissive and eager sensuality. Nubile she certainly was, but in a way that Walton chose hopefully to consider somnolent, unawakened. Her kisses, proffered shyly for the first time in the dusk of late May, were—after his experience with Irene—startlingly chaste; and yet again, perhaps because he chose to do so, he found in them a feathery suggestiveness that excited him. And, if he also felt a peculiar reluctance to pursue matters beyond these fleeting kisses, on consideration he decided that the cause lay in his reaction to the excessive sexuality of his relation to Irene and its dissolution in fracases and rejection. In a curious way, it now seemed to him as though the whole affair with Irene had not been real, but another long fantasy. And surely, given his fascination with Joanna, the outcome, in whatever form, could not fail to be a happy one. Was she not, at last, the princess realized?

She was also, though he gave less thought to so mundane a résumé, a senior at Wellesley College, one hundred miles from Amherst, a creditable though not outstanding student; a shy, dreamy, not uncomfortably lonely girl little known to her classmates; the daughter of Professor Seth Gaylord of the Department of Geology at Hobart College, a scholarly widower who cherished her, his only child, with a reticent laissez-faire affection; and in a vague way she intended, upon her graduation from college, to keep house for him.

Barely twenty years old, so some six months' Walton's junior, she seemed sometimes as wise and mature as a Delphic priestess, sometimes essentially still a child. She reveled privately and secretly in the poetry of Emily Dickinson, in what she had read of the Eastern scriptures, and in dreams of her own, of which even Walton saw only corners and tiny segments, as she raised for a transient moment the curtain that usually concealed them. She exulted openly in all flowers, shrubs and flowering bushes, in classical music, in children—whom she regarded not at all with a maternal or even adult eye, but as her true confrères, citizens of a kingdom of Heaven which she could not define but which, it seemed to Walton, she inhabited whenever genuinely happy.

The three weeks of May remaining after Walton first met Joanna were inevitably, since the concluding ones of the final college semester for both of them, among the most crowded of the calendar. Yet, after that first walk out into the countryside (they stayed, forgetting altogether Joanna's obligation to her escort at the dance, for two hours), everything else in their schedule was secondary to their sudden, immediate and absolute absorption in each other.

What was said on that first walk? What, in effect, happened? Walton was later to wonder himself just what element in those two hours made their memory at once so poignant and so tenacious. It eluded his grasp; he remembered precisely and graphically only her sitting under a yellow willow tree, and looking at him with that grave, inquiring glance that filled him both with pride and uneasiness.

To be sure, they talked—told each other the contexts and events of their lives. She listened, wide-eyed and genuinely pained, to the story of the difficulties of his family and his sense of obligation to them, told perhaps the most honestly it had ever been. He listened to her recital of the cloistered life she led with her father, after her mother's death, (sufficiently early for it to have for her the wistful quality of a delicate pastiche, touched only faintly with grief)—listened, to this tale with a feeling that it was drenched in peace, as quiet and unhurried and drowsily comforting as a village green on a summer afternoon.

And they shared, equally and responsively, as each asked of the other what were his hopes and plans, an awkward silence, a faltering and vague reply and then delighted laughter. Neither knew what he wanted from his life; each was comforted to find the other so uncertain. Each, Walton realized, in sudden understanding that sent a flare of warning up in his mind, had led, in different ways, a limited, confined and sheltered life: neither had sufficient adventurousness to yearn to explore beyond familiar territory. They might conceive wistfully of such a possibility, but that was all: each found compensation in retreating inward.

But she did not know this about him, Walton realized with a peculiar mixture of panic and exultancy. To her, his achievements in college meant that he had an outgoing, even daring aggressiveness that constituted the central basis for her admiration, even easy worship of him. To be at home both in the outer world of activity, the rough-and-tumble of competition, and in the quiet and sensitive one of apperceptions—this was, for her, his unique quality.

All this, of course, not at that first meeting, but as the weeks passed. Walton might groan at the discrepancy between her vision of him and the actuality, yet it also gave him strength and pride and a fierce determination to approximate more nearly her evaluation. And above all else, security—a point of departure, a home-bred confidence in his own substance and potential, from which to sally out and *try*. With this (it seemed to him entirely new) support, he found it comparatively easy to give no more than a moment's attention to the lonely night signals, the sky rockets that continued from time to time to light up, briefly and luridly, in sinister admonition, his otherwise peaceful and exalted meditations about Joanna and himself.

It was perhaps not wholly naïve of Joanna to think of him as a doer, a man who overcame obstacles—real, hard, physical, factual ones. By this time in senior year, he had no activities weighing on him except the preparations for final examinations. The obstacle he met then, in seeing her regularly, was not one of tasks and obligations, but simply that of the distance between them, the lack of a car and of any considerable funds. It was the way in which he managed to circumvent these difficulties that constituted his achievement, for her.

This he accomplished in a variety of ways. Fortunately, there were several classmates who drove to Wellesley with some regularity, to see girls at the college or at nearby Dana Hall or Pine Manor. Walton kept a close watch on their schedules, and went along, sharing expenses, on two weekends and twice in the middle of the week, staying at a tumble-down rooming house in Wellesley for from one night to three. When they failed, he hitchhiked or, on one occasion, took a long, dreary all-night excursion on a milk train.

Both of these ways of travel contained their small triumphs, totted up new items on the slowly and cautiously growing account of manhood. Hitchhike he had before, but always with several other fellows from Amherst. As he set out for the first time alone, all the scareheads he had assimilated at home over the dangers of this practice, the thefts and murders and other brutalities of the open road, swarmed through his mind. And he was, after all, no hero. This salient and central knowledge was always with him, and he waited, for his first thumbing of a ride, until he saw a solitary woman driver approaching him.

She was cheerful and pleasant and matter-of-fact; he next hailed a conventional-looking family. Courage grew, and by the end of the second trip he had ridden several trucks and seedy-looking cars carrying only men.

What was the harvest? The realization that people—anonymous people at large—were neither desperadoes nor raucous deriders of what he considered his own obvious shortcomings. No one was waiting for the chance to jeer at him—no one but himself.

And this realization grew into something more positive when, at ten o'clock one Friday night, he persuaded one of the train crew to accept him as a passenger on the slow local milk train. A working passenger—for through the night he helped this man unload the heavy cans, learned to tilt, roll and lower them: learned more than he had ever known before about the silent comradeship of shared labor. Then, at six in the morning, as the train grunted slowly into the Wellesley station, the two, equally dirty and sweat-stained, clasped hands for a moment before Walton jumped down to the station platform.

"So long, kid. Good luck."

The words kept echoing in his head as he trudged wearily through the streets to Mrs. Waters' rooming house. They continued as a leitmotif to his thoughts while bathing and shaving and dressing. As he ascended the hill leading to the campus, he found that although he was whistling a popular tune the lyric he fitted to it ran, "So long, kid. Good luck."

And when he sat over breakfast at a little table across from Joanna, he felt, without any conscious articulation of it, even to himself, that a man's body was sitting in his chair, that the hands holding the knife and fork were a man's hands, and that for the first time he was looking at Joanna with a man's eyes.

Looking at Joanna . . . It was not, it seemed to him now, only he who had changed. A flush animated her usual pallor—an ivory pallor, to be sure, in which Walton found a deep aesthetic satisfaction. But this delicate color, its faint rosiness, lent new life to the exquisite image—new life and womanliness. Touched off by his own assurance, by the excitement of this surprise visit—for he had given her no warning—or by whatever combination of forces at play in that attic room of her imagination (so he thought of that intensely private inner existence of hers, that would bubble up so unexpectedly in the midst of some even, uninspired and negligible conversation: as taking place in a locked and unviolated attic room, half necromancer's study, half little girl's play-room—but wholly exquisite, virginal, fresh and cool)—affected by whatever cause or causes, the girl had become a woman. Still fragile, spirituelle, but in her own delicate way a spirited woman.

And through that long and deliciously warm and drowsy day, it came to Walton that it was actually possible to realize in fact, in action, in perpetuity, the dream that his first vision of Joanna had stirred into life. How quiet it would be with this girl, he had thought then, seeing her framed in the shaft of afternoon sunlight. And now: how satisfying, how fulfilling, to be with this woman—to share her imaginative perceptions, her gentle joys, and as well to draw her, slowly, with tenderness and care, into a full immersion in the currents of sensuality.

These meditations in a sun-flecked grove of trees on the bank of the campus lake, lying back on a soft growth of moss, side by side in the somnolent hum of midafternoon. And if a shadow, no more extended than the passage of a thin trailer of cloud across the sun, flickered over him then, remembering his earlier fears and recognizing the emphasis upon the *tenderness and care* with which he would initiate her into the intimacies of their life together—if a moment's premonition darkened this sun-drenched afternoon, he turned and saw her, drowsy, relaxed, even dewy, and was reassured. For the miracle of this new bloom and down on her held true, still rounded and softened the semiangularity that had been, he felt sure now, only her virginal remoteness.

Under the intentness of his scrutiny, she blushed but smiled. And now it seemed to him that with her unaccustomed rosiness, her dewiness, this new ripeness that was more an aura of her awakened happiness than a physical reality shaped and expressed in the curves of her slender body and young flesh—now it seemed to him that they had reached some sunny hilltop he had long envisioned, after a difficult and often hesitant climb. He rolled over and took her in his arms.

Joanna's responsiveness was, to Walton, unique. When he and Irene had lain in each other's arms, he had been aware always of her hunger, her desperate searching, almost her pain, in this cleaving of flesh to flesh—and it had affected him with an equal urgency, and yet too with fear, it seemed to him later, fear that he could not satisfy so furious and demanding a passion. But with Joanna, here, now, it was like dancing—at once innocent and freer. As his kiss deepened and lengthened, she responded, content to follow, yet making—by instinct only, surely—of her giving, her response, a separate complementary act of faith and commitment.

Walton's embrace tightened; his hands roamed over her as he had never allowed them to before—had neither dared nor felt the urgent need to. And still she responded; her hand followed his and confirmed its action. The acceleration of her breath excited him; the acceptance in her eyes deepened; and her slim body moved in a sweet agitation against his.

Until the sudden crashing of heavy footsteps through the undergrowth of last autumn's branches pried them apart in abrupt apprehensiveness, to stare, wide-eyed, at each other and then around them. They saw no more than a large, blurred figure moving away, then heard his laugh and a girl's voice saying, "You have to walk softly, even when you carry a big stick."

Walton, as quickly relaxed, turned back to Joanna, but she drew away, seemed almost to shrink from him. The fear was still in her eyes —or was it shame, or guilt? She had withdrawn, he saw instantly, into that protective remoteness from which she had emerged only that morning.

"Baby," he said softly. "Jo, darling. Don't let it upset you."

She shook her head, not, it seemed to him, as a negative gesture, but as though dazed and trying to recover her wits. She started to speak, but although her lips formed words, she made no sound.

Walton reached out to draw her close, but although she did not shrink back again she would not permit him to draw her to him—so that his hand remained on her shoulder with a space still between them, leaving him in so strained and awkward a position that he was forced to release her.

"Joanna," he said reproachfully. "Come back. Where have you gone? It was just an accident; he didn't know we were here."

She looked at him intently then, with so rapt and prolonged a gaze that he became uneasy. Vague premonitions of disaster swept and swooped and swerved through his mind: a series of disconnected images and scenes, all threatening to Joanna, all suggestive of her vulnerability: her extreme, unbearably raw sensitivity to everything harsh, loud, brutal, cynical. Catherine on the wheel—the night behind his closed eyelids was filled with the lurid light that disclosed these fantasies.

All in a moment; all in response to the shock and terror and pain in her eyes—and then, understanding no more, he was filled with a protective indignation and tenderness. And this time, when he drew her close, held her with his arms around her and her head on his shoulder, she did not resist, but rather clung to him. The lover had become the guardian, the champion, the father.

After what seemed to Walton a long time, she lifted her face and said, slowly and painfully, "I can't—explain. Maybe—sometime—but not now." And then, in a sudden tumbling, anguished rush of words, "But I was so happy. I was so happy. I was—"

And tears.

This fragile body shaking in his arms, the desperate need and trust with which she clutched him, the soft, tear-streaked face in childlike contortion—these. Walton felt his chest swell with tenderness and power.

"Sweetheart," he said at last. "Little Jo, never mind. Never mind. I'll take care of you." And then, with a suddenness that startled him— so that he listened to the words hanging there, it seemed to him, in sibilant, whispering echo on the golden, fragrant air, lingering there in perpetuity for later lovers who might listen in the same remote, in-toxicated wonder that he felt, hearing them: "Joanna, let's be married. Let me really take care of you. You'll be happy again—the way you were. We'll be happy. Let's be married, right after Commencement."

She stopped sobbing and lay still in his arms. So still that it seemed to Walton he could hear every sound in the many miles surrounding them: the lisping dialogue of the first leaves and the young breeze that had wandered along, the individual accents of single insects moving contentedly, in desultory comfort, from blossom to early blossom, the plaintive meaningless yap of a dog, distant footsteps on dead autumnal branches, scuffing through leaves; and yes, the very immemorial creak and groan of the round earth itself, turning on its sound but rusted axis, tried, tested, but stained and crusted with the barnacles of outer space. Stillness.

And then, finally, she stirred and tightened even more her hold on him.

"Yes," she whispered. "I want to, but, Walton, we can't. Father and your family and we don't have any money and it's too soon and—oh, everything." She snuggled closer, trying, it seemed, to burrow her face through his jacket, shirt, his very skin, for refuge within, there where the blood beat its steady course through him. "But I want to."

Family . . . money . . . For a moment, his determination faltered; he felt the familiar reins tighten on him, in him; his whole purpose stammered.

She felt it, released him and sat up, regarding him gravely, searchingly, strangely dignified by her tear-smeared face, and at the same time so intense, so urgent as to be almost frightening.

"And there's me," she said. "I'm queer—I don't know, sometimes it seems to me crazy, really. And so afraid of so many things. You don't know, and I can't tell even you."

Walton felt his new surge of resolution like some triumphal martial music.

"I don't need to know," he said—and it seemed to him that his voice rang with power. "I know enough. And we can be good to our families while still having lives of our own. And I have money for the summer from what I made this year on the paper. We'll do it, right after Commencement. And you won't be afraid any more."

She was in his arms again, her love and gratitude storming him; he suddenly knew for the first time how what seemed to be strength could feel quite helpless and overwhelmed by militant weakness. And his hand, stroking the silken hair as she whispered, "I feel so safe," seemed somehow to have lost its capacity to feel: there was, he realized, no sensation in it. He had to look to make sure that it was still moving in that gentle, rhythmical motion.

But so their plans stood late that evening when, both subdued, he quietly kissed her good night and made his way back to the village and the rooming house. And so, still, throughout the long rainy Sunday that followed, a strangely uneven, ragged, ominous day, breaking into weeks of sunshine. During much of it they sat huddled, it seemed to Walton (against what threat?), in a silence interrupted only by one or the other saying, "Are you sure?" or "Don't you think?" or "If we waited?" and instant reassurance, hot hands caught and tangled, a straining together, and the long desperate kisses, it would seem, of lovers about to be parted forever.

It was Walton who offered most of the reassurances, but when, late that night on the glistening roadside drenched in the now-abated rain, he stood alone, signaling for a ride, all the desolations of doubt filled him. The dreamlike moment was over— the ecstasy and the power vanished. Now, soon, he must face Marcia and the ineluctable facts of his life.

Marcia Nicholson came down on the Amherst Commencement like the Assyrian. Her purposefulness and powerful determination were evident as she stepped from the train in Springfield: vigilant custodian of Elinor and William; autocratic director of the logistics of luggage— indeed, commander-in-chief of the whole expeditionary force. For a fleeting moment, Walton, meeting his family with a painfully bewildering mixture of emotions, searched for the cocked colonial hat of the first American army—in so persuasive an illusion did he see, under the unfashionable black straw hat with the single white feather and jet hat pin, the lineaments of the Father of Our Country (Was this a whisper from the great collective unconscious that we have become a matriarchy?) landing at Trenton, enduring at Valley Forge, arriving for the ultimate meeting with Cornwallis.

What particular fortifications was she storming? Walton wondered uneasily as he dutifully kissed her and then Elinor, who greeted him with the automatic smile and the little tottering step that were the insignia of her disease, and with a stranglingly tight embrace that was the token of her genuine feeling for him. Finally his father, and for Walton the real greeting—quiet, warm, simple. When they first appeared, Walton had been momentarily distracted from his speculation about Marcia by the sight of his father, leaning on his cane, off to one side of the central grouping of Marcia, obsequious porters and hostile conductor, and by the ambiguous subtleties of his expression: patience? amusement? a prayer for the strength for tolerant forbearance?

But what was on Marcia's mind? As the strange procession made its way to Ez Barker's car, Walton's attention was pulled away from its embarrassing (since they were the fixed object of all observers) progress to a consideration of that familiar set, grimly determined expression. Could she know? How could she know? And how could he, aged twenty, about to take his diploma and embark on manhood, still quail inwardly over this manifestation of displeasure in a sixty-year-old woman, dressed in black neither elegant nor dowdy, but individualistically old-fashioned, a woman who still wore high dickies and spats over oxfords and whose rather fine features lost their distinctive caste only, ironically, through being set in an expression of such defiant haughtiness as to tempt parody? How could she so affect him? What was this power?

He did not know, and he realized at this moment that he also did not know whether he preferred Scylla or Charybdis. If Marcia had somehow, by whatever unpredictable prescience, guessed at his intent to marry Joanna, he knew that the next few days would be dominated exclusively by a struggle between her and himself. This might be true anyway, but more surely if she were forewarned. If, however, he could postpone any announcement of his and Joanna's plans until Commencement was over, then the central conflict of these next days would be an interior one between his hard-won determination so to devote himself to his family as to make their stay a genuinely happy and memorable one, and his dread of the appraisal and speculation of all of Amherst, confronted with his family.

His crippled family, he thought. The comparatively new fierce tenderness he felt for his father, up there ahead, dragging his bent legs along beside Ez's slow, attentive gait (all the rancors of senior year's estrangement from Ez vanished, melted, as Walton observed the respect and friendliness Ez showed his father, noted how Ez, the self-conscious, seemed completely at ease despite the many staring eyes and gaping mouths)—this tenderness would see Walton through the shrinking panic that he knew he would feel when he and William walked across the ball field to attend the Commencement game.

But, despite the attrition of much guilt, there was not the balancing, compensatory love and sustaining defiance to offset the uneasy shame of escorting Elinor, as Marcia had insisted, in a fiery secret letter, that he must do, to the Commencement dance at the fraternity house. In quick, mute despair, observing her trip, totter and right herself with the aid of Marcia's extended arm—here, now, on the steps leading from the station to the parking lot—he could see her as she would be in the midst of that gay, colorful, beautiful throng at the dance, wearing some outmoded dress that Marcia had secured for her in the fond, perverse conviction that it was more "refined" than current styles, and with the blank, frightened expression in her large, once beautiful (since animated) brown eyes. Sleepwalking, lost across the border of the secret world she inhabited.

To be sure, she was not so finally lost to the world of common reality that she could not participate in it. But such participation was really marginal, superficial: *she* was not there.

What fierce colors, he wondered, what passionate visions, however distorted to normal eyes, what appetites and dreams did she entertain beneath that blank surface of conventional platitudes: "This is a nice dance" . . . "Do you like Amherst?" . . . "Walton is my brother, you know" . . . and vacuous replies (how many times he had winced, hearing them. Winced! Good God in rage, black Almighty raving God, *suffered*): "Yes, I do like Amherst" . . . "Yes, I love to dance" . . . "I'm having a very good time" all half murmur, half mutter, for the light was out, extinguished, so that the good brother who had cut in on them, tapped Walton on the shoulder and said politely, "May I?"—the good brother must cock his head, beg her pardon, ask her again what she had said and finally, desperately, pretend he understood while praying silently to be delivered from this dilemma into which he had entered, in the bonds of brotherhood, for the sake of Brother Herrick—yet knowing all the time that it would not be much longer, for Brother Herrick had a holy sense of duty to both this strangely disquieting sister of his and to those friends who stood by him in his travail. And Brother Herrick, meanwhile, harried, hot eyes burning with anxiety, trying to decide whom he might ask next, without feeling too humiliated—hectically nervous about the one he had just left, but painfully reluctant to ask another.

And then there was his mother. To the casual eye not a cripple, not even, perhaps, strange; rather a distinguished woman in repose, though dressed a bit eccentrically. But the disfigurement, the crippled member, was in her, he sometimes thought, though mostly hid from view, to the worst degree of all. A black fungus ate through her whole system, so that she would erupt, she, the indomitable but gracious great lady, would erupt in sudden hot volcanic gusts—when feeling slighted, when ignored, when contradicted, when not recognized as the indisputable arbiter—and the lava and ash would make a ruin of the fairest site. William, however his legs looked, was too gentle, too kind, too toughly weathered by life, to make any trouble past visual; Elinor would never, in her terrible meekness (Walton shuddered again over what could be, must be, imprisoned behind this final, almost inanimate meekness)—Elinor would never, beyond the initial impression she made, embarrass him by anything she did. But his mother might, as like as not, halt the actual Commencement procession—stand there in the path, cry "Stop! It's the wrong music" and shoo them all back, in helter-skelter confusion, president, recipients of honorary degrees, band and all, tumbling over each other, to the spot from which, in pristine dignity, they had begun. All life was only a rehearsal to her.

Rehearsal? For what great unlikely day? God hold it off!

Marcia knew. No spy, no intelligence service, no informer had assisted her to this knowledge. And, indeed, she did not know who, exactly what, when or how. She knew simply, with that deep animal intuition peculiar to women (since women, in crinoline or organdy, wool or lace, cotton or rayon, despite whatever battery of man-made machines, whatever putative social and economic equality with men, to assist them in a conviction of having at last escaped the sheer heavy weight of their origins—women, however protesting, do remain in deep, enduring touch with the roots of nature)—she knew. And when, the first day's activities done, the class oration delivered, the class poem read in the grove exercises, the president's tea attended (and Mr. Luce had shown Walton's parents an attentive deference that had even contented Marcia), she bustled Elinor to early bed and persuaded William that he should stay on the porch of their small hotel and continue to enjoy his conversation with Professor Howe—then, then, she closed Elinor's bedroom door behind her and faced Walton.

She drew herself a little more erect, nervously and characteristically smoothed her dress over her hips and crossed the room to where he sat.

"Now we can talk," she said. "I know my boy has something on his mind."

Walton steeled himself.

"How do you know?" he asked, not quite sharply.

"Oh, I know, I know." She shook her head sagely, smiling half-sadly, half-playfully. "And you know, too. It's no ordinary mother-son relationship we have. We—feel things about each other that coarser-grained people never experience. Something has happened to you, something that's important to you—and so to all of us."

He looked at her steadily, but he did not yet trust himself to speak. She dropped into a chair beside him, adjusted the pince-nez that often wobbled so perilously on the bridge of her aristocratic nose, and folded her hands in her lap. After gazing at them speculatively for a moment or two, she looked up sharply, and again directly at him.

"Is it a girl?"

Here was the moment he had dreaded, presented in the way he had dreaded. Those keen eyes, burrowing into him, the sharp voice, demanding to know, the severe look, compounded of apprehensiveness and grim authority. And where, he wondered hopelessly, was the new strength of manhood now? Again, he could only nod miserably; this time he did not even meet her eyes.

"I see. Who is she? What's happened?"

It was as though he wrenched some part of himself up, tore it loose from its comfortable connections, because he must find something, however cruelly unfair to this anonymous part of himself, with which to confront her. His voice was level, his eyes defiant.

"Don't talk to me as though I were a defendant in court, Mother."

Her voice softened with an incredible—a sickening—alacrity, he thought.

"Walton. Of course not. I'm nervous and tired; it's been a great strain to bring Elinor and your father all this way. Now, dear boy, I didn't mean to upset you. I want to hear all about her." Her smile was suddenly so bright that it must have pained her as much as it did him, Walton thought.

And then, at this moment, she removed her glasses, and rubbed tiredly at her eyes. As he saw the raw deep marks left by the abrasive claws of the pince-nez, he felt something wince inside him, both from the pity he felt for her poor face and the indignation he felt over the revelation that compelled his pity. Here, in these two deep indentations on either side of her nose, in the raw, pinched skin, she inadvertently, it seemed to him, revealed the hurt, tired, lonely, defeated woman forever hidden under the matriarch with whom he must do battle.

And so, though such was not his intention, he spoke in reply softly, almost gently.

"Her name is Joanna Gaylord, Mother. I've seen a lot of her this semester. She goes to Wellesley and her father is a professor at Hobart College. She's graduating this week too."

Still holding her glasses in her hand, she looked forlorn, defenseless. And her voice was too eager, too patently soothing.

"I'm sure she's lovely. I hope I shall have a chance to meet her. Perhaps you can persuade her to visit us sometime next year."

Despite—because of?—Marcia's dislike of cigarettes, he lighted one, blew out a long thin funnel of smoke as though he were expelling his very final breath.

"We are going to be married," he said.

The silence was prolonged, solemn, epoch-making. And when Marcia finally spoke it was in a whisper. No acting this, all roles at last cast aside in this ultimate low-voiced protest.

"No, no, no, no."

The silence persisted. And suddenly Elinor was in the open doorway, eyes dilated, face contorted in fear.

"What is it?" she demanded, advancing toward them with more vigor than she had summoned in years. "What's the matter? What have you done to Mother?"

Marcia put on her glasses, straightened her shoulders, stood up.

"Nothing, dear," she said soothingly. "Mother's just tired, that's all. And you must be too, dreadfully tired. We'll all go to bed shortly," all the while skillfully steering Elinor by the shoulders past a low coffee table, a stuffed chair, a standing lamp, with the professional adroitness of a nurse wheeling a patient down a cluttered hospital corridor.

The last glimpse Walton had of Elinor's face, over her shoulder and past Marcia's, was threatening and black. Gone that terrible frenetic meekness; hate emerged, bringing her face to corrosive life.

"I heard Mother say no no no that way and I know you told her something dreadful like you want to get married and leave us or go off to Europe and I have no life at all. I'm sick of it," she shouted. "I tell you I'm sick of it and I won't stand for it."

And Marcia's ssh, wheeling her away, and Walton sat and stared at the wall, at the insipid little rose pattern of the paper, and thought longingly of a hypothetical improbable someone somewhere who would comfort him. A bleak thought caught at him (would he not have to *take care of*—those were the decisive words—Joanna, too?) and he thrust it away savagely, with an impersonal will. At least he didn't feel it to be his own. He would, he told himself resolutely, remember that moment in the woods by the lake, before the trampling footsteps (the Spoiler, he thought suddenly and only half comprehendingly) broke into it. He would invoke the dewiness, the rosiness of the awakening Joanna—

Marcia again closed the bedroom door behind her, gently but with finality. Her face was composed now; she looked quiet and purposeful. And, although something about the exact moment she had chosen—for he rejected superstitiously the possibility that she had simply returned after calming Elinor—for her re-entrance froze him, made him feel, as so many times before, quite helpless to cope with her, he nevertheless felt a grudging admiration for the skill and promptness with which she could adjust yet another of her multitudinous masks.

"Now," she said almost briskly, "we really must talk."

Walton sighed heavily and resumed his empty staring at the wallpaper.

"But first I want to be sure that we don't raise our voices," Marcia continued, with a significant movement of her head in the direction of the closed door and an almost archly conspiratorial expression. "You heard what she said, Walton. That little girl has had a terrible experience, a wretched time. And those of us who are strong must make sacrifices for her. It's hard, but it's right. It's simply a law of life. I should know. I, above all people, should know."

Walton felt strength surging back into him. It was, although familiar, incredible to him that she should put her case so transparently.

"No, Mother," he said clearly and directly. "I don't think it is a law of life. I don't believe either that it is any real help to Elinor if I don't get married. And I don't believe that, because she has been so sick and had so rough a time, I should give up my own life and be, in a different way, as unhappy as she is."

Marcia had turned glacially cold.

"So," she said. "You are already planning to desert us. Oh, Walton, I don't know what I've done to deserve this. But I can bear it—" the ice melted—"I can bear anything. After what I've been through, all my life, I can and will endure anything, up to the time when I finally break. I have my honor and my pride."

Walton groaned in impatience, and in ultimate frustration rubbed savagely at his head.

"Mother, I give up. I'm not deserting Elinor. I'm not deserting you—or Dad. I'm not deserting, that's all. If you want to know a law of life, there's the law that everyone has one life to live and that it's his inalienable right to live it. And believe me, I've gotten a mighty slow start. No, wait a minute—let me finish.

"I am going to live in Cleveland. You know that. You know that I have a job, and that that job is in Cleveland, not in Africa or anywhere else. And by now you should know too that, whether or not I live at home with you, I'll still be there to help, and want to help. Joanna and I have talked a lot about that, and she understands and agrees that I should even come down early every day in the winter to fire the furnace and to stoke it up every night. I'm not going to leave Dad in the lurch on that—or other things."

Her face was haughty and scornful.

"Furnaces," she said, "are not what I'm thinking about. We made a real sacrifice to put you through college in the East, and we've taken care of the furnace all that time. What I'm thinking of is the companionship, the help, and the sharing of this lonely burden I've carried for so many years. Your father is a good man, but he's left everything to me. I'm not blaming him, it's not his fault he's crippled, but he hasn't even done what he could. Everything—the raising of you children, the running of the house, the managing of our trips and vacations— all this has fallen on my shoulders. And at last, now, when it seemed that there was going to be someone who would share the load with me—you, and after all we've done for you—you are going to run away and get married. Married! Desert your family for some strange girl with a pretty face you barely know.

"No. Don't you interrupt me. Now it's my turn. You'll help your father with the furnace! Let me tell you, I wasn't worrying about your father, when he's let me carry the full load all these years. And he has his books. What I'm talking about is my loneliness—and the loneliness of that little girl in there. I've been dreaming, so foolishly, of the rides you'd take us on in the country (we've never had a car) and now it's all gone, all, all gone."

She covered her face with her hands, her shoulders shook, and for the first time in many years, Walton heard his mother cry.

He heard her cry and sat there, bound and trussed by conflicting emotions. Despite the reality of tears, he could not determine the genuineness of her feeling. He felt a strong need to comfort her, yet at the same time a wary disinclination, a distaste almost, remembering all the times she had deceived and trapped him—not, to be sure, consciously, yet all the same effectively. He had a muddled sense of being committed irrevocably to a cause lost at its inception and simultaneously unable to free himself from this commitment without a punitive and unbearable guilt.

This long moment carried too great a weight; overburdened, it split and broke into fragments. His voice, he knew, was cold and bleak, instead of furious, only because it came from his now uninhabited self.

"I could feel sorry, Mother, if there was any real justification for what you said. Oh, I don't mean the part about the load you've carried; it has been awful. I mean your insisting that I'm—just, well—"

And suddenly he wasn't bleak and cold, but close to tears himself. He felt so finally, futilely but genuinely sorry for both of them, for her, for himself, for all of them—for Joanna too. They were all so pathetic, all so inadequate for the tough complexities of life, so fearful, so guilty, so ghost-ridden, so lonely.

And so hopeless? With the tears unshed but bubbling up hot, it seemed to him, in his throat, he clung to her now and she to him. And then, gulping and sniffling, she gasped, "Oh, my boy! My big, handsome boy! How I love you!" and he stiffened as though someone had pointed a gun at him.

Oh, yes, she meant it. This was not histrionics. But he was being held up as surely as if by a highwayman. He tried to move away, but she clutched at him until, in sudden desperation, he wrenched himself free.

It was at that moment that they heard William's cane in the

hall and looked at each other with the identical expression of guilty children, caught and exposed at their mischief.

This was the way he felt, Walton thought in bewilderment; and this was the way his mother looked. Then the door opened, and his father appeared.

For a moment William's face retained its glow—the glow, Walton suddenly realized, with which innumerable times he returned home from a day of work and comradeship, and which seldom endured, once home, for more than half an hour. Then, as though abashed, he averted his eyes and, without a word, turned in the direction of the other bedroom.

"William!"

Slowly he swung around and faced them, as though expecting a disciplinary reproof. That was the stance and the expression, and yet Walton understood at this moment that this was not their meaning. His father, not unlike himself, was always wary at the evidence of an imminent row. Yet friction, hysteria, recriminations, accusations—these were their daily bread. The punishment William Herrick awaited was not for any offense of which he was guilty, but rather that payment he made every day on the note he had undertaken when he married Marcia Nicholson. His expression reflected his dread of the coming scene; his anticipation was like that Walton had felt contemplating some outrageous act that Marcia might perpetrate at Commencement.

"William," said Marcia, wiping her eyes and blowing her nose, "you'd better sit down and listen."

And how many times had she said that! Walton thought wearily. Dully he watched his father obediently lower himself into a chair, and from nowhere, it seemed, caught in echo, as though played back, William's reflexive movement when he had first appeared, sensed the tension in the room, and attempted to avoid participation, to elude them. There was another element here—as though, Walton thought, his father somehow felt himself the outsider and Marcia and Walton the —the couple. As though (Walton's mind stammered) he, William, were a cuckold—and, being unworthy, must accept his state.

In red rage, Walton broke in.

"Dad, what I've told Mother is that I want to get married. I didn't mean to tell either of you until after Commencement; I knew there'd be trouble and I didn't want to spoil these days. But she guessed."

What he saw first now in his father was dismay—unguarded despair and gray fatigue. Then, almost immediately, the proportions were righted, the world tilted back into place: his father was his father, and, what was more, the head of the house; he had never spoken with a more convincing authority.

"That's a big step, son. We weren't prepared for it, so it's no wonder your mother is upset. But, now it's out, you'd better tell me about it."

There had been the moment of recognition, and from it Walton drew the knowledge that he had not before had—perhaps hadn't wanted to have: that his father, too, had counted more heavily than he, Walton, had dreamed, on having him back with them, assuming his share of their common problem. But the very fact that Walton now really understood this, fully comprehended that there was here, in his family, a unanimity of need for him, and that his compulsive sense of duty to them was not simply a subjective condition in himself—this, and the twin vision of his father stricken by the news and then rallying soberly but gallantly—the very sequence which William's reactions had epitomized made it possible for him at last to tell his story fully. Not simply Joanna, but, for the first time, his rejection of the Pearson Fellowship, and President Luce's subsequent intercession with Mr. Cotterill.

As he talked on and on, he became aware of a shift in weather: Marcia's grimness softened, if only in recognition of her interest in the story as story; and in his father's face he saw a respect, an affection and a pride that warmed him through, and finally emboldened him, at the conclusion of his account, to say quietly and firmly, "So you see, I have not, as Mother has thought, intended in any way to desert you. But I do say that if I want to get married I have a right to."

William, all eager life again, leaned forward, eyes glowing, and struck his hands on the arms of his chair.

"So you do, son, and you give me new heart. If, in some ways, we could have worked out some of our problems more easily were you to be coming home alone to live with us, we have no right to ask you to do so if you are sure you have found your right wife. And, since you say that she and her father are to come here for Commencement Day, we shall soon have a chance to meet her. I am proud of you for the confidence that President Luce has in you, and for your manly facing of the temptation to go to England. Perhaps you should have gone. I don't know. But at my time of life, with the burdens there are to carry, I cannot pretend to be anything but grateful that you're coming to Cleveland and still want to help us."

Marcia sniffed, but it was not a strong sound.

"You always sound like a sanctimonious preacher," she said, but without conviction.

Both men laughed, but Walton halfheartedly. His own thoughts had not been too different; he wished, as he often had before, that his father wouldn't deliver his sentiments in such formal terms. But his main point was won, and as Ez Barker had said, "Who do you think you are, God? Nobody else gets it with spangles all over it."

And so the days passed, as they always do, regardless of what dread anticipation. And if, with all the anxieties attendant upon the custodianship of his family, Walton did not really have any full sense of Commencement as one of those pivotal, one of those solemn fete days that, transcending the regularities of the calendar, stake out the progress of a human life—at least the dominant reason for this omission, this loss, was the subordination of Commencement in his thoughts and feelings to another epochal day just before him: that of his marriage.

And this realization, this hovering and constant vision in turn supported him through the days preceding Commencement. True, his parents had not fully and openly granted their approval, and he would not be twenty-one until November. Even his father had said "if you are sure you have found your right wife." But *his* intent was clear, and Marcia had not reopened the topic, except for occasional sarcastic references to the state of matrimony and the blessed ignorance of those looking forward to it. From time to time he saw her regarding him with one of her significant expressions (this was the word for them, the only right word, though Walton could never answer the question "significant of what?")—but she did not speak to the point again until the actual eve of Commencement.

So the image of his marriage to Joanna supported him through the trials of the pre-Commencement weekend. When he and his father attended the Amherst-Williams baseball game, Walton had only to remember William's prompt and vigorous support of the marriage, despite the blow its announcement had given him, to rally everything positive and loving in himself and thus overcome his dread of the curious scrutiny William's crippled legs would evoke. At the fraternity dance, the thought of Joanna as his wife was soothing and healing to the raw wounds reopened by the experience with Elinor so close in actuality to his anticipation of it. And, after his mother's half concession, he worked so single-mindedly to remember to observe the special attentions that made her happiest that none of the outbursts he had feared from her occurred; during three days, she retired in outraged pride to her room only once.

And so, at nine o'clock on the night before Commencement Day, as Walton walked briskly from the fraternity house to the hotel to say good night to his family, he had a strong sense of achievement. The race was nearly run, and this time there was, at last, a prize. Only with this thought did he realize that not once since the discussion with his parents had he felt any recurrence of his shadowy anxieties about the marriage itself, about his capacity to take care of Joanna, about— he had not put it this way before—her capacity for marriage.

Reviewing this earlier uneasiness, he felt no fear. Perhaps, he thought, as he mounted the steps of the hotel porch, he had not before understood to how large an extent they had been related to, and unconsciously confused with, those he had felt about his family's reactions.

Marcia was alone in the sitting room of the suite, wrapped, despite the balmy June evening, in her bulky winter robe.

"Elinor's asleep," she said, extending her cheek for his dutiful kiss. "Worn out. Your father's reading. We can talk."

Walton smiled.

"Fine," he said, and agreeably inquired about her estimates of various friends and professors she had met in these last days.

Marcia answered, but briefly and bemusedly. It was clear that this was not the sort of thing about which she wanted to talk, and at last she ventured a question of her own.

"Joanna," she said, and made of the name something strange— not distasteful, but necessarily still subject to gingerly appraisal, as though it were an unfamiliar spice being tested on the tongue. "She's coming tomorrow?"

"Yes," said Walton, "with her father. The Wellesley Commencement was yesterday."

Marcia sighed.

"And what are your plans?" she asked in a tired, resigned voice. "I've been waiting for you to tell me."

In direct response and proportion to her passivity, it seemed now to Walton, his voice became more tentative.

"Well," he said, "we thought we'd get married here the day after tomorrow, so that all of you could be there. I've spoken to the college pastor about it. And then take a week's honeymoon in New York and come back to Cleveland and stay at home, if that's all right with you and Dad, until we find a house of our own."

Again Marcia sighed.

"What does her father think about this?"

"She says he was surprised," Walton replied gravely, "but, after a long talk, is satisfied."

Marcia flared up.

"She says . . . she says! When did she say? Have you called her up long distance? And who is he to be satisfied? He'd better be satisfied, now that she's got you."

Walton noted with a recurring surprise the obverse of his earlier discovery. This was what he needed to make him firm and strong: her anger, her outburst.

"Mother, that's ridiculous," he said. "He feels about his daughter, of course, as you do about me. And, yes, I did call her up, night before last. Why not? We have to make arrangements."

"Oh, go on, go on. Make your arrangements. Don't think about me; don't pay any attention to your family." Marcia began rocking violently in her chair. "The world belongs to young people; it's not the way it was in my day. My day! I never had a day; I was robbed of my youth, taking care of my family, and I'm still doing it." Her tone was bitter, at once contemptuous and pathetic.

"Mother," Walton began patiently, "I thought we'd had all this out, and that you understood. I thought—"

"I understand, all right. I understand only too well. After all the care and love I've given my boy, he's going to marry some common girl whom he's known just a month! Oh, I understand."

Walton waited until he could control his voice.

"You have no right to say that. You must stop calling people whom you haven't even met common. Stop using that word altogether; this is the twentieth century. And I've known her six weeks, during which I've seen her at least twice a week. And some people you get to know better in a month than you do others in a year. If you're going to talk this way to Joanna, we'll get married alone: I won't even let you meet her."

There was iron in his voice, his look, his bearing: he could hear and feel it himself, and its impact on Marcia was visible and immediate.

"Oh, I won't, I won't," she muttered. "You know I won't. Oh, Walton, don't you understand? It's all so sudden, and I didn't count on it. It's so strange. Life's so strange, so unreal. Why, I don't even know what she looks like!"

Walton drew out his wallet, and handed a photograph to Marcia.

"I was going to show it to you the other night," he said steadily, "but you didn't ask me, and anyway I didn't think you'd want to see it then."

An extraordinary change in Marcia's attitude occurred. It was first perceptible in her posture, which straightened. At the same time her carriage, her whole body, seemed more relaxed. In silence she examined the picture for several minutes, and then at last looked up at him and smiled.

"Why, she's fair," she said—and Walton thought with surprise that he had never heard her use that word before—"and, really, very aristocratic looking. There's a sweetness, a refinement, about her face, too. And she looks rather tall and graceful, really a lady. I wish you'd shown me this before." Her voice rose excitedly. "William! William! Come and look at this picture of Joanna."

At the sound of his father's rousing himself, Walton took the photograph from her, saying, "Let me show it to him," and opened the door to the bedroom.

William also looked in silence. Then Walton perceived that his father's eyes were unaccustomedly filled with tears.

"She's lovely, son," William said, and waved his gaunt hands in exuberance, flourishing the photograph. "Like a wildflower."

Marcia sniffed from the doorway, but eagerly took the extended photograph. When, back in the sitting room, she finally turned to Walton again, her face was flushed and animated to a degree Walton had not seen in her for years.

"She'll be good to Elinor," Marcia half crooned. It seemed to Walton now that she was, in this strange reversal, actually mesmerizing herself. "I can tell that from the way she looks. She'll be kind to Elinor and even, perhaps, help her very much. Perhaps it will all be for the best, after all. Oh, I'm so relieved." And then, in another sudden shift of mood, half accusingly, "Why didn't you let me know this? Why didn't you tell me the kind of girl she was? It would have made all the difference in the world to me. I'd never have been so upset at all."

Walton let this pass—this and other similar exclamations through the next half hour. He was sufficiently leery about the duration of this intoxication to prefer not to risk any interruption that might serve as an irritant. But, when he rose to go, Marcia put her hands on his shoulders and spoke in still a different key.

"My fine big son is going to be graduated tomorrow," she said softly, in an almost exalted tone, her eyes suddenly dilated and shining, "and the day after that he's going to be married. And there's just one thing I want him never to forget. Listen to this, Walton; I don't want you ever to forget. No one ever replaces a mother and a mother's love. Marriage is important in life and you must be faithful and good to your little wife. But a wife is not the same as a mother. The mother comes first; you should put her first, and her love. Nothing—do you hear—nothing ever comes before a mother and a mother's love. Then we'll all get along together fine."

Despite the sudden freezing horror he felt, Walton managed to nod and to mutter, "All right, Mother. For Pete's sake, they're not the same thing at all. Good night"—and, moving to the door, "Good night, Dad."

As he stood in the doorway and heard his father's hearty "Good night, son, and congratulations. Get a good sleep. Big day tomorrow," he turned back, drawn by an irresistible compulsion, and saw the burning inquiry still in her eyes, the imperative ardor, and—yes, the fear.

Awkwardly he made his way back to her, reinforced the kiss with a clumsy, self-conscious hug and went hurriedly out again.

There was one really bad moment on Commencement Day. It had nothing to do with the meeting of the Herricks and the Gaylords. Professor Gaylord was a chubby, quietly genial and absent-minded man, whose shining pink scalp, round spectacles and beaming round face made Walton think of a beardless, almost hairless Santa Claus. Although both he and William were too shy to talk much, it was clear that they liked each other immediately.

Nor did Marcia have much to do with Walton's bad moment. He knew the symptoms: she was wholly reconciled now, and putting every effort into charming Joanna. Walton was even amused at the resultant exhibition, and Joanna's half-awed, half-frightened reaction. It was perhaps her inability to know what to make of Marcia that led her to seek out Elinor, and this, in turn, insured a new endorsement, partly genuine satisfaction, partly self-vindication, from Marcia.

No, throughout the long and festive day, everything between the Gaylords and the Herricks went well beyond Walton's fondest hopes. The moment that upset him came outside the hall in which the exercises were held, and after the graduates had filed out, followed by the swarming audience.

Still in his cap and gown, holding the diploma that certified him as a graduate of Amherst College *cum laude,* peering about for his family and Joanna, he suddenly bumped into Miss Crider, who beamed at him sadly and let her plump hand rest longer than usual in his extended one.

"You got your editorial check all right? I hear you're going to be married, so you'll need it. Congratulations. I'll really miss you, though, Walton, you and your soft soap. You made my life easier and more fun. Plenty of apple polishers around but all except you lazy. Plenty of hard workers around, but all except you dull and literal-minded. Where's your family? I'd like to meet them."

"I don't know," Walton had begun, resuming his examination of the milling and swirling crowd, "I've been looking—" when she interrupted him with a tug on his arm.

"Here's someone else to congratulate you," she said, and some sly inflection in her voice warned him even before he turned back— to face Irene Wertz.

She had changed, outwardly at least; she looked—in comparison to a year ago—suave, sleek. Her complexion was impeccable, her silk foulard dress and her small hat fashionable—and she wore them well. There was no trace of her old slumping posture, and her smile was composed and cordial as she extended her small hand.

"Yes, I do congratulate you, Walton," she said softly. "On both —your marriage, too."

There was a mockery in her eyes, though, and this, together with the realization that his contact with the silky skin of that small hand still excited him, totally discomfited him. So discomfited him that he blurted out, "Thanks. How's Nick?"

"Nick? Nick who?" She seemed genuinely surprised for a moment; then that familiarly derisive smile, the old gaminlike jerk of the head and shoulder (it seemed to him that he shivered, as though feeling with his hand that bare satiny shoulder under the silk) and "Oh. Him. Sure. I don't know; I haven't seen him in months."

It was an open question for several minutes thereafter whether something (himself?) was salvaged or destroyed just then by the intrusion of Marcia's iciest tones: "Here he is. But he seems to be busy."

Her haughtiest glance swept over Miss Crider and Irene, then thawed as she turned to Joanna and, putting her arm around her, went on, "Joanna and I thought *you* would find *us.*"

Walton tried to rally his scattered powers, but it was a feeble effort.

"Mother, I particularly want you to meet Miss Crider, who's been so kind to me all through college and given me so many jobs. And this is Miss Wertz. My mother. And this—" stretching out his hand to take hers—"is Joanna Gaylord, my fiancée."

Joanna smiled hopefully and murmured her greeting. Marcia unbent a little for Miss Crider the Provider, but it was too late, for

Miss Crider's shrewd eyes had observed and understood, and her response was curt. Marcia, in turn, ignored Irene.

And Irene stared at her, long and thoughtfully, then turned back to Walton with an eloquently quizzical expression, shrugged her shoulders (those shoulders!) and walked away without a word. Miss Crider said briefly, "Good-bye, boy. Good luck," and stumped after her.

"Common!" Marcia sniffed.

Walton felt the beseeching quality in Joanna's hand, clasping his, and said nothing. But, as they moved off to join Elinor and the two men, he was caught in such an eddy of anger, longing and dismay that he felt a sudden bitterness in his dry throat, not unlike the effect of heartburn. And he only understood his dominant feeling a half hour later when, lighting a cigarette, he smelled the scent on his hand, recognized its heavy bitterness as Irene's.

Joanna's hand was long and thin and bony. Walton had never thought of it that way until that moment outside the Commencement hall, when, in the presence of the other women, he had reached for it. Now, here, in the drawing room they had reserved, with good-byes said, the long, dark, rainy ride in Ez's car to Springfield over, the exciting midnight lights and bustle of the railroad station, the formalities of tickets and luggage and the knowing smile of the porter all successfully encountered, and the door of their little room locked against the world —now, here, as the train roared through the night and they sat, man and wife, on the made-up bed and sipped champagne (her first, his second), he reached again for her hand, held it, rubbed his thumb against the knuckles, and thought: this hand, this wife, this girl, this long and thin and bony hand, and remembered Irene shrugging, moving her bare shoulders, her whole body, under her silken dress, and walking away. Out of his life.

Now he shrugged, impatiently, angry with himself, angry almost— it seemed—at Joanna. To exorcise what was troubling him, he tried to recall Irene, red-eyed, plaintive, self-pitying and accusing—but he put too much will into the effort; it was self-defeating.

And then he became aware of Joanna's grave and steady look of inquiry, and tightened his hold on her hand.

"Are you sorry?"

There was such a burden of feeling on the frail words that it seemed that they must break. Fear, hope, tenderness, despair, trust, timidity—there was no way to define the quality of the question. But

Walton felt a rush of protective love. He raised his tumbler.

"To my wife," he said. "The most beautiful and desirable woman in the world."

And all in a moment she was shining again, as she had, in one surprising burst of feeling that infused every feature, every gesture, every expression at the wedding, so that Marcia (of all people!) had exclaimed, "She loves you, Walton. You must be very good to her."

"I like being a woman." She said it shyly, almost primly, with that peculiarly poignant inflection that both enchanted and alarmed him.

"A married woman," said Walton, and looked at her boldly, possessively, with what felt to him like a husband's look.

She closed her eyes. "Married," she murmured.

And there—there, Walton thought, gazing at those long golden eyelashes spread softly just above her high cheekbones. There—the vision, that first sunlit moment again, framed in the rectangle of light and shadow. His Renaissance princess, with the dull golden hair and the long pale face. He leaned over and kissed her softly.

As he had hoped, she stirred under the kiss, and the faint rustling of her wedding clothes evoked and then replaced that other rustle; her reaching arms recalled that long moment in the woods by the lake; her soft breath on his cheek restored the promises they had made this afternoon. And then her eyes opened, and in them was such a depth of love and acceptance and trust that he closed his own, blinded. He was aware of the trembling of his hand, and, opening his eyes, drained his glass. Then, gently, he took hers from her and put his arms around her.

And it was the way it had been before. Slowly, tenderly, he wooed her out of her wedding suit, turned off the lights until only one dim wall lamp was burning, coaxed her into drinking her champagne between kisses, soft but inflaming kisses, and whispered softly ardent words to her that brought that rosy color flooding back into her face. And she closed her eyes again and he spilled some champagne on her bare arm and kissed it away, until she opened her eyes and they were full of happy tears and she drew him closer again and silently besought his hands upon her.

And, as before, the bloom and dewiness possessed her, and they clung, intoxicated, to each other until this seemed unbearable, then without a word began feverishly to rip away their remaining clothes.

When there came a knocking at the door. It was a sharp, imperious knock, repeated almost instantly. They sprang apart, staring, and though Walton saw and recognized the look on her face, he did not think about it, did not reach out to reassure her. He could not, for as the knock sounded again, louder and more impatient, a desolate sense of doom swept over him, a great sweeping indictment of happiness and love, and swarming in a hundred different shapes from the outlands of childhood, behind the closed door, along the dark hallway the attic steps, the dark street after the closing of the doors, the harsh voice of his mother calling, "Walton, what are you doing there," and beyond childhood at school and then in college open up freshman the many voices but most of all the knock open up we know you're there hiding in the playground the schoolroom the coat closet from the goblin face to the dormitory the Spoiler is at the door despair.

And in a cracked voice he called, shivering as he stepped into his trousers, pulled on his shirt, "Wait a minute! Just a minute!" For he would face it. He always had he always would.

And opened the door a crack to see a blue cap, a conductor's face as ordinary as a conductor: "We know they missed one drawing room at the station but they didn't give us the number. Sorry, sir. But may I see your tickets, please?"

Fumbling. Relief and relief-induced anger. Dropping his wallet. Trembling fingers. And there—there.

"Drawing room B, 315. That's O.K. Sorry to trouble you."

And the closing of the door. And the drawing of the bolt. And turning, there where she was, tumbled under the tumbled covers, face white, strained, and in the eyes that same mortal hopelessness and terror. And a great fatigue washing through him, a chilling current of despair.

"Oh, darling, don't look like that. Jo. It was just a stupid mistake. Damn him! Don't, please don't. It will all be all right."

But it wouldn't be. She knew it, and he knew it, and she knew that he knew it, too. It wouldn't be all right.

JOURNAL: 9

from the journal of Walton Herrick . . .

Sept. 10, 1953

Back to Bergson and that first entry so long ago: "We are more fully alive and this increase of life brings with it the conviction that grave philosophical enigmas can be resolved or even perhaps that they need not be raised, since they arise from a frozen vision of the real and are only the translation, in terms of thought, of a certain artificial weakening of our vitality."

I have sat here for some twenty minutes, pondering this single sentence. And now, as I flip back over my journal, I find that most of the entries after the first few have been devoted to "grave philosophical enigmas." I have seduced myself away from my original intent: "not to analyze, describe, record . . ." but "to invoke." I have, I now think, *raised* the enigmas, tried to *resolve* them—for is the philosophical discourse of our time about man not predominantly the psychological? And only now do I see that, in swerving away from my sound original purpose, I have occupied myself with that "frozen vision of the real"—and become again the victim of an "artificial weakening" of my "vitality."

Words—to exorcise words. And yet I had to set it down this once: set it, so to speak, on the floor and hold it there firmly with my foot, stand on it, lest it escape me again. For what I see now is that even in my most recent entry, in which I did really discover something—this obsession with mastery, this superimposing of the fantastic upon reality —I tended to philosophize it away, to *generalize* it away, to try to master it. . . .

Yesterday I came upon a poem, the last line of which has sung in my head ever since: We are vulnerable or dead.

It makes me want to open all the doors and windows of my house.

It makes me want to take off my clothes. It makes me want to ventilate my mind, to learn to listen, to watch, to inquire, to explore. It makes me want to open myself, to have no secret compartments in my nature or my life—to immerse myself (Bergson again) in the great sticky river of life. No insulation, no protective armor, no automatic closing vents. Open to shame, to suffering, to fear, to humiliation, to rejection. And so to fulfillment, to joy, to courage, to humility, to acceptance.

"Not an eternity of immutability, but an eternity of life . . . In it we live and move and have our being."

Tomorrow night I leave for the Vineyard.

1953

September 12

HAVING boarded the huge flat-bottomed ferry running between Woods Hole and Vineyard Haven, Walton stowed his bags in a luggage compartment and went up to the top deck, where he bought a paper cup of coffee. It was early morning, and he had sat up on the train until almost three, drinking bourbon and meditating. The last hour or two of his vigil he had been relaxed, confident, even elated. Loosened into peace, he had felt fatigue and anxiety slip their moorings, as now the ferry, after several horrendous blasts, lurched out of the Woods Hole slip, to begin its trip through the treacherous channel.

These were his visits to Sequester Meadow, he had thought before going to sleep—these times when, bound to a destination he loved (on the train, hooting its lonely midnight way up through Connecticut, he had watched, rapt, the occasional lonely blinking lights, and chanted silently to himself, "Home, home. I'm going home. Julie. The kids. Home"), he wrapped his arms around himself with the happy illusion that he was embracing his world—that, all forgiven, shriven, he was being welcomed back into the place, the context, the life, the immediacy that at other times he evaded, entertained in a gingerly way, or even fled from.

Most transitions terrified him. Getting from here to there, out in the open where no mask could be sufficient, no shelter provided, required strenuous muscular effort of will. Ordinarily, of course, he didn't realize this. In fact, the few times such a concept had bolted nervously across his mind, he had worried, not that this was his disability but that he should sporadically entertain such fantastic nonsense. But now, shooting, spun on the moonlit rails in the middle of the night—shooting along with the swaying and the rocketing of the train, soothed by the bourbon and the imminence of the haven, of home—he had fully grasped it, if only through his present freedom from fear, his free yielding of himself to the train's reckless speed, this seldom experienced abandonment of self to what might come, adapting of self to *a place in*. As he could *not* now, here, this morning, he thought to himself, for the ferry had rolled a little in the brisker white caps past the lighthouse, spilling hot coffee onto his hand.

It was a blue-and-white day, with a stiff breeze, fresh and invigorating. But the lack of sleep and the excessive drinking had left Walton feeling let down; the breeze he accepted stoically, as he might a cold shower, but the boat's motion made him uneasy.

As it always had, he thought grimly. No matter what the size of the boat—he was always at the mercy of that alien element, water. Not in any realistic way, though: for now, as so often before, he suffered the hallucination that the ferry would roll over. Paralyzed where he stood, terrified, he experienced the great engulfing moment that swallowed the cries of the children aboard; the frantic, possessed efforts of passengers to save themselves; the tremendous sucking into the watery abyss of the pathetic, valiant figures who strove to dive or flail their way out of the catastrophe. As for himself, he accepted it passively, not ungallantly, but with a last despairing thought of Julie and the children waiting at the dock.

Growling with nervous disgust, he drained the last of the black coffee, scalding his throat, and made for the lunch bar and a second cup. When he emerged again, he glanced at and then away from the stacks of life jackets in their racks beside him, before going directly to the center of the deck, to the place where he could best hear the laboring of the motors below, detect the first cough or rattling of phlegm in the gigantic throat. There he planted his feet wide.

It was then he almost jumped, with the certainty that someone had spoken in his ear. He looked to the left and to the right: no one. But he knew. It was the Spoiler: he would have exchanged his pork-pie hat for a jaunty yachting cap; his jacket would sport gold braid, and a silk scarf, tucked into the form of an ascot, would have replaced the bow tie. And—hideous thought!—surely he was trying to grow a mustache. As yet there was only a faint dark stain above his lip. But, on closer examination, Walton could imagine a few long, silky hairs, which wisped out delicately to produce an obscenely effeminate air.

It had been so long since he had suffered this hallucination that Walton literally shuddered. He set the coffee, now sour to him, down on the deck and strode resolutely toward the front rail, to wash the image away in salt wind. But the voice went with him, and the first words (reminding him forcefully of Abe Fortune's postscript about the devil) were: "You jerk! With your alcoholic dreams of happy reunions, of home and rosebuds! You can't stand two days of it without breaking out in hives. You belong alone, outside, looking in. Think of the family picnics, the diapers, the tears and running noses!"

Walton struck his forehead with his clenched fist, saw a plump middle-aged woman looking at him apprehensively, and plunged away, back to the side rail, where he stood for some minutes, oblivious of the wind, the boat's motion, of everything except his desperate attempt to regain control of himself.

Control? To regain *himself*—that self he had felt so sure of last night on the train, the self to which he felt, after all the strains, conflicts and betrayals of the summer, he had finally come home. He snatched at symbols of peace and rationality, remembered the journal entry about trying to force his will upon reality; the night he had thought he heard Julie's voice in the kitchen at home, and the laughter of the children; the words he had written, as well as spoken to Dennis, about getting down on his knees. But to no avail; they whirled in his head, cutting back and forth across one another, without warmth, without life, without sustaining meaning.

In despair, he began to pace the deck, but was stopped short by a large knot of people. He turned sharply, to skirt them, only to bump into a little girl of five or six. He caught her by the shoulders, to prevent her falling, and found himself staring down at the back of her head, and feeling a sudden loosening of the torment in him.

Her long hair had been caught up on the top of her head and pinned there—awkwardly and insecurely, for it was already beginning to slip. Loose tendrils curled up and away from her tender little neck, and when she twisted in his hands and turned her slightly dirty, impish face around to gaze up inquiringly, there was something in the easy, trusting movement that deepened the relaxing of his tensions. Suddenly, as though there were a rushing and gushing of waters within him, he was afraid that he was going to weep.

But he managed to say, "I'm sorry. Are you all right?"

"I'm o-káy," she said, giving the second syllable a lift upward, and then raced off to her mother, the loose knot of hair bobbing with each stride.

Walton turned and stared out at the water, but did not see it. He did not try to explain what had happened: "Shut up," he growled to himself at the impulse. "Don't think about it; don't touch it." He stood there, soaking in the healing flow of life. And when his eyes cleared, he gazed at the expanding shoreline of East Chop, the curves of the harbor ahead, in quietness and comfort.

As the ferry forged closer and closer to the dock, Walton moved again to the prow to watch, amongst the throngs of waiting people, the tiny individual figures of his family identify themselves. At last he made them out: Jenny standing on the plank seat at the edge of the dock, Julie's arm around her, Peter shading his eyes, staring up at the top deck of the boat, Tim capering about, waving his arms and shouting. And when Walton could finally see and be seen clearly, he stayed a little longer where he was, holding the moment.

For now he could see them, really see them, sharply delineated in the bright, electric air, each in movement, each so poignantly and fluidly alive, so peculiarly himself, that Walton's throat ached. This, he thought, *is* life, is my life, our life.

Julie, head thrown back, strong but delicate chin braced (quivering a little, he remembered) against the air (in premonition of what ambush, what surprise attack?), eyes searching the sun, the source—for portents? And then the identification, the discovery of mortal man, her husband, and a slim brown arm thrust out and up in welcome and a straining forward, a reaching that would, he knew, in a few minutes be close and fierce in mingled laughter and tears ("Why do you always cry when you're happy, Mom? When you're meeting someone?"), so surprisingly fierce a spirit in so gentle a nature, laughing and weeping into the sun in my arms.

Jenny, clasped now in her mother's other arm, yet pressing away; already, though half-formed, all compact of independence, in wriggling motion that was not rejection but insistence on autonomy. Walton remembered the morning he, cross and sleepy, ordered the children to remain upstairs and not bother him while he hurriedly prepared to go to work. Remembered this and, three minutes later, the hurried, still awkward footsteps of Jennifer on the stairs. Exasperated, he said, "I thought I told you to stay upstairs." And she, stamping for emphasis, "And I told me to come downstairs. I told me and I am me." As now, Julie was forced to put her down on the dock, and Jenny, head back to look up at her mother, was stating her case with assertive arm and foot, before scrambling back up on the bench.

Tim. Whom I called Buddha-in-rompers. Tim, whose first word was no version of Mother or Father, but Light, pronounced "Laaht"— as carried into the living room, his arm outstretched and pointing, to the chandelier, a lamp, a wall button, or best, the sunlight pouring through a window pane: "Laaht! Laaht!" More light—so now, chin on chest in meditation, whose eyes would be bright with love, he waits, then sees, and his arms go out—to hold. Round. Holding the light.

And Peter, erect, fists clenched—in tension or in preparation for the indifferent world out there he had discovered early? This is my son whom I failed in the first years, bringing him to premature loneliness and vigilance so that now he stands, head thrust slightly forward in guarded inquiry about life: What's ahead, what's in store for us? Peter, who last spring had said, "I always expect something bad. Then when it's good, I like it even better." Not cynical, but toughened, serious, alert, standing guard with responsibility.

This is what it means, Walton thought, and felt a sharp pang that Maria was not there too, vivid and staunch, grasping at life with both hands.

This was what it meant. He waved, reaching out through the glittering spokes of light to them, his life. Then he turned to join the line of passengers, those waiting to cross over the gangplank onto the island.

This tingling of his sunburnt flesh, this taste of salt, and its crust on his eyebrows, this easing welcome aching in his limbs as he stretched out in the porch chair—this peace, this coming home at sundown. The Colonel's incomparable old-fashioned in one hand, Walton drew deeply on his first cigarette of the day and looked out on Menemsha Pond.

He had always loved the end of day, whether in summer shadows lengthening across the grass, in autumn the flaring colors in the trees gleaming a last brave minute in the light of the round red sun's departure; whether the early winter night had fallen and, with shades drawn against the cold, the fire flared in the hearth and ruddied the faces of the children; or in spring the paler sun had retreated slowly, leaving a thin white light, vibration rather than color, in which the delicate green shoots and sprouts quivered into life, and there were buds upon the maples and their husks upon the ground. In whatever season, end of day. Home, come home, the long task done, the journey ended and the rest begun. Systole and diastole, and one clear marker on the calendar of life: another day.

And here, now, rocking on the old screened porch, with the shimmering stillness of Menemsha Pond far below and the dark shadows already gathering in purple pockets in the hills across the pond, he was at peace. Peace was not absolute quiet; it lay, delicate and throbbing in his hands—animate, pulsing in the long grasses of the meadows between him and the Pond. It flicked those silvery burnished waters with a quiver, stirred the dark blue and green of the pines on the bank, brushed clean his mind and burned with this salty tang upon his lips.

Peace was audible—in the creaking of the rocker, in the soft voice of Julie within, preparing supper and answering Jenny's piping questions, in the shouts of the boys in the meadows below. Peace was polyphonic and it spread through time, through the day's movements, so that these voices were the recurring statements of earlier moments in the morning and afternoon, bringing them back to mind in their first brilliance, though muted and slowed in the adagio of end-of-day. Peter and Tim, brown and glistening, racing into the surf with cries of exuberance as croaking and raucous as the very gulls'. Jennifer, pushing and patting at the dark brown sand of her castle, pressing her hands' imprint on the castle's turrets; withdrawing them, to regard with grave intensity her mark. Then finally lifting her smudged face to him, and there, under her sun-softened hair, in her eyes a dark discovery. And pushing herself up, displaying all the sand and mud clinging in the soft creases of her neck and inner elbows and the cracks under her knees, running to Julie, calling, "Mommy, Mommy, come see."

And Timmy, staring at him seriously, almost mournfully: "Daddy, I must talk to you in privatcy." Then, behind the sand dune, earnestness wide-eyed, "Daddy, I almost died, didn't I?"

"You were pretty sick."

"And if I'd died, I'd be dead forever in heaven, but it wouldn't be me, would it?"

"Tim, that's something none of us knows—just what happens after death and whether we're still ourselves, or even what that means then."

And after a silence, grass-plucking, low-voiced, "I don't want you to die, Daddy."

"Well, I hope I won't for a long time. There's still a lot of life I want to live."

"And I want you to. I want my Daddy to live to a hundred trillion." Hugging and, as rocked in the seesaw of his father's arms, laughing, laughing and howling with delight. But when set down, after catching his breath, eyes suddenly widened: "I'm glad you came, Daddy. When I was sick. When you're away, it's a little bit like you're dead, isn't it? I mean, you're not there, are you? And you wouldn't be here if you were dead." And from that silence, "Daddy, can you float with just your nose and tummy and toes showing? I can. Come see." Tugging. "Come see. Quick."

And through it all, Julie . . . After that one first look, after that first frightened plunge into the clear depths of her eyes—to find there no doubt, no reservation, no accusation (she did not know then; there had been no letter; reprieve, reprieve)—always Julie, Julie everywhere. Administering lunch after the long, happy morning of being shown and being told—all the achievements and adventures of the summer (Had he really been *here* that weekend of the hurricane and Timmy's illness? No, that had been somewhere else, a place to be found only in the geography of the emotions, not Chilmark, not home, not here), all the plans for the next weeks. (Dad, did you see this? . . . Daddy, I made it. . . . You know what we're going to do? . . . And I can swim a hundred yards. . . . Dad, Daddy, Dad. Come see. Look.)

Lunch, then, and again the sense of admission, of a place in a world where lunch was not a meal, but a benison, like the Colonel's unexpected blessing, with the children's bowed heads exposing the backs of their necks—spoken in low, embarrassed gruffness: "We thank thee, Lord, for this food and that we are all together again. Amen."

And Julie on the beach, in a new black bathing suit, hugging her knees and slender brown legs in an ecstasy of thoughtfulness (What do you see there? What do you think you see? How can you know in your clean vision?), rocking on her heels, squinting into the sun with wrinkles around her eyes that lent a further sweetness to her face. Julie laughing into the sunlight, Julie abandoning herself to the sun, eyes closed, stretched out beside him, with his hand on her foot, he holding it as though it were a talisman.

Those feet. He had forgotten until now that day so long ago, when, bored and dry at a meeting in a basement room, he had tried to amuse himself by looking out the window flush with the sidewalk beyond it and, watching the multitudinous feet passing by, imagining the persons they supported.

And then a pair of feet, so small, so slender, so tenderly arched that one could not conceive of them as providing enough support for any human body. And the realization, suddenly shaken by a gust of passion and tenderness: those are the feet of Julie Norton. Julie, Julie, Julie . . . And he would have run from the room, out to overtake her, to clasp her and stammer his new knowledge of love. . . .

The sun was gone; as though by way of announcement, the screen door slammed. The Colonel, smiling. "Ready for a refill? I'll join you now—and Julie in a moment."

Walton held out his glass, and was caught up by another memory of the day: the Colonel taking off his shirt and trousers at the beach to go for a swim. Odysseus, stripping off his rags. A used body, heavy and gnarled. A lived body. It suited the man, as Walton knew him—scarred, heavy, powerful, with the gentleness of real strength, not at peace, but alive, aging but vital.

The Colonel returned, holding the door open for Julie and for Jennifer, who was proudly and precariously bearing a tray of hot hors d'oeuvres.

She plunked it down on the low table beside Walton, with such force that all three adults half reached to retrieve the shattered pieces. But the tray and plates were intact.

"These are hot dogs," said Jenny, poking at them. "They don't look like hot dogs, but they are hot dogs. They are baby hot dogs, little eensy-weensy hot dogs, for my doll. But you may eat them, Daddy, because Mommy says so, even if they are for my doll. And you're not a doll, are you?"

There she stood, fists tightly clenched, wringing her arms in her excitement. An expression, Walton remembered, that he had first used about Maria, when she was a little girl. For it was the same motion, the swift pounding at the air, not in anger or hostility, but in excited joy. The images of Maria, of the little girl on the ferry that morning, and Jennifer herself merged for Walton, as he snatched her up and hugged her, assuring her that he was not a doll.

But she would not be held. She would not be claimed. One of her tiny hot dogs in each hand, she scrambled off his knees, down the porch steps, and ran off through the tall grass, calling "Pee-tuh! Tim-mee!"

Walton sat rocking in contentment and looking from Julie's characteristic swift brushing back of hair from her forehead to the Colonel's familiar ruminative expression, as he stroked his chin with one hand and with the other supported his glass on his knee with thumb and forefinger, the other three fingers, gnarled and broad and palely freckled, spread in relaxation down his leg.

"How does it happen," Walton asked, "that everyone calls you the Colonel—as though there weren't any other colonels? I hadn't thought much about it, but that was the way it was with my father too, in Cleveland. To many people he was always known simply as the Professor."

Colonel Norton lifted his shaggy brows, and the wrinkles around his eyes squeezed themselves into sharp relief.

"Why, I don't know," he said. "It's only the people around here, of course. No one in the service—no military men—would think of—"

Julie broke in, smiling.

"It's because they trust you and want you to take charge. Lots of us spend our lives looking for someone to take charge. That's part of why I'm often so hard on Walton. I want him to."

The Colonel cleared his throat and looked away. Walton grinned.

"I'm all ready to," he said, "after I've had about three days, like this, of just complete indolence."

"I'll bet you *are* tired," said the Colonel.

"Maybe I won't give you that long," Julie said airily. "I've got a lot on my mind."

Walton looked at her sharply, but her expression told him little. It was mischievous—or flirting? They all fell silent now, and he brooded a little on Julie, on the swift dartings of her moods, like small fish, swerving, turning, flicking their tails and reversing themselves, then sweeping off in another direction—within the bowl, the tank, of their marriage? But then— Suddenly he felt drowsy, disinclined to pursue his conjectures.

The advancing dusk, swift now at the end of summer, turned the air lavender, except for the red glow low in the west. Wherever the children had gone, they were silent, and all the world was still, so that when a sharp, cool breeze arose, it seemed audible in itself, a sibilant sigh that needed no instrument for its music.

At that moment, Peter's voice, low but clear, was heard from around the corner of the house, just behind the Colonel's chair.

"Now you listen, Timmy, because what I got to say to you is important."

"Me too," said Jenny insistently, "me too."

"Yes, you too," Peter replied, with a note of condescension in his voice. "You too. Maybe you can understand some of it."

"I can," piped Jenny. "I can understan' it. Yes, I can. I can too."

"Well, anyway," said Peter. "What I mean about fighting, Timmy, is that you can't say it's good and you can't say it's bad. Grampa told me that, and you know he was a great fighter—"

"In the army," Tim whooped eagerly. "He was a colonel in the army. That's why people call him Colonel. He killed a million Frenchmen or something."

"Not Frenchmen, Tim! They're our friends. Those were Germans in the First World War. And not a million. And anyway he wasn't glad to kill them; he told me so. You make it sound like it was fun. But Grampa was sad. Only he had to, or they'd kill him and conquer the world. Now listen—"

"Pow!" yelled Tim. "First World War! Pow! Pow! Pow! Uh-uh-uh-uh-uh-uh—" The air shook with the vibrations from his machine gun. And "Pow! Uh-uh-uh-" went Jenny.

"Lis-*en*," said Peter. "If you don't shut up, I'm not going to tell you, and it's very important."

"I'll listen," Tim promised in a breathless voice.

"I'll listen too," said Jennifer, and, more reflectively, "Pow!"

"Well, then," Peter went on in a milder tone, "fighting is not just good. And it's not just bad. It's what you're fighting for and who you're fighting against. It's *why*. So when you say you hate Jerry Perkins because he has a boat and won't take you out in it, and you're going to beat up on him, that's foolish. Maybe it's mean of him not to take you, but it's not worth a fight. That's what Grampa says—that a man's not always brave because he fights, that sometimes it's braver not to fight. Especially when it won't do any good, or save people's lives, or protect them from bad men. So, if there's no point in a fight, you're not a coward not to. And that's what I meant to tell you, because you're talking about beating up on Jerry, but you're mad really at Bill Lane because he called you a coward and he's a lot bigger than you—"

"He did not!" said Tim, and Walton could envision him, red-faced and indignant. "And I am not, and it's not fair for him to say so."

"You see, Timmy." Peter's voice was earnest. "You're all mixed up. You say he didn't say it and then you say it wasn't fair of him to say it. But that's all right; everybody gets mixed up. Are you worried about whether you are a coward, Tim? Because you're not. After Bill Lane called you that and began to tease Jenny, you went right up and took her hand and led her away. So you're not a coward, because he might have hit you but you were brave enough not to run away and leave Jenny. Anyway, Grampa says a brave man is one who is afraid of something and does it anyway, to help someone else, like Mommy said Daddy did because he doesn't like airplanes but he flew here to help you when you were sick. So he's a brave man and Grampa's a brave man and you and I are brave men—boys."

"That's good," said Tim. "I like that."

"I'm a brave man, too," Jenny asserted, then drifted off into a meditative tone: "Grampa talks a lot."

Through the men's explosion of laughter on the porch, Julie called, "Come in and get washed for supper, children. Peter! Timmy! Jenny! Supper!"

They scrambled up the steps, Peter in the lead, yelling, "I'm going to sit beside Daddy!" And the others, "No, me!" . . . "No, *me!*"

At the candle-lit table, Tim, his scrubbed face shining, turned to his father. "I'm brave, Dad," he confided. "I'm a brave boy, like you."

Julie was writing poetry again, including a long poem still unfinished. All she told him about it was that she called it "Meditation."
STOP

He had told her the outcome of the conflict at the Foundation, and about Leon Goodman's intervention, leading to several conferences with the partners of the Colosseum, a leading publishing house, who had offered him a senior editorship he was inclined to accept. STOP

Julie had called her father in to hear the news, and Walton had answered their questions and volunteered information about so radical a shift in jobs, the nature of the work, the large salary, and his feeling of ambivalence about working for P.H. He awaited only Julie's approval to accept the Colosseum offer. STOP.

The Colonel had gone off to bed, and Walton had poured a bourbon for himself, a Scotch for Julie. Julie had told him many stories about the children's summer, her talks with Maria. . . . STOP

Walton had told her of the experience with Abe Fortune, the discussions about the governorship, Jane's trouble. STOP

That was the way it had been—dry, informative, almost formal, awkward. No, perhaps not. That was the way he had felt. Julie had been warm enough, gay enough, humorous and tender about the children, shy, and pleased about her poetry.

And now they were silent. Julie was mending shirts and sweaters and rompers, smiling at him once in a while (was there something wicked in her eyes?), sipping her drink, humming to the soft music of the radio, which they had left on in the kitchen. Walton was smoking his pipe and brooding.

Who then was this woman his wife? Where had the peace of sundown gone? Where had it fled, the certainty and the love, the warmth and the security?

He did not know. He thought, in bitterness and in distress, that that must be his epitaph. He visualized the stone:

WALTON HERRICK
1907-19—
HE DID NOT KNOW.

What was this wall between them, after the closeness and comfort of the day? Or was the wall within him, separating his present uneasy self from the free, fulfilled man of the afternoon? And why so uneasy? Was the change exclusively in himself, or had something darkened Julie's happiness? Even so, why should the slightest frown, perhaps only of preoccupation; the merest flicker of impatience; the most superficial suggestion of sarcasm in her voice—and, he always kept forgetting, she could wield sarcasm as a whip when she herself was really stung—why should any of these be sufficient to upset his equilibrium?

Julie stirred, put down her sewing, and went to the kitchen to turn off the radio. When she had resumed her seat and taken up a shirt of Tim's, she looked directly at him.

"I know all about you and Gail," she said and—in parody of demure smugness—"I know all about it, and I am prepared to forgive you."

Walton stiffened. The familiar red clouds began to sift through his brain.

"You do?" he said coldly. "You are?"

Her eyes were dancing.

"Yes," she said saucily. "Gail was here the weekend after you came up to see Tim. She thought you'd already told me." She bit off a thread. "I wish you had," she said softly.

"That weekend was hardly the time," he replied stiffly. "And since we didn't—"

She flapped a derisive hand at him.

"Don't say, 'And since we didn't really finally go to bed together.' Gail says it was all her fault, but if I know anything about you, Walton Herrick, it wasn't you who stopped short of the bed."

"No," said Walton in a low voice, staring down at the pipe he held in his hand. "No, it wasn't."

"I'd been gone a couple of weeks, of course. I can understand how you must have become unbearably lonely." Her smile was gone, her lip slightly curled, her eyes beginning to grow hot.

Walton exploded to his feet.

"Goddamnit!" he said. "Don't go getting so damn superior and sarcastic! How did you leave me? With a look of hate that I can't ever forget, that's how! You couldn't have made it plainer that you didn't give a damn about me or what I did." He drained his glass in a gulp and stalked over to the decanter for more.

"So now it's my fault." Julie's voice was icy. "I was prepared for that, because it's always my fault. What I couldn't guess, though, was just how you'd manage to work out the details this time. But you're very ingenious, Walton. The greater the challenge, the more ingenious."

He grunted in exasperation, shaking his head from side to side.

"Look—" he said.

"No," said Julie hotly, "you look. Just once, you look. What you saw was hate, all right. Hate for you, that you could be the way you were. But I don't hate, and look hateful at, someone I don't give a damn about. And looking hateful doesn't mean I don't give a damn about what that other person *does*. I'm not going to let you slip that in that way, you slippery man, you."

"I wasn't trying to slip anything in, goddamnit." Walton realized he was bellowing, as much from the feeling of blood in his head as from the noise he made. "I was drunk," he said more quietly, "and lonely and hurt. That's what I was."

"Good," said Julie, clipping off the word. "Good. I'm glad you were hurt. I was hurt too. But I suppose that *that* thought, any thought, about my hurt is too vague a concept for you to grasp."

"Julie. Julie," said Walton, a strange feeling of desperation coming over him, "Julie, *all right*. I did it. But I didn't do— We—" He stopped short and stood there, feeling like a schoolboy apprehended in a moment of adolescent crime.

"I know all about just what you did, and what you didn't do. And I'm not so small as to pretend I don't, and let you trap yourself into lies. What I don't know and would like you to tell me is whether you also went to bed with that Karen Kuddly-Kiddly that Maria met at lunch."

Walton struck the side of his head with the heel of his hand.

"Stop torturing me," he said. "Is this a criminal court? Why are you firing questions at me like some damned prosecutor? And I didn't go to bed with Gail, so don't say did I go to bed with Karen Kodály *too*."

"Very well," said Julie, with the smile he dreaded—half malicious, half self-wounding, it seemed to him. "Very well. Did you go to bed with Karen Koh-dah-yee or did you only almost go to bed with her?" She sang softly, in derision, "I'm carin' for Karen, She's carryin' a torch for me." Then, flatly, "I want another drink."

Walton came to her obediently, "Now don't go off the deep end," he said placatingly. "Take it easy on the drinking. I did *not* go to bed with Karen. I saw her just once, after that lunch. You knew all about her before you and I were married, and nothing's ever happened since we were married." He stayed for several minutes by the liquor, prolonging the preparation of Julie's Scotch and soda. He felt both ashamed and propitiatory. What made him so need to pacify her? He didn't with other people.

As she accepted the drink, Julie smiled at him. Warmly and sweetly, he thought with sudden renewed fury. Sure, sure, nail him to a cross and then, when his answer came out the way she wanted, all was forgiven, come home. What arrogance! What superficiality! And now her voice, mollified, with that undertone of complacent womanly sniffles: "Well, that's good anyway. How near did you come? I don't care, if you really didn't, however tempted, and didn't *because* you chose not to."

"Not near at all. And I'll be goddamned if I'm going to say anything more about it. Or anything else." He poured another drink. "You'll just have to take me the way I am. I can't help it if I'm attractive to women."

For a sickening moment the full force of his fatuousness hit him like a blow, but Julie gave him little time to recover. Her voice was again glacially sarcastic.

"I'll be glad to take you the way you are, if I can find out what you are—or who you are—besides fatally attractive to women. And it's you who'd better watch the drinking."

He groaned.

"Julie, let's stop, stop. I'm no match for you. You can riddle me full of holes any time you want to. You're always too quick for me. But I won't give in. Let's stop before we can't stop."

"I can riddle you full of holes because you *are* full of holes. That's why. And of course you want to stop: who's getting hurt now? Why do you suppose I'm too quick for you? Because I'm telling the truth, and that scares you. That's what *you* call quick!"

He set down his glass, and covered his face with his hands. His head was literally whirling, yet now as he heard her speak again, her voice once more softened, this very relenting in her somehow angered him more, made him want to strike in his turn.

What she said was, "Do you think I like to have to say these things?"

For a single flashing instant he wanted to blurt out the story of his affair with Sonia, strike Julie with it, wound her. But he held himself rigidly in check. Smarting with, it seemed, a thousand stings, he said with painful slowness, "I don't know why, when I'm alone, I can think and see things so clearly, and when I'm with you they evaporate into thin air. Julie, I did work hard this summer, at myself. I kept a journal—"

He finally looked directly at her and on her face saw an expression of expectancy and, it seemed, even of tenderness. "I—I—I can't seem to tell you what I want to," he finished miserably.

She was soft and sweet and kind.

"Tell me about the journal," she said.

He came over to her, feeling the lump in his belly relax, the tension that squeezed his ribs relent and subside. He told her, stumblingly at first, then with slowly increasing ease.

She interrupted him.

"Read me some," she said. . . .

When he finally stopped, he had been reading aloud for two hours. Each time that he had finished an entry, he had looked up and found her eyes bright and attentive; each time, she had said, "Go on. I want to hear more."

He read her the first entry, omitted the second as not likely to be so interesting to her (she said, "All right, but I want to hear them all eventually"), read the third one, about his "grandfathers" and the two clowns (she whispered something when he described his "black grandfather's" turning away from life, and then read, "This is what Julie means about me," but would not repeat what she had said). Then he read the fourth one—the one he thought of as "Timor Mortis and the Face at the Window"—and saw that her eyes were wet; finally, omitting only the references to Karen and Sonia, he read the entry of July 18, ending, "Having been trained, and having accustomed myself in the darkness of my soul to another atmosphere, I must learn to breathe the true air that surrounds me."

They were silent then, looking at each other. Looking, Walton thought, and seeing each other. He felt tired and relaxed and at peace. With an effort, he rose, took their stale glasses, and went to the kitchen. When he returned with a fresh glass for each, he said quietly, "Come. Let's go to bed."

Julie rose and held out her arms. As he stood, arms flung out to either side to protect the glasses, she hugged him and laid her cheek against his chest. "That's all," she said. "That's all I ask. For you to be open and honest with yourself, about yourself. To—to listen to yourself." But as she clung to him and they made their awkward progress to the bedroom, she added sharply, "And to me, too. Don't forget that."

He laughed. Setting down the glasses on a chest of drawers, he let out the most vigorous roar of laughter he had known in a long time.

Julie looked up at him demurely and, when he had subsided, announced (that was what it was), "I like you to laugh at me."

She eluded his grasp, snatched up from the bed her nightgown and robe, and escaped into the bathroom.

Undressing, Walton wondered over the sudden return of his uneasiness. He had heard the door close and then he was abruptly aware of a familiar panic rising in him. Familiar? But not identifiable. Or was it? A story flashed into his mind—one of an American friend of Freud's who had been living in Vienna for a year with a mistress and then, when his wife came over from the United States to join him, found himself impotent with her. What had Freud's comment been? It eluded him and he thrust the whole anecdote away, squaring his shoulders and quickly pulling on his pajamas.

Julie was wearing a new robe and nightgown of pale green. Her black hair was freshly brushed. She looked, he thought, like a sacrificial victim, and instantly rejected the thought as absurd. She looked radiant.

"Well," he said. "Just that. My God. Well!"

She swirled. "You like?" she asked. "Ees good? O.K.?"

"I do. It is. O.K."

The brilliance of her eyes made him lower his.

"Julie," he said, "shall we talk a little longer? I've always liked anticipation, and I want to tell you about those men at the Colosseum."

"Anticipation?" she asked loftily. "What in the world are you anticipating? Sleep, perhaps? And dreams?"

"No," he replied, leaning into the words. "You. You, my dear wife."

"Oh, la!" she exclaimed. "You are bold, sir." Giggling, she subsided on the bed and affected a hoarse whisper. "All right, big boy, I'm with you."

Walton laughed nervously. At least, it felt like nervous laughter, but there was no recognition of it in Julie's expression, and he plunged ahead.

"Well," he said, "I answered Leon Goodman's letter, just saying that I'd like to explore the new possibility. We had lunch—you know, it's funny; Leon's always a behind-the-scenes man, the prototype of the liaison man, the negotiator, the suggester, the bringer-together. He's so much this, and so often does it by letter or telephone, that I always find myself surprised when I'm actually with him. It's almost as though I hadn't realized I knew *him*—really knew him. And then I find I'd forgotten what a really nice man, what a really good man he is."

Julie laughed.

"He's a pasha. A little Jewish pasha with horn-rimmed spectacles, whom I always see holding a long water pipe and looking over it shrewdly at the world."

Walton, lighting his pipe, nodded thoughtfully.

"You do have to say Jewish when you're talking about Leon. He's so genuine a citizen of the world that I don't mean it in any parochial sense. Yet his Jewishness and his goodness are all mixed together; without being one, he couldn't be his particular kind of other." He broke off. "What are you grinning about?"

"About your careful way of being sure that I'm not saying anything anti-Semitic. It's so silly."

"I was not!" Walton began. "I was—" and again broke off, with a laugh, at first rueful but gradually becoming real merriment. "All right."

She squeezed his hand.

"So what did Leon say?"

"He suggested I go into publishing. His firm are the attorneys for several big publishing houses, among them the Colosseum. And just as many other people do, the partners there turned to him for suggestions, because their top editor is retiring. And he proposed me."

"But why wouldn't they want someone already in publishing?"

Walton shook his head.

"I asked that. And Leon said they had the feeling that if they get someone with a good background and reputation from outside, they'd prefer it, having already plenty of professional editors. Think it will interest more writers—especially those in public life. Anyway, it appealed to me. I've often thought I'd like book publishing. My teaching's obviously given me the background for judgment of books, the Foundation for administrative work. What I don't know anything about is selling books, marketing them. But I guess there'll be plenty of others to teach me about that. But about the owners—

"There are three of them, equal partners. The only one you've probably heard of is Sean O'Neill. You know—on television—the Information and Interpretation program? And he's a popular lecturer."

Julie nodded.

"Of course. Did you like him?"

"He's very charming. I've talked most with him—the first time at his country house. It was like being in Hollywood, or at least my idea of what Hollywood is like. We had a swim and sat dabbling our feet in the pool while talking about terms, and then lunch in the patio beside the pool—all sure out of my league."

"Your league's bigger than that," Julie said indignantly.

"Maybe. Maybe not. Anyway, he's my one doubt about the job. But I guess we'll get along all right. He's both very Irish and very sophisticated. Full of blarney, yet with real steel in him too, articulate, not above slapstick, yet at times strangely dignified and with a little Irish poetry in him. I suspect he has a hot temper from the way, when I crossed him in a discussion of current books, he got a look of almost poisonous sweetness in his eyes, which struck me as probably being inhibited anger. Like me, he doesn't like being contradicted. What are you laughing at?"

Julie's shoulders shook.

"You know, the only thing that equals your sensitiveness to other people's emotions is your misreading of what those emotions mean. With you, everybody either feels like you or is the opposite."

Walton felt a vast contentment. "That's pretty close to right," he said, and laughed. "You're sharp tonight."

He could not have described the look he saw in her eyes, but he knew he was not misinterpreting her emotions now. His own feelings throughout the evening would cause the hardiest psychological seismographer to despair of charting them, but now, now he was clearheaded as he had rarely been; he felt that he fitted his body, that he possessed his own feelings.

"And the other two?" Julie asked.

Walton grinned.

"The other two? Well, Julian Price may not be the proverbial silent partner, but he doesn't talk much. He's dark and hook-nosed (O'Neill's freckled and light and very lively), and he sucks on his pipe in a sort of melancholy way. He has kind eyes (don't start laughing; I'm not going to analyze his emotions) but sometimes they look sort of clouded with pain. Cyrano de Bergerac. He's tall and has a deep voice; O'Neill's short and has a rather high voice. And yet I guess O'Neill's the husband."

Julie raised her eyebrows.

"The what?"

"I think O'Neill's the dominant one of the two, the initiator, the more decisive one—"

Julie interrupted.

"Oh," she said gravely, "is *that* what a husband is?"

Walton winced, then laughed.

"Ouch," he said ruminatively, and then plunged ahead. "Well, anyway, Price has obviously a great range of knowledge of the book business. He may have less flair, but he has more depth, and I imagine keeps the whole enterprise going day by day, overseeing both big and small details."

Julie sighed and took a small sip from her drink.

"I don't see anything left for the third partner."

"But there is. The financial side. He has the best mind for figures of the three and I believe has a large private fortune. His name is Brooks —Hiram Brooks. Straight New England granite, either from Maine or Vermont. O'Neill's Irish Catholic, I think Price is Jewish, but Brooks is what I'd call Congregational-atheist. That is, raised the one way, but believing in nothing now but profit and rectitude. He was O'Neill's original partner—Price came in some few years later—and the two of them must have made some pair: Saint Patrick and Cotton Mather without the theology. I'm sure that it's Price who reconciles the elements."

"You make it all very vivid. Now describe Hiram Brooks."

Walton scratched his head.

"That's a tough one—to make you see him. He looks as though he came out of *Pickwick Papers,* and he's stout—but he's not like Pickwick. Let me fix my drink first."

When he returned with a fresh drink, Julie looked at him thoughtfully.

"You drink more than you used to," she said.

"Yes," Walton replied, "but—"

He stopped himself, sat down on the bed, and went on more slowly. "Just yes, I guess. This summer, anyway . . . Now Brooks. He has a massive gray head, balding on top (he's the oldest of the three, about sixty, I'd say), and he wears the funniest little half-moon glasses—for reading, I suppose, but he seldom takes them off. He looks over the top of them at you and his eyes are a frosty, glinty blue. He dresses very plainly, rather formally, but wears old-fashioned double-breasted vests or waistcoats. That's what throws you. He seems flinty—stern New England—and yet he affects those strange glasses and vests. And what's more, he talks like a blend of Vermont and Oxford, which is pretty damned hard to do. Abe Fortune's assumed kind of speech—you remember?—isn't a bit stranger than the broad *a* coming in the midst of Brooks's nasal sentence. And he drawls. And while he talks, he sort of beats time with his half-moon spectacles, which are attached to a black ribbon—you know, pince-nez. He's a good raconteur, and greets everybody as though he were the returning prodigal son, but when you get around to talking about money—wham! all the joviality and Oxford accent are gone, and the steel trap snaps."

Julie shivered.

"Walton, they sound awfully formidable. I know it's one of the best publishing houses, but are you going to like working for them after P.H.? You don't much like to be bossed. Yet you won't even consider being governor, and you want to work for three men like that."

"Two. Price will be good to me and for me. And I'm not unformidable myself, ma'am, begging your pardon. I'm no governor. Haldane hit it on the head when he said I was a good poet, but a bum politician. Working on books seems to me, after the Foundation and the Congressional investigation, an ideal life. I'm hungry for it."

Julie pursed her lips in thought.

"I'm glad it's not me. I'm glad I'm a woman. Won't you have to be a good politician to deal with Mr. O'Neill and Mr. Brooks? After P.H., who—whatever troubles you had this summer—*is* your friend and so gentle a man?"

Walton shrugged.

"I think I can take care of myself. Maybe in this work I can be a poet-politician. And working for P.H. had become hard for me especially because he is a friend, and gentle. You know, I told you how he referred back to the time I'd not backed him up on his project? Well, I've never said this to anybody—and I couldn't to him—it was because the others really did convince me it wasn't a good project, and that I'd backed it in the first place because I'd misjudged it, or even perhaps only because it was P.H.'s. I think it'll be great to make a fresh start with new people, with whom I can be reasonably impersonal. I need that. The mixture of business and friendship is a mistake I've always made, and I'm determined not to do it this time."

"You really are sure, aren't you?" Julie looked half-curious, half-amused.

"Are you against it? You sound so wistful. Yes, I do want to do it, to make a clean sweep. They've offered me a five-year contract. I held out for that; they wanted three, but it's all new to me and it's going to take time to get broken in. And that's all the security I want. If it doesn't work out, I can always go back to teaching. As a matter of fact, I miss it, though I don't miss the academic life. Anyway, I'm a teacher or a book man, not a politician or a public life man."

They were silent. At last Walton raised his head from his study of the pattern in the quilt and said, looking directly at Julie, "So what do you say?"

She hesitated.

"You're not just asking me about the job?"

He covered her hand, looked at her urgently.

"No, Julie, not just the job."

She slipped out of bed and walked silently over to the window. Drawing the curtain to one side, she looked out into the darkness.

"I love the man who wrote the journal," she said slowly. "I don't love the man who made a pass at Gail two weeks after I left. My best friend—I'll never feel the same about her again."

"But, Julie—"

"Wait a minute. That doesn't mean I can't understand how it happened. I understand better after hearing you read tonight, but most of all, I guess, because of Dudley's visit here."

"You mean when he and Cynthia—"

"No. No. I was going to tell you. Much earlier in the summer he came up alone for a weekend. It was just after he'd been out home with you—it must have been the weekend of you and Gail. I never thought of that. Did he—"

Walton nodded.

"Yes, he was there. At the party. He went home alone, first. But you mean he came right up here then? And never told me? Dud Foote?"

"That's right," said Julie, and he could not fathom her expression. "He told me that you'd told him about our separating. But of course he didn't mention Gail, and I didn't make any connection until now."

Anger surged through Walton.

"And you let him come? And the son of a bitch never said a word to me and went on being *my* good friend. Some friend! To say nothing of Cynthia, coming on the next week or so. My God, that night at their house! I went to dinner and they had a fearful row. She was accusing him about some woman—"

"Me," said Julie, and this time the mixture of pride and amusement was plain. "Cynthia told me. Everybody tells everything sooner or later, it seems. But, Walton, wait a minute before you get all enraged. I think Dudley was sort of in love with me—or thought he was: sometimes they're hard to separate. And he felt terribly disillusioned about you, though he didn't say why—except that he couldn't understand your being willing to accept the separation, until I made it clear to him how I had insisted. For I found myself defending you. Almost all the time. No, that's not fair; he didn't keep after you; I was always bringing you up. But, Walton, nothing happened. Except talk. And now I know he'd just seen you with Gail and felt badly about me."

Walton's throat felt so swollen that he could barely force the words through.

"Dud Foote!" he repeated thickly. "Goddamn it to hell! After all—"

Julie interrupted him.

" 'After all you've done for him!' I know, I know. But he wasn't really disloyal, except by your code. And your code, darling, is pretty elastic. How can you be so hard on Dudley when you and Gail—"

"I don't know, but it's not the same thing," Walton cried passionately.

"It's not. That's right. Your friend, who falls in love with me, comes up and we have long talks. My friend, who's always been a little in love with you, almost goes to bed with you. If it's a question of loyalty, she was more disloyal than Dudley, just as you were readier to betray me than I was you. Walton, remember what you just read to me tonight about loyalty and constancy."

Walton bowed his head.

"Yes. Julie, I do see what you mean. I won't even pretend that I was going to tell you about Gail—and I don't know how much my reason was self-protection and how much not wanting to break up your and her friendship."

"Telling me wouldn't break it up," Julie said. "I'd have gone to her as she came to me. And it's made a dent, all right, it's changed, but it hasn't broken. And just the same way, when Cynthia got some sense of how Dudley was feeling, she and I had a real straight talk, and became friendly. We're not likely to be real friends, but we get along fine. She said she did with Lydia, too."

"Lydia!" Walton jumped to his feet. "Either I'm going crazy, or everybody else is. I didn't know the Footes had seen her. I seem to be the only one who doesn't know anything. Julie, I just can't get over Dud."

Julie's face was suddenly set in firm lines.

"You must. Because it's life, Walton, and you can't make the rules. You can't sit on your throne and legislate. And then do whatever you want to, and see no connection. Especially when you know better. And you do—right there in your journal."

"My God, Julie," Walton cried in exasperation. "I wish I'd never read it to you."

"I'm sure you do," she said calmly. "Right now. But not earlier and not later. Not tomorrow and not next month. And maybe some other times. But not most of the time."

He looked at her now, and it seemed to him that he had never seen her before. With all that he had made of her—yes, that was it: all he had made of her—he had not seen, not known *her*. And however much she had flailed at him (flailed? flayed him), whatever perfectionist demands she had made on him, however much she had hated him in May—he had done this one unpardonable thing: he had not seen her, heard her, known her. He felt an impulse to fling himself at her, grasp her knees, beg for forgiveness. He said: "Julie, read me one of your poems."

She shook her head.

"Not now. Not tonight. Sometime. Soon, maybe. But not now."

He accepted this. And, although all his failures, his unimaginativeness, his *sins* were over him like a shroud, he forced himself to say quietly, "Then let's go to bed."

For a moment, with the lights out, he lay there stiffly, miserable in self-hatred and inadequacy, yearning for oblivion.

And then she turned to him fully, whispering, "I'm glad you're here." Woman. Woman against him, pressing gently, giving, accepting. His dull distress turned to a new panic. He was afraid, shrunken with fear and guilt and shame. Within himself, he cowered abjectly.

Julie drew back. He heard the rustling of her withdrawal, a husky whispering sound that somehow echoed his own inner withdrawal. He lay there, bleak, desolate, unable to move even his hand.

Then she was back, her hand stretched out to him. "I want you," she said. "Don't be afraid because you're all exposed. Stay with me."

And slowly he felt himself surge back into himself; he felt her flesh, herself; he knew himself, and rose and went in to her, in gentleness and strength. And he was aware, as he had not been before, of their separate rhythms, and taught himself to find hers. It was not, he thought fleetingly, to possess but to join. When he said, "I love you," he had never said it before. And they climbed the mountain and were at peace.

JOURNAL: *10*

from the journal of Walton Herrick . . .

Sept. 13, 1953

Despite all yesterday's emotional turmoil, I awoke this morning far earlier than usual. The sun was just rising, and I could see, as the shade over the window billowed lazily, a glimpse of the shining green world outside. I lay there for a little while, hearing Julie's soft breathing beside me and knowing an insistent kind of peace, but not its source, feeling it stir and move within me, easy yet unfamiliar, flow and ebb with a tidal movement. It was as though Nature had finally taken me in, accepted me too at last as some part of her green and stretching world. If it was my blood articulating differently from its wont, then my blood was sap, compact of sticky, moving, living stuff.

Nor did I know what part dream had in this, only that it did have some, together with the reunion with Julie, since I had awakened to this new knowledge, come out from sleep filled with this certainty. From my thirtieth year on, I have not been a mystic, since then seldom even felt any sympathy for the mystics' stammering attempts to give voice to vision or their elaboration in symbolism of religious experiences. I cannot set down with any precision what happened to me this morning; I can only tell how I felt. I was filled with an exuberance, a joy wholly alien to any previous experience; the words "the wet green world" came to my mind again and again; I knew that I was alive in a sense that I had never been alive before, had an unreasoned sense of my own identity, separateness, and at the same time my interconnection with all other living, growing things.

This world that I was at last a part of was wet, green, mucoid with life. It left a luminescent trail, like that of the snail, everywhere in my imagination. I plunged my bare hands, my arms, up to my shoulders into it, held them there, and felt crawling and writhing over them and clinging to them hundreds of tiny living things. I, so pitifully fastidious that a caterpillar, even an inchworm, on my bare skin could—to my shame, of course—make me shudder! And I knew that today I could embrace Julie and the children with a new knowledge at once of their separate bodies and selves, each distinct from the others and from myself. There would be an end to that blurring, merging even, of myself and them in my apprehension of them.

Where had I been all these years? In some sterile clinic, I told myself; I could almost smell its disinfectant, antiseptic corridors, see its barren, white-painted rooms, empty of all life, filled with the odors of medication and preservation.

This was true, but in another sense, I had been in the Deep Freeze. My flesh had never been informed of me, my heart had beaten like a clock, the fluid in my veins had been as static, as glass-encased as though captive in a test tube.

But now life moved, raced, echoed through me. Surely, if my heart and brain, my sinews, bones and muscles were all mine, all interfused and mine, my life, my loves, my work, my intent must have undergone the same alchemical transformation. I could feel hatreds, jealousies, intolerances, self-pitying complaints falling off me like dried, flaked skin. There was oil in the new skin that lay beneath.

And so, reaching out a hand to touch Julie, I drifted back into sleep, exhausted by happiness. . . .

When I awoke again, the feeling was gone. I was alone, and I knew a moment's inconsolable desolation; it was as though a window had been cut through the wall of my life's prison, a window through which I could view the green promise of life as I had dreamed of it—only to have disappeared again, so that it seemed the window, and the view it held, had been only part of the recurring dream.

But after a little, groping cautiously back, I recaptured my vision, not of course in its former intensity but fully enough to believe, to know a reassurance that was like fire in my bones. Then I could relax and ask myself about this celebration of life.

For that is what it was. Exhilaration is another thing, and familiar enough to me: it may be induced—by a clear, cold day, by success, praise, physical exercise, alcohol, the titillation of sexual invitation. But this exuberance, this new sense of life in oneself and life everywhere around one, of discreteness, separateness, and yet unity—this is what children have as their birthright, although, only too often, briefly. I have seen it shining from Tim's face as he gazed, with what people facilely call three-year-old innocence, at the moon, the sea, or simply a string of lights. Maria carries it about with her as though it were secreted in the pores of her face. Considering the strains and pulls and division of loyalties to which she has been subjected, I cannot understand it. But a sure test of the validity of what I say about her is to invite her to join in any expedition, any enterprise of a new or unfamiliar sort. Her eyes become enormous, her face luminous; she says "Yes" with her whole body—and would, if it were an invitation to a rocket trip to the moon.

This is not indiscriminateness; this is a continuous celebration of life in recognition and anticipation of its wonder, its diversity, its vitality. This is what it is to be alive, and to value it. It transcends—no, it includes —both the tragic sense of life and the comic. I think of Alyosha Karamazov watering the earth with his tears, and of the joyous laughter of the great boisterous comic spirits. There is no incompatibility between these, although it takes a Shakespeare to feel and communicate both with equal ease and integrity. And to talk of it to those who have never experienced it, who are not free to experience it, is as futile as to preach to a congregation of chipmunks.

Why is there so little of this natural exuberance, this joy of living, this sense of profound life, among us? Why are our feelings so alien to us that we cannot find them, and must turn desperately to the drugs of sensation for a substitute?

I shan't list all the reasons that are given us: technological growth and standardization of living; the acceleration of the pace in urban living; our Puritan heritage in conflict with our glamour-and-sex-charged commercialism, etc., etc. But this last is not a conflict; it is cause and effect: suppress the natural joy in life, and you invest manifestations of it with the special spiced-up and spurious value of a rare and secret commodity; you invent and glorify evil. This is your true Garden of Eden story.

And of course I don't know an answer; the answer is manifold. But I do know the fact: the increasing hundreds of thousands (millions?) of human beings who never celebrate life in the sense of what I have just written, who live out their days in dull despair and numbing opiates, and wake at night from a nameless terror, crying out, "Who am I?" and "Why was I ever born, to bear this desperate burden of my unknown self, fearing the dark and hating the light?"

And I among them—I, never having known, until this morning, this degree of peace and joy and certitude. I, hitherto crippled and sick, and now made well again.

I remember the dream about the little duck, the waltzing decoy. If he was inviting me to self-knowledge and life, an understanding of my beginnings and a participation in my present, *who* was employing the decoy; who had set him there in my path?

And why should a toy represent, or at least introduce, real life? Have I been so confused that the fantasy world I have so often invoked has been reality to me, and the natural world artificial?

Sept. 14

Yesterday was so good a day. And the vision holds—its luminescence gone, its fire cooled, but its meaning clear and steady. I want to say more, after all, about what I called yesterday the inability to celebrate life.

There is abroad a malaise that is too complex to be defined easily. Students and interpreters of this uneasiness, this insecurity, this sickness of the Soul, abound; but most of them spell out their interpretation in terms exclusively religious, psychological, political, scientific, sociological or economic. It is that we have lost our religious sense, one says; another: our understanding of science has outstripped our understanding of ourselves; still others blame the pace of twentieth-century life, the competitive nature of our society, or the loss of faith in traditional ethical values. Some believe that the sense of inner emptiness that assails so many of us leads us to a search for God; others, to the psychological search for the Father (or Mother); still others, to that for a classless society or a discovery, on some new frontier, of that heroic life so pitifully absent in an age replete with comfort and mediocrity.

I believe, flatly and simply, that we are searching for ourselves, our selves—that, through whatever complex of factors, most of us have lost the clear identifying sense of just who and what we are—each of us, just what his real potentialities and limitations are, what that peculiar hallmark of identity that enables him to feel that he not only inhabits but *fits* his skin, all of a piece, body, mind and spirit, thought word and action one, so that he has made, each to his degree, his peace with himself and gained sufficient self-knowledge to be ready to turn outward to move among others with good will and genuine interest; to engage, in a spirit of mutuality and with a sense of discreteness, friendly otherness, the individuals he meets.

But I suspect too, or did on rereading this last paragraph, that one must continue to endure tensions, conflicts, and one must be ready to speak from his guts, not loosely and indiscriminately, but within the context of encounters and oppositions, when the occasions warrants,

The Hands of Esau

when the stakes, the values involved, are high enough to warrant it. Such stakes are self-respect, respect for other selves, respect for life. Yet one cannot be free to do so until ready to sacrifice the love or even liking of others whom his thrust hurts, frightens or angers. This has been hard for me unless fiercely aroused: and then, no longer free-speaking from my insides, but blurted out in violence.

Love . . . that word. I read in a book review in yesterday's paper: "There is nothing new that anyone can say about love. Hence, it is hardly fair to complain . . ."

Quite possibly this is true. It is always difficult to distinguish between a strikingly new way of saying a familiar thing and actually creating a combination of genuinely new juxtapositions of elements to effect an original idea or insight. Even if this latter seems to be achieved, it is of course impossible to verify conclusively the achievement, for there is no universal census taker of all private conversations and diaries under the sun.

Yet there is a proposition of opposite polarity in which I believe: every individual is unique. Therefore, nothing that has been said about love—or about anything else, for that matter—can be duplicate or duplicated, short of conscious and literal plagiarism or quotation. Two people cannot say the same thing, if one includes in the saying inflection and emotion, the whole mysterious complex of brain wave and sentiment, of ennobling emotion and irritated ganglia. What makes opinions, sentiments, prejudices, feelings representative, or even what we call universal, is the way in which two (or two thousand, or two million) responses converge within a single orbit of acceptance, so that one, or another, or even many, may experience recognition and agreement. So, in one respect, men become mankind. But within each, however close he may feel to another, despite enormous distances of time or space, there is his particular version, stamped, however faintly, with the trademark of his sole personality.

Love . . . I have little patience with all the favorite distinctions between sacred and profane love, spiritual and sexual, love of man for woman, of mother for child, or of saint for God. Love is love—for whatever. It is not an itch or a sentiment or a delusion. My distinction would be rather, in whichever of these relationships, one between love, which is the celebration of life in oneself and in someone else, a celebration consummated in the meeting of two personalities which delight in each other—a distinction between this celebration and a desire for, or infatuation with, some other person or object, with the motivation of possessing, absorbing, using, exploiting that other, or oneself being possessed, absorbed, used.

Reciprocity is essential to love. One person may worship another, but not love him unless the feeling is shared. One may not love nature, books, music—however much one may admire, revere, be awed or thrilled by any particular manifestation of art or nature. Such experiences are unilateral; love moves always to and from.

And this, inevitably and ultimately, brings us to sexuality and to marriage, where the interpenetration is most complete—that of bodies and feelings and, in marriage, of sustained closeness through daily living and through having children together.

Where there is a love of personalities combined with sexual delight in each other, one reaches the ultimate, I think, in man's capacity to answer and confront that universal loneliness that is his lot. Were I now arguing with someone, I know that I should have to defend my statement against the charge of supporting a romantic fallacy. There would be two reasons for this, I think: an inadequate attention to my words, and the rarity of the experience I have just cited. There is abroad so easy and superficial a mouthing of "when love and sex are joined" that my supposed listener would be almost bound to assume I was falling into platitude, unless he had followed very closely my definition of love. Then, too, the genuine combination is so infrequent that skepticism must be expected.

I don't feel arrogant in writing this way. The Colonel took the children off somewhere early yesterday, to give Julie and me extra time to sleep. And when she came back to bed, after seeing them off, we made love again. In full sunlight, with the windows open, with no stimulants, none of the sense of secretness or that faintly wicked titillation induced by darkness, isolation, music, alcohol, blurring and beautifying the lover. There were, in our true daylight nakedness, all our unheightened humanness and mortality. It was a little frightening to me at first, and then filled me with a kind of wonder and joy I had never experienced before.

It was so *real*. Her shoulders, her breasts, her thighs, her belly, her buttocks were so real. The shock of their delightful reality defies setting down, yet I must try to find some way to express the difference of this experience from the erotic experiences of the past, to keep it really mine, not just a diffused remembrance of "a happy time."

In my adolescence I wrote of *She*, have sought She ever after. But this was and is Julie, a woman, not a dream. The mother of my children, my wife; and my delight in her body was in both it and that it is hers, and that she is mine, and yet her own. She there, I here, and in our eyes and hands the knowledge of our rewon innocence, the joy of our discreteness.

There is something of what I mean about marriage in these words, and I do marvel that we can feel this after so many years. Perhaps we do the more because of our long-sustained misunderstandings and quarrels and open conflicts that have so often kept us apart, while at the same time we kept reaching for more growth, refused to stay for long in our separate cells, refused to accept the sentence of isolation and resignation.

Yet this suggests that if we came to accept each other more fully and steadily, there would be a vitiation of the strength of this experience, perhaps even satiation. I do not think so as I write today. I no longer believe that the sexuality of husband and wife loses edge and flavor and fulfillment through familiarity—unless one means by familiarity simply the rehearsing of the same stances and movements. When one entertains that deep life Bergson wrote of, is alive in one's bowels, with a full sense of self and other, dullness, repetitiveness, staleness are impossible.

I said we made love. A tired phrase, a euphemism, and it smacks of invention. But this was not, is not invention; this is creation, which comes from inviting your soul to open, to explore, to find, to celebrate. We did not make love; we loved. Guilt, shame, fear: after the first full naked moment, I was at last without them; I was with Julie.

And so marriage and family. I am not talking now of serenity, untroubled peace and cooperation, so often invoked and so frequently the masks for indifference, withdrawal, mechanical and apathetic obedience to the *rules* of a household. For God's sake, if there are five or four or even two individuals in a home, how can there *not* be wrangling, quarrels, disagreements, outright fights?

And there is no need, surely, to stress the richer meaning that marriage and parenthood have simply from the fact of having lived and living together, close, side by side, face to face. I began with love as the celebration of life consummated in the meeting of two personalities which delight in each other. To sustain this, in marriage, between parent and child, or in friendship, is to take into account how few moments of ecstasy, or even delight, there can be in proportion to unheightened ones, to accept this as fact, to learn to move in the natural rhythm of waxing and waning in longer cycles, and, when hard-pressed, to fall back on the foundation sills of having come through things together, now locked in angry disagreement, now in common joys. Impatience, irritability, selfishness, hurts inflicted and received, rejections, even cruelty—these do not finally matter, however much they scar, if deep in the belly there is the solid knowledge that both—or all—have been *there* (however differently each might describe the terrain) instead of somewhere else.

That is where I've failed Julie, and I thank God if it is not too late.

It seems it is not, and yet last night I woke up panting and sweating from a dream in which she was gone, and I alone with my faithlessness. There was something outside the window where I stood gazing, something on the grass . . . But I cannot bring it back.

There is more, however, that I want to say about love—about what love is not. Love is not present if one thinks to do or feel or "sacrifice" something because he *should* do it. Duty is another matter, whether in terms of a genuine sense of obligation, commitment, or responsibility grounded in reality, or falsely conceived as the rationale for what is actually the fear of some vague but powerful retributive or punitive "justice," my sardonic, watching Truant Officer.

The confusion of love with self-abnegation, self-denial, stems for most of us—perhaps all in the Western World—from the Christian religion. And what a travesty of the teachings of Jesus! I do not have the knowledge of his words and the gospels that my grandfather Herrick and my father had, but the central concept of love that I find in the words and acts of Jesus is present alike in the first and in the last great story of his life, the Nativity and the Crucifixion, and in each alike the symbol is one of abundance. The sense behind both the Coming and the End seems to me that of bringing more abundant life to more fellow humans, and much of the life in between the two, many of the deeds and the parables and sayings, stress this same concept. The extra mile, the cloak as well as the coat, the paying of equal wages to those who worked a half day and those who worked a full one (my grandfather's famous heretical last sermon comes to mind); the courtesy to Mary Magdalene and the justifying of Mary to Martha—all these suggest to me a *fullness* within that will not measure out meanly, count off Peter against Paul, insist upon deserts in accordance with some literal reckoning. The humble beginnings in the manger, with the attendance of animals and the shepherds; the anguished ending between two thieves—these have again and again been cited as the exaltation of the humble. I do not think this their primary meaning. I believe that worldly status is beside the point. True, Jesus constantly reminds us to humble ourselves, to remember the increased spiritual difficulties confronting the wealthy, the proud and the powerful. But these exhortations and stories have reference to the state of the soul. The usual disdain of sin and sinner, of foolish and fallen, and the romantic reversal of this position, are equally irrelevant to the state of one's soul. It is not that it is good to be a thief or a prostitute or a dumb beast—only that this, taken in itself, is not pertinent. What is relevant, what is even central, is the equality of human souls before God.

But while this means that men are equals *sub specie aeternitatis*, it does not mean that they grow equally in stature and in their capacities to experience the good things of life. "To him who hath shall be given . . ." A hard saying, it is often remarked—but this is true only if one views it in naïvely materialistic terms. To him who has life in abundance within him, more life shall accrue—this is the meaning to me, and I find it irrefutable. And so it follows, to me, that those who advocate selflessness, the denying or belittling of self, have hold of a half-truth that will sting them with its poison.

And so it is, to me, that only through seeking, and at least partially finding self, can one love. And only in this way, not through self-denial, can one know humility. The equating of selfhood with arrogance is another favorite misreading of the Word. Humility has no intercourse with either self-inflation or self-depreciation; it can exist only where there is honest self-appraisal, where one neither makes claims for qualities one does not have, nor pretends to be less than one is. It is the condition of humility to know one's limitations and one's potentialities and to know the nature of the world in which one lives, and one's relation to it. How can one appraise properly the vastness and the diversity, the unique qualities of all created things without knowing first who oneself is? And can one truly evaluate oneself without knowing the context within which one exists?

Love, then, is the truest celebration of life—within and without. And in retrospect, flashing even across the shadowy and troubled years, the despairing passages of my life, the icy wastelands where I wandered only half alive—that love I found manifest in the person of my father which is in heaven.

I wrote that last without premeditation, but I think of William Herrick, who had no childhood in any recognizable sense, and yet, being one of those rare people truly "once-born," who triumphantly though unostentatiously went straight from that mortal welter of pain and affliction that replaced his opportunity for childhood, into maturity and love.

I think of his unconquerable love—for life, for people and for God as he knew and communicated Him—and I believe that he is in the Heaven I have never believed in: that, if it was not there, it had to be created for him, as a receptacle for his love.

Sept. 17

These past three days have been so full I've felt no need and found no time to write. But at last, tonight, I've stirred myself, written to P.H., resigning; to Sean O'Neill, accepting his offer; to Abe Fortune, inquiring about Jane. And I've had a *good* talk with the Colonel. But first, an experience with Peter this afternoon.

We were off by ourselves, having gone to Vineyard Haven for the heavy weekly shopping for groceries. On the way back, we were quiet, having exchanged only a word or two, when Peter said, quite abruptly, or more as though to himself than to me, "But I still don't see how the seed gets in there."

It was hard to say, for a moment or two, which of us was more confused—he, because he hadn't realized he was going to say it aloud, I, because at first I didn't understand. Then, in a flash, I did and realized that a long-anticipated time had come—a time at which, I'd promised myself, I'd deal openly and fully with him, not stammer and retire as my father had with me.

A last doubt assailed me: eight was awfully young. But I dismissed the doubt as motivated by a wish to evade the chance, and plunged ahead. I talked for fully five minutes, and as I realized that I was clear, plain, with what seemed to me just the right combination of down-to-earthness and reverence for the wonders of the subject, I became really exhilarated with the sense of an important job well-done. I concluded, triumphantly but modestly, with something to the effect that this was the real story of life, its generation and birth, and this was why love, though often referred to too easily, was the key word and experience in life.

For a moment, I looked straight ahead, watching the road, and needing to be sure my emotions were wholly under control before I looked at Peter again. For, throughout my account, he had sat silent, eyes bright and fixed attentively on me. Then, toward the end of my recital, a new dreaminess had come into them, caused, I felt, by a sudden full realization of all the different aspects of this mysterious center of life to which I had been introducing him.

When I felt myself fully under control, I turned to Peter again, a little surprised that he had not yet broken his silence. His eyes were still dreamy, but now they brightened and he looked at me with all possible candor. "Dad," he said, "when do you think I can have a new bike?"

I told Julie and the Colonel this story tonight, and even through their laughter the Colonel began nodding his head. "He got what he needed," he declared. "Children instinctively absorb just the amount that's right for them, and then shut the receiver off and think about something else. Don't worry; he was listening."

If it had been someone I liked less than the Colonel, I would have been annoyed; when I'm telling a good story like that, it irritates me to have someone misread my intent and—say, in this case, think I'm hurt over Peter's inattention while I'm really delighted to tell the story for its humorousness, even if the humor in it is at my expense.

Then Julie picked it up, and added earnestly, "Of course he did, and it's wonderful that you did it the way you did."

I groaned, and muttered, "Oh, for Lord's sake, I thought it was a funny story."

Julie looked at me sharply, appraisingly, but when she came over to my chair she ran her hand over my head. "I'm tired, and I'm going to bed and read a little while," she said.

I nodded, was aware the Colonel was looking at me closely, too, and closed my eyes. Something was ticking away; I heard myself distantly thinking to myself: Watch out. You're getting ready to blow.

It had something to do with what seemed to me now their failure to see how much I'd changed—that my motivation in telling a story like the one about Peter was very different from what it would have been five years, two years, even six months ago. Then contradictorily, I thought, with further irritation, for Christ's sake, I can't be perfect.

All this I caught and can set down now, clearly and comfortably, I think, because of what the Colonel said next. He said it quietly, but with an expressive warmth, and after his first few words I opened my eyes and gave him my attention.

"Walton, I'm not given to speeches. But I must say to you how good I feel about you and Julie. She didn't tell me much this summer; she and I don't discuss our intimate feelings. But I knew things weren't right between you. And now you've been here almost a week, and it's clear to see that things are mending. You know how much she means to me: my child, my one. And you and I are very different sorts of men; we find it—I hope I'm not presumptuous in saying 'we'—hard to unload ourselves to each other. So, I'd like you to know that I've always been glad Julie married you and that I've always been confident that your marriage would be a strong and lasting one."

His face was red with the exertion; I felt ashamed and humbled, yet incongruously proud too. Before I could thank him, he added, with an effort, "Just one thing more that I've always wished I'd learned before *my* wife died. Men and women are different, by nature. I mean utterly, irreconcilably different. Don't either of you try to change that, or take over part of what's rightly the other's. There's a lot to be glad for in that difference."

I wrote above that I had a good talk with the Colonel. That was it: the longest one we've ever had.

I don't fully understand yet that last statement of his. Its surface meaning is simple, yet the effort it cost him, and my estimate of him, make me sure there's much more in it than I as yet see.

Something else has come through to me, though: what Freud said about the man who was impotent with his wife after living away from her with a mistress for a year: "I didn't know he was so decent and honest."

And so enough. Let me remember what I wrote, not about the ecstasy in the celebration of life (that too, though, that too), but especially about the daily living together and about being *there*, whether in anger or joy, in irritation or in understanding.

DEPOSITION: *8*

1

[Sonia Wilenski is lying negligently on her side, propped on an elbow, telephone clamped between palm and cheek. She is dressed in a man's shirt and in shorts, and with her free hand is poking languidly at a small abrasion on her knee, which she has drawn up awkwardly within reach. As she talks, her gaze roams from the offending spot on her knee to the picture of herself on the wall to a package of cigarettes on a nearby chair. She then stretches her arm out, straining, but her finger tips fall just short, and she resumes her previous position, to watch absent-mindedly the curtain flapping over the open window.]

SONIA (after a long silence): Honestly, Evvie, you sound as though the world had come to an end. Well, I suppose you *could* say its foundation's been shaken. Don't groan; I've heard worse. What did Herrick say in his letter to you?

[Evelyn Onslow is seated in a straight chair beside the telephone table in the foyer of the apartment she shares with her mother. She is wearing a light print dress; her hair is freshly brushed; she sits up very straight, but her gaze is downward in meditation, and her expression suggests the raptness of a religieuse at devotions. When she speaks, it is softly, but with precise clarity.]

EVELYN: All he said was that he had decided to accept this offer from the Colosseum and had written Mr. Gates, resigning.

SONIA (bending her neck uncomfortably to examine her thigh, where she has pushed up her shorts. A scratch? a lump? a pimple?): Well, Gates hasn't let *his* secretary see that letter. And if he's answered it, he dictated the letter to someone else. Herrick tell you he'd take you along with him?

EVELYN (hesitating, her eyes brighter): He—said he'll have to see what the situation is at the publishing house.

732

SONIA (yawning and pushing her shorts back down): How'd he seem?

EVELYN: Seem? Mr. Herrick?

SONIA: Oh, come off it, Evvie. "Seem?" "Mr. Herrick?" Yes, seem. In the letter. Your great big hero man. Jolly? Sour? Scared? [Sonia rolls over on her back and stares up at the ceiling, scowling. Evelyn flushes, and draws herself even more primly erect, as though she were actually facing her interrogator.]

EVELYN: Sonia, I don't like you to talk that way. Anyway it wasn't the kind of letter that would give you a feeling of how he was. It was just a note. But he seemed to be in good spirits.

SONIA: Christ, Evvie, you do talk the goddamnedest language. "He seemed in good spirits"! [Evelyn's lips are set firmly. She sits in silence.]

SONIA: Ev-vie! Now, honey, don't get mad. You know I love you dearly, just the way you are. For Christ's sake, who else would I sit and talk to by the hour on a moonlit late summer night when I might be out getting laid. Oops, there I go again.

EVELYN: You talk so much about sex I'm not very worried about what you do.

SONIA (laughing. She has discovered a hangnail on the hand holding the telephone and has begun to pick at it): Nope, it's up to me to do the worrying, but if you mean you think I don't have any sex life except talk, you can think again, old girl. Who do you think is going to take Herrick's place? Gatesy hasn't had anybody in for one of those long heart-to-heart chats.

EVELYN (She has lifted her head and there is an expression on her face as though she is summoning resolution. She thrusts her chin out; her mouth quirks.): I only got my letter yesterday, and I suppose Mr. Gates got his at the same time. I don't see any very logical candidate. Probably they'll get somebody from outside. Sonia! [Her voice changes, becomes very determined in a characteristic way, as though she is forcing herself to say something that shyness and self-consciousness make difficult.] Sonia, are you doing anything special tonight?

SONIA (hoisting herself up to a sitting position): Besides yakking with you? Nope. Wanta come over? Come on. You can sleep over. And get some gin on the way. I feel like getting looped.

EVELYN (full of animation): I'd love to come. And Mother's Cousin Sadie is here for a week, so it'll be all right for me to leave her. [Hesitates, and then juts her chin out again.] Maybe—maybe I'll even get drunk with you.

SONIA (lets out a whoop): That'll be the day! Hurry up now.

[Evelyn hurries about the apartment, putting things into her overnight bag. She writes a hasty note to her mother, including Sonia's
telephone number, props it up on the mantel, takes it down again and
writes at the bottom of the page: P.S. Good night, Cousin Sadie. A
last look around, a re-examination of the contents of the bag and the
bills in her pocketbook. Then she turns out all the lights except the
lamp on the mantel, which shines full on her note, decides the room is
too sepulchral, and relights a standing lamp on the other side of the
room. She leaves, testing the door lock from the outside and half runs,
half skips to the elevator.

Sonia has risen and lighted a cigarette. She stretches, and walks
slowly over to the window. Pulling up the shade, she looks out at the
moony night over the roof of the next apartment building. She stands
there for a long time, and finally puts out her cigarette on an ashtray
on the window ledge, absent-mindedly, without looking at it. She turns
around abruptly, stamps her bare foot on the floor and, seizing her head
in both hands, gives it a savage yank. "Goddamn him!" she says. There
are tears in her eyes.]

2

[An hour later. Sonia's apartment. Evelyn, holding her second
gin and tonic, is seated in the one easy chair, a new acquisition—really
sprawled out in it. Her shoes are off, her hair a little disheveled, her
cheeks pink. She looks, and speaks, either unusually elated or anxious;
her expression and tone hover between the two states. Sonia is again
sprawled out on the bed, with a pitcher of martinis beside her and a full
glass in her hand. They have not returned to the subject of Walton
Herrick's resignation, but have been talking about the theater—Sonia,
caustic and well-informed; Evelyn, not so well-informed but full of
questions and opinions as to what the theater *should be*. At last they
fall silent. Sonia drains her martini, whistles and pours another.]
SONIA: What you want, Evvie?
EVELYN: Want? You mean out of life?
SONIA: Nope. Out of me.
EVELYN (hesitating for a moment, then speaking rapidly): Sonia, I know
    I haven't any right, but *did* anything happen between you and Mr.
    Herrick? One of the girls in the clerical department told me that
    everybody knows it did, that Mr. Gates fired Peggy Thomas for
    telling him about it, and that that's part of why Mr. Herrick is

leaving, and that Peggy Thomas is threatening to write Mrs. Herrick all about it.

SONIA: Christ, hasn't she done that yet?

EVELYN: Oh! You mean it's—

SONIA: Yes, it's true. And it's just about true that Peggy managed to inform several hundred people, so that I feel like I'd been a front-page story in one of the tabloids or like everybody was free to come in and watch me take a bath. I wasn't going to tell you tonight, but I'm going to quit too

EVELYN (obviously distressed, but perhaps not clear herself about what): Oh, Sonia, how awful for you! And for Mrs. Herrick! But I don't believe so many people know about it. I only heard about it day before yesterday.

SONIA: Don't be foolish. Everybody knows you adore him and they'd be afraid to tell you, lest you tear their eyes out. And don't feel sorry for me; it's my own damned fault. And I don't like working for Gatesy anyway; he's such a prissy little man. I never have any trouble finding a job; I'm a damned good secretary.

EVELYN (warmly): I know you are. But Sonia, how could you do it? I mean for yourself—and for his family too.

SONIA: I told you long ago, I don't know his family. It's not up to me to take care of them. But I'm mad at myself for taking such damned poor care of myself.

[Evelyn starts to rise from her chair, sinks back, then determinedly does stand up and makes herself another drink, a stronger one.]

EVELYN (drawing a deep breath): I shouldn't have said that. I *am* getting drunk. Sonia, I certainly can understand why you couldn't resist him.

SONIA: Couldn't resist him! Hah! I'll tell you, it was he who couldn't resist me. [Pauses, snorts at herself, sighs] And then could.

EVELYN (taking a big gulp of her drink): I knew that—that he fell hard for you that very first night when we all had drinks together. Did you—was it—

SONIA: Nope. We drew up the blueprint that night, but nothing really happened for three or four weeks. Then for a couple of weeks it was almost every night. After that, only once or twice.

EVELYN (at first dreamily, then intensely): I'm a coward. If I wanted something like that, I'd never dare do it. Usually I think of not doing it as being good, but tonight I feel all different. I just admire and envy you, and sort of despise myself.

SONIA (laughing, not very successfully): You can admire me all you want, but don't envy me. I gave myself a pretty raw deal.

EVELYN: It must hurt awful. Sonia, don't answer anything you don't want to, but—but is he a wonderful lover?

SONIA (jumping up and draining her glass, then pouring the last from the pitcher, to stand, staring enigmatically at Evelyn. Finally she speaks derisively): Want some? Of course you do. He's got some kind of extra—class, I guess I'd call it—until you get up too close. And he makes most men seem such slobs. Maybe what makes him so attractive is that he's full up with problems, with tensions. All the time he wants to and he wants not to. Even when it comes to taking a drink or lighting a cigarette—pipe, I mean. And that endless tension in him generates some kind of special heat and magnetism, I guess. The old-fashioned way to talk about it would be to say that good and evil are always at war in him.

[Her voice has slowly softened, and she begins pacing the room. After a moment, she stops by Evelyn's chair.]

SONIA: Is he a good lover, you want to know. What's a good lover? To me, a good healthy animal who is also a man who knows his own mind and is ready to take the responsibility for whatever he does and therefore can have all the pleasure from it too. I thought Herrick was like that, but he isn't.

EVELYN: I know he suffers a lot. Sometimes I hurt for him, when he's so tense and tired, and carries such a load of work.

SONIA: Well, I'm not sorry for him. I'm sorry for me. Lover? Those two weeks we had a wonderful time in bed. Yes, it was exciting. But all that time I thought it was me he was in love with, little old Sonia Wilenski. And it turns out he isn't in love with anybody, except maybe himself. And when his need for safety, which he thinks of as guilt, is stronger than his need for kicks, he just makes one of his courtly bows and says it's been fun. And me, poor dumb fool that I am, let him see how much he's hurt me. I don't know whether I'd rather kick him or me. Yes, I do—him. I'd like to roast him over a slow fire.

EVELYN (earnestness and newly slurred speech produce a comic effect, but neither of them notices it): Sonia, I know you're wrong about this. You've misunderstood him. He's the kindest man I've ever known. He does more good to more people. With all he has to do, he'll always listen to the least important person in the place who comes to him with a problem. And help them. At least three or four times I've heard someone leaving his office say, "You've saved my life." He'd never be so cruel.

SONIA (after staring at her in wide-eyed incredulity): My God, Evvie, you're stark, raving crazy in love with him! You really do believe he's godlike, don't you? Well, just let me ask you one question. Have you ever been in bed with him?

EVELYN (blushing bright red): You know I haven't. But, Sonia, don't you see—[her voice softens] the one thing he couldn't give you is the love he feels for his wife?

SONIA: Tears and spit! I'm going to make martinis and get lousy roaring drunk. Some love he feels for his wife! [Pouring gin and a little vermouth in the pitcher] I'll tell you what I think: I think he hates women. No, wait a minute. I don't mean all the garbage about latent homosexuals: he's not that. And I don't even mean that he knows this himself. But maybe he had the kind of mama—hold still, damn you [there is a brief balancing of ice cubes, the pitcher and a tall spoon; then all is righted]—the kind of mother who, you know, possessed him so that he thinks of only two kinds of women: the mamas, whom you placate, and the pretty women, whom you fuck. Or try to. I've known men like that. Call them men [her voice rises as she finishes stirring and pours a fresh martini, which she then holds aloft as a toast]—yes, call them men, damn them. What's so sacred about the word "men"? Why should we use it as though it means strength and honesty and courage and sense, and then say of all men who aren't like that that they're not "real men"? Who ever saw a real man? Who the hell established that ideal, anyway? Let's face it, Evvie, men are selfish slobs. They haven't got the guts of women; they haven't got the sense. All they're good for is inventing things, having theories, dealing with anything but another human being. If we're good-looking, their contempt (which is really their lack of confidence in themselves) takes the form of their greediness, their goddamn greedy eyes and hands. If we're homely, they let the contempt show openly in what they say and do. Just what have they got that gives them the right to be so contemptuous, except that little dangling thing between their legs which more often than not they can't get up, anyway? Do they have children? Do they raise children? Do they keep house? Do they do anything, except sit around and look important and dictate? The sons of bitches, they make me sick. Dictate! Do they even make love? No, they make *war* in bed—Herrick too; that's what I meant—and if we're too strong for them, they say it wasn't fair, we don't fight by the rules of war. You're damned right we won't, not when they make the rules.

EVELYN (standing and waving her empty glass): Hurray for women! Secretaries of the world, unite! [Pauses for a hiccough, then speaks with exaggerated gravity] Some of those things, though, Sonia. You'n I haven't borned children, haven't raised 'em. How do we get off, talking about that?

SONIA: No, but we can. And I hope you will. I don't know about me; I don't know if I want to bring anybody else into this goddamn screwed-up world.

EVELYN: Sonia, I'm drunk; yes si am. And it's lovely, it's perfeckly lovely. But I do want to know this. Do you really think Peggy's going to tell Mrs. Herrick? Thassanawful thing to do. And Peggy's mean, I know she's mean enough to do it, too. But do you think she will? Do you really think she really will?

SONIA: Yes, I do. I wouldn't be surprised if she's done it already.

EVELYN: Thass lovely. Just lovely. And now I'm going to bed and think about it all, all of it, until I fall asleep wish will be soon, I promise you, very soon. Ssh! Sleep to soon.

SONIA: Here, let me fix the bed. I wish you weren't so sleepy. I got a lot more to say.

Evelyn Herrick, just before sleep, found herself walking down a rose-trellised walk to greet her husband. There, in a field beside the' house, were his children, playing happily, and they waved and shouted, "Hi, Mother Evvie!"

Hearing them, Walton turned to her and said, "How can I ever thank you, dear, for being such a wonderful mother to them?" His eyes were so full of love, and she knew that he meant they'd make war in bed again tonight, and he would win. She loved losing, and since it was married war it was perfectly respectable as well as wicked and wonderful. The roses were so sweet, they smelled heavenly. She held one up for Walton to smell. . . .

[Sonia Wilenski sits in a puddle of martinis. Stripped down now to her underwear, she sits on the wet floor, chin on raised knees, and stares before her. Every little while, she unsteadily raises her glass and sips.]

SONIA: Damn him. Damn him. Goddamn him.

[But she will not give up—for him or for any other man. She will plant her feet and stay in there.]

MANUSCRIPT: 5

Friday, September 25

I have not yet recovered from the shock of Wednesday's talk with P.H. When he asked me to lunch at the Century, I thought he wanted to sound me out about Walton, that he still hoped that Walton would change his mind about resigning. I figured that he was turning to me both because I am an old friend of Walton's and because I am (he'd told me) the only person at the Foundation to whom he had mentioned the resignation. I thought either that he wanted my advice about handling Walton, or even perhaps that he wanted me to go up to the Vineyard and try to persuade him to change his mind.

And then, in the library, over our drinks, he straightaway offered me Walton's job! And by the end of lunch, though I said only that I needed a few days to think it over, I knew I'd take it. In fact, that night, after telling Cyn, I called the Head in Cornell and told him that I wanted the two weeks' leave they'd given me to finish up here at the Foundation extended forever. That's what I said: extended forever. I don't like the Head. And of course he doesn't like me now, if he ever did. But, for all his blustering, I'm sure he can arrange for someone else to handle my advanced courses. Anyway, they'll have to send the police after me to get me back.

And this morning, I told P.H. I'd take the job.

So much for the facts. Why do I set them down, in a haphazard journal that I turn to only about once a month? Whom am I telling these facts to?

I think I wanted to see how I felt as I wrote them. About taking *Walton's* job. P.H. and I were both uneasy about this aspect of it. But at last he looked me in the eye (I like this guy; he's very human and fair,

739

and he cares about honesty even in all the small relationships—where most people don't worry about it)—he looked me in the eye and said, "I think we both feel a little strange about its being Walton's job I'm offering you. But, Dudley, I did everything in my power to get him to stay. I got Haldane's approval to raise his salary and even to make him a vice president, in charge of humanities. He was adamant. So it's not a question of his ever feeling that you took the job away from him. In fact, when he's so fond of you, he's bound to be terribly pleased if you take it over."

Later, that seemed a funny phrasing to me: "when he's so fond of you." Maybe it's true, though. *When* he is fond of me . . . For I don't feel he is consistently any more; perhaps Julie has told him of my visit. But both the feeling he gave me when he came up to the Vineyard because of Tim, and his silence during these weeks up there, when I know he's written to others besides P.H., suggest some alienation.

Anyway, all that later. Then, at that moment, I thanked P.H. for telling me what he had and told him it did make a difference to me.

"Good," he said. "And one other thing. It's hard for me to say, but I think I'm glad Walton decided as he did." He stopped talking abruptly right there, and we sat looking at each other as though each of us was asking the other a question and at the same time waiting to be asked one.

Finally I said, "You mean Sonia?"

P.H. frowned and shook his head. And yet he was not quite saying no to my question.

"Does everyone know about that?" he asked with a kind of humorous despair. "Thank God, the girl's shown some sense. She's given me notice and leaves at the end of next week." He hesitated and then went on. "That's part of what I meant—that he could do such a thing, with someone right in the office. And—how well do you know Julie?"

It was my turn to hesitate.

"She's lovely," I finally said.

P.H. spread out his hands, palms up.

"Well. There. Something's happened to Walton. And another thing —he feels, I know, that I should have backed him all the way on the Kiefer appointment, and I simply couldn't. He himself wouldn't have been happy staying. But I felt I owed him every inducement."

"It's not easy to owe something to Walton," I said, I guess a little ruefully.

P.H. smiled faintly.

"No," he said. "It's not. I don't think he's conscious of it, but he asks you to pay for it with something that looks like loyalty but is closer to devotion. And that devotion must not be slavish, yet in another sense it must be absolute. He wants friendship on the basis that each really knows and accepts the other, warts and all, yet unconsciously he insists on establishing what the warts are. It's difficult."

I agreed. Yet here I am, becoming successor to the man who gave me a chance to be here at all, my old friend, toward whom I don't feel very friendly any more. Now it is Cyn and Julie who are friends, and Cyn has been sweeter to me than ever before since we left the Vineyard. I think I have that one licked—with Cyn as my real life wife and Julie my faraway princess (Jesus, isn't that what I wrote about Walton's attitude toward her?)—not to be revisited.

In looking back to check that parenthetical point, I've just reread a lot of this, and it seems to me that the writing's gotten progressively worse. I think I'm going to give it up, but the uneasiness of my feeling about Walton makes me want to give my original intent ("Study of a Friend") one last try. What I'd like to do is just start fresh and do a serious, impartial, analytical sketch, as though I had never written or thought about him before. There's something I need to clarify for myself.

WALTON HERRICK

When I try to think what Walton *is*, I am distracted by what he *does*. He is the kind of man to whom it is important that his friends— and who is not his friend?—have a clear idea of him. Most people live not caring much whether they are "understood," but to Walton it is essential that he be understood.

"And who is not his friend?" There it goes . . . the resentment again. He has often told me, through the years, that I am one of his best friends. After a certain point, I did not doubt it; but still he insisted, almost as though he were afraid he would not be believed. It must be hard for Walton to believe that he can be a friend. He is continually imposing tests upon people (many, I am sure, unconscious) to discover whether they love him for what he is, or for some other reason. Like King Lear, he gives you one third of his kingdom, but he also wants the verbal, public assurance that you love him. Walton has given his kingdom away many times, and has banished many people—if only to prove that he can get along by himself. Then he has to turn to someone else.

Sometimes, as we have talked, I've felt that he was trying to invent sins and weaknesses, that he might plead guilty and be forgiven. For when Walton is not giving away his kingdom, he is, like Tartuffe, claiming to be depraved. He may be, for all I know, but I do not think that sins have much bearing on friendship. This is Walton at his worst, the man who claims to see in you a certain weakness—maybe you look sallow that morning, or have just said you don't want a drink—and allies himself with that weakness, "understands" you and then proceeds to outdo you in confession. Thirty minutes later he will have moved on to another scene, another action, and be enjoying, in a hearty way, the disposal of his morning's work, or be engaged in a flirtation—happily compiling more sins, I suppose—and there you are left standing, with your face wide open, and a foolish idea of Walton in your outstretched hand. "Put it on the desk," he says, scarcely looking up from the telephone.

To accept all this, I have to go back to Montaigne and be reminded that inconsistency is the nature of man. But then, Walton, too, has read Montaigne. He would be the first to agree that he is inconsistent. Yet—and I feel funny writing this—I'm beginning to think that there is one consistency in Walton. And were I to expose myself to it, it would put an abrupt end to our already dwindling friendship. Walton wants power. Certainly, when the sheep and goats are counted, Walton will be found standing rather self-consciously on the side of the goats. He is generous; he is not prejudiced against Negroes or Jews; he is intellectually committed to the Life Force. When Walton judges a project, it is important to him that the plan has a semblance of flesh and blood. Yet, with all this, he insists on proving that he is stronger. Stronger than what? Ultimately, I am not sure, but in the immediate situation it seems to mean, "Stronger than you." His moment of confession, when he relates a love affair he had ten years ago, is followed by a retraction. In case you thought he was turning into St. Francis of Assisi, he hastens to assure you, with a hearty roar, that he is really a country boy with simple tastes. Someday I would like to see Walton suspend his damned intelligence; cease weighing and judging; cease being conscious that he is Walton Herrick.

I have, several times last April and more often since I came to New York in June, found myself defending him against the criticisms of those who think, although they have no clear evidence, that he is a high-powered operator, a man who gets things done without intellectual or even ethical reservations. On the other hand, I have found myself agreeing in trite phrases with those who regard Walton as a kind of superman, a chevalier without fear or reproach. These latter are mostly women, though there are exceptions. People seem to see Walton in black or white, and I have seen some people pass from one extreme to the other.

Right now, tonight, Walton does not seem so remarkable to me. He is not, by a long shot, my idea of a great man, either for good or evil. The need to exercise power, of which I have spoken, is an irritation, not a danger.

Though I haven't seen much of him at the Foundation, I can tell from incidents and what people say that he is fair and considerate at work, and gives others opportunities to earn and claim credit that another man in his position might not allow. But I have often seen Walton enter a friendly conversation on terms of equality, and then abruptly shift his ground, make his power known, by generously offering to do something for somebody. To those who need his help, to a man who needs a job or a woman who needs excitement, this must be a tremendous lure. Then, I imagine, the retraction often follows, and liking turns to dislike. I see some of this in his relation to Dennis Byrnes at the Foundation.

If Walton would only let life alone, if he would only let it happen around him and *to* him. . . . If he would believe, as I do, that he is not so remarkable, that he is—like the rest of humanity—at the mercy of wind and weather, he would be a happier man.

There are parts of him I simply do not understand, and I'm not sure I want to. I do not understand the mechanics of his life, how, with one hand, he can juggle the wife, the children, the lawn mower, and with the other, the mistress (or, at least, other women), and the real commitment to thought and to his work. Not that he's juggling very well right now. But this split in his life, which seems to alarm some people, is, in my opinion, a dislocation in the machinery, not a planned program of Machiavellianism. God knows, it must cause him enough sheer discomfort, if nothing else.

Walton has been advanced, not because he has particularly wanted it, into a position of great prestige and real power. His decisions at the Foundation and, I suppose, in the publishing job, can appreciably alter the lives of those who come into his orbit. I think it's a pity that he can't find some job that would give him a chance to forget himself. The ability to take life easy is perhaps the one consolation of unimportant people. To be a part of things, instead of trying to control or understand them—this, in my opinion, is happiness. . . .

That's about it. Yet of course he still escapes me. My analysis of his need for power, for proving that he's "stronger than you are": even as I reach for this understanding, it eludes me. Is that so? It seems to me that the actions of his that I would use to illustrate these points illustrate something else, something, however, that I can't pin down.

Enough scribbling. I give up. I have the responsible post, with authority and position, I've always wanted and doubted that I could ever secure. My energy must and will go into that. I think I'm relieved that I must put the Montaigne translation aside, too. I'm not a writer of any sort, but I can see now that I had to believe I might be, to offset my dissatisfaction with an associate professorship.

So good-bye, Walton Herrick; I've got my own job to do now, my own life to live, my own soul to probe in the trials of work and family. *That* will never mesmerize *me,* however.

You did for a while, though. It really seems to me now that there's something appropriate in my succeeding to your job, just because of that preoccupation with you—and Julie. I guess I really felt inferior to you and found my own importance only in studying you, in being associated with you. To find myself, I had to replace you. And if I've lost a friend in the process, I've gained one, too. We're quits.

September 26–28

It had been a week now since the Colonel had taken the children down to Northport to open the house there, with the maid's help, and start the children in school. His offer had come unexpectedly the night after his brief talk with Walton, and had so obviously been a source of satisfaction to him that Julie and Walton capitulated after only brief hesitation.

It had been a week, then, since the two of them had been left alone together in the Colonel's house, and there was another week remaining before they must return home and Walton take up his new job with the Colosseum.

The Island was quiet; all but a few summer visitors had left. The mornings and nights were cold, but day after day warm, sparkling, golden. They took long walks, sunned on the beach, twice dared the water. They slept late and breakfasted lazily on the porch. They read in the evening, usually aloud, one to the other. Walton read the remaining journal entries, sometimes editing as he went along; Julie read him the fragment of her poem, *Meditation,* which he found delicate and haunting, saved from over-delicacy by a certain sinewy precision of expression, protected from a too lyrical emotionalism by an occasional tough-minded and humorous word or passage that broke into lines of tenderness and beauty like astringent laughter, not changing a mood so much as bringing it sharper lines of definition, rooting and then trimming the emotion.

"It's as though A. E. Housman were a woman and had raised a family," Walton declared excitedly.

They talked far into the night—about the children, the future, the sources of their past misunderstandings. They made love. And on the nights when they were too tired, they still went to sleep in each other's arms.

745

To be sure, it was not, as Julie pointed out the third or fourth night, a second honeymoon. It was something quite different, for which no traditional name had been established. Reunion? Maturity? Consummation? Words. And it was not all bliss and serenity. Sometimes, in their talks, Walton would feel a recurrence of impotent rage over what was to him Julie's biting intolerance of a fuzzy opinion of his, or her impatience over what she found to be his literal-mindedness. Occasionally she would chide him for blurring over a statement of his feelings or for refusing to dare a wholly honest reply to her question; then he might sulk or slam a door in rage. But on each such occasion one of them would seek out the other, suggest a walk or a drink; reconciliation was always achieved quickly, and without explanations or apologies.

"We're so funny," Julie said as they started out one day. "Actually we're both terribly dependent on each other, but in such different ways. I get bossy and critical of you because I don't want to be submerged in you just because I'm so proud of you; yet, when we're with other people, I lean on you awfully. And you're all independent with other people, but at home depend on me to plan everything and ask my advice as though I were wiser, and are cautious about saying something you think I won't like, and are less honest than you are other times. So sometimes you're my father, and sometimes I'm your mama."

"Mama!" Walton had snorted indignantly. And yet the word returned to him, without his fully understanding the association, the very next day, as he was driving back from Edgartown, where he had gone to buy champagne for a surprise for dinner.

As he came to the traffic circle in West Tisbury, where the roads from Edgartown and Vineyard Haven meet and merge, he was suddenly struck by the sunlit peace of the little village. As he passed the schoolhouse, it seemed to him that it was his school, he had gone there—or rather it had been there for him in the life he hadn't taken. Here were the missing roots: had he dreamed, not once but often, of being raised in this place, healthy, cheerful, growing up in the knowledge of home and self under these great spreading trees, striking out sturdily on his own down that narrow road beyond the school that led to farms and woods, through the inviolate peace of the island, and coming back in the morning past the glistening wet meadows or over the icy winter puddles to the sound of the school bell? Could he go back and take this other road? He pulled the car up off the road he was on, with an almost mystical intimation of change, with the same deep stirring of animate peace in him that he had known that first

Sunday morning up here. And the words that flashed through his mind were "mama" and "Sequester Meadow"—the one opposing the other, the other answering the one.

As he started off again, toward home, he thought soberly that of course he could not go back and begin again, but as a man could find a man's equivalent, with all the mistakes and fears and guilts and shames of the road he *had* taken, absorbed and recognized and packed together in him, a part of him. And he could help Julie teach the children how to take the right life. That was what he had thought, he realized a moment later with surprise: teach them *how to take the right life*—how to be themselves.

Yet, by the time he reached the Chilmark post office, the feeling of uneasiness that had hovered on the edge of the scene, throughout all these good days with Julie, returned. Only this time he had a flash of recognition as he worked the combination of their post office box and pulled out two letters, hastily scanning the postmarks and handwriting. One from the Colonel, the other from Abe. He slumped in relief against the wall.

So he had still been fearing Peggy Thomas' poison-pen letter all the time. Did that explain the haunting uneasiness he felt from time to time, like a sudden shadow slanting across the sunlit grass?

Grass . . . something on the grass. "Splendor" spun trivially, mechanically into the web of his mind. But that strand wouldn't hold; he was blocking out something. He put his hand to his forehead and then stared at his wet fingers. Wet . . . morning . . . one morning he would come to the kitchen window, he had thought, and avert his eyes from—what? from what?

The obscenity in the grass. Dizzy, he yet held the vision steady: he must not retreat now. He must look; though it sicken him, destroy him, he must look. And he did. Holding to the desk beside him with one hand, clutching the two letters in the other, swaying alone in the tiny post office, swinging over the edge of the world, sickeningly into space, he looked.

He did not know what it was. Vomit? Excrement? A foetus? But there it lay, its essential horror in its palpitating expressness. He had seen it before—in a butcher shop? Yes. No. Once when their old dog had thrown up shortly after eating, the effect as though his food had taken on the imprint of his intestines and come back up through his throat like a model of his innards. Yes. No.

His dying father. Cancer of the large intestine. An exploratory operation to deflate the vast swelling. Hopeless. And when the nurse was not there to change the dressing and William was groaning in pain, Walton had done the job, and had looked upon his father's glistening exposed guts. Row upon row, coil upon coil. . . .

And so, one morning, with the sunlight gleaming on the dewy grass, he must look and see. His own guts? He did not know. But there, glistening, the obscenity . . .

It was over, the day grown suddenly cooler, the sun duller. Walton walked slowly back to the car, climbed in painfully, like an old man, and opened Abe's letter.

The letter was short, but full of good cheer. Jane was well enough to leave the sanatorium, but she was to continue therapy with the doctor in charge of her case; Abe had rented a small house near the institution to facilitate her visits. Their return to Stamford was at least a few months away; for the present politics would have to wait. Not that it mattered: nothing mattered now but Jane. "Over and over I keep thinking what could I have done these years that I didn't do? I finally think I know. I was always kind, often thoughtful. But I didn't open myself. I didn't tell her my thoughts, give her the chance to tell me hers. I think we often live our marriages only as an extension of our single selves, appropriate the other, instead of exploring her, *meeting* her. Or him. And now with us any exploration must be that much gentler, more careful.

"I hope all goes well with you and your Julie. My dear friend. Abe."

Walton's eyes blurred. "My dear friend." My *dear friend*.

He sat there, his head whirling less and less, until finally he felt quite steady. Suddenly he remembered that he had thought, earlier on the ride, of the evening ahead, of the evenings he and Julie had been spending together, alone. He had thought, "We talk endlessly together, far into the night. We make love, unless too tired. Then we fall asleep in each other's arms."

But was that so? What was the meaning of his need to drink so much? Wasn't it rather that each night he anticipated making love with —dread? No. A feeling of guilt? Perhaps. For certain, with uneasiness. And drank, to find out whether this would make him feel erotic or enable him to fall asleep without making love.

Was that so? He didn't know. Was he feeling again, but hiding the feeling from himself, a doubt and fear about his manhood? On first coming in to a woman, he always had, except—strange—with Julie at the beginning, and this summer with Sonia. But he didn't think that was it, yet ever since that golden Sunday morning of which he had written there was some strange mixture of reluctance and apprehensiveness and—duty (what did that mean?) in his feelings as he approached bedtime.

And just now—in the post office—the realization of his dread of a letter to Julie from Peggy Thomas. And the thought that in the midst of their joyousness and ecstasy (yes, despite all this, there had been ecstasy again) everything was still precarious, they were on the edge of—what?

Again he did not know, or what *that* had to do with the imagined scene on the grass at which he was afraid to look.

They had not explicitly referred again to the question of Walton's returning to the house in Northport, yet several times Julie had referred to something "they" must do in October, or about "Christmas this year." Must it be left implicit? Was he afraid to put it into the open?

What had Abe said? "But I didn't open myself." And if he, Walton, did not open himself, would it be through fear or a desire to relieve himself of guilt, or through conscience? That word. It was so long since he had used it, even in thought.

The probable answer was for all these reasons, and perhaps more. But then, *then,* everything out on the table, there would no longer be any reason to turn and look over his shoulder. The Truant Officer was irrelevant if one was no longer a truant.

He started the motor and drove slowly toward home.

The champagne, the lobster, the salad—all delicious, all consumed. The candles guttering; Julie, with the yellow orchid he had brought her in her hair, flushed and smiling, spinning in her fingers the stem of the glass that held the little last of the champagne.

Walton felt a deep glow all through him. The afternoon's intent was forgotten, spent; he knew a richness in his blood, a sureness in his bones that felt like—coming home. I am a man, he thought without embarrassment, and with no self-consciousness said aloud, as though he had newly minted the tired words, "I am a lucky man."

She lowered her eyelids against the full hot force of his eyes, and then opened them again to face him fully, woman, her eyes intensely bright. "You are a good man," she said softly.

What he felt was of that order of shock that in a moment invades one's whole chemistry. "One cannot," he remembered in a flash a doctor's having once said to him, "endure such a shock without undergoing total change—throughout one's system." Walton could not now remember to whom or what the man had referred, but at this moment he took it home to himself. He sat there, rigid, immobile.

"And what's more," said Julie, "I never want to leave you again. I never want you to go away again."

She rose and came over to him. The light in her eyes suddenly terrified him; her fragrance as she came into his arms or, rather, as she drew him into hers, dizzied and smothered him; the warm weight of her on his lap seemed insupportable because of his own rigid insubstantiality.

"Julie," he said, his voice muffled against her bare shoulder, that suddenly tasted salty, too real; "Julie," he cried so hoarsely that she sprang up and away from him, "Julie, I must tell you now—"

She stood there, staring in bewilderment, an arm thrown protectively up, as though to shield her face. He knew even as he looked at her that he would always remember her as she was at this moment, and the sense of living through such an irretrievable instant, where roads (why always roads?) forked and one chose one's direction, quieted him.

"I'm sorry, darling," he said. "I didn't mean to frighten you. Sit down. It's just so hard to say, and when you said that about being a good man, and then that you'd—never want me to leave again, I couldn't stand it. I want it so—" he leaned forward in his earnestness, and found more strength than he had hoped for, to go on—"and I can't have it unless I tell you. I have to take that chance."

Julie's eyes were huge, her voice low but controlled.

"What are you saying?"

Walton's hands tightened on his knees.

"All this," he said, "all this has been so wonderful. Yet under it —I don't know; it can't last without telling and everything being out. Julie, I had an affair this summer. With someone you don't know—a girl at the office, P.H.'s secretary."

All the time he went on, in a gushing torrent of words, she sat motionless, pale despite her tan, stricken, eyes wide and haunted. And, as he rushed to his incoherent conclusion, he stood up and came to her, dropped on his knees and poured the last words on her lap, before burying his head in it: "And I don't want anything ever hidden, ever standing between us again. So even if you can't accept me now, even if you throw me out again, I had to tell you, I had to be all here, bare and exposed, like you said the very first night. Hiding nothing."

He felt her stiffen, pull away, and he released her and sat up.

"I—I—I—I—" she said slowly. "How cruel and selfish of you to tell me, to wait until the moment—" she faltered—"and then tell me, then, then, *then*." She beat her fists on her knees. "To talk all about

Gail and Karen and Dudley, that night, and say nothing about this, nothing, and let me—let me take you to me, and all the time . . ."

Her voice diminished; in a convulsive movement, she drew her shoulders in and up, until they seemed to touch her cheeks in an agonized effort to comfort herself, or to shrink into invisibility. Then, in a moment, she sprang up and confronted him, so militantly that he too rose in hasty reflexive alarm. Her eyes were blazing in maenad fury.

"You destroyer!" It was a choked scream. "You're hateful! And I hate you. I hate you!"

The first stinging slap stunned Walton. The second, rocking his head violently, gave him the dizzy sense of things coming loose inside it. Yet he stood there, hands at his sides, knowing only that that was all that was left for him: to stand and endure. A terrible passivity entered him, drowning even the pain, as he waited for and received a third slap, a fourth.

And then she burst into a terrible weeping and fled from him. He heard the bedroom door slam, the bolt drawn. And still he stood motionless, as the dying candle throbbed, went out, throbbed again, like the echo of the blows, the voice and the door, and finally was spent. He stood there then in the darkness, barely alive, hearing only the desolate sound of her inconsolable tears.

It was sometime in the early dawn when he awoke from his trance (it had not been sleep) in the armchair at the sound of shuffling steps, at once quick and hesitant. It was the child sound, he thought dully, the night-time child sound, and did the halfhearted best he could to pull himself together to reassure and comfort.

And it was a child, though Julie, still dressed, though rumpled, hair disheveled, the flower crushed, her face in the dim light dirt-and-tear-streaked. She flung herself into his lap.

"I'm so cold," she cried through chattering teeth. "Hold me, hold me. I'm freezing. My heart is freezing."

His arms tightened around her; he crushed her to him, muttering broken words and sounds of love and comfort.

"So cold," she whispered, and choked. "So dying. So cold," clinging to him, rooting at him, burrowing into him.

And in the bleak, thin light, he felt the kindling of a flame in him again and, clasping her to him as though someone were trying to tear her away, he staggered on stiff joints down the hallway and dropped, still clutching her, to the bed, where for a long time, an endless time it seemed, of warming, nourishing, protecting, salvaging the flame, they lay clasped.

Until she began to murmur feverishly, "Love me, love me, hold me. Warm me. Oh, love me." And in a paroxysm of frantic haste Walton tore at her clothes and his own, ripped at the blankets, to clasp her again, hold her until he could leave the print of his hands on her hot, convulsed, twisting body.

"Make love to me," she whispered hoarsely, weeping. "Oh, love me, warm me, love me."

And he did. Silently, sternly, promising, offering, thrusting, cherishing, fulfilling. And held her in the circle of his arm, in sleep, thereafter.

But to awake, and part. She white, hurt, shaken, the smile of waking stricken from her, the desperate loneliness and the unbearable knowledge of betrayal returned. Refuge now in bitterness, sarcasm. Strike. Strike back with words like spears.

"Oh, come *on!*" In emulation of teasing coyness. "How do we really compare in bed? How am I going to compete if I don't know my competitor?"

And over a tasteless breakfast, half-eaten, half-left, with eyes always averted, a sudden springing up in fury, ripping off sweater, skirt, tearing at hooks and eyes, terribly reminiscent, that scene again unbearable:

"There! Now tell me, you! Are her breasts better? bigger? Her arms rounder? Her shoulders?" Twist-swinging: "Her back, her butt? Can she grind and bump like this? Bump bump. No, look. Look, I tell you." Challenging. "Come and take me, if you're man enough for me. Not for that little floozie. You don't dare. You don't *dare*. Mama's boy." Marching naked out of the room.

And all the time, that terrible passivity again. A vision of hell. Punishment that must be endured. Nowhere to turn, no move to make, only to stand, motionless, hands at sides, head bowed, endure. . . .

And later—it must have been afternoon—Julie appeared quiet, subdued, hesitant.

"I thought I'd like to take a walk." Swallowing, as though unable to pronounce the words. "Would—you like to come?"

Silent acceptance. And silent walk, over the dark brown sands, wet from an unnoticed rain, under the dark blue gray and purplish clouds of fall, through the chill wind that whined malignantly (Now is the winter of our discontent)—he docilely and numbly following her erect figure where the path between dune and sea was narrow, or walking stiffly by her side, aware without looking of her fixed, unyielding profile. And turning without a word to retrace their forlorn and meaningless steps.

Then, almost home, her raised head and the timid smile, the soft words: "I want to make you a nice supper. Fix me a Scotch, will you?"

And though still silent, the negative peace of a hot supper, favorite dishes and, once, the pressure of her hand on his shoulder as she bent over him to take his plate. Silently, the dishes, he washing, she drying. And there, in the kitchen, her raised face—grief and need commingled, lost, oh, lost: "Please take me to bed." He heard or saw the word *Daddy*. Please, dear Daddy.

And this time sweetly, deeply, slowly, as though drinking at him, as though measuring him, imprinting him, tasting the strange mixture (as he felt it) of his ardor and his utter passiveness to all her moods. Greeting and farewell, tender reunion and impenetrable sadness. And the quiet turning of her back to sleep. . . .

He could not come up out of the darkness, out of oblivion's protective arms. He could not bear to die to consciousness. He could not. But he did.

To see her standing there, dressed, even hat and coat, and the small suitcase there beside her.

"I—I'm going home," she said in a small voice. "Like the bad novels, the soap operas—only to Daddy, not to Mother." Her voice broke. "I don't know what we'll do. I don't know. It's mean to leave you to close the house, but I can't help it. I don't know what's the matter with me, but I can't find myself." She stopped, choked. "I'm lost, and I have to see my father. And don't come home, Walton. Don't come unless I call you. I don't know."

And even as he fully woke, with a chill at the back of his neck and over his scalp, and stretched out a hand and cried, "Don't! Oh, Julie, don't—" she was gone, and frozen, paralyzed, in the grip of some ultimate cold like stone, he lay there, alone, listening to her diminishing footsteps.

The Eye of God

How art thou fallen from heaven, O day-star, son of the morning! How art thou cut to the ground, that didst lay low the nations! And thou saidst in thy heart, I will ascend into heaven, I will exalt my throne above the stars of God; and I will sit upon the mount of congregation, in the uttermost parts of the north; I will ascend above the heights of the clouds; I will make myself like the Most High. Yet thou shalt be brought to Sheol, to the uttermost parts of the pit.

Save me, Oh God; for the waters are come in unto my soul. I sink in deep mire, where there is no standing: I am come into deep waters, where the floods overflow me. I am weary with my crying; my throat is dried: mine eyes fail while I wait for my God.

O God, thou knowest my foolishness; and my sins are not hid from thee.

I AM JEHOVAH THY GOD, WHO BROUGHT THEE UP OUT OF THE LAND OF EGYPT: OPEN THY MOUTH WIDE, AND I WILL FILL IT.

There is an evil which I have seen under the sun, and it is heavy upon men: a man to whom God giveth riches, wealth and honor, so that he lacketh nothing for his soul of all that he desireth, yet God giveth him not power to eat thereof, but an alien eateth it; this is vanity, and it is an evil disease.

If I take the wings of the morning, and dwell in the uttermost parts of the sea . . .

I AM HE; I AM THE FIRST, I AM ALSO THE LAST.

The wicked are like the chaff which the wind driveth away. There- fore the wicked shall not stand in the judgment, nor sinners in the con- gregation of the righteous. The way of the wicked shall perish.

For all his days are but sorrows, and his travail is grief; yea, even in the night his heart taketh no rest. This also is vanity.

If I take the wings of the morning . . .

I FORM THE LIGHT, AND CREATE DARKNESS; I MAKE PEACE, AND CREATE EVIL. . . .

Thou hast set our iniquities before thee, our secret sins in the light of thy countenance. For all our days are passed away in thy wrath: we bring our years to an end as a sigh.

If I take the wings . . .

I AM THAT I AM.

Lighten mine eyes, lest I sleep the sleep of death.

If . . .

I AM.

Better is an handful with quietness, than two handfuls with labor and striving after wind.

October 1

WAITING for Clarence Kiefer, Walton downed one drink quickly, then sipped slowly at a second. He was nervous. He was, he must be, exaggerating the significance of this meeting. But after two grim days of lonely packing and closing of the house on the Vineyard, and several more aimless ones in New York, alternately sitting and brooding in his small hotel room and pacing the avenues disconsolately, any meeting was an event. And the impulse to call Kiefer was not simply a whim. For Walton, the summer's painful sequence had begun in the spring with the conflict at the Foundation over Kiefer's appointment. Seeking the man out now was an act of reassessment.

For whom had he fought so stubbornly and bitterly? He understood sufficiently, of course, the principle he had been defending— even, he thought, to what extent it really was a considered and objective position he had held, and to what rather a clashing of egos, with a resultant rationalization to justify stubbornness.

But, all the same, there was a man intimately bound up in the issue, a man with a fine record, a man whom he had talked to half a dozen times in the last two years and liked, respected. Yet did he really know him? Rehearsing disconsolately the summer's events (the newspaper account of Dudley's appointment to his old post had somehow filled him with melancholy, serious doubts about the course he had taken, and about the new work in publishing)—rehearsing the whole dreary story, he had suddenly thought, "Kiefer! Who is Kiefer?"

And now, seated alone at a marble-topped table in a little café on lower Fifth Avenue, his nervous anticipation slowly wore off and was replaced by a weary, almost bored regret that he had made the appointment. What could come of it? It had been an act of superstition, he thought now, as though in exploring more intimately the calibre of the man he had backed he would find some touchstone to his own nature, some reassurance or denial of his own integrity, of his intent through this whole thorny summer.

A few minutes before five: Kiefer was not late; Walton, lacking purpose until work began next Monday, had been early. Through the window he watched the people on the pavement. October had entered crisply, the warm and lambent sunlight cooled by a light breeze, the air golden and clear.

Friends met, stopped and talked just outside the window. Laughter exploded, so genuine and hearty that passersby turned, looked and smiled, in sympathy or in reminiscence. Walton could not take his eyes from them; his heart shivered, and there was a ball of lead in his belly, but he continued to stare at them as though he would consume them with his eyes. And then a woman joined them—a woman of about thirty-five, vivacious, warm, vital-looking. One of the men addressed her laughingly, and when she replied she laid her hand upon his sleeve.

There was a shadow across his table, but at first, so rapt was his attention on the group outside, Walton supposed that it had somehow emanated from them. Then he was aware of the presence of a man beside him.

For just a moment, startled, he did not recognize as Clarence Kiefer this man of middling height and heavy stature, whose awkward solidity and bland expression were belied by the owlish intensity of his eyes behind horn-rimmed spectacles.

"I'm not late, Dr. Herrick?"

"It's good to see you, Mr. Kiefer."

Kiefer was worried. He was afraid.

"In the event that this gets out, Mr. Herrick—" Was the light that bent a ray from his shining glasses simply a gleam from the setting sun, fracturing the window, or did it shoot outward from some antediluvian fear, visible thousand of light years later in the suddenly panicked eyes of Clarence Kiefer? "In that event, Mr. Herrick—" he paused to take a mincing sip of his pale highball—"in that event, it could prove very embarrassing to me. An administrator in my position is vulnerable in a peculiar way. In this time of charges and allegations, guilt by association . . ." His voice trailed off, and he concluded with a halfhearted wave of his pallid, freckled hand.

"We are all vulnerable," Walton replied flatly. Maliciously? Misery breeds malice. "To be alive is to be vulnerable."

"But not to the same degree," Clarence Kiefer insisted earnestly. He had a way of nodding his head, of bowing, almost, as though he were agreeing endlessly with himself. This Walton had never noticed before, and it irritated him. "Consider the position of the dean of a nationally renowned graduate school—"

" 'Consider the lilies of the field . . .' " Walton broke in rudely.

Kiefer drew his head back—like some affronted stork or crane, Walton thought. No, he belonged to some sturdy branch of the rodent group—a muskrat, a woodchuck. No bird he. "You are jesting. But this is no matter for levity. To me, Mr. Herrick. You sought me out. You offered me this post—or at least led me to believe that, subject to the approval of your Board, I should have it. I dealt frankly with you, reviewed the whole story of my associations, however tenuous, with groups now unfavorably regarded as connected with—" he paused, swallowed some unacceptable designation (much, Walton thought, as an indignant child might gulp an unpalatable dose of medicine), and finished, the capital letters glistening with majesty—"The Left. I realized that this was possibly indiscreet, but it seemed a Noble Cause, in the service of My Country. And I had every confidence in you. Frankly, I assumed that your position in the Foundation was impregnable, unassailable. It had not occurred to me that, if they rejected me because of my marginal association with The Left (mind you, all years ago, years ago, in those years when the Blood is hot), they would also—reject you. Even though, years ago, we belonged to the same association. In the event that my candidacy was unsuccessful, I had assumed that you would still be there, to insure that there was no bandying of my name."

Walton poked savagely at his pipe.

"They didn't reject me," he said shortly, "except as the director of this one project. They wanted me to stay, offered me a vice presidency and a raise. But after what had happened I didn't want to stay."

Kiefer pawed at the air and began to bow again.

"Very well, Mr. Herrick, very well. For you, I might add. But this is what I meant when I said that I am left vulnerable. Exposed, I might say, however unjustly. Just suppose what might happen, in the event that our president learns that I was considered a—a Security Risk."

"Why should he?" Walton asked abruptly. "I can tell you for certain that Philip Gates, the head of the Foundation, is most discreet."

Mr. Kiefer nodded, several times. "I am sure, sure that that is true. Certainly. But what is to prevent—say, even one of your trustees from mentioning all this, however casually, to just one—one, I repeat—friend? And this friend in turn tells two or three others. Then, in the event that—"

"What is to prevent one of us from slipping in the bathtub and breaking his neck?" Walton inquired roughly.

Clarence Kiefer was pained. A red flush had crept up his neck and was now staining his face.

"It's all very well for you, Mr. Herrick," he bleated—and again, as though completely out of control, his head commenced to bob—"all very well for you to jest about it and treat it lightly, as though it was no responsibility of yours. But I must protest that, as Dean of the Graduate Faculties of Dunston University, I am in no position to be amused by the course events have taken. That a youthful adventure, undertaken in a spirit of idealism, should threaten my whole career, now at its peak, is hardly a development to be dismissed lightly. All through a gesture undertaken in patriotism—"

Walton felt an almost unbearable impatience. This—this lobster was not the man he had defended.

"How much time," he asked abruptly, "do your administrative duties allow you to continue your scholarly work?"

Kiefer seemed as pleased as though Walton had congratulated him on the birth of a son.

"Almost none. One could say none at all. Administration consumes a great deal of time, a great deal."

Walton said nothing, simply stared at him, and it was as though Kiefer divined his thoughts, for the red flush, which had subsided, mottled his cheeks again.

"Mr. Herrick," he began, and his voice was a painful rasp. "Mr. Herrick—"

Walton laid a hand on his sleeve. His waspishness had broken, and he was ashamed of his rough handling of this—this poor sheep. *By what authority?* had suddenly pounded through his head.

"Mr. Kiefer, I'm truly sorry that I've been so unsympathetic. I've been having troubles of my own, and I've allowed them to make me deal shortly with you. Please accept my apology. And let me add this: I'll call Philip Gates tomorrow and ask him to make doubly sure that everyone with knowledge of this matter honors strictly its confidential nature. I'm really sure that you'll have nothing to worry about."

Kiefer's anxious eyes searched his, and apparently found the reassurance they sought. He relaxed, his hectic color receded, and he ventured a few amenities—an inquiry about Walton's new work, the current news, the beauties of October. Then he rose, rather awkwardly, and expressed his thanks, took his leave.

Walton watched his hunched shoulders pass through the door. Then he slumped back in his chair. So that was that. He ordered another bourbon.

The universal solvent. It might get to him in time, he thought—what Abe Fortune called "the broth." When in trouble, alone, discouraged, have a drink for comfort. When in cherished company, elated, after victory or recognition, have a drink to celebrate.

In cherished company . . . He recalled, sipping the new bourbon, the little group of two men and a woman on the sidewalk outside the window earlier. "I all alone beweep my outcast state . . ." How did the rest go? "Like to the lark—" The poet remembers his "sweet love": irony of ironies. When alone, an outcast—from himself, Walton thought, as well; self-banished, too—not only bourbon, but also a woman. Always. Always? Yes, always a woman. Looking back down the corridor of years. Exiled from Joanna and self, from self and Lydia, from the vague remote others, always to turn to another woman—to carry on, he had almost thought, his vendetta. Vendetta! Then did his mother's arm reach so far? Poor mother, poor Marcia Herrick: for just a moment he felt the pity and tenderness he had bound tightly in him these long years now. Then, watching a handsome couple enter the café, he thought again, always a woman.

And now—this summer—at last, even with Julie. But it was different: fool or not, he had told her; he had never told before, and he felt a perverse, self-wounding, festering pride—until he remembered his conversation with the Colonel.

He had called home once. On reaching New York, that first night, he had been unable to keep his hand from the telephone. Julie had been out, the Colonel's voice gruff but kind. Julie and the children were fine; he and Julie had—he coughed, cleared his throat—talked of their trouble.

"I've been very plain with her, Walton. I can't pretend to sit in judgment; I'm pulled both ways. But I know that the only good outcome is for her to ask you back. That's the way it must be: life must go on. But it will take time. Julie has a very stubborn streak in her— sometimes, I think, an unhealthy will to self-mortification. Her heart is more innocent than wise. As was her mother's."

Where had the Colonel learned to talk like that? Where had he kept his poetry all this time? And then his voice changed; there entered a note of almost comic despair.

"Walton, why did you tell her, man? Why didn't you pack it away in yourself and take your medicine like a man, in silence? That's what I was trying to tell you about men and women, up in Chilmark. There's never lived a man whose eye didn't wander, and foot follow after. And when a break comes, it's never because of just one of the two."

Walton stammered something incoherent, and the Colonel's voice changed again.

"Listen, son, remember this. What I said to you in Chilmark about my—feeling for you, and you as Julie's husband—that's unchanged. Remember that. And I'll call you at the hotel in about a week. Good night, son."

Son. His own father. Was it that he had never had a father to defy, to rebel against, because William was not such an image, was not *the father*—was this why, why . . . He became confused, lost the sequence of his thought, and, observing that his glass was empty, ordered another drink.

Which must be the last, he told himself with as much sternness as he could summon. And then dinner—alone. Why was the thought of being alone so dreary? Why, when alone, could he never draw upon the resources he knew he had: books, meditation, even writing again after so long? What was so dreadful about being alone? What had he once written about this in his journal?

And where were his friends? Why must he be alone? Abe Fortune —the only man who came to mind. What was the unique thing Abe meant to him, that no other man did? And why, again why, double-damnable why, searching his mind for others, could he think only of women: Sonia, Gail, Karen (far away), even (strange and ambiguous) Lydia.

He shook his head, sipped his new drink. What had his father told him long ago? "There's some taint in the Herrick blood, son, that can't withstand strong drink, once begun. That's another reason I hope you won't drink. There's Lloyd, as you know, but it was true of my father too, when he was a young man, before he had the Call. And his father, Aaron—and my great-grandfather Peletiah was the worst of all. I've never touched it, and I hope you won't."

The line of drunken Herricks! Walton wished he could conjure them up now, sit them down with him here, at this table, and inter-rogate them: old hoarse-voiced Uncle Lloyd, whom he had grown to love in those last years, for his humor and vitality; Grandfather Cor-nelius, the reformed and inspired, who had still gone off the edge of propriety at the end, preaching radical love and practicing some sub-stitute with his nurse; Aaron of the stormy temper, wasting his life on the farm and his anger on his children—what drunken furies he

must have indulged on Saturday nights, before harnessing the team on
the Sabbath and driving morosely to church, with a fresh cut on his
cheek from his unsteady hand, and his head still wet from the vigorous
application of the pump, in hope of shocking the ache from it.

And this left his own father out; he was sorry, but it did. He
realized that he was trying to feel the devotion, the tenderness, he regularly and spontaneously accorded him. But it would not come: tonight
it was not there, not in him.

Uncle Herbert Nicholson could sit with them, though he would
probably be painfully uneasy. But he was a brother of the cup. Not
so *his* father, the Thunderer. It suddenly amused Walton, filled him
with a wonderfully free sense of the comic that the only two male
forebears he really knew anything about who did not belong in this
tavern's company were his gentle father and the austere and terrifying
James H. Nicholson. What a pair they would make, sitting at a table
for two in the adjacent dining room, where spirituous liquors were not
served!

One's forefathers could be good company, Walton thought, realizing that he was no longer alone. He turned to Peletiah to apologize for
not having included him in this summary.

But Peletiah was not discomfited. His was a crab-apple sort of
old age, not sour but tart. Peering into the murky depths of a heavy
silver tankard, he remarked to Walton that a good disposition and a
good digestion were life's greatest boons—and the first depended on
the second. "But not wholly." A smile cracked the reddened, veined
knobs of his cheeks. "A good digestion is your one requisite, but the
other is a freedom to speak what Nature has generated in your mind.
Relieve yourself of whatever unprofitable and malign thoughts your
natural humors and vapors have cast across your contentment and
comfort and self-pleasuring. Nature has given us orifices—vents, as you
will—for the passage in of good things and the casting forth of that
which is not congenial to the human constitution. And you do not speak
your mind, however hot or mean or even poisonous (all the more, if
poisonous) at the time, these matters pack up sorely within you. But
withal, keep your bowels open as well."

Walton observed that Cornelius Herrick was pained, that Uncle
Lloyd guffawed.

"But the pith of the matter," Great-Great-Grandfather Peletiah
continued, "is not to keep too nice a conscience. There's the heart of it.
Uncles and aunts I have had, and cousins to surfeit. Wherefore my
changing of the spelling of my name to Herri'k. I'd have none of them,

with their finicking consciences, and that apostrophe was an admonishment to them. It earned me the title of Eccentric, which I wear the more easily for the knowing that its alternatives seem to be Fool and Sheep. It's a wise man knows his own father and his own natural talents. Mine —talents, that is—have been to accommodate myself to myself, and to no one else. Spare me the man that's finicky—the man who will not do this or that because 'twill harm Sophia Wentworth or Hector Jones. What won't harm someone else? You can't take a hundred steps outdoors without stepping on an ant or bug. And the man that will always be about doing God's will is worse—put two such together and you'll see why. For each such man there's another God, disagreeing with the first, and then unnecessary words or fisticuffs. Why do we have our Selves, if not to service them, indulge them, take care of them, watch out for them? Show me a man that's not selfish, and I'll show you one of Nature's fools. Now up with your tankard, boy, and stop puttering around in your insides. Life's an impossibly painful matter, and spirits impregnate spirit. I grieve when I think of those poor Red Men before our grandfathers brought them Fire Water."

Cornelius uttered a loud, distinct groan. Lloyd shouted, "Another round! Go on, old fellow! Don't stop now. We're going to put the boy straight yet. Beer does more than Bunyan can, to justify God's ways to man."

Great-Grandfather Aaron was staring before him, glassy-eyed. There were fumes in his head, Walton thought, and—who could endure so emancipated a father as Peletiah?

Uncle Herbert's chair was empty, Walton realized next, and spotted him at the bar, three shot glasses lined up before him, dividing his attention between the bartender's discourse and the group at the table, for he kept throwing oblique, worried glances over his shoulder at the Herricks.

And out behind the bar, through the open door, the Hon. James H. was concluding a glacial period while William Herrick nodded in perplexed acquiescence, his hands together, finger tips tapping finger tips, upward, Walton remembered having once thought, as if in prayer.

The waiter (Dennis Byrnes? He had an epicene kind of surliness) brought a fresh round of drinks.

"Cheers," said Uncle Lloyd.

"Now, women," said old Peletiah Herri'k. "Aaron's a good boy, a bit bad-tempered, but honorable. Women plague him, that's his trouble."
Great-Grandfather Aaron broke off his obsessed staring, swung his head around and fastened Peletiah with a wild, wrathful eye, but his father's

old, red-rimmed sky-blue eyes twinkled imperturbably. "Women," he continued, "are necessary." He paused, quaffed. "But that's the most you can say for them—both the best and the worst. If they're plump in those regions God meant them to be, that's natural and pleasant. If they're skinny there, that's unnatural and unpleasant. But what bothers me, son—" and he turned to Walton, put a hand on his shoulder—"is that everyone in your time (and I speak as the eldest here) seems to want them to coruscate, wants them to assume roles, capacities beyond 'em: Saints and Sirens and Successes. It's not peculiar to your time, of course; Aaron felt much of this. His wife was to him, and to that underdeveloped boy there [he pointed to Cornelius] a Saint. The difference lay in what it meant to them. That scrawny Cornelius (a heathen name), who, as I recall, charges me with darkening his childhood with my drunkenness (I can't remember his prissy language) found her sainthood admirable, and blamed his father for all her troubles. While his father—that's Aaron—hated it and tormented her and himself because of it." He swallowed a long draught. "This is the burden of what I have to say. She was no Saint, no more than my early lamented wife. (I was relict in my time of four. A man has to keep his feet warm of a winter's night.) She was a woman who made the mistake of thinking that if she did what she had the arrogance to think that others wanted her to do, she would please them—and *God*. And that's where the misery comes in. Women are necessary—but they're not that necessary."

Aaron picked up his glass in one massive hand and shattered it against the wall. Walton could see Uncle Herbert, aghast, staring at the spot on the wall as though it were the stigmata of Saint Sebastian, then, with shaking hand, pick up the last of the three shot glasses before him, and hurl its contents down his throat.

Beyond the open door, in the dining room, the Hon. James H. Nicholson rose, bowed coldly to William Herrick and departed, leaving William to raise his hands to Heaven and mop his perspiring forehead. Poor Dad, thought Walton.

And then an inspiration. "Go out in the lobby," he said to Aaron. "There's a man there, tall—very tall—who's looking for you. You can't miss him—he's used to frightening people. I think you'll enjoy talking with him."

Aaron's chair crashed on the floor as he left.

"Why, there's William," said Cornelius. "In the dining room. He's alone; I must go keep him company. Gentlemen, excuse me." He bowed.

"His loss is our gain," muttered Uncle Lloyd.

At the bar, Uncle Herbert was staring in a stupor at three newly full shot glasses.

"Now," said Great-Great-Grandfather Peletiah, "let's consider the present." He turned and directed the full blue fire of his eyes at Walton. "That of course, refers to you, son. I don't suppose we've all been summoned to this epiphany simply to sit and drink. At least, *I've* never found life that pleasantly uncomplicated. I've spoken of women, mind you, as much as I care to. But you don't seem able to forget them. If it's not your mother mollycoddling you, it's a wife you're quarreling with, or a wench you're running to or away from. It doesn't become you, a man of some position in the world of affairs. Running for governor, aren't you?"

"No, I'm not," Walton replied. "There was some talk of it, but I'm not."

"Governor!" The word came resonant from Jas. H., who had entered with Aaron. "Of what state, sir, if I may ask?"

"Connecticut," Walton replied, and hastily added, "I don't mean that I am, but—"

"Connecticut! My state, sir. Senator Nicholson, James H. Nicholson. It's a pleasure to meet you, Governor Herrick."

Walton found it futile to explain, and the pleasure in the eyes of his handsome, elegantly erect grandfather, as they shook hands, forbade it.

"A governor," said Cornelius Herrick, "is a father, one who teaches."

"A governor, sir," said Jas. H. Aaron (the two had gradually merged), "is one who commands, controls, rules, by properly appointed authority."

"A governor," said Uncle Lloyd dryly, "is a device for regulating, and usually reducing, speed." He looked challengingly at his father.

But Cornelius was locked in steadfast appraisal with Jas. H. There they were again, Walton thought, facing each other as they had in his vision of childhood, contesting for supremacy. Yet perhaps Cornelius was also challenging *his* father, the Nicholson-locked Aaron. And Jas. H.'s son?

Walton wheeled to consider the bar, and the irony came home: Jas. H. practiced at one bar, Uncle Herbert at another. But Herbert was nowhere to be seen. He had fled.

And so did Aaron—now. With a demented howl he ripped himself from the contours of Jas. H. and raced out into the night.

"Love," said Cornelius firmly. "Radical love."

"Justice," replied Jas. H. forcibly.

"Gentleness," said Cornelius.

"Firmness," said Jas. H.

"Sympathy."

"Integrity."

"Peace."

"Duty."

"Stuff and nonsense," snorted Peletiah. "I'm older than the two of you put together. Let's have no more of this. We're here to help Walton, not to weaken him with this milksop talk. We were about to instruct him with regard to women."

"There will have to be less noise here," said the House Dick, "and let's have no more talk of women, old boy. No women in here." He flashed his badge.

He looked like—like Mr. Remington, his mother's nemesis, Walton thought.

"El Hani!" exclaimed Cornelius, turning very pale.

"Sam Burgess," said Jas. H., with marked satisfaction.

On second thought, Walton decided he looked a little like Dudley Foote—or was it the Spoiler?

"Who are you calling 'old boy'?" demanded Peletiah wrathfully. "You young whippersnapper! We'll soon take care of you."

Uncle Lloyd unbuckled his peg leg. "Here, Gramp," he said, handing it to Peletiah, "hit him with this."

Everything is coming apart, Walton thought.

The House Dick fled, muttering maledictions. . . .

They saw the women at the Wailing Wall—shrouded in black, pale, care-worn, faces lined. They were huddled together: old Hephzibah, Elinor, Cora, Cousin Gertrude and Ludie—who was feigning grief, peeping plaintively from behind her veil. Beside them, arms thrust out in protection and anguish, stood Marcia, the priestess. She tore her hair, strewed ashes upon the others and herself, led their dismal chant.

They saw the women at the Sewing Circle: Catherine Herrick, as grim as though she belonged in the first group, vivacious Rosalind, William's Dickensian companion Mrs. Harris, Patience Nicholson, Aunt Emily Herrick, Lloyd's Celia. They chatted briskly, sipped their tea, resumed their needlework. "The distaff side," said Jas. H. approvingly. He had avoided looking at the other women.

They saw the women of the Chorus Line: Carol Seixas, Irene Wertz, Karen Kodály, Gail Arbuthnot, Sonia Wilenski. ("Giddy chicks," said Uncle Lloyd, and chuckled. "Foreign dolls.") It was true, Walton thought—what Peletiah had said about him and women. When they reached this part of things, they were *all* his. But no, a second line appeared, none of whom Walton knew, but Lloyd waved and called out, "The Can-Can! Give us the Can-Can!"

It was then that Ludie tore off her black cloak and rushed to a place beside one at whom Jas. H. was glowering. "Emmy Burgess!" he exclaimed. "Brazen hussy!" Walton did not know to which one he was referring, but watched with amused sympathy his Aunt Ludie's gartered leg kick high.

"Enough!" shouted Peletiah. "Saints, Successes and Sirens." They were back in the Tavern, and as Walton turned to glance at the bar, his blood chilled. The Truant Officer was sitting where Herbert had been—and beside him Hawkshaw the Detective, finger astride his nose.

"This has been an unruly gathering," said William Herrick I, the Great Original. "And when one investigates families, it is not seemly so to disport yourselves. The Herrick line began in America in dignity, peril and honest toil, but knew early the harsh hand of indignity. Terror and shock and death visited us, ripped away our fairest rose. This has been the black cloud in our inmost heart ever since, and I suppose some such to have occurred among the Nicholsons.

"Life is painful, and its beauty and dignity are found and maintained only when one accepts and celebrates all of it, the pain and the joy, the work and the rest, the wars and the peace.

"You, sir," he went on, pointing a finger at Peletiah, "are an old rascal, showing our women in the guise of death's heads or dancing girls, and presenting the scene of decent needlework as only the occasion for trivial gossip. You demean them and yourself."

Walton gazed at him with interest. He saw no resemblance to any other Herrick—rather, he thought suddenly, to Huntingdon Haldane.

"All we know," said Peletiah rather snappishly, "about your tragedy is that some men paid fines for frightening your wife, and that she died shortly after. Tell us what happened, and take the curse off us."

William I shook his head gravely.

"It is not a matter for light recounting. Nor does the single isolated incident, the narrative detail, matter. Something of the sort is in every human experience. Ask yourself of your own, and turn your revelry into sober thought on the condition of your own life, your own soul."

"Sir, you are arbitrary." Jas. H. was glowering.

The Great Original looked at him coolly.

"I had hoped to restrict my comments decently to my own family. But since you break in, sir, with a comment so obviously ironic, coming from you, I shall add this. I have reprimanded my sometime grandson for his treatment of women. He would never have found reason, sir, for his presentation of lamenting women—death's heads, I called them—but for your kind of man. Why turned you always your back on life?"

"I demand," said Marcia Nicholson, tossing her haughty head, "a place in this council."

Aaron Herrick (where was Jas. H.? Gone, fled, averted) bellowed angrily, "A woman!"

Walton watched, fascinated, as Herbert Nicholson flung himself from some obscure corner directly at Marcia. "No, not a woman, not a woman!" he cried hysterically. "You're all blind. And you—" he pointed a shaking finger at Walton—"You! Why do you write of love and not of hate? What makes you think you can exorcise the basic emotion, the spring of all we feel? You fool! I left you a poem."

William I shook his head sadly.

"I shall not stay. I ask of all of you only this. What do you think America is *for*? Why do you think we carved and chopped it out of a wilderness? You, sir—" he pointed at Cornelius—"you have had some experience of life. You struck out for yourself, however soft you finally became. ["Soft?" said Cornelius. "Hard."] But are you aware, are you capable of understanding my pride that this son of yours—and he alone in the whole line—was named for me?"

"Me?" said Walton's father, and covered his face.

"You," said Old William. "You were the warrior. For as you yourself might have said, 'The ways of the Lord are wondrous strange.' You are the lion heart."

But not a father, Walton wanted to cry out—not a father to me. He held his peace.

"That's what they always say," Marcia commented bitterly. "How can he help being brilliant with the father and grandfather he had?"

Lloyd's face was composed in a way Walton had never seen it; he was looking at his brother, and his eyes were shining. "William. Bill," he said. "Look up. It's so."

And William, who had never been called Bill, looked up.

"Where are the girls?" asked Peletiah-Lloyd.

"*Senator* Nicholson!" sneered Herbert. "He never was elected."

"Patience," said Patience.

"Tea," said Catherine Herrick.

"Girls!" snorted Marcia-James. "Nasty sexuality! Prurience! Lust! Filthy sex!"

"It tickles," said Ludie plaintively.

Old William turned to go. Then he paused and swung back to Walton. "Live with your pain," he said gravely. "Embrace it. You have in you the means. Stand up. Be a father to yourself."

He was gone. With confidence, Walton turned to look at the bar. There was no one there. Yet he saw Cornelius' eyes, following his gaze, grow wide in fright—heard him murmur again, "El Hani!" Then, with an effort, he composed himself and said, to no one in particular, "This is a ridiculous gathering, and William is waiting for me. My son," he concluded pointedly, gazing in a reproachful way at Lloyd, who was imperturbably restoring his leg.

"And my brother," retorted Lloyd, without looking up.

Cornelius stopped short, looked Lloyd full in the eye, hesitated (his face had a sweetness, a thoughtfulness that Walton had never observed before), and spoke.

"Yes," he said, "and your brother. We'll come back to you."

And shortly they did, Cornelius pacing himself slowly to stay beside William's shuffle. The three of them drew chairs together, Cornelius facing Lloyd, William by his side. Walton moved his own chair, to hear the better.

" 'And Rebekah his wife conceived.' " Cornelius was grave. " 'And the children struggled together within her; and she said, If it be so, wherefore am I thus? And she went to inquire of Jehovah. And Jehovah said unto her,

> " 'Two nations are in thy womb,
> And two peoples shall be
>   separated from thy bowels:
> And the one people shall be
>   stronger than the other people;
> And the elder shall serve the younger.

" 'And when her days to be delivered were fulfilled, behold, there were twins in her womb. And the first came forth red, all over like a hairy garment; and they called his name Esau. And after that came forth his brother, and his hand had hold on Esau's heel; and his name was called Jacob: and Isaac was threescore years old when she bare them.

" 'And the boys grew: and Esau was a skillful hunter, a man of the field; and Jacob was a quiet man, dwelling in tents.' "

They were all silent.

"I have read in Jacob Boehme," said Cornelius, "that Esau betokens the first power of the natural, created Adam, and Jacob betokens the power of the other Adam, Christ."

William had kept his head bowed. Now he looked up, directly at his father, his eyes clear and shining.

" 'Behold, Esau my brother is a hairy man,' " he recited, " 'and I am a smooth man. My father peradventure will feel me, and I shall seem to him as a deceiver; and I shall bring a curse upon me, and not a blessing.' "

He turned his shining gaze upon Lloyd, who stirred from the depths of his chair, grunted, coughed, and then let the veils fall back from his eyes too. He shifted his gaze to his father, who waited, hands clutching the arms of his chair, braced.

" 'Bless me, even me also, O my father.' " Lloyd's voice was hoarse, croaking, but the words were clear. " 'Hast thou but one blessing, my father? Bless me, even me also, O my father.' "

Cornelius bowed his head now, but William, sitting erect, looked commandingly at Lloyd.

Lloyd slouched back again, and this time his words were not so clear. One shaking hand held the stump of a dead cigar.

" 'The days of mourning for my father are at hand; then will I slay my brother Jacob.' "

" 'And Jacob,' " said Cornelius in an impersonal storyteller's voice, " 'went out from Beer-sheba, and went toward Haran.' "

William lifted his head and chanted, " 'And behold, a ladder set upon the earth, and the top of it reached to heaven. . . . Surely Jehovah is in this place; and I knew it not.' "

There was again a long silence, once more broken by Cornelius the storyteller.

" 'And it came to pass, when Jacob saw Rachel the daughter of Laban his mother's brother, and the sheep of Laban his mother's brother, that Jacob went near, and rolled the stone from the well's mouth, and watered the flock of Laban his mother's brother. And Jacob kissed Rachel, and lifted up his voice, and wept.' "

And now Walton observed that a change occurred; the three men relaxed and smiled, each to both the others: they were joined in some invisible ring of feeling.

Cornelius declared, "We are now at the banks of Jabbok, where

Jacob wrestled with the angel. And when the angel was gone, 'Jacob lifted up his eyes, and looked, and, behold, Esau was coming, and with him four hundred men. . . .' " He paused, and then, as though in benediction: "Jacob 'bowed himself to the ground seven times, until he came near to his brother. And Esau ran to meet him, and embraced him, and fell on his neck, and kissed him: and they wept.' "

Walton looked at the three bowed heads—Cornelius' shiningly white, his father's with the heavy gray bush from ear to ear, and Uncle Lloyd's gleaming bald pate.

Then they lifted their heads and turned, all three to him, to recite together, " 'Now Israel loved Joseph more than all his children, because he was the son of his old age: and he made him a coat of many colors.' "

Walton felt the hot tears in his eyes, and bowed his head. So, he thought, I have not understood. I have understood very little. And my sons? Peter, Tim? I have much to learn.

When he looked up, they were gone. Cornelius and William had left the room; Lloyd had returned to the table. Slowly, Walton followed.

"Just in time," said old Peletiah, Ur-Abraham. "The women! Old Adam said we have not treated them with respect. Let's respect them for a little. More ale!"

"No," said Cornelius with firm authority. "Grandfather, enough of this horseplay."

But it was too late; they were already there, scattered through the room. Chiffon and silk, demure organdy and sultry satin. Slave girls and empresses, sorceresses and soubrettes: Herrick's Circus, the Greatest Cliché on Earth.

The Blue Danube soared through the room, shivered the crystal chandeliers, stirred the heavy draperies over the tall windows. Marcia was waltzing with Aaron, leaning gracefully away from him as he swung her gallantly: supple young Marcia, smiling into his fierce eyes, knowing an abandon that released her wholly from the years of servitude to come.

Dear young Marcia, thought Walton, go backward, on backward, never turn forward. And then he saw, transfixed upon a huge green cross, Jas. H.—head bowed, beard upon chest, blood trickling from his great sinewy hands and feet—saw him rouse as the gleeful Herbert thrust the Vinegar Sponge into his face, rouse, look wildly upon the dancing Marcia, there with Aaron, shudder and give up the ghost.

"Blasphemy, blasphemy! How perfectly dreadful!" chanted the long black line of Elders.

Herbert threw the sponge high in the air, uttered an exultant shout, and flung himself into the arms of the astonished Lloyd.

"Waltz with me! Waltz, my dear," he cried, and Lloyd gallantly responded, thumping his wooden leg resoundingly, and laughing, laughing hoarsely with his head thrust back to bay at the chandeliers.

Herbert leaned back against Lloyd's strong arm, and in imitation of Marcia simpered up at his escort, and around at the other dancers, a provincial lady aping the great world.

But not for long. With a wild cry Ludie, dressed only in a white camisole laced with scarlet ribbon, and in long black stockings, her dark hair flying, raced across the ballroom, flung Herbert spinning away and, with one supple twist of her body, thrust herself into Lloyd's embrace.

"Off with her head!" shouted old Peletiah, hopping about so lustily that the ale slopped from his mug, to mingle with the vinegar on the floor.

Walton turned away, dizzy. There were quiet figures in the corners of the room. Joanna, head bent, hands folded in lap, contemplating (in sorrow?) the floor. Walton's heart ached. But in a moment he saw his father shuffle over, stop before her, resting on his cane, and incline his head in gentle question. She looked up; Walton saw her gladness, her welcoming smile, and turned away. Of course, he thought, of course, and walking on blindly and rapidly, almost trod on Lydia and Jas. H., holding converse on cushions spread on the floor.

They were rapt, not even aware of him, and he paused to listen.

"There are four modes of life," declared the handsome, vital young lawyer, "and only four. They are gambling, politics, sex and scholarship. Call them what you will, these are the four elements of human life as surely as fire, air, earth and water are of nature. They, and the mixtures that emanate from them, comprise every human experience. I challenge you, my dear Lydia, to mention one sphere of endeavor that does not partake of one or more of these elements."

Lydia threw back her fine head in delighted laughter. She was wearing a pale reddish-brown chiffon, caught up in pleats on her bare shoulders, and flowing down over her body in delicate, mobile lines. (Dear Rusty, dear divinely freckled, sumptuously made Lydia, what will you say?)

"Business," Lydia suggested.

"Compounded, in varying degrees, of gambling, politics and scholarship," replied Jas. H. exuberantly. "Another?"

Lydia's eyes grew thoughtful.

"Motherhood," she suggested.

"Sex, pre-eminently," replied Jas. H. "With admixtures of all the others."

Lydia's eyes danced now as they looked directly into his.

"I love politics," she declared. "Most of all."

Of course, thought Walton, of course. And he leaned forward and asked, a little belligerently, "Haven't you left out art, the creative act?"

Imperturbably, without turning to notice him, young Jas. H. replied, "Sex."

Walton moved off in a melancholy way and, observing Cornelius in a big armchair, thought, "Religion!" But Gail was gracefully settled at his feet, her arm resting across his knees, her face lifted in adoration. Cornelius was stroking her hair.

Catherine Herrick was watching. Patience Nicholson was watching. Aaron's wife (What was her name? Lucinda?) was watching. Elinor and Cora and Cousin Gertrude were watching. The night has a thousand eyes.

Who was the Old Witch? Marcia? That German governess, Fräulein—Hess? Old Peletiah's wife, Hephzibah? Walton rubbed his hand tiredly over his forehead: he didn't know.

But he knew who the Young Witch was, and his loins stirred. Wearing a gold belt and a gold patch between her thighs (*ces barbares marchent tous nus*) and a shining golden cap on her head, Sonia-Irene was dancing with a dervish, Joseph of the Many Colors. The waltz had ended, and they flung themselves (*shuddering gold-licked flesh*) into barbaric rhythms; they rocked and rolled.

Old Peletiah, dressed like a rooster, hopped and swung, horny and raucous, red-faced and lecherous—swung Peter Pan, slim and elegant (crow, Karen, crow), stamping out the measures, ducking, weaving, puffing and blowing.

Down behind the bushes (no bulrushes these) by the end of the ballroom, savage old Priapus Nicholson rolled Emmy Burgess in the tall grasses, while the Elders watched. (Oh Susannah, Moses, in the bull rushes, rushes to victory. Victory, victory, how perfectly splendid!)

Walton sat down, lowered his despairing head into his hands. Where was Julie? Where were Julie and the children? Not here, never here—there was no place for them here, in this antibiotic community. They belonged in life, far, far from here. *How art thou fallen from life, O earth worm, son of the mud! How art thou cut to the ground, that didst lay low the dollies!*

The band broke off. "Silence!" screamed Peletiah. "Silence! For the Parade of the Seven Deadly Neuroses!"

And to "Pomp and Circumstance" there rolled through the ball-room, on resplendent dollies of the sort employed by furniture movers, the pageant of Seven Walton Herricks. The first stood upright, arms folded over chest, adamant, while P.H. pleaded with him to stay, Julie pleaded that he come close, Haldane pointed out the logic of the situation. The second—but why go on? Walton thought desperately to himself. They were all there, the same old ones, the inescapable ones of time immemorial ("Time is indivisible," muttered Henri Bergson in his ear. "Reality is mobility itself. The more or less lengthy changes we witness within us and in the external world take place in a single identical time. Listen to the uninterrupted humming of life's depths") —lust and wrath and sloth and all the rest.

"I can't," he cried out to Bergson. "I can't listen. I can't hear!"

And he couldn't look. He couldn't see. The platforms holding the Seven Neuroses became linked, spun round, formed a Merry-Go-Round and commenced to whirl at a tremendous speed. "Faster," cried the Duchess. "Faster, faster!"

The whole ballroom began to spin on its axis, like the great globe itself, dissolving, fading, to leave not a rack behind. To Walton, it was as though he were on a rollercoaster, rushing through space, catching an isolated glimpse, now and then, of this one, that pair, another—flash—another—flash . . .

On what level of reality did all this occur? *Eye do not know. Eye can only suggest, reticently, objectively, that it is Life commenting on itself. (If Eye take the shank of the morning, and loaf in the nearest parts of the pool . . .)*

It was all breaking up, dissolving, whirling in a glittering phantasmagoria, caught in snatches—part *Walpurgisnacht,* part ascension. The sky was filled with insipid and anemic herrick-angels and nicholson-angels, their pale wings beating ineffectually. And below, red glow, the Young Witch was dancing the Hornpipe with Peg-Leg Lloyd (all naked she, her full breasts jouncing); and Peletiah raised the flagon to the flaccid lips of the Old Witch, while Herbert, astride a cracking broomstick, made an obscene gesture. Old Witch, Young Witch . . . women.

"But I never meant to do it," Marcia said. "Walton, I was always so afraid. I don't know of what, but so terrified. I never meant to—"

He reached out a hand, drew her frail old body into his arms, and kissed her forehead.

"No," he said. "I guess you never did."

The waiter tapped his shoulder again. He looked like Otis Varney, poor son of a bitch, but his hands were as well kept as those of P.H. "It's closing time, sir," he said. "Our revels now are ended. But there's a place open three doors down the street. I'd suggest the Bide-a-Wee, sir."

"Go," said Walton, waving a paw at him. "Go, put pebbles in your mouth." But he paid the bill and staggered away.

It was cold outside—brilliantly, Octoberly cold.

"Poor Tom's a-cold," Walton muttered. "And it's all over, and all still to be done." The cold he felt inside matched the night's weather. He must go back—back to lights and warmth and music and the sirens'—

Sirens! A wail cut through the night, sliced it into quivering halves, came nearer, nearer, and swept past in one prolonged desolate ululation. Cut time obliquely, and it's you, *you* there in the police ambulance.

Shivering, Walton huddled back in the cab he had just entered, and said, "Take me to one of the big midtown hotel supper clubs. I don't care which."

ON ANOTHER LEVEL,

after Clarence Kiefer left, Walton sat alone at the table for some time, brooding over a glass that he kept full. His thoughts were melancholy, complex and inconclusive. Images of his family, unconnected fragments from his whole life kept interswirling in his mind. It seemed to him that somehow, in some vague way, great segments of his forty-five years had broken loose, like individual bergs from an ice floe, and were floating out away from him, leaving him free—

Free from what? for what? A hand tapped him tentatively on the shoulder. He looked up to confront a short man with bright eyes and bald head (everyone was bald, it seemed, tonight)—a man looking at him at once urgently and tentatively.

"You're—Walton Herrick?" the bright, birdlike man asked. "Is that right?"

"Yes," said Walton, rising. He could feel his head clearing in the act. Demand-supply. This man really had something to say to him.

"My name is Heathcote," the man said. "Nathaniel Heathcote. I— well, I guess I owe my life to you. Mr. Herrick, you changed the whole course of my life. Do you remember?"

Walton, flushed, strained to remember. "Nathaniel Heathcote. Why, you— But—"

"I remember the words," said Heathcote, almost reverently. "Asked about me, sir, you said, 'We would conduct the same careful exploration, and if nothing new and pertinent turned up, we would make the same decision.' About me. Not such daring words out of context, perhaps. But we all know the context—that of McCarthy America. I'd waited and waited to hear words like that, and I'd little thought I'd hear them in defense of me—no, not in defense of me, but in justice to me. And I thought it was you, and I had to thank you. And Marian wants to thank you, too."

"Marian?"

She was even more birdlike. Her face was thin, her eyes bright, too, but brown to Nathaniel's blue. Her chin was sharp, her nose a blade, but the face was true—and a benediction.

"Oh, I do," she said, only breathing the words.

"Well," said Walton, and thought, Will my goddamn eyes never stop blurring? "Well. Well, I'm glad."

They were gone, and he stood there for a moment, swaying—not only from liquor, although he knew now that he was half-drunk. You never know, he said in heavy silence to himself, you never know. He didn't know; he was suddenly bewildered and, looking at his watch, had difficulty reading the time. Well—Kiefer and Heathcote. Well.

It was a quarter to eleven, and he'd been sitting and sitting. No good end to that: he signaled the waiter, who scurried over.

The waiter looked like P.H., it seemed to Walton, but he was as obsequious as Otis Varney.

"Yes, sir," he said, bobbing his head. "Yes, sir, check, sir, we're closing soon, sir. But if you want to go on, sir, there's a place three doors down the street, named the Bide-a-Wee."

Walton waved him away.

"Don't want to go on," he said. "Check, please."

He paid the bill and walked slowly away.

Outside October was here. It was brilliantly cold. Walton shivered, even before he heard the wild keening of an ambulance siren. But the sound made him colder, chilled him through. He waited, desolate, till the big black car with the red bull's eye had shot by. Then he turned to the doorman.

But the doorman was scrambling around for another client farther down the street. Beside him, instead, was a hunched beggar, a man with a raw face and a self-induced hump to his back, holding out a dirty checkered cap.

With a shudder, Walton looked into the burnt-out face of Herbert Nicholson. He drew out his wallet and placed a dollar in the cap. Then he looked earnestly into the drugged, opaque eyes.

"Don't hate," he said hopelessly, and ran down the street to a cab. . . .

There was the unimaginative and conventional but stirring blare of horns and roll of drums. That was the last of the conventional and unimaginative. From the moment Lucy Banks stepped into the spotlight, the room was transformed. Once she began to sing, it was enchanted.

Walton knew of her career only remotely. But he did know that, from its inception in Harlem, it had been one steady progression upward—the triumph of both a personality and a talent, so subtly fused that one found it hard to separate them. And—thanks to the many billboards—he knew that this was her first appearance in this renowned room of this world-famous hotel, hence genuinely the culmination of her career.

Arriving just before her appearance, he had been placed at a tiny table in a far corner of the vast ballroom, clearly maintained for that rare customer, the single man. Now, as she began to sing, his mind was whipped free of all its obsessions of these last months; he was totally and happily her prisoner.

How to define her power, her unbeautified beauty? Tall, bigbosomed, her hair swept up carelessly, her large but shapely hand swinging the microphone as though it were a baton, the mirth that rippled over her large body as though from some inner tidal wave— these were all part of her presence.

But her style—it troubled description. How to say in words the way she would break off in the middle of a lyric line to talk satirically or sadly to herself; the way she would suddenly break into a heavy, raucous chant that reached down into your bowels and stirred you, shocked you into urgent primitive life. She, shouting blues, was an incitement to the blood, just as she, singing low and sad, was the mother of life. And she, talking rhythmically and bitterly, pseudo-scandalized at the ways of men and half scolding, half burlesquing her own sarcasm and incisive satire, transcended the Female Yelp even as she embodied it.

She was magnificent. Most of all Walton admired her for never being more exactly, more completely Lucy Banks; everything for which she was known, her idiom, her subjects, her change of pace—everything remained unaltered. The only concession to the place, the occasion (this was the first time not only she, but any Negro entertainer had ever performed here), was the slightly prouder tilt of her head and, during a moment's pause for emphasis, the way she looked out, squarely at the audience, her fine dark eyes majestic but inscrutable.

It was historic. As she sang on, between the wild and prolonged bouts of applause, Walton's head cleared and his heart swelled. It was a proclamation, a fiat, not just for herself, but for her people. He found himself remembering faces: early cooks; his father's janitor friend at Western Reserve; the boy in college whom he had not known well, but with whom he had spent illuminating hours; a host of anonymous faces, haunted, sad, proud, angry, life-worn; but most of all the elegantly chiseled features of his closest friend at Columbia, Oliver Hastings, aristocrat sans portfolio, sensitive, lonely, patient, passionate, no more at home with the rank and file of his race than with white people. But persevering, praising alike (where had he heard that?) the joy and the pain in life.

Friends. They came swarming into his mind now. Not a host— only a few, but surging up in him, their faces, their *quality*. Bill Corwin of the early games in the attic, Red Stewart, Ez Barker, Anna Manges (not strange to think of her among the men), Nathan Langbaum, with whom he had taught—the man he thought of now, as always, as Buddha in a business suit, a rosy round man with the clearest, most compassionate eyes he had ever seen—Leon Goodman, Abe Fortune, William Herrick (but he belonged, belonged in this roll call) and—who?

Who? Whose name was nagging at him? He saw the face—dark, smoky and prophetic at times, at others lighted up with that illumination that shines through the pores, a short, square, stocky man with the chest and shoulders of a fullback and yet the delicate sensitiveness of a concert master in his reaching out to touch others (the tip of the finger extending to the hand of Adam there on the Sistine ceiling).

Who? *Who labored with me, for me, and against me for me . . . and never gave in to the temptation to—* To what? To destroy me? Why? The patient-enemy. (What does that mean?) A light. (More light.) As Lucy Banks reached the climax (climbed the mountain) of a chiseled high note and bowed to thunderous applause, Walton knew: the doctor, the psychoanalyst (buffeted twentieth-century redeemer: *Eye hate you. What am Eye saying?*).

Yes, him: Mort Gauss, who labored with me, for me, and against me for me—to whom I will return. Soon. Ask not when. It is now.

And you, Lucy Banks? Old young brave champion (*What do you think America is for? Why do you think we carved and chopped it out of a wilderness?*), God bless you. And friends swam before Walton's eyes—Mort Gauss, Oliver Hastings, Nathan Langbaum, Abe Fortune and Lucy Banks.

The thunder of the surf retreated, the light was gone, and people retired into the quiet chattering of their tables. Yet was he restless. What *was* America for? He saw it spread on the round living globe: the high breathless mesas of New Mexico, of Wyoming and Colorado, the million dazzling lights of San Francisco, the pines and red earth of North Carolina, the morbid prairies of Nebraska, bright Florida and blond Nevada, the strange moonscape of Utah, cliffs of the Wasatch Range that were pyramids and hieroglyphs, portraits of esoteric pharaohs carved by nature out of solid rock, and prehistoric elephants lying on their sides, great gray-green greasy Limpopo Utah. And the Salt Lake, that first view of frozen arctic splendor. And the green and fertile hilly farms of southwestern Iowa, where the grant wood households sat on the lawns in Sunday picnics and rocking chairs. Or snow in the dawn of the Sierra Nevadas, clusters and thickets of snow on the silent pines; bright Venus shining over the high Colorado mesa till the moon rose, huge, round and orange, oh thou America.

Much have I traveled in the realms of gold, and many goodly states and kingdoms seen. And yet, Connecticut, when first I saw you— the greenness and the softly rolling hills, a gentle landscape, tried and quiet—I came home.

Home. The lights were bright again, and the voices rose, sharply, querulously. Yet Walton felt his head clear, said good-bye Lucy Banks, and turned to consider his problems. Consider? Listen. Why, that last night when he left Sonia, why had he felt so purged, so sure, so strong that he could tell Dennis Byrnes what to do with his life? He had always thought that this was the way he would feel when he resisted the ubiquitous temptation, said *no.* But *then* he had said both and been canceled out. He had said no and done yes and kept the no intact since it was good-bye.

Or, even more central, how could he do this and—in a breath, a whistle, a passage of hours—reach the Vineyard and be there for Julie? Hoist the petard! He did not know, he did not know, he did not know. The epitaph.

And there—a couple leaving. Surely it was Gail—and surely Dudley Foote. No. A resemblance. No. An actuality.

They were gone. He did not know. And if it were an evening of coincidences, why should it not be? Only in novels did people fail to materialize, appear in unpropitious clusters—since this would be improbable. In life it happened every day. (And that's where I am, back in life.)

So he would go. Another waiter to hail and board, another doorman, another taxi.

"The Bide-a-Wee, please. Do you know where it is?"

Good-bye, Lucy.

It was dark, a cellar, a hole under the earth, a cave in which to lose yourself. Be lost.

It was murkily lit by red lanterns. Walton stumbled to the bar, groped for a stool, and slowly accustomed his eyes to the gloom. Midway in our life's journey . . .

No one else was sitting at the bar; only a few shadowy people were scattered here and there in booths. The bartender, thin, furtive-eyed, scant-haired, said nothing, merely stood before Walton and waited.

"Bourbon," said Walton. "Do you have anything to eat?"

The bartender turned a liver-spotted profile to him. "No food," he muttered. "Too late." But when he returned with the drink, he leaned suggestively across the counter and half hissed, half whispered, "Not unless you'd like a good steak sandwich. I've got a small porterhouse left, Grade A. It's against rules to serve so late, but I'll give it to you in a back booth for five dollars, if you want."

Walton observed him in silence for a moment, literally shocked by the man's expression. You would have thought that he was speaking of an international crisis and that millions of dollars were at stake. Instead of five and a steak, Walton thought without amusement. But what did it matter?

"All right," he said. "Rare. And bring another drink with it. Which booth?"

With a deepening of his conspiratorial expression, the bartender jerked his head to the right. "Come on," he said. "I'll show you."

Carrying his glass, Walton followed him in the relatively simple maneuver of crossing the room to one of three booths against the rear wall. The man flicked the dust, real or imaginary, off the dark table and motioned Walton to a seat. He raised an anticipatory finger. "Real juicy," he whispered. "Rare. The real McCoy." Then he was gone into the shadows.

Sipping his drink, Walton felt a vague uneasiness. Was there something really wrong with the place? Why had that other waiter recommended it? Why had the name stuck tight in his mind? Why, in short, had he come? Bide-a-Wee!

He reached for his pipe, couldn't find it, cursed and slumped back, disconsolate. Dully he looked at the other booths, their occupants now fairly visible. In the very next one, a woman was looking directly at him —directly, appraisingly and now, it seemed, suggestively. Walton felt a little heat stir in him.

She was not beautiful, not even pretty. She was thin, and her eyes— or, in the dusk, the effect they gave off—were almost rapacious. Yet she also gave off something else (A scent? Impossible at that distance. But a chemical excitement, somehow)—something that titillated Walton, that stirred him as the movement of Sonia's shoulders had.

He turned his head away. It was as though he could hear a voice out of nowhere, it seemed, and the voice lighted the place, filled it with the radiance of—of humanity, he thought. Whatever that meant. No, he knew: Lucy Banks, singing of love, ruefully, cynically and yet tenderly. And then there was another voice, a man's, quiet, deep, resonant too, saying, "All right, Walton. But if you ever want to come back, the door will be open." His spine thrilled to it now; he was going back into that room and—and seek the truth.

And yet a third voice, soft, husky, saying, "You are a good man, and I never want you to go away again." His eyes were swimming in tears; he thought again, as he had earlier in the evening, that one had to go back and feel the clichés, live them, and then they regained the freshness that is life. And through the tears he saw Julie's beloved face as clearly as though she were there beside him.

"What in hell are you looking at?" The voice, strident, angry, was somehow familiar, stirred memory, and memory stirred the bristles of Walton's hair.

It came from the next booth, the one in which the blonde woman was sitting, but it was not her voice. All Walton could see of the man opposite her was the dark back of his head, over the wall of the booth.

"A man who wants a smoke," she replied silkily, indifferently—and to Walton, "Have a cigarette?"

He rose automatically and took one from the package she held out to him, unable to avoid the brushing of his hand against the long cool fingers that clung to the nearer side of the package.

Lighting it, he said, "Thank you," and looked down at the man with the familiar voice, who glared back at him openly.

It was a face he knew, knew strained with hatred and outrage, black with wrath at everyone, everything. It was Louis Jacoby, the little dark man who had come to their home with the Varneys and flung the cat at Gail.

Jacoby achieved recognition at the same time. He laughed, without mirth.

"Well," he said. "Well, it's the Hero. It's the president of the SPCA. Or is it the NAACP? And what are you doing here in this dump? I thought you were a big wheel."

Walton stared at him a little dazedly.

"Hello," he said at last. "And thanks again for the cigarette." He had resumed his seat when he heard the woman say, "Introduce me, Louis. You're a crude bastard."

Jacoby heaved himself up, had difficulty catching his balance, and bowed in burlesque dignity.

"This is Mr. Walton Herrick," he said, "big wheel, or ex–big wheel at the Schuyler Foundation, who once bounced me from his house. And this—" he bowed again—"this is Madame Magda Lupescu."

"You jerk." Her voice was lazy but venomous. "I'm Gwen Davies. And I'm glad to meet you. It's been getting a little dull and stuffy in here."

Jacoby looked at her scornfully.

"*You* find it dull," he said savagely. "That's too damned bad. Too damned bad. You bitch."

"Shut up, Louis," she said, and turned that same disquieting look on Walton. "It's so nice to see a man. I want another drink, Louis." She moved her body, and it was as before.

The bartender was there. He materialized. There was no sense of his having walked, run or flown there. First he wasn't there; then he was. He brought Walton's sandwich.

It was exactly as Walton had expected: a thin cube steak on soggy toast, a greenish slice of tomato, and a little wilted lettuce. He felt a wild desire to crack the plate over the man's head, but held himself under tight control.

The bartender was appraising him closely.

"It's a little smaller than I thought," he hissed, "so I'll only charge you four seventy-five. I'll get your drink right away, Mrs. Davies." After a quick look at all three, he was gone.

Walton ate doggedly. He could hear the other two, back in their booth, arguing fiercely, Jacoby in rasping half sentences, Gwen Davies coolly, cuttingly. He had just finished his meal when he felt her hand on his shoulder, smelled the heavy wave of gin and perfume, and looked up to find his eyes and nose inches from her décolletage.

"Move over," said Gwen. "I want to talk to you." As she bent down, her hand rested heavily on his thigh.

Over her shoulder appeared Jacoby's dark threatening face.

"Stand up, Herrick," he said thickly. "I don't give a shit how big you are."

The bartender, alert to the need for strategy, held out one imploring hand to Jacoby, even while he slid the check across the table to Walton with the other.

Walton's whirling head cleared.

"Listen," he said coldly, "all of you. I don't want to talk to you," and he gently pushed Gwen to one side and stood up, facing Jacoby. "And I'm not going to beat up on you; you've done it to yourself. As I have to myself. And—" he swung around to the bartender—"I'm paying you exactly three dollars, one-eighty for the two drinks and one-twenty for that miserable steak. And nothing for yourself. Good night."

He did not look back, but went through the door and began striding vigorously up Fifth Avenue, once more beneath the stars.

How long he walked the frosty avenues he didn't know. He turned east, then north again, then east, then north, west, north once more— wherever a brighter light shone down the street, he swung, to pass it, look in, not lonely, not cold, without by choice, his own, to move on again in the direction of home. Taking the long way home, he thought. And it seemed to him that old Peletiah patted his shoulder, and chuckled, "Good for you, son. And remember what I told you." And the first William: "Be a father to yourself."

At last he came to a vast excavation, where a new building was to house some giant corporation. He climbed the low fence, went slowly down the steep bank from the level of the street. At its foot, in the depths of the gigantic scooped-out cavern, he seated himself on a block of concrete, and looked up.

Above him towered a crane, its empty maw hanging listless, open. Beyond and above it, the blazing stars.

The night traffic sounded dimly, remotely. Here there was silence, and emptiness. Here, in the womb of Manhattan, there was only himself. Tomorrow the builders would come and their work would begin. Tomorrow and tomorrow. And he would take up his new work, and he would go back through the door that had been kept open for him, in pursuit of himself. Committed, he would begin the long journey back to Julie and home, a journey that might or might not be consummated. But he knew where he wanted to go; he knew where he belonged.

All that tomorrow. But now he was finally alone. He was alone and still and empty. Stripped down, he thought, to the thing itself, the poor, bare, forked animal—to the irreducible minimum.

Curious, numb with the cold, he waited for life to begin. It did, within him. Life stirred.

AUTHOR'S NOTE

A novelist's comment attached to his work seems to me almost always pretentious, and I am embarrassed that I feel I must write one. Yet, in fairness to so long a work, projected so far ahead, I do want to say that, while I have attempted to bring this single novel to some sense of resolution, I have subordinated this attempt to my larger concept of the whole series. Hence the present incompleteness of the portraits of a number of characters, and of many relationships between characters.

I want also to take the opportunity to dedicate in advance the whole series, *The Generations of Adam,* to my wife and intransigent love, Mary Tuttle Haydn, and to express my deep and glad indebtedness to a number of friends: to Jerome Nathanson, to Simon Michael Bessie, to Marc Friedlaender, to Mavis McIntosh, to Charlotte Payne, to Harry Ford, to Jerry Mason, to Alfred Knopf, Jr., to Cass and Jane Canfield, and especially to Norman Kelman.

Hiram Haydn

December 8, 1961

DATE DUE			
JUL 24 82			
AUG 6 82			
AUG 27 82			
SEP 10 82			
NOV 1 82			
JUN 20 83			
APR 10			
OCT 21 1966			
AUG. 31. 1976			

c. 1

Haydn, H.
    The Hands of Esau.

2c

RLIN

NFC 86